The Tectonics of the Appalachians

a volume in the
REGIONAL GEOLOGY SERIES

edited by
L. U. DE SITTER

THE TECTONICS OF
THE APPALACHIANS

BY

JOHN RODGERS

WILEY—INTERSCIENCE

a Division of John Wiley & Sons, Inc.

NEW YORK · LONDON · SYDNEY · TORONTO

Library of Congress Catalogue Card Number: 72—116771

ISBN 0 471 72930 2

Printed in the United States of America

10 9 8 7 6 5 4 3 2 1

à la memoire de

PAUL FALLOT

grand géologue

grand savant

grand monsieur

Editor's Note to Regional Geology Series

The aim of this series on Regional Geology is to add to the available geological literature concise descriptions of large structural units, independent of national boundaries.

It is important that the personal opinion of an author, formed by his work and experience in the structural unit he describes, comes clearly to the attention of the reader. Theorizing about the geological history of a particular kind of structure too often does not take into account the great diversity of the observed phenomena, and then generalizes in an unwarranted way. We aim to give a better basis to these general concepts and thereby stimulate a deeper understanding of the relations between different kinds of structures.

Some of the books describe classical territory where new work has brought new conceptions, others are concerned with hitherto relatively unknown regions, but always the surveys are presented from a fresh aspect.

L. U. de Sitter

Contents

The Tectonics of the Appalachians

CHAPTER 1

Introduction

Geographic Setting

The Appalachian Mountains (Fig. 1), taken in a broad sense, are that chain of relatively low but steep mountains that follow the east or, better, the southeast coast of the North American continent. They extend across nearly 20 degrees of latitude and more than 30 of longitude from Newfoundland in easternmost Canada to Alabama in the southeastern United States, a distance of more than 3000 kilometers (about 2000 miles); placed on the continents of Europe and Africa at the same latitude, they would extend roughly from Warsaw to Casablanca. In 1540, the would-be conquistador Hernando de Soto crossed the southern part of the chain, and that part appeared (unnamed) on a map of 1543, after the survivors of his expedition had returned. The Spaniards named these southerly mountains for the Apalachees (Apalachis), a tribe of North American Indians who lived in northern Florida and southern Georgia well south of the end of the chain; they were first encountered by Pánfilo de Narváez and Cabeza de Vaca in 1528 (near the present Apalachee Bay), and de Soto spent with them the winter before his expedition to the mountains. The tribe itself was virtually destroyed in early eighteenth century hostilities between the Spanish and English colonists and their Indian allies, but the name Appalachian Mountains came gradually to be applied to the range farther and farther north, ousting local names such as Allegheny in Pennsylvania and the Virginias. Geographers and geologists now apply it to the whole chain, even the portion on the Canadian mainland, and I am using the name here with this broad meaning; the geographers tend to exclude Newfoundland, but geologically that island is also Appalachian and therefore included in the discussion.

Geographically the Appalachian Mountains are not a single continuous range but a complex of mountain groups; most of the groups run roughly parallel to the chain as a whole, though none extends even half its length, and in general they overlap one another with rather vague boundaries. Intercalated between the more linear mountain groups are similarly linear valleys, some narrow, some broad and fertile and locally even surrounding small mountain groups. There is no continuous "crest" to the chain; in some places a group of mountains near the center is the highest, in others the highest is along the northwest side. The highest and largest mountain group lies in western North Carolina and adjacent states; Mt. Mitchell in the Black Mountains near the southeast side of the group rises 2037 meters (6684 feet) above sea level, and Clingmans Dome in the Great Smoky Mountains along the Tennessee line rises 2024 metres (6642 feet). Next highest are the White Mountains of New Hampshire, culminating in

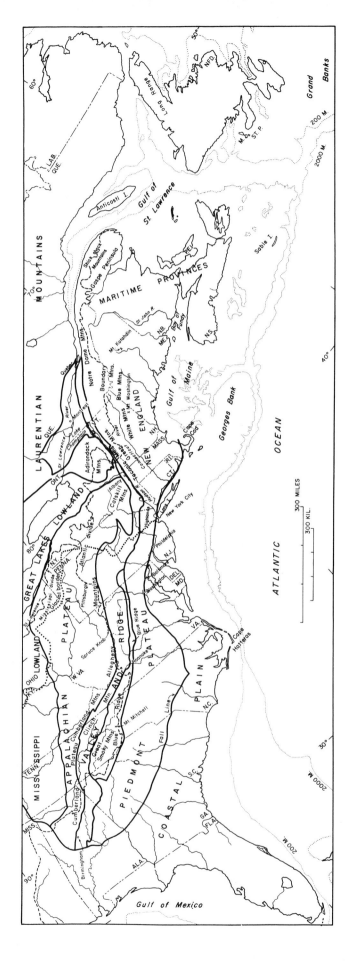

FIGURE 1.   General map of Appalachian Mountains showing principal features.

Mt. Washington at 1917 meters (6288 feet). Outside these two groups and the isolated Mt. Katahdin in Maine (1605 meters—5267 feet), no peaks rise above 1500 meters (5000 feet); the Adirondack Mountains of northeastern New York (highest point Mt. Marcy at 1629 meters—5344 feet), although sometimes geographically included with the Appalachians, are geologically unrelated as they are an outlier of the Laurentian Mountains of Quebec across the Saint Lawrence River. Summits over 1000 meters (3000 feet) are found not only in the groups already mentioned but also in the Shickshock Mountains of the Gaspé Peninsula in Quebec, in the Boundary Mountains along the Quebec-Maine border and the Blue Mountains in western Maine, in the Green and Taconic Mountains of Vermont and Mt. Greylock in northwestern Massachusetts, in the Catskill Mountains of southeastern New York, in the Allegheny Mountains of Maryland, West Virginia, and Virginia, in the Blue Ridge of Virginia, and in the Cumberland Mountains of Virginia, Kentucky, and Tennessee.

In a rough way, the Appalachian chain separates the drainage flowing directly into the Atlantic Ocean from that flowing north to the St. Lawrence River and the Great Lakes or west to the Mississippi, but the divide only locally corresponds to the highest part of the mountains. In New York, indeed, it abandons the Appalachians altogether to swing through the Adirondack Mountains around the headwaters of the Hudson River, whose narrow, tidal fjordlike estuary neatly divides the chain into two nearly equal segments and leads to the two lowest passes across the divide, which lie on either side of the Adirondacks, 44 meters (145 feet) above sea level from the upper Hudson Valley into the Champlain-St. Lawrence Valley and 130 meters (430 feet) from the Mohawk Valley into the interior lowland of the continent. In the segment southwest of the Hudson, the mountainous axis of the Appalachians is flanked almost throughout by broad belts of lower hills, which are more or less dissected plateaux; these in turn are flanked by broad plains, the Atlantic Coastal Plain on one side and the vast interior lowland of the Mississippi and the Great Lakes on the other. Including the hilly belts, the chain is here 350 to 500 kilometers (200 to 300 miles) wide; excluding them, it is 100 to 200 (60 to 120). The drainage divide here keeps about 200 kilometers (130 miles) away from the edge of the Coastal Plain, at least as far north as Pennsylvania. In the segment northeast of the Hudson, on the other hand, the waters of the Atlantic wash directly against the southeastern foothills of the chain, extend well into the chain in the Gulf of

Maine and the Bay of Fundy, and cross it entirely in the Gulf of St. Lawrence; on the northwest no plateau is present and only the relatively narrow St. Lawrence and Champlain Valleys separate the Appalachian ranges from the Laurentian Mountains and their outlier, the Adirondacks. Across the Maritime Provinces (Nova Scotia and New Brunswick) and the Gaspé Peninsula, the chain reaches its maximum width—600 kilometers (350 miles)—but elsewhere it is narrowed by the sea.

The southeast coast of North America is bathed by the cold Labrador current on the north and the warm Gulf Stream on the south and is subject to mildly monsoonal winds (though the mountain barrier of the Appalachians tends to temper these); hence the climatic zones are much more compressed than on the Atlantic coast of Europe, and the climate is more continental except where the sea penetrates deeply as in the Gulf of St. Lawrence. One end of the Appalachian chain lies in latitude $51\frac{1}{2}°$N off the extreme eastern projection of the continent in a maritime subpolar climate supporting spruce forest not far south of the limit of tundra; the other end lies in latitude $32\frac{1}{2}°$N well within the continent in a continental subtropical climate not far north of the limit of evergreen broad-leaved trees. In the higher mountains, moreover, the climatic and vegetational zones are displaced southward; Canadian plants are known on the highest mountains in North Carolina, and the summit of Mt. Washington and the highest parts of the Shickshock Mountains in Gaspé and of the Long Range in western Newfoundland are above timber line. The entire chain is well watered; the average annual rainfall ranges from 80 centimeters (30 inches) in the north to 130 centimeters (50 inches) in the south, and locally reaches 200 centimeters (80 inches) in the highest mountains. All was originally forested; by the early nineteenth century a large part had been cleared for farming, but since then considerable portions have slipped back into woodland as farmers migrated to the fertile plains in the center of the continent. In the twentieth century the growth of cities and then of suburbs has transformed much of the central part of the chain into an urban landscape, but even now deep forests exist within 100 kilometers (50 miles) of New York City.

The existence of this mountain barrier, not very high but organized in depth, had a considerable effect on the history of the North American continent. By the middle of the eighteenth century, the Spanish had a firm grip on the southern part of the continent including the shore of the Gulf of Mexico, the French possessed the great interior basins of the St. Lawrence and the Mississippi, and the English were settled only along the Atlantic seaboard between the mountains and the sea. Yet over a million Europeans were living in the English colonies, far more than in all the rest of the continent put together; hemmed in by the mountains, which helped to protect them against invasion from the west, they had developed cities, communications, governments, and the beginnings of a spirit of solidarity. After the Seven Years War, the British took possession of the entire French empire on the continent and ousted the Spanish from Florida, but they also attempted to confine the colonists to the seaboard, reserving the interior for the Indians and fur-traders; the attempt contributed its share to the colonial discontent that resulted in the American Revolution. Once independent, the Americans burst across the mountain barrier and swept westward, ruthlessly brushing aside both the Indians and the Europeans who stood in their way, until in less than a lifetime the United States occupied a swath straight across the continent. Indeed the most conspicuous irregularity in its borders, the southward projection of Canada along the St. Lawrence and between the Great Lakes, still reflects the original Appalachian barrier.

Geologic Setting

Geologically the Appalachian Mountains are that belt in eastern North America where Paleozoic (and some Precambrian) rocks were deformed in Paleozoic time; they lie between the stable interior of the continent, where the Paleozoic rocks lie flat, and the Coastal Plain, where undeformed Cretaceous and Cenozoic sediments lap over and bury the older rocks. Triassic rocks, preserved in a series of fault troughs along the chain, also overlap the deformed Paleozoic rocks and contain fragments of them; traditionally therefore the deformation in the mountain belt has been dated at the end of the Paleozoic, and in fact for generations American students were taught that it was the event that marked the end of the era. We now know that deformation (and also igneous intrusion and metamorphism) began in the Appalachians in the latest Precambrian and took place at several times during the Paleozoic, and that the tectonic history of the mountain belt is complex. In some portions of the belt, however, only one period of deformation has been important.

The tectonic trend lines of the Appalachians (fold axes, trends of foliation, elongation of igneous bodies or groups of bodies), though locally irregular, are for the most part remarkably even and parallel to one another and to the general trend of the chain. Taken broadly, they outline a series of arcs convex to the northwest and most marked along the northwest side, which correspond to structural sections of the chain; the arcs are separated by more angular recesses. The southernmost arc extends from central Alabama to southern Virginia (750 kilometers, 500 miles); on the southeast the trends are nearly straight, but on the northwest they are strongly arcuate, especially in east Tennessee, and the arc is broken in two by an indentation in northwest Georgia. The second arc extends from southern Virginia to the vicinity of New York City (650 kilometers, 400 miles); its curvature is most pronounced in Pennsylvania. The third and largest arc extends from New York City to the Gulf of St. Lawrence (1200 kilometers, 700 miles); the curvature is strongest in southern Quebec and southeastward and in Gaspé, and there is a hint of reverse curvature in between along the northwest side of the chain and also in Cape Breton Island at the east end of Nova Scotia. These three arcs are commonly called the Southern, Central, and Northern Appalachians, or the Tennessee, Pennsylvania, and Quebec salients. Finally, the island of Newfoundland exposes a fragment of a fourth arc, extending up to 600 kilometers (up to 360 miles) along strike at an angle and in a position to suggest an offset to the right across the Gulf of St. Lawrence. Considering their geologic cross section and history, these arcs group themselves in pairs into a southern and a northern segment, corresponding to the two geographic segments separated by the Hudson River. Of these, the southern segment not only has priority on the Appalachian name but includes the regions of "classical Appalachian structure"; on the northwest, where this segment has been studied in detail, it has a simpler structural history than the northern segment, but its southeastern portion is perhaps the least known part of the entire chain.

The Pleistocene continental ice sheet covered the entire northern segment, even its highest peaks, and encroached slightly on the southern, as far as a line from New York City west-northwest to the southwestern part of New York State; farther west the glacier advanced well to the south (as far as 38°N latitude) on the interior lowlands along the western foothills of the chain. Apparently there was no local glaciation farther south, though periglacial phenomena have been found as far as the North Carolina mountains and though there were local glaciers in several parts of the northern segment before and after the continental advance. As far as the continental glacier reached, fresh rock exposures are found, abundantly in some areas but rather sparsely in others. The irregular cover of glacial drift, though largely of local origin, has been moved enough to be of no use in mapping the underlying bedrock; in some areas, notably on north-facing slopes such as the northern slopes of the principal mountain groups of New England, it is very extensive and bedrock exposures are few. Elsewhere it is thin and discontinuous so that bedrock exposures are relatively abundant, but even so the area covered is generally much larger than the area exposed. Where artificial exposures are available, they commonly show that the natural exposures are only of the more resistant rocks and give a distorted notion of the proportions of rock types present. Where the cover is thin, the topography may express the underlying bedrock fairly well, but glacial modifications of the topography are always significant and locally extreme.

Beyond the glacial limit, the cover of glacial drift is replaced by a mantle of residuum derived by weathering from the underlying bedrock; talus, colluvium produced by mass wasting, and normal alluvium also occur but generally not over large continuous areas. The residuum is very irregular in thickness, for weathering penetrates some rocks more deeply that others and along joints rather than between them; in the southern states it averages tens of meters (yards) thick over some rock types. In such areas, bedrock exposures can be found only in the deeper stream valleys or, for the more resistant rocks, on the higher mountains. Commonly, however, the topography is very delicately adjusted to the underlying bedrock and provides many valuable clues for geologic mapping. Even more important is the residual mantle itself and the soils developed upon it; in certain regions one can make a detailed geologic map with no more than a handful of exposures per square kilometer (square mile) simply by careful study of the residuum, which not only reflects the original rock but may preserve fossils or even the attitude of bedding or foliation. The largest areas of poor exposure are over the complex metamorphic rocks in the low plateau on the southeast side of the chain in the southern states; the techniques of mapping such areas are only now being worked out, and our knowledge of their geology is still unsatisfactory.

Geologic Subdivisions

The southern segment of the Appalachian Mountains can readily be divided into four belts or provinces, which persist the length of the seg-

ment through both the southern and the central arcs of the chain. Farthest northwest is the Appalachian Plateau province. Some parts of the province are true plateau, but more of it is thoroughly dissected by deep, narrow valleys, and some is truly mountainous; its highest point is Spruce Knob in West Virginia at 1481 meters (4860 feet). Various parts bear various names; for example, the Catskill Mountains of southeastern New York and their southwestward continuation—the Pocono Plateau of northeastern Pennsylvania, the Allegheny Mountains from north-central Pennsylvania to southeastern West Virginia, the Cumberland Mountains in southwestern Virginia, southeastern Kentucky, and northern Tennessee, and the Cumberland Plateau from central Tennessee to northern Alabama. The northwestern border of the province is fairly sharp in the north where the hills drop down to the plains bordering the eastern Great Lakes, rather vague in Ohio where they dwindle into the glaciated plains, and increasingly abrupt southward across Kentucky into Tennessee, where a lower, steplike plateau lies at their foot. The southeastern border is very abrupt except in a few places; commonly one drops 300 to 500 meters (1000 feet or more) within 2 or 3 kilometers (1 or 2 miles) into a broad valley.

The province is characterized primarily by flat-lying or nearly flat-lying sedimentary rocks, chiefly Carboniferous at the surface except in New York where they are Devonian, but in many parts there are gentle folds and in some places steeper folds and a few faults. Many small farmers cultivate the narrow valley floors, but except for its northern glaciated rim the region is not agriculturally significant; lumbering is locally important. On the other hand, it contains great resources of mineral fuels—bituminous coal, oil, and gas—and many important industrial cities are located in its valleys or around its edges.

The second belt is called the Valley and Ridge province; it is the most characteristically "Appalachian" of all from the physiographic point of view. Narrow ridges, a kilometer (mile) or less across, persist for tens or even hundreds of kilometers (miles) strictly parallel to each other and to the trend of the chain, some high and even-crested, some lower and "comby," that is to say irregularly serrate. Outstanding examples are Clinch Mountain, which extends for 200 kilometers (140 miles) across Virginia and Tennessee, cut across by only one stream and rising at its northeast end to 1434 meters (4705 feet) above sea level, and the ridge called Shawangunk Mountain in New York, Kittatinny Mountain in New Jersey, and Blue Mountain in Pennsylvania, which extends for 300 kilometers (200 miles) but is broken in several places as at the well-known Delaware Water Gap. Between the ridges are similarly extensive parallel valleys, some narrow and infertile, some broad and very fertile indeed. There are also belts a few kilometers (miles) wide of irregularly knobby country beside ridges or between valleys. The proportions of valley and ridge differ from one part of the province to another; in particular the southeastern side is nearly everywhere a single broad valley, 10 kilometers (5 miles) or more across, though low minor ridges or knobby belts and here and there a higher ridge, always with the same trend, diversify its floor. This continuous and fertile valley is not followed by any one stream for more than a small part of its extent; called collectively the Great Appalachian Valley, it goes more commonly by local names—Wallkill Valley, Kittatinny Valley, Lehigh Valley, Lebanon Valley, Cumberland Valley, Shenandoah Valley, the Valley of Virginia, the Valley of East Tennessee, and Coosa Valley.

The Valley and Ridge province is underlain by a diversified sequence of Paleozoic sedimentary rocks (Cambrian to Carboniferous) that have been strongly folded and faulted but not metamorphosed, except for cleavage in the shale and limestone along the southeast side. The broader valleys are among the finest farming regions in the United States and are noted for their dairy cattle, fruit, and tobacco as well as the usual grains. Mineral resources are also present in the province, notably anthracite coal in Pennsylvania, zinc, lead, and barite in Virginia and Tennessee, and iron in Tennessee and Alabama. These and the electric power produced by the dams of the Tennessee Valley Authority (TVA) system in the southern part of the province have stimulated the growth of industry.

The third belt in the southern segment is called the Blue Ridge province. Though it does not extend the full length of the segment, it reaches from northern Georgia to southern Pennsylvania, and farther northeast it is represented by the low Highlands of northern New Jersey and adjacent Pennsylvania. In the Central Appalachians it is mostly a single massive ridge 10 to 20 kilometers (5 to 10 miles) across, which rises abruptly from the Great Valley on the west and drops off nearly as abruptly on the east, though with more foothills and subordinate ridges. Only three rivers cross this part of the ridge; southwest of the third, at Roanoke, Virginia, where the province enters the Southern Appalachians, it broadens out into the culminating mountain group of the entire chain. Two principal ridges diverge southwestward from Roanoke; they rise 500 meters (2000

feet) or more above the adjacent provinces and mark the borders of the province, which is 100 kilometers (60 miles) across at its widest, extending from South Carolina to Tennessee. The southeastern ridge retains the name Blue Ridge and is here the main divide of the Appalachians, but the northwestern ridge, the Unaka Mountains (including the Great Smoky Mountains and other named mountain ranges), is the higher and more massive. Extending across between these two ridges, like the rungs of a rope ladder, are additional mountain ranges, notably the Black Mountains including Mt. Mitchell, the highest point in the Appalachians. The two border ridges, and with them the province, end abruptly in northern Georgia.

The northwest face of the Blue Ridge province is everywhere composed of Lower Cambrian or older sedimentary rocks, emerging from under the younger and weaker rocks of the Valley and Ridge province or thrust over them, but much of the crest of the Ridge exposes a still older metamorphic basement in the core of a complex anticlinorium. The cover rocks are also metamorphosed, only mildly on the northwest side but more and more intensely southeastward, especially across the broad part of the province, so that in that direction the distinction between cover and basement becomes obscure.

The Blue Ridge province is the least settled part of the Appalachians, though even here there are many small farms in the narrow valleys; conversely timber is important. Iron and especially copper have been mined in quantity in the belt, marble occurs locally, and important pegmatite districts provide mica and feldspar, but the special value of the region is as a recreation ground for the American people. Many famous summer resorts lie in and around the mountains, and a national scenic highway 900 kilometers (550 miles) long, the Blue Ridge Parkway, follows the crest of the ridge linking the Shenandoah National Park athwart the Blue Ridge in northern Virginia with the Great Smoky Mountains National Park on the North Carolina-Tennessee border.

The fourth belt is the Piedmont Plateau province, which slopes gradually southeastward from the southeast foot of the Blue Ridge to the Fall Line where the Appalachian rocks disappear under the sediments of the Coastal Plain. Southwest of the end of the Blue Ridge province, the northwestern edge of the Piedmont stands a few hundred meters (yards) above the Great Valley. Some irregular mountain groups, none very high, rise above its northwestern portion, but except for a few linear ridges in west-central Georgia the rest of the province is a nearly featureless upland plain dissected about 100 meters (a few hundred feet) by an intricate dendritic network of streams. The province is largely underlain by crystalline schist, gneiss, and gneissic granite, but in some belts the grade of metamorphism is lower. The age of the rocks is mostly uncertain; Paleozoic fossils have been found in a very few places, but at least some Precambrian is also present. In addition, several fault troughs containing unmetamorphosed Triassic sedimentary rocks parallel the general trend, and dikes of Mesozoic dolerite are widespread.

The province used to be more thoroughly farmed than now, but much of it has gone back to scrub timber, on which a pulp and paper industry is growing. Dairy produce in the northern part, tobacco in the central part, and cotton in the southern part are the money crops. Gold used to be an important mineral resource, but now mineral production is chiefly of base metals and sulfur from sulfide ores and of mica and feldspar from pegmatites. In addition to the older cities strung along the Fall Line, many small and medium-sized industrial cities have sprung up along the numerous rivers that traverse the province; the manufacture of textiles predominates.

In contrast to the distinct belts of the southern segment, the northern segment of the Appalachian chain cannot be neatly subdivided. The Appalachian Plateau province ends with the Helderberg "Mountains," a mesalike step below the Catskill Mountains overlooking Albany, New York. In front of it the lower Hudson Valley, representing the Great Appalachian Valley, merges with the Mohawk Valley, an eastern projection of the lowland around the Great Lakes, and both these roles are played by the upper Hudson-Champlain-St. Lawrence Valley, lying between the Appalachians proper in New England on one side and the Laurentians of Quebec and their outlier, the Adirondacks of New York, on the other. Along the upper Hudson and east of Lake Champlain, the underlying lower Paleozoic rocks are as deformed as in the Great Valley but along the Mohawk, northwest of Lake Champlain, and in the wide part of the St. Lawrence Valley around Montreal, they are as flat-lying as around the Great Lakes, though disturbed by normal faults. Finally, at Quebec City, the valley narrows again and, save for the Isles of Orléans (close to Quebec) and Anticosti, is drowned by the estuary of the St. Lawrence.

Except for the Hudson and Champlain Valleys, then, the Northern Appalachians correspond only to the Blue Ridge and Piedmont Plateau provinces, and even these are hard to distinguish. The northern New Jersey Highlands, mentioned just

above as representing the Blue Ridge, continue northeast as the Highlands of the Hudson, which breaks through them in a spectacular fjord, but beyond that neither eastern nor western boundary is clear. In general the Highlands or "Blue Ridge" trend continues northward across western Connecticut into the Berkshire Hills of western Massachusetts and the Green Mountains of Vermont, but along the New York border, from extreme northwestern Connecticut to the south end of Lake Champlain, a separate range, the Taconic Mountains, is interpolated on the west, and the eastern foothills, less distinctly separated, drop off only gradually into the parallel Connecticut Valley. The Green Mountains continue northeast into the Sutton, Notre Dame, and Shickshock Mountains of Quebec southeast of the St. Lawrence Valley and estuary. The last outpost of the "Blue Ridge" trend is the northern Long Range in the Great Northern Peninsula of Newfoundland. All these mountain ranges, except perhaps the Shickshocks, have in common an anticlinorial structure; a basement core is exposed intermittently from central Vermont southward and in the Long Range. The Connecticut Valley to the east of the Berkshire Hills and Green Mountains is itself not distinctly marked off north of Massachusetts and is only vaguely continued in the upper St. Francis and upper Chaudière Valleys near the southeastern border of Quebec, the upper St. John Valley in northern Maine, and the Restigouche Valley and Chaleur Bay along the north edge of New Brunswick.

The rest of New England, the Maritime Provinces, and Newfoundland presumably correspond to the Piedmont Plateau province. Some of each approximates a slightly dissected plateau sloping seaward, but elsewhere the topography is diversified by linear ridges and hilly belts, and to the northwest rise the highest mountains in the segment, the White Mountains of New Hampshire and others nearly as high northeastward into Maine (lower hills continue this trend southward across central Massachusetts and northeastward into northwestern New Brunswick). The several arms of the sea also diversify the topography. In southern New England the rocks are much like those of the Piedmont, but northeastward the grade of metamorphism falls (though granite bodies abound), and Paleozoic, especially middle Paleozoic, fossils are somewhat more common. One Triassic fault trough underlies the lower Connecticut Valley, and another the Bay of Fundy and the Annapolis Valley of Nova Scotia. Furthermore, a large, irregular, mostly little deformed, mainly postorogenic basin of Carboniferous rocks extends from central New Brunswick and northern

Nova Scotia across the Gulf of St. Lawrence into southeastern Newfoundland. Finally, the south margin of the segment is framed by a low, mostly drowned cuesta, underlain by Coastal Plain sediments and crowned by the terminal moraines of the continental glacier—Long Island, Block Island, Martha's Vineyard, Nantucket, the shank of Cape Cod, Georges Bank across the mouth of the Gulf of Maine, and Sable Island Bank off Nova Scotia. Southeast of Newfoundland, and at least as big as that island, is the massive continental projection of the Grand Banks, offset to the right from the continental shelf to the west. Apparently, like that shelf, its outer part is underlain by 700 to 3000 meters (2000 to 10,000 feet) of Mesozoic and Cenozoic sediments, thickening seaward and overlying crystalline rocks of undetermined but probably sialic composition.

In much of the segment, particularly its northeastern part, lumbering (especially for pulp) and fishing are the principal occupations. In the less rugged uplands, small farms are widely scattered and fairly numerous, though less so than a century ago; in the lowland areas, farming is on a larger scale and commonly devoted to dairy produce or to local specialty crops like potatoes and cranberries. Nowadays the tourist trade is of great and growing importance. Mineral deposits are scattered here and there: gold was once important in southern Nova Scotia; base metal deposits are known in northern New Brunswick and elsewhere; there is an important iron deposit in Newfoundland; much coal and some gypsum and salt are mined in the Carboniferous basins in New Brunswick and Nova Scotia; important asbestos deposits are associated with bodies of ultrabasic rock along the northwestern ridges, especially in Quebec; granite, marble, and slate are quarried, especially in Vermont; and pegmatites are common throughout New England, except central and northern Maine. So far large-scale industrialization is mainly confined to southern and central New England and southeastern New York, where in fact the Industrial Revolution first came to America in the middle of the last century.

Growth of Geological Knowledge

Our knowledge of the Appalachians began to accumulate about the time the United States achieved its independence, although at first it was more mineralogical and lithological than properly geological. The first geological synthesis of the country was that of William Maclure,

published in 1809 in Philadelphia and Paris accompanied by a colored geologic map (a second edition was published in 1817; see Maclure, 1809, in the bibliography). Maclure had traversed most of the United States west to the Mississippi River, and the geological subdivisions shown on his map are readily identified with the geologic provinces recognized today, but his terminology was entirely Wernerian. Thus the sediments of the Coastal Plain he classed as Alluvial; the flat-lying Paleozoic rocks of the Mississippi Valley and the Appalachian Plateau as Secondary or Flötz; the deformed but unmetamorphosed rocks of the Valley and Ridge province as Transition; and the crystalline rocks of the Blue Ridge, Piedmont Plateau, and New England as Primitive (some of the Triassic basins were recognized and correctly delineated and were classed as Old Red Sandstone, a subclass of the Secondary). Thus rocks of Paleozoic age were assigned to three of the four major subdivisions, depending on their present attitude and condition, which was evidently accepted as primary. The tectonics of the Appalachians presented no problems to one who believed that the rocks were originally deposited as we see them today!

At the time Maclure was writing, the new concept of faunal succession had just been introduced by William Smith in England and by Cuvier and Brongniart in France, but it did not reach America for nearly a generation. It was first used here by Lardner Vanuxem and others in subdividing the sediments of the Coastal Plain and showing their equivalence with the chalk and the Tertiaries of Europe, but the outstanding early application was to the Lower and Middle Paleozoic rocks of New York State by James Hall, Vanuxem, and their associates, beginning in the late 1830's, hardly any later than its application to the corresponding rocks in England and the Rhineland. The Paleozoic rock succession in New York is well displayed and for the most part structurally simple, and it was described in detail in four reports published in 1842 and 1843; moreover, fossils are abundant through most of it, and the faunas were described by James Hall in a whole series of quarto volumes published over the next half century. As a result the "New York system" became the standard for North American stratigraphy, above all for the flat-lying Paleozoic rocks of the Great Lakes-Mississippi lowland, whose stratigraphy was rapidly worked out in the following decades.

Simultaneously with the work in New York, the brothers Henry D. and William B. Rogers*

---

*No relation to the present author.

worked out the rock succession in the Central Appalachians in Pennsylvania and the Virginias; this succession has many obvious similarities with those in New York and the Mississippi Valley but also some notable differences, over and above the much greater deformation it displays. Thus it is roughly ten times thicker than that in the Mississippi Valley and contains much less limestone and more clastic rocks (the New York succession is intermediate in both respects, and indeed thickens and coarsens eastward across the state); also its upper part is Upper Paleozoic and thus completes the "New York system" (in fact, in North America the Upper Carboniferous is now universally called the Pennsylvanian system).

Meditating on these relations, Hall in 1857 (Hall, 1883) was the first to point out that as a general rule belts of mountains and mountain deformation are belts of thicker and coarser sediments. Hall attempted to explain the belt of thicker sediments by the course of a great ocean current and the deformation simply by subsidence of the sediments, but whatever his explanation, his profound generalization was quickly recognized as valid on both sides of the Atlantic. Not long after, James D. Dana (1873, p. 430 ff.) called the trough of thicker sediments a "geosynclinal" and explained both the trough and the deformation by lateral compression in the Earth's crust, an explanation that met with far more favor than Hall's.

The contribution of the Rogers brothers to North American stratigraphy is overshadowed by their contribution to its tectonics; naturally stratigraphy and tectonics were worked out together. In a joint paper (Rogers and Rogers, 1843) published near the end of the period of their most active work, the brothers described and illustrated the folds of the Valley and Ridge province with extraordinary exactitude—their length and regularity, their parallelism even through arcs of many degrees, their consistent asymmetry and relation to thrust faults—and they drew the conclusion that such a regular system of folds could not have been formed by the local uplift of each individual fold by vertical forces but must reflect a regular system of forces acting tangentially across the folded belt. This force system they envisaged as resulting from catastrophic volcanic explosions to the southeast, near the centers of curvature of the arcs, by which the whole sedimentary cover was shaken as one shakes a blanket held along one edge, the folds being frozen into place as the lava solidefied. As later with Hall, the Rogers brothers' explanation met no acceptance (again Dana's idea of lateral compression in the crust was preferred), but their clear generalization of the facts greatly influenced

geologists working in deformed belts on both sides of the Atlantic. To this day, structure like that of the Valley and Ridge province in Pennsylvania is considered typically "Appalachian."

In southwest Virginia, which encroaches into the Southern Appalachians, W. B. Rogers encountered and accurately described the great thrust faults there associated with or replacing the folds, although he and his successors for a generation or so considered them all upthrusts along very steep planes. His work was carried southwestward across Tennessee by James M. Safford and into Alabama by Eugene A. Smith. Safford (1869) discovered and described the outlying faults and folds of Valley and Ridge type on the Cumberland Plateau, and Smith and one of his associates (Smith, 1893), finding that one of these has a reversed asymmetry, first clearly suggested the idea of an underthrust. Finally, toward the end of the century, the newly created U.S. Geological Survey sent a group of young men (M. R. Campbell, C. Willard Hayes, Arthur Keith) to map the Southern Appalachians on newly completed topographic base maps; from their work (after some false starts) emerged the evidence that the thrust faults are not as steep as had been thought, so that lateral thrust was greater than upward thrust, the recognition of truly low-angle thrust faults (which followed the recognition of such faults in northwest Scotland, Scandinavia, and the Alps), and finally a long synthetic report by Bailey Willis (1893) on the mechanics of Appalachian deformation, based in part on experimental work (and influenced of course by Heim's monumental study of Alpine mechanisms). (More detail on the growth of tectonic ideas in the Appalachian Valley and Ridge province is given in Rodgers, 1949.)

In sharp contrast with these conspicuous successes in interpretation by the geologists working in the Valley and Ridge and Appalachian Plateau provinces, the many able geologists who studied the crystalline rocks of the Appalachians during the nineteenth century produced little more than imprecise lithologic maps. Lacking the aid of fossils, they in effect organized their information on classical Wernerian lines; for one or two decades, even the Wernerian terminology was retained, and later on, after it was discarded, the rocks were classed into supposed age subdivisions (Laurentian or Archean, Huronian, Taconic, Montalban) very largely on metamorphic grade. The numerous state reports of the nineteenth century are now of value, as far as concerns these rocks, almost exactly in inverse proportion to the amount of historical interpretation that was attempted. In the southern segment, all the crystalline rocks came to be considered Precambrian, the roots of an ancient continent Appalachia that persisted throughout the Paleozoic contributing sediments to the "true" Appalachian belt to the west. In New England and Canada, fossil finds prevented this convenient synthesis, but after Logan's original insights, such as recognition of the thrust fault still called Logan's line (Logan, 1861), little progress was made in deciphering the tectonics or the geologic history, except that evidence accumulated for several episodes of severe deformation distributed through the Paleozoic era.

With the introduction of the petrographic microscope, a formidable new tool became available for studying the crystalline rocks, but in the Appalachians, through the first quarter of the twentieth century, it was used mostly to study igneous bodies and their origin; the broader questions of tectonics and historical geology were passed by. A conspicuous exception is the work of Florence Bascom and her students and associates, especially Anna Jonas Stose and George W. Stose, in southeastern Pennsylvania and adjacent Maryland, but even here, where a few fossils are present to help date the rocks, a heated controversy arose over the age and structure of one of the major terrains.

At the beginning of the 1930's, however, Marland P. Billings began studies in the crystalline rocks of New Hampshire that combined careful petrologic study of the igneous and metamorphic rocks with detailed structural analysis and close attention to stratigraphy (Billings, 1950). These studies opened the way to general interpretations of the geologic history of New England. Similar work, much of it by Billings' students, soon began elsewhere, and it is now in progress in each of the New England states and Canada. This work is steadily broadening our understanding of the Northern Appalachians; indeed, ideas are still changing so rapidly that any attempt at synthesis, even if it appears adequate now, can hardly remain so for long. In the southern segment, too, modern work combining stratigraphy, structure, and petrology has begun, notably the work of Ernst Cloos and his students in Maryland and northern Virginia and of Philip B. King and his associates on the borders of Tennessee and North Carolina—to be sure, much of this work has been done in the Blue Ridge province and adjoining parts of the Piedmont, and vast areas of the southeastern Piedmont remain virtually untouched. Altogether, a great renaissance in Appalachian geology is under way, no longer concentrated chiefly on the Valley and

Ridge province but rather on the crystalline rocks north and south.

This book attempts to outline the tectonics of the Appalachian Mountains as presently understood. The different provinces of the chain are taken up not in a geographic nor in a geologic order, but in the human order in which our basic understanding of their structure has been achieved, that is to say roughly the order outlined in the preceding paragraphs. For none of the provinces is a wholly acceptable and noncontroversial interpretation yet available, but the facts are better known and the problems better posed, if not better resolved, in some than in others, and from them one can proceed to the less known, where we may not even be asking the right questions.

Sources and Acknowledgments

The literature on the geology of the Appalachian Mountains is of course extremely large, having accumulated over more than 150 years and being concerned with an area close to the main early centers of population and higher education in the United States and Canada. Fortunately general geologic maps of all the states and provinces (or at least of their Appalachian portions) are now available, although a few are rather old and obsolete (a list is given in the Appendix, p. 226–229), and in recent years several outstanding collections of research papers have been dedicated to different parts of the chain (Lowry, ed., 1964; Clark, ed., 1967; Neale and Williams, eds., 1967; Zen, White, Hadley, and Thompson, eds., 1968; Kay, ed., 1969; Fisher, Pettijohn, Reed, and Weaver, eds., 1970). Most of the states and provinces have active geological surveys, producing detailed maps and reports, and the two national surveys have also been very active, commonly in cooperation with the local surveys. Summary articles and reports have been less common, generally covering only a state or part of a state or province; indeed their absence is the main reason for the present book.

It goes without saying that I am deeply indebted to all my predecessors and colleagues who have worked in the Appalachians, but especially to the innumerable persons who have accompanied me in the field, either in my field areas or in theirs or just on general excursions. I owe my first introduction to Appalachian geology, and indeed to geology in general, to the geological and paleontological group at the New York State Museum in the early 1930's: Drs. C. A. Hartnagel, D. M. Newland, Rudolf Ruedemann, and Winifred

Goldring. Later Profs. C. M. Nevin and K. E. Caster at Cornell, Profs. Charles Schuchert, C. O. Dunbar, C. R. Longwell, and Adolph Knopf, and also Mrs. E. B. Knopf, at Yale encouraged my continuing interest in Appalachian structure and stratigraphy. On the United States Geological Survey I was particularly fortunate to be associated with Josiah Bridge and Philip B. King in work in the Southern Appalachians, and was further encouraged by D. Foster Hewett, Hugh D. Miser, George R. Mansfield, and Charles H. Behre, Jr., who supervised various projects with which I was connected. It would be impossible to enumerate all the others from whom I have drawn inspiration and advice over the years or even their organizations, but I do wish to mention the groups at the Tennessee Valley Authority and the various state surveys, notably those of Tennessee and Virginia. Finally, although I have never been either their student or their colleague, like all others concerned with the Appalachians I must pay tribute to the work of Profs. Marland P. Billings and Ernst Cloos, who have led the way in the major reappraisal of the geology of the crystalline Appalachians that mainly distinguishes the current epoch in Appalachian geology.

The idea of writing this book grew out of the invitation, extended to me in 1957 through the kind offices of Prof. Paul Fallot, to be a visiting lecturer at the Collège de France in Paris. In 1960 I presented eight lectures there on the tectonics of the Appalachians, and an expanded form of those lectures, the first draft of this book, completed with the invaluable support and criticism of Prof. Fallot, was hectographed and distributed in, I think, 65 copies. On my return to the United States, I commenced a second draft, whose preparation proceeded from 1961 to 1964, when it was largely halted by administrative duties that I was not allowed to escape. This draft was finally completed early in 1968, and the final revision was then begun. Various drafts of different chapters have had the benefit of friendly criticism from many colleagues, students, and other friends—I would be quite unable to enumerate them all, but I am deeply grateful. The library, secretarial, and drafting facilities of the Department of Geology and Geophysics of Yale University were at my disposal (when I was able to make use of them), and I heartily thank all those who kindly helped me in these parts of the work. Several ideas developed in the course of preparing the book have been published as separate articles from time to time, but these articles have all been reworked for the present volume.

CHAPTER **2**

The Appalachian Plateau Province

If one proceeds by train or automobile from Chicago in the central lowlands of North America eastward toward Pittsburgh, one crosses first the broad, flat glacial plains of northern Indiana and western Ohio. Beneath lie nearly horizontal middle Paleozoic sedimentary strata, mainly limestone, but the bedrock is almost entirely concealed by glacial drift, and what hills one sees are moraines or other glacial features. In east-central Ohio, however, the countryside changes; one leaves the glacial plain and encounters hills underlain by Carboniferous clastic rocks, dipping very gently but steadily eastward at five to ten meters per kilometer (a few tens of feet per mile). Soon one penetrates an intricately dissected hill country; the tops of the hills rise gradually higher but the individual rock layers drop gradually lower, so that one traverses higher and higher beds. Coal mines make their appearance on the hillsides, and one has entered the Appalachian bituminous coal field. Finally, in the heart of the field, one arrives at Pittsburgh on its three rivers, sunk in narrow, steep-sided valleys nearly 200 meters (600 feet) below the tops of the nearby hills.

If one proceeds farther east, the regional dip ceases to be steadily eastward; instead it reverses and the beds outline broad, gentle synclines and anticlines, although the dip exceeds 5 degrees only locally. In general, lower and lower beds rise

to the surface eastward in ever more rugged country—the Allegheny Mountains—until one reaches the Allegheny Front at the other margin of the coal field, the other edge of the outcrop area of the Carboniferous rocks.

The bituminous coal field thus lies in the heart of a great structural basin or synclinorium, commonly called the Appalachian coal basin or the Allegheny synclinorium (Kay, 1942) and roughly coextensive with the broad part of the Appalachian Plateau province. In the Carboniferous rocks, the lowest part of the basin lies southwest of Pittsburgh in extreme southwestern Pennsylvania and beyond in western West Virginia; here are preserved what may be the youngest Paleozoic rocks in the entire Appalachian region (Dunkard group, generally classified as Lower Permian). The middle and lower Paleozoic strata beneath all thicken eastward, however, and hence in them the low point of the basin is displaced progressively eastward into the belt of gentle folding southeast of Pittsburgh. Probably the upper surface of the Precambrian basement at the bottom of the sedimentary column slopes southeastward under the entire province. The stratigraphy of the synclinorium and of the Valley and Ridge province to the southeast is very well summarized by Colton (1970).

From western Pennsylvania the synclinorium

extends northeast and then east across southern New York State into the Catskill Mountain region, gradually shallowing eastward between the southward regional dip off the Precambrian core of the Laurentian and Adirondack Mountains and the uplifted lower Paleozoic rocks of the Valley and Ridge province. In the opposite direction it extends in full width entirely across West Virginia but then contracts notably, as though its southeast flank were bevelled by the margin of the Valley and Ridge province, which here trends west-southwest. Beyond West Virginia the synclinorium becomes shallower and is complicated by several notable folds. In Alabama it widens and deepens again into the Black Warrior coal basin and then disappears under the overlapping Cretaceous rocks of the Coastal Plain.

Northwest Flank of Main Basin (Southwestern New York to Southwestern West Virginia)

The two flanks of the main Appalachian coal basin, although about equally wide (100 to 150 kilometers or 60 to 80 miles), are quite different in tectonic detail. On the northwest flank, the dip is almost steadily into the basin, nearly due south in southern New York, off the Precambrian shield to the north, but swinging through southeast to nearly due east in Ohio and Kentucky, off the broad Cincinnati arch, the next major structural element to the west; the angle of dip averages perhaps 5 meters per kilometer (perhaps 25 feet per mile) in the Carboniferous rocks at the surface but nearly three times as much in the Lower Devonian (Oriskany sandstone) beneath. Except near the bottom of the basin or at the two ends, the dip is broadly even, but where detailed maps are available (e.g., Fettke, 1954, and Cate, 1962, for western Pennsylvania), there are scattered and apparently planless irregularities—folds of erratic trend, domes, noses, etc.—whose structural relief is rarely more than a few tens of meters (a hundred feet) (Fig. 2A). An apparent exception is the Henderson dome (Fettke, 1950) in eastern Mercer County, northwestern Pennsylvania, an isolated circular dome 8 kilometers (5 miles) across with 45 meters (150 feet) of closure at the surface and more underground.

In the northeast part of the basin in north-central Pennsylvania and south-central New York, more regular folds like those on the southeast flank encroach well onto the northwest flank; these are considered below along with the folds of the southeast flank. In the deepest part of the basin from Pittsburgh southwest there are also some vaguely continuous low folds, roughly parallel with the folds farther southeast, and similar folds extend from western West Virginia into eastern Kentucky, though here they diverge more from the "Appalachian" trend and strike nearly west. They appear to lead westward into an east-west zone of small faults, the Paint Creek-Irvine-Kentucky River fault zone, prominent because there is nothing like it either north or south. The faults of this zone appear to be mostly steep; they have generally been considered normal faults, bounding small grabens, but strike-slip movement may be important. They extend roughly westward up the flank of the basin and across the crest of the Cincinnati arch and die out on the upper southwest flank of the arch—a total length of about 250 kilometers (150 miles). The basement beneath is faulted, and apparently movement began early in the Paleozoic, for the basal Paleozoic clastic strata appear to thicken abruptly southward in the vicinity of the fault zone (Woodward, 1961). Farther west, in the southern part of the large Illinois-western Kentucky basin west of the arch, the same trend is continued by the more prominent Rough Creek fault zone, some 200 kilometers (120 miles) long, which includes horsts as well as grabens and may also represent strike-slip movement. If one includes some faults on the east flank of the Ozark arch still farther west in Missouri, this east-west line of faulting extends in all nearly 750 kilometers (500 miles) across the gentle warps of the continental platform. Clearly it has little if anything to do with the Appalachians.

Altogether different from these folds is the solitary Burning Springs anticline in West Virginia, which extends north-south for 50 kilometers (30 miles diagonally across the deepest part of the Carboniferous basin, breaking the outcrop area of the Permian (Dunkard) rocks into two parts. The coffer-shaped anticline has a maximum structural relief of 500 meters (1650 feet), a flat top more than 1 kilometer (about a mile) wide, and very steep dips on the sides; it is far higher and sharper than any other structure in the main coal basin except along its southeastern edge. Moreover, the ends of the fold are almost as abrupt as the sides, the structural relief fading away in a few kilometers (miles) at either end. In its isolation and its discordant trend, this fold appears quite un-Appalachian.

The gentle northwest flank of the Allegheny synclinorium, with its persistent regional dip, is in no way different either in size or in steepness from the flanks of several other basins farther west in the flat-lying sedimentary cover of the central

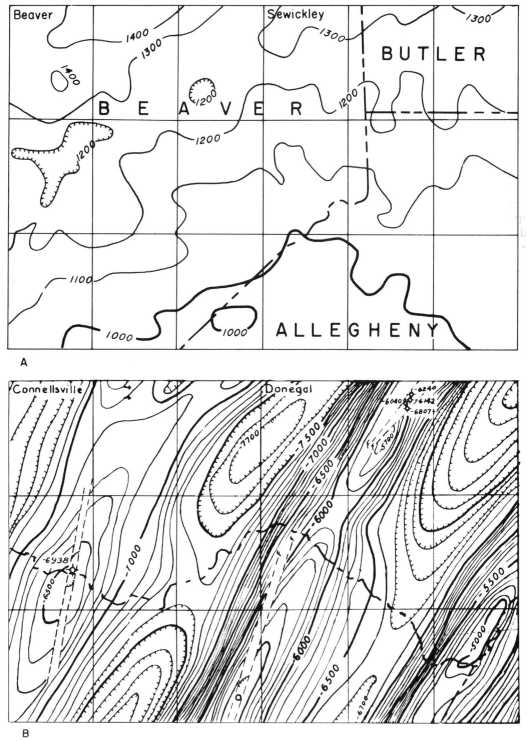

FIGURE 2. Structure contour maps in the Appalachian coal basin of western Pennsylvania. After Fettke, 1954. Each area represents two 15-minute quadrangles (names given in northwest corner); contour interval 100 feet. (A) Area on northwest flank of basin: Pittsburgh quadrangle lies next southeast of area shown. Contours on Ames limestone (Upper Carboniferous); all elevations above sea level. (B) Area on southeast flank of basin; Pittsburgh quadrangle lies next northwest of area shown. Contours on Oriskany sandstone (Lower Devonian); all elevations below sea level. Separate figures give elevation of sandstone in wells in "graben."

14

platform of the continent. Oil wells that penetrate this cover to the underlying Precambrian basement rocks are widely distributed over the platform; moreover, the basement comes to the surface to the north in Canada and certain adjacent parts of the United States and also in the center of the Ozark arch in southern Missouri. Such data make it clear that the basins and the intervening arches are also present in the basement surface; if anything, indeed, they have higher and more marked relief on that surface than in the upper part of the cover, and in several regions it appears that the basins subsided actively, either continuously or intermittently, during the Paleozoic era. Similarly on the northwest flank of the Allegheny synclinorium the Paleozoic strata thicken gradually to the east and southeast, from the Cincinnati arch (which was a shoal during at least part of the Paleozoic) to the bottom of the synclinorium (and well beyond), so that the surface of the basement slopes to the east with a somewhat steeper dip than that of the Carboniferous rocks at the surface, on the order of several tens of meters per kilometer (100 feet per mile).

Furthermore, the broad basins and arches of the central platform exhibit innumerable low minor erratic folds, domes, noses, etc., and the irregular minor features on the northwest flank of the Appalachian coal basin resemble these considerably more than the typical "Appalachian" structural elements to the east, such as those on the southeast flank or even in the bottom of the basin. Where such features have been best studied, in the Mid-Continent oil fields of Kansas and Oklahoma, they present several common characters. Their areal arrangement ranges from a rather imperfect alignment, commonly within fairly narrow zones, to what seems to be complete planlessness. The most marked anticlines are fairly long and continuous, but they are separated by flat basins or irregular structure rather than true synclines, and they nowhere form regular systems of parallel folds. More commonly the beds are warped into irregularly distributed complete or partial domes, rarely more than 100 meters (a few hundred feet) high or a few square kilometers (1 or 2 square miles) in surface area. The structural relief of these anticlinal elements, which have been studied in detail because of the oil they contain, increases with depth almost everywhere; the increase is fairly regular in certain of them, but more commonly it takes place by jumps, especially across disconformities. The dip remains less than 2 degrees, however, over most of the platform, and dips approaching 10 degrees are at once very local and extremely rare; the common use of great vertical exaggerations in cross sections of these

folds leads to a very inaccurate picture of them.

During earlier years, several different theories were proposed for these platform structures, including simple compression of the cover, torsion in the cover, and differential compaction of the sediments. The view now generally accepted (Powers, 1931; Clark, 1932; McCoy, 1934) is that they are chiefly the result of small, intermittent movements in the basement, repeated at the same spots during the Paleozoic and transmitted upward through the sedimentary cover; differential compaction has played a significant but not dominant role. The nature of the stress in the basement is not at all clear; in some cases it may have been simple compression of inhomogeneous material, but in others it may have produced strike-slip movement along certain lines, presumably preexisting lines of weakness. There seems no reason to doubt that the scattered irregular minor features on the northwest flank of the Appalachian coal basin have a similar origin.

The Henderson dome in Mercer County, Pennsylvania, is somewhat different. According to Fettke (1950), a well drilled on this dome found that brecciated Upper Ordovician (Reedsville) shale replaces several hundred meters (well over 1000 feet) of the normal overlying section (Upper Ordovician and Lower Silurian) and that the dome is absent in the beds below; he interprets the dome as the result of diapiric intrusion of the shale into the overlying strata. No reason for the localization of the intrusion so far from other structures is apparent. Another equally speculative possibility is that the well encountered a buried Silurian "cryptoexplosion" structure, like several exposed on the platform to the west and southwest whose ages range from Late Ordovician onward (Bucher, 1936; Born and Wilson, 1939); the dome in the overlying Carboniferous rocks might then have been produced by the relief of later, possibly orogenic, stresses over the preexisting weak spot.

The Burning Springs anticline also requires an entirely different explanation from the other structures of this flank of the basin. Despite its isolation and aberrant trend, I believe it is intimately related to the more regular folds on the opposite flank, and accordingly it is discussed with them.

It has been suggested (Clark and Royds, 1948) that the east-west fault zone across Kentucky reflects strike-slip movement in the basement; if so, the slip was left-handed—that is, the north side has moved west relative to the south side—and could hardly have been produced by compressive stresses oriented across the Appalachian orogenic belt. The zone may, however, merely mark the boundary between two basement blocks with any sort of relative movement.

Southeast Flank of Main Basin (East-Central New York to South-Central West Virginia)

The structural features on the southeast flank of the Appalachian coal basin are quite different from those on the northwest flank; there is no sharp boundary, but the belt of transition is not very wide, at least in the central part of the basin. Instead of low, irregular structures on a general regional dip, one encounters a succession of roughly parallel anticlines and synclines, mostly many times longer than broad. The crests and troughs are not even but rise and fall irregularly, and the folds also show some sinuosity in plan, particularly near plunging ends where individual folds die out and are replaced, en echelon, by others. The character of the folding is well shown by the structure contour maps published by the state surveys of Pennsylvania (Fettke, 1954; Cate, 1962) and West Virginia (McCord, 1960; Haught, 1968; also county oil and gas maps by Haught and others, 1955–1968).

The folds in this part of the Plateau are particularly well displayed in southwestern Pennsylvania, between Pittsburgh and the Allegheny Front at the east edge of the Plateau province (Fig. 2B). Their wave length, crest to crest or trough to trough, ranges from 10 to 20 kilometers (6 to 12 miles) and their structural relief, crest to trough (i.e., twice the amplitude), from 200 meters or less (500 feet or less) for the less regular folds near Pittsburgh to 800 meters (2500 feet) for each of the three large anticlines—Chestnut Ridge, Laurel Hill, and Accident or Negro Mountain (the first two appear in the east half of Fig. 2B)—that dominate the structure farther east and bring the highest Devonian rocks to the surface. Southeast of them, at the south edge of Pennsylvania, another still higher fold, the Deer Park anticline, indents the edge of the Plateau itself, bringing up a good part of the Upper Devonian shale section. Dips are mostly less than 10 degrees, except locally on the flanks of the largest anticlines. No regularity to the plunge of the folds is apparent; the crest of a given anticline may show several high and low points, and they may be opposite either high or low points on the adjacent synclines and anticlines. Likewise there is no evidently consistent asymmetry to these folds; here one flank and there the other is steeper. Faults are rare at the surface, but drilling has revealed a number at depth in the Devonian section (especially in the Huntersville chert and the Oriskany sandstone). Generally these have been interpreted as high-angle faults commonly bounding long, narrow graben along the crests of the anticlines (see Fig. 2B; it is in the anticlines of course that drilling data are ordinarily

available). Gwinn (1964), however, has accumulated much information showing that the faults are thrust faults bringing one or other flank up over the crestal area; the faults flatten down dip away from the crests.

Northward the strike of these folds, which is about north-northeast near Pittsburgh, swings in a great arc through due northeast in northwestern Pennsylvania to east-northeast and north of east in north-central Pennsylvania and south-central New York, and Woodward (1957a) reports tracing some of the axes, with a trend almost due east, into the Catskill Mountains of southeastern New York. This arc is roughly parallel to the arc made by the much steeper folds in the Valley and Ridge province in central Pennsylvania, though the center of curvature may be a little farther southeast. The wave length of the Plateau folds remains roughly the same throughout this arc, but the amplitude falls off northeastward; in south-central New York State the largest anticlines stand less than 300 meters (1000 feet) above the adjacent synclines, but in nearby Pennsylvania they are somewhat higher. There is a fairly consistent southwest plunge from this area toward the deeper part of the basin in southwestern Pennsylvania; east-north-eastward in northeastern Pennsylvania and southern New York, Devonian rocks completely replace Carboniferous rocks at the surface. Here also the folded belt encroaches considerably onto the northwest flank of the synclinorium, probably because the synclinorial axis shifts to the southeast in the older strata there exposed. As these folds are superposed on the southward regional dip they show a consistent asymmetry, the southeast flanks of the anticlines being the steeper. Faults are present here at the surface as well as underground, including small thrust faults of a few meters (feet) throw, dipping northwest on the steeper southeast flanks of the anticlines.

The Plateau folds can also be followed southwestward far into West Virginia, but significant changes appear just south of the southern border of Pennsylvania. The easternmost anticlines increase in amplitude and steepness southward across the western county of Maryland into eastern West Virginia, exposing thick and weak Devonian shale strata beneath resistant Carboniferous sandstone and conglomerate units (Pocono and Pottsville sandstones), which in turn underlie coal measures. The area is thus one of strong relief, anticlinal valleys lying between coal basins rimmed by outward-facing cuestas; Spruce Knob, the highest point in the Allegheny Mountains and indeed the entire Plateau province, is on the easternmost such cuesta, facing east toward the Valley and Ridge province.

Of the larger Plateau folds in southern Pennsylvania, only the two eastern ones extend south into this belt of stronger folding. The Deer Park anticline strikes southwest diagonally across the west end of Maryland, its height fairly constant at about 1600 meters (5000 feet). The syncline between it and the Valley and Ridge province, the Georges Creek coal basin west of Cumberland, Maryland, still preserves strata of the same Early Permian age as the youngest rocks (Dunkard group) in the main synclinorium southwest of Pittsburgh, but here they are involved in a fold of unmistakable Appalachian trend with dips up to 30 degrees. West of the Deer Park anticline, the Accident anticline rises south-southwest into Maryland, but then ends abruptly 20 kilometers (13 miles) from the state line; 12 kilometers (7 miles) north of west and just inside West Virginia, the Briery Mountain anticline rises as abruptly to an even greater height—1300 meters (4000 feet)—and trends on south-southwest. Some 25 kilometers (16 miles) on, there is a smaller and less distinct westward offset, beyond which the fold is known as the Etam anticline. Dips of 25 degrees are present along the northwest flank of this line of folds, and dips of 40 degrees occur on the Deer Park anticline near where it enters West Virginia.

Because of the difference in strike and despite the offsets, the Deer Park and the Accident-Briery Mountain-Etam folds converge southwestward; where they meet, the traces of individual axes are hard to follow, but in effect the two folds are replaced by the still higher and steeper Elkins Valley anticline, whose west flank has a relief of nearly 3000 meters (9000 feet) and steep, locally overturned, dips; wells suggest thrust faults not far underground (Reeves and Price, 1950, p. 2111–2112 and Fig. 5B). From the point where it replaces the other folds, it extends 70 kilometers (45 miles) south-southwest; the trend is somewhat sinuous, however.

The Elkins Valley anticline lies some 40 kilometers (25 miles) west-northwest of the edge of the Plateau; as the average wave length of Plateau folds is about 15 kilometers (9 miles), there is room for one or two additional pairs of folds between. Behind its higher part, there are two fairly large anticlines (Glady Fork and Horton anticlines), with dips to 35 degrees and heights of over 1000 meters (3500 feet). Northward the eastern anticline plunges and disappears and the western is offset to the east, forming the lower Blackwater dome only about 700 meters (2000 feet) high. Southward the two join, about opposite the abrupt south end of the Elkins Valley anticline, and rise into the Browns Mountain or Pocahontas anticline, the highest of all the Plateau folds in Pennsyl-

vania and West Virginia. In its core the uppermost Ordovician strata (Juniata redbeds) are exposed, thrust northwest over Middle Devonian shale, a stratigraphic displacement of nearly 1000 meters (over 2500 feet); the total relief of the fold is over 3000 meters (nearly 10,000 feet). Indeed, both physiographically and structurally this anticline resembles the folds of the Valley and Ridge province as much as those of the Plateau, and it is often assigned to that province. It trends about S30°W, parallel to the boundary of the Valley and Ridge province 12 to 15 kilometers (8 to 10 miles) to the east, and extends for over 100 kilometers (65 miles) before it plunges down, near the well known resort White Sulphur Springs, and is lost among a group of 6 to 8 small, parallel, closely spaced folds with the same trend. No other large fold appears to take its place; thus the belt of stronger folding along the east side of the Plateau, which narrows southward as the folds become higher and fewer, terminates here. The group of small folds, which involve only Upper Devonian and Lower Carboniferous beds (one fold has a relief of 500 meters—1,500 feet; the others are all much smaller) and are accompanied by some minor thrust faults, spreads westward about 25 kilometers (15 miles), but does not extend far along the trend, for, just to the east, the boundary between the provinces abruptly changes direction to S60°W and starts to bevel across the Plateau folds instead of lying parallel to them. At the same point a major thrust fault, the St. Clair fault, appears at the surface along the boundary.

The folds west of the Accident anticline, on the other hand, all decrease in relief in northern West Virginia and show some curious changes and offsets, especially along two transverse lines that extend about N80°W from the two prominent offsets in the Accident-Briery Mountain-Etam trend; for convenience these two lines are here termed the Morgantown-Sang Run and the Fairmont Rowlesburg line. The Laurel Hill anticline indeed practically disappears at the state line, but its trend is continued beyond the traverse lines by the Preston, Hiram, and Webster Springs anticlines, each offset to the west and each lower than the preceding one (maximum heights are 400, 150, and 75 meters—1200, 500, and 250 feet).

The Chestnut Ridge anticline is more nearly continuous, but it too drops off markedly and offsets slightly to the west as it crosses each of the transverse lines. Farther west, the southern of these lines separates an area of especially weak and irregular folds coming out of Pennsylvania— relief on the order of 50 meters (150 feet)—from north ends of two more anticlines, the Wolf

Summit and the Arches Fork. These and the southwestern extension of the Chestnut Ridge anticline here stand generally 100 to 150 meters (250 to 500 feet) above the adjacent synclines; they trend generally southwest into central West Virginia but are quite sinuous, and each shows at least one sharp westward offset, across which their axes are not certainly continuous. Because of their southwest trend, they diverge more and more from the south-southwest-trending folds to the east; between appears a large triangular area with, at the surface, an almost steady northwest regional dip of 20 to 30 meters per kilometer (100 to 150 feet per mile) broken only by a few weak terraces or folds like the Webster Springs anticline. Finally, 90 kilometers (55 miles) southwest of the Fairmont-Rowlesburg line, the Chestnut Ridge anticline, or rather its offset, the Orlando anticline, bends off toward the south and fades away entirely, and the other two are lost in a transverse zone of small folds—domes and basins—with as much as 150 meters (450 feet) of relief and curious blunt ends, in places offset from one another along N20°W lines (the west side offset south); the zone itself is elongate in the same direction.

West of the Arches Fork anticline and its continuations is an area almost devoid of structure, perhaps the flattest part of the bottom of the Appalachian coal basin. Yet cutting diagonally across this seemingly structureless area is the Burning Springs anticline described above (p. 13), with nearly vertical sides and a structural relief of 500 meters (1,650 feet), far higher and steeper than any other fold on the Plateau west of the Chestnut Ridge and Elkins Valley anticlines. It extends for 50 kilometers (30 miles) in a somewhat sinuous north-south line between remarkably abrupt terminations, each hooked to the east (the north end also sends out a prong to the north-northwest—Smith, 1948—and farther northwest the low Cambridge anticline or monoclinal flexure can be followed for 125 kilometers (80 miles) across eastern Ohio). The northern termination is far from any other distinct folds, although from the west end of the Fairmont-Rowlesburg line, about 60 kilometers (35 miles) to the east, a vague low fold (the extension of the Littleton anticline north of the line) extends westward toward it. The southern termination, on the other hand, is close to the north end of the transverse zone of short folds mentioned above; the nearest folds are perhaps offset parts of the Arches Fork anticline.

In the northern part of this transverse zone, where it crosses the trends of the Arches Fork and Wolf Summit anticlines, the individual folds trend southwest, but farther south, where it forms the west side of the triangular area of northwest

regional dip, several folds with south or south-southeast trends also appear. One, the Mann Mountain anticline, can be traced for about 60 kilometers (35 miles) along the zone, though its maximum relief is less than 100 meters (only about 250 feet); its trace is somewhat sinuous, but the longest straight stretch trends N20°W. Finally the zone approaches the boundary of the Valley and Ridge province close to the southwest end of the group of small S30°W folds around the end of the Browns Mountain anticline, and it marks an abrupt change of trend between these folds and a few folds trending S60–70°W on the Plateau to the west, near to and parallel with the province boundary.

Taken together, the transverse zone and the Burning Springs anticline extend roughly N15–20°W for 200 kilometers (130 miles) entirely across the state of West Virginia; thus the Burning Springs anticline is not as isolated as it at first appears but rather forms a northward extension of the transverse zone from the southeast flank of the coal basin with its fairly regular folds across the floor of the basin toward the northwest flank. The two together may appropriately be termed the Burning Springs-Mann Mountain line.

The only folds of any size on the Plateau west of this line are the pair closest to the Valley and Ridge province—the Abbs Valley anticline and the Hurricane Ridge syncline south of it. Their mutual relief, only about 200 meters (500 feet) where they begin in the south end of the transverse zone, increases rapidly southwestward and reaches 1000 meters (3000 feet) where they cross into Virginia. At about that point, the Richlands thrust fault appears along the northwest flank of the anticline, about 7 kilometers (4½ miles) northwest of the St. Clair fault along the province boundary; westward it increases in throw, bringing up Upper Devonian shale, and gradually approaches the St. Clair fault (it is here accompanied by smaller thrust faults in the steep beds just to the northwest). About 60 kilometers (35 miles) from the state line, the two faults merge in the eastern part of a very complicated area centering around Big A Mountain; beds as low as Middle Ordovician appear on the tapering end of the fault sliver between them, apparently on the south flank of the Hurricane Ridge syncline (elsewhere no beds older than Devonian appear along this flank beneath the St. Clair fault and its branches).

The rest of the folds on the Plateau west of the Burning Spring-Mann Mountain line are all low—130 meters (400 feet) or less in relief. They trend generally west-southwest but are sinuous and irregular, though some show considerable continuity, notably the Warfield anticline which appears about 25 kilometers (15 miles) east of Charleston, West Virginia, and can be traced into Kentucky. On its south flank, for some kilometers (miles) east of the state line, is a zone of somewhat steeper south dips, locally faulted, and the whole belt of deformation apparently merges westward into the eastern end of the Paint Creek-Irvine fault zone (see p. 13). These folds seem intermediate in character between the higher and more regular folds on the southeast flank of the coal basin and the low irregular domes and basins on its northwest flank.

The folds on the southeast flank of the Appalachian coal basin run so generally parallel to those in the nearest part of the Valley and Ridge province (north of the sharp change in strike opposite the south end of the Browns Mountain anticline), showing the same curvature across Pennsylvania, that no one has questioned that they are equally a part of the Appalachian fold system, formed at the same time and by the same forces. They are, however, much lower and more gentle, and there is little transition from one to the other, save for the Browns Mountain (Pocahontas) anticline, which is intermediate in every respect. In Pennsylvania, the flanks of even the largest folds on the Plateau average no more than 15 degrees at the surface, whereas the northwesternmost fold of the Valley and Ridge province, the great Nittany arch, is the broadest, highest, and steepest fold in the northwest half of that province; Cambrian rocks are exposed on its crest, and its northwest flank is overturned till locally the beds dip no more than 30 degrees southeast. One is forced to admit therefore that the forces acted very differently in the two provinces, presumably because of differences in the geologic material to be folded or in its attitude relative to the forces. The sharp boundary, where the nearly flat beds of the Plateau give way to the steeply dipping or overturned beds on the northwest flank of the Nittany arch, has been called by Price (1931) the Appalachian structural front. According to Price the front coincides with the line where the sedimentary rocks to be folded, at least the Middle and Upper Paleozoic rocks, were the thickest, that is, with the central line of a zone of weakness where the basement surface was most deeply depressed at the time that Paleozoic deposition was coming to an end and deformation was beginning. Southeast of the front, both Precambrian surface and Paleozoic strata would then have sloped gently northwest, and under forces "from the southeast" they would fold readily, whereas northwest of the front they would have sloped gently southeast and would resist deformation.

More recent compilations of thickness data cast

doubt on this view, however. The Carboniferous strata show relatively little change in thickness across Pennsylvania, but what maximum they have is farther east in the anthracite region. The underlying strata, on the other hand, especially the Devonian and Silurian, show an immense thickening to maxima deep in the Valley and Ridge province.

Whatever the explanation of the Valley and Ridge folds and of their sharp western boundary, the gentleness and breadth of the folds in the Appalachian Plateau has suggested that they are also deep. According to Sherrill (1934), who carefully studied the asymmetry of the folds in Pennsylvania and southern New York, if only the regional dip at the present surface is taken into account, the folds show a slight southeast-facing asymmetry, opposite to that typical for the Valley and Ridge folds, but if the folds are projected down to the upper boundary of the basement, the asymmetry can be fully accounted for by the regional dip of that boundary. From this argument, and from the argument of Ashley (1908) that even the strongest, most "competent" layers in the sedimentary column are far too weak to support arches of such a size even without an overburden of weaker rocks, Sherrill concluded that all these folds are the results of deformation in the basement, producing folds in its upper surface which were then reflected upward through the sedimentary sequence.

Drilling on the crests of many of the larger anticlines on the Plateau has shown that they certainly persist, with little change in amplitude though with steeper dips and more faulting, as far as the Lower Devonian (the Oriskany sandstone, an important source of natural gas in the region). In 1955, the Sandhill well of the Hope Natural Gas Company in Wood County, West Virginia (Bayles and others, 1956; Woodward and others, 1959), begun in Upper Carboniferous rocks on the flat top of the Burning Springs anticline near its highest point, was completed to the Precambrian basement. This well penetrated a normal succession of strata about 1250 meters (about 4000 feet) thick down to the Lower Devonian (Huntersville chert, next above the Oriskany sandstone) with little evidence of disturbance or any but flat dips. It then entered a 600-meter (2000-foot) zone of intensely deformed rocks, with irregular steep dips and faults, in which the Lower Devonian sequence (Huntersville, Oriskany, and Helderberg formations) is repeated several times. Woodward (Woodward and others, 1959, p. 18) estimated the excess over the true stratigraphic sequence in this zone at 505 meters (1658 feet), almost exactly equal to the relief of the fold. Below this zone, the well reentered flat-lying Lower Devonian rocks and showed no signs of further disturbance through 2150 meters (more than 7000 feet) of strata to the Precambrian basement.

The elevation of the basal Devonian and Silurian strata below the disturbed zone is very nearly the same as their elevation in wells in the basins on either side of the anticline, if account be taken of the regional dip. Thus there are three numerical agreements in the data: the elevation of the Silurian strata under the anticline agrees with that in the basins on either side; the width of the flat top of the anticline agrees roughly with the depth to the center of the disturbed zone; and the structural relief of the fold agrees very closely with the excess thickness in the disturbed zone. The logical conclusion from these data, drawn by all who have studied them, is that the anticline is present only or mainly in the Carboniferous and Devonian strata and closes out downward in a zone of disharmony.

The duplicated Lower Devonian section found in the Burning Springs anticline, though spectacular, is not unique; for example, one of the wells in the Giffin dome on the Chestnut Ridge anticline 80 kilometers (50 miles) north of the Pennsylvania-West Virginia state line (Gray in Schaffner, 1958, Pl. 8, p. 76; Gwinn, 1964, Fig. 11, p. 879) penetrated the Oriskany sandstone three times in 550 meters (1800 feet)—the structural relief of the dome is about 800 meters (2500 feet)—and another well, 75 kilometers (48 miles) southwest along the same anticline, penetrated 750 meters (nearly 2500 feet) of Upper Silurian strata (Salina group) (normal thickness about 250 meters—850 feet) without reaching the base, with salt beds through several hundred meters (feet). Ludlum (1958) and several others have therefore suggested that all the larger folds on the Plateau close downward in a zone of disharmony, which would also have to be a zone of decollement. Rodgers (1963, p. 1533) pointed out that the Burning Springs anticline lies along the western edge of thick salt beds in the Upper Silurian (Salina group); they have been found in wells all across northern West Virginia, western Pennsylvania, and southwestern and south-central New York, but they appear to be absent (though anhydrite is present) in the Sandhill well and in all wells farther west and southwest. He therefore suggested that a large block of the Devonian and Carboniferous strata under the Plateau slipped a quarter to a half mile relatively northwestward on these salt beds. The block would consist of the wedge between the Burning Springs-Mann Mountain line and the Fairmont-Rowlesburg line plus the belt between the Chestnut Ridge anticline and the Valley and Ridge province from the latter line northeastward as far

as Clearfield in central Pennsylvania, southeast of which a number of small transverse faults cut the folds. He further suggested another large block in north-central Pennsylvania and south-central New York but indicated no boundaries; the presence of a decollement there has been confirmed by the work of Prucha (1968) in a salt mine in one of the northernmost anticlines in New York, and the limit of more than very mild folding corresponds quite well with the limit in this area of relatively thick salt (75 meters—250 feet) in the upper part of the Upper Silurian Syracuse formation (Rickard, 1969, Pl. 8). According to the decollement concept, as worked out in detail by Gwinn (1964), the Plateau folds are simply buckles formed within or at the leading edge of such a block as it slipped (Fig. 3), and the transverse lines and other offsets of folds are the result of strike-slip movement within it or at its lateral margins. Well information (Reeves and Price, 1950, p. 2110 ff.) in the Elkins Valley and Briery Mountain anticlines and exposures of Silurian rocks in the Browns Mountain (Pocahontas) anticline indicate, however, that the postulated zone of decollement must descend to deeper strata under those folds; the thick shale sequence (Reedsville or Martinsburg shale) in the Upper Ordovician is a reasonable possibility. In other words, in contrast to Sherrill's view, all these folds would be the result of deformation within the Paleozoic cover, the basement beneath being undisturbed.

Pine Mountain (Cumberland) Thrust Block

In the Cumberland Mountains along the state line between Virginia and Kentucky, about 35 kilometers (22 miles) southwest of their common corner with West Virginia and 40 kilometers (25 miles) northwest of the continuation of the St. Clair fault, a low anticline appears in otherwise virtually flat-lying Upper Carboniferous coal measures, with a small thrust fault on its northwest side. West-southwestward the fold rises rapidly and the fault increases in throw, and at a locality on the state line called Skagg Gap, only about 10 kilometers (6 miles) beyond, the south limb of the fold has a dip of 33 degrees, strata on the crest stand at least 1000 meters (3500 feet) above their position at the south foot, and the north limb is entirely cut out by the thrust fault, which here throws weak Upper Devonian black shale (Chattanooga shale) against the flat-lying Upper Carboniferous strata to the north (a large part of the increase in throw of the fault occurs abruptly at the gap).

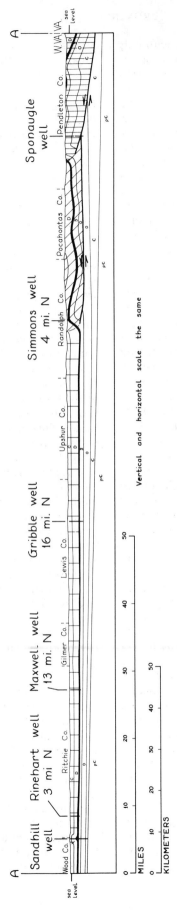

FIGURE 3. Interpretive cross section of Appalachian Plateau and western edge of Valley and Ridge province in West Virginia, passing through Sandhill and Sponaugle wells. Widely spaced vertical lines—decollement in Upper Silurian; diagonal lines—decollement in Middle or Upper Ordovician; closely spaced vertical lines—decollement in Lower or Middle Cambrian. Stratigraphic units (top to bottom): Carboniferous (including Permian); Devonian (heavy line — Lower Devonian); Silurian; Ordovician; Cambrian; Precambrian basement. From Rodgers, 1963, Fig. 2 (reprinted with permission from the *Bulletin of the American Association of Petroleum Geologists*).

21

From Skagg Gap the fold and fault, with only gradual changes in height and throw, continue west-southwestward for 200 kilometers (125 miles) through the otherwise flat-lying coal measures of the Plateau, extending in a nearly straight line across the southeast corner of Kentucky into eastern Tennessee (Fig. 4), roughly parallel to the nearest folds and faults of the Valley and Ridge province some kilometers (miles) across the strike. Throughout this distance resistant sandstone layers (Lee group) at the base of the Upper Carboniferous, upturned on the south limb of the fold, uphold a prominent and continuous linear ridge called Pine Mountain; at its north foot lies an equally continuous linear valley, the trace of the fault appearing in the valley or on the north face of the mountain. Pine Mountain stands 300 to 600 meters (1000 to 2000 feet) above the valley, and ridge and valley cut sharp and straight through the essentially planless dendritic topography eroded in the flat-lying beds on either side. Along the last 8 kilometers (5 miles) of the Pine Mountain fault in Tennessee, the throw increases somewhat and Silurian and locally uppermost Ordovician strata appear along it. The fault is compound where it has been studied in detail; near its southwest end there are at least 7 separate fault planes in the thrust zone (Englund, 1968, p. 29).

The southwest end of the fault and fold is even more abrupt than the northeast. The strike of the dipping sandstone strata that form Pine Mountain (Lee group) swings through a sharp right angle from west-southwest to south-southeast, and the fault does the same (merging with the minor Terry Creek fault that extends a few kilometers— miles—northwest from the junction into the flat-lying strata), and mountain and valley, fold and fault (here called the Jacksboro fault) cut transversely 13 kilometers (8 miles) across the grain of the country and emerge at the edge of the Valley and Ridge province. Here the tipped-up strata forming the mountain make another sharp right angle to the northeast and merge with those in the hogback (locally called Cumberland Mountain) that marks the border of the Plateau province for many kilometers (miles) to the east-northeast; on the other hand the Jacksboro fault and the flat-lying Carboniferous rocks west of it project another 15 kilometers (10 miles) south-southeastward, causing an abrupt offset in the boundary between the two provinces, before the fault and with it the boundary curve away to the southwest into the normal Appalachian strike.

This extraordinary fault thus detaches from the main Plateau a nearly rectangular block of virtually flat-lying Upper Carboniferous coal measures 200 kilometers (125 miles) long and 13 to 40 kilometers (8 to 25 miles) wide, surrounded on all sides but the northeast by strongly upturned older strata. The basin so formed is called the Middlesboro or Cumberland coal basin; its flat bottom is interrupted only by a few narrow belts of disturbed (tilted and brecciated) rocks that run transversely across the block, generally at angles of about 60 degrees to its long sides (the hogback on the southeast side of the basin shows some deflections where intersected by these belts), and by the extraordinary Middlesboro (Ky.) "cryptoexplosion" structure (Englund and Roen, 1963). The detached nature of the southwest end of the block was recognized in the middle of the nineteenth century by Safford (1869, p. 54–55, 68–69, 141–143), but a northeast border was first discovered by Wentworth (1921) in the present century. Wentworth recognized that a belt of disturbed rocks crossing the otherwise flat-lying Carboniferous strata southeast of Skagg Gap represents a transverse strike-slip fault, the Russell Fork fault, extending from the gap for 40 kilometers (25 miles) southeastward to the edge of the Valley and Ridge province at Big A Mountain. The abrupt increase in the throw of the Pine Mountain fault at Skagg Gap thus results from its intersection with the Russell Fork fault and the addition of the right-handed strike slip of that fault to the relatively small throw of the thrust fault northeast of the gap. According to Wentworth's estimate the strike slip on the Russell Fork is 3 kilometers (2 miles) and that on the Jacksboro fault 15 kilometers (10 miles), so that the block pivoted on its northeast end; later detailed work has confirmed this estimate. Wentworth seems to have thought that the Pine Mountain fault under the block continues to dip southeast at the same angle as where the surface trace of its main branch appears on the face of Pine Mountain —10 to 15 degrees near Skagg Gap—cutting diagonally downward across all the underlying strata.

A few years later, Butts (1927) reported the discovery of several curious areas of badly deformed Ordovician and Silurian rocks surrounded by and apparently underlying nearly flat-lying Upper Cambrian strata (Maynardville limestone and Conasauga shale) on the crest of the broad, flat-topped Powell Valley anticline, the first fold south of the Plateau border along the narrower southwestern part of the Middlesboro coal basin (the fold plunges and disappears northeastward some kilometers—miles—short of the Russell Fork fault). These areas lie just north of the Tennessee state line 20 to 30 kilometers (13 to 20 miles) east of Cumberland Gap at the extreme west tip of Virginia, 6 kilometers (4 miles) south of Cumberland Mountain along the Kentucky state line at the Plateau border, and 25 kilometers (16 miles) south-southeast of Pine Mountain and its fault.

Butts recognized at once that these areas are windows and that the fault around them is the Pine Mountain fault, which, instead of cutting diagonally downward across the strata, must follow the Devonian (Chattanooga) black shale under the entire Middlesboro basin and only start to cut down again under the Powell Valley anticline, where erosion has fortunately exposed it (Fig. 4B). More recent work by Miller and his associates (Miller and Fuller, 1954; Miller and Brosgé, 1954) plus some drilling (a small oil field was discovered in the deformed rocks beneath the fault) have completely confirmed Butt's interpretation and have shown that here too the Pine Mountain fault is compound, with slices as much as 50 meters (150 feet) thick between its branches. Furthermore, Miller and Brosgé have successfully applied the window interpretation to a whole series of anomalous areas of Ordovician to Devonian rocks extending 25 kilometers (15 miles) east-northeast along the axis of the anticline, and there may be more as far again to the northeast (Miller, 1962).

Finally, Rich (1934) showed how the whole structure—Pine Mountain fault, Middlesboro basin, upturn at the Plateau border, and Powell Valley anticline with windows—is the natural result of movement on a thrust fault that followed weak layers in the stratigraphic column for long distances and jumped from one weak layer to another by cutting at high angles across the stronger intermediate strata—thus, in the cross section through Butts' windows (Fig. 4B), near the Plateau border it jumped from the weak Middle and Upper Cambrian (Conasauga) shale up to the weak Devonian (Chattanooga) shale, and at Pine Mountain it jumped from the latter shale to now eroded higher layers or perhaps to the former land surface. The plunge and disappearance of the Powell Valley anticline northeastward from the window area is the logical consequence of the pivoting action that had already been deduced by Wentworth, and the transverse disturbed belts within the coal basin are evidently incipient strike-slip faults within the block that failed to develop like those at its ends, to which they are roughly parallel. Later work, well summarized by Harris (1967, 1970), has shown that part of the fault was itself folded by further growth of the Powell Valley anticline, probably by the same process over another fault deeper in the sedimentary column; thus Rich's demonstration that the fault followed the weak layers as much as possible is fully confirmed. Furthermore, drilling within the coal basin (Young, 1957) has repeatedly reached the fault, which lies near but not at the base of the Devonian

(Chattanooga) shale (mostly in its lowest tenth) and is recognized by shearing and carbonization of the bituminous shale and by the presence of pockets of natural gas under high pressure. At the southwest end of the block, the fault must lie a bit deeper, in shale close to the base of the Silurian (basal Rockwood formation) or in the uppermost Ordovician (Sequatchie formation) near the northwest side of the block but at the top of the Lower Cambrian (Rome formation) under the Powell Valley anticline.

Folds and Faults on the Cumberland Plateau

About 40 kilometers (25 miles) southwest of the Jacksboro fault at the southwest end of the Pine Mountain block, the rough Cumberland Mountains, eroded in the coal measures, give way to the flat-topped Cumberland Plateau, upheld by resistant sandstone layers (Lee group) at the base of the Upper Carboniferous from which erosion has stripped the coal-bearing strata. The rocks here dip east-southeastward at less than 10 meters per kilometer (only 40 feet per mile) off the Nashville dome (the southern extension of the Cincinnati arch), which lies to the west; farther south the dip decreases to barely 5 meters per kilometer (barely 25 feet per mile) near the Tennessee-Alabama state line. In northern Alabama, however, it swings fairly abruptly from eastward to southward around the southeast corner of the Nashville dome; hence the outcrop area of Upper Carboniferous rocks widens to form the triangular Black Warrior coal basin, lying between the older rocks exposed on the south flank of the dome and those in the Valley and Ridge province (the third side is the Cretaceous overlap of the Coastal Plain which terminates the exposed part of the Appalachian mountain belt). Only the north margin and part of the east margin of this basin are plateaulike.

From the middle of Tennessee far southwestward into Alabama, the Plateau is split lengthwise by Sequatchie or Browns Valley, eroded where the straight Sequatchie anticline, 335 kilometers (over 200 miles) long, has lifted up the resistant Carboniferous (Lee) sandstone layers and exposed the less resistant strata beneath. Along the high central segment of this strongly asymmetrical anticline, the lowest rocks exposed are Ordovician or uppermost Cambrian (Knox group), and here the steeper northwest flank is broken by the Sequatchie Valley thrust fault (Milici, 1963). To the southwest the fault seems to die out, but to the northeast it disappears beneath the surface (thus it

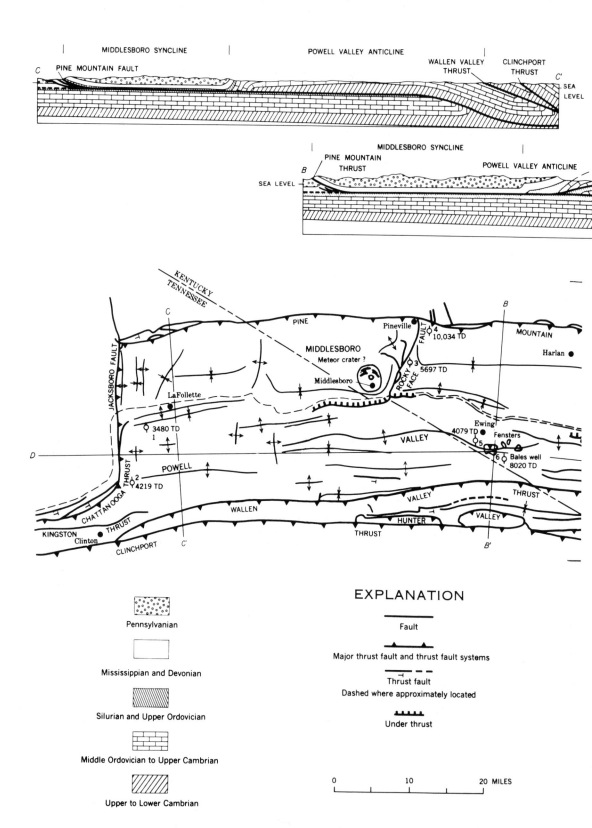

FIGURE 4. Structure map of the Pine Mountain thrust block, from Harris (1970, Fig. 1, which gives original sources of data). Skagg Gap at north-northeast corner of block, Big A Mountain at east-southeast corner, and village of Cumberland Gap, Virginia, in west tip of state of Virginia, just east of corner with Kentucky and Tennessee. Dashed line is province boundary; from Big Stone Gap to the Jacksboro fault it follows Cumberland Mountain.

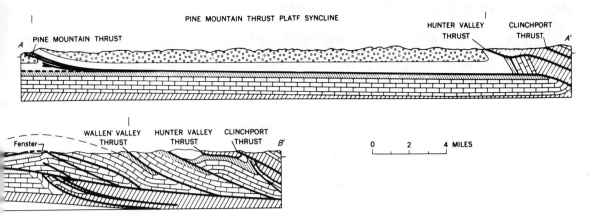

PINE MOUNTAIN THRUST PLATE SYNCLINE

PINE MOUNTAIN THRUST

HUNTER VALLEY THRUST

CLINCHPORT THRUST

A   A'

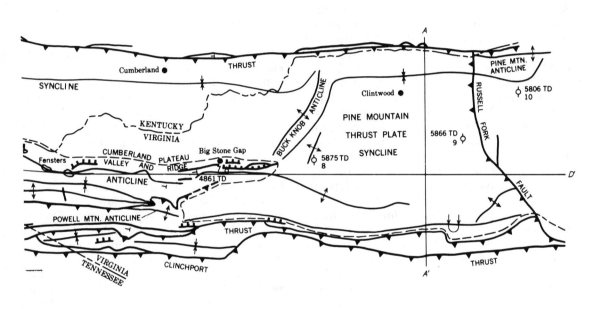

Fenster

WALLEN VALLEY THRUST

HUNTER VALLEY THRUST

CLINCHPORT THRUST

B'

0   2   4 MILES

A

Cumberland   THRUST

SYNCLINE

KENTUCKY
VIRGINIA

Fensters

CUMBERLAND   PLATEAU   Big Stone Gap
VALLEY   AND   RIDGE

ANTICLINE   4861 TD

POWELL MTN. ANTICLINE

VIRGINIA
TENNESSEE

CLINCHPORT   THRUST

BUCK KNOB ANTICLINE

Clintwood ●

PINE MOUNTAIN

THRUST PLATE

SYNCLINE

5875 TD
8

5866 TD
9

PINE MTN.
ANTICLINE

5806 TD
10

RUSSELL FORK

FAULT

D'

THRUST

A'

THRUST

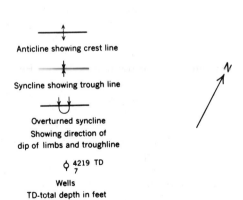

Anticline showing crest line

Syncline showing trough line

Overturned syncline
Showing direction of
dip of limbs and troughline

4219 TD
7

Wells
TD-total depth in feet

N

was cut by a well 20 kilometers—14 miles—northeast of its northeastern surface termination); at both ends the fold plunges rather gently, dying away over a distance of 50 kilometers (30 miles) to the northeast and 80 kilometers (50 miles) to the southwest. The strike of the anticline is roughly that of the folds in the Valley and Ridge province to the southeast but straighter; it is separated from them by a band of nearly flat-lying Carboniferous rocks, which is about 13 kilometers (8 miles) or more wide in Tennessee and still wider in Alabama (Walden Ridge).

The bold isolation of the Sequatchie anticline helped to confirm Price (1931, p. 34, 44) and Ver Wiebe (1936, p. 924, 934–935) in the view that the Appalachian folds could not have been formed by forces transmitted through the sedimentary column (here across the 13 kilometers—8 miles—or more of flat-lying strata separating it from the Valley and Ridge province) but must have been continuously supported from the basement below, as Sherrill argued for the folds in the Plateau in Pennsylvania. On the other hand, the evident similarity of the fold to the Pine Mountain fold and fault in trend and position (the ends of the two are only 55 kilometers—35 miles—apart) led Rich (1934, p. 1595) to suggest that it too is the result of thrusting along weak layers in the sedimentary column, but with considerably less displacement. Rodgers (1950) explored Rich's suggestion, citing as evidence a line of transverse structures at the northeast end—the Emory River line of disturbance—which he thought was a strike-slip fault analogous to the Jacksboro fault, and two areas of younger rocks surrounded by older rocks in the Valley and Ridge province to the southeast, which he interpreted as windows like those Butts found behind the Pine Mountain block. (These are the two windows next to the Chattanooga fault southwest of Harriman; more recent work [Tiedemann, 1956; Swingle, 1961] has confirmed that they are windows, but interprets them as windows through a different thrust fault [Rockwood fault], which comes to the surface at the west edge of the Valley and Ridge province [Chapter 3, p. 52].) The weak layer along which thrusting took place would be the Middle and Upper Cambrian (Conasauga) shale along the high part of the fold but perhaps the Devonian (Chattanooga) shale toward the north end; the total displacement would be no more than 3 kilometers (2 miles) near the north end and probably steadily less southwestward.

More detailed work around the Emory River line by Stearns and his associates (Stearns, 1954, 1955; Wilson and Stearns, 1958) has confirmed that it is a zone of strike-slip faulting, but has

shown that it does not end at the northeast end of the Sequatchie anticline but continues into the Plateau rocks farther west. Here it is related to another, much shallower bedding thrust fault, the Cumberland Plateau thrust, which has moved as much as 3 kilometers (2 miles) following various weak layers between the resistant Upper Carboniferous sandstone strata (Lee group). Because this fault is so shallow, some of the details of its cross-cutting from one layer to another can be determined with considerable precision, and some have been checked by drilling. Figure 5 is a diagrammatic representation of the steps in the fault surface and the resulting folds; the principle is precisely that enunciated by Rich in 1934 for the Pine Mountain fault, and its explanatory power is evident. Stearns believed that the shallow Cumberland Plateau thrust fault is folded by the deeper Sequatchie anticline, being present in the flat-lying strata on either side; it would thus be older. Milici (1963), on the other hand, showed that it is mainly a northeastern and northwestern continuation or offshoot of the northeastern (subsurface) part of the Sequatchie Valley fault, where that fault jumps up into the Upper Carboniferous—in my opinion, a very satisfactory interpretation.

All these structures end northeastward against the Emory River line of disturbance. The southwest end of the Cumberland Plateau fault is still unknown; presumably its displacement, like that of the Sequatchie Valley fault, decreases in that direction, and it may die out long before reaching Alabama. A number of small transverse faults are present in the Carboniferous rocks of the Black Warrior basin south of the southwest-plunging end of the Sequatchie anticline in Alabama; Rodgers (1950, p. 676–677) suggested that they are analogous to the Russell Fork fault at the northeast end of the Pine Mountain block.

Because of the irregular course of the boundary between the Plateau and the Valley and Ridge provinces in northwesternmost Georgia and northeastern Alabama, the Plateau block east of the Sequatchie anticline widens there to 40 kilometers (25 miles), but it too is split lengthwise by a staggered line of three additional anticlines—the Lookout Valley, Big Wills Valley, and Murphrees Valley anticlines (the latter two accompanied by thrust faults)—closely comparable to the Sequatchie anticline both structurally and topographically. These folds have the general trend of the nearby Valley and Ridge folds, but each runs out at one end to a reentrant in the province boundary and dies out at the other within the flat-lying Carboniferous rocks of the Plateau. Their combined length, not including 15 kilo-

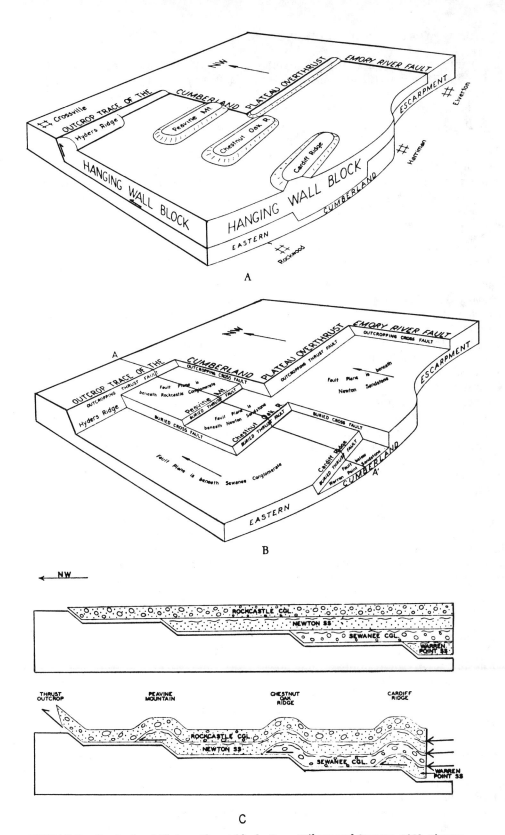

FIGURE 5. Cumberland Plateau thrust block. From Wilson and Stearns, 1958, Figures 7 and 8 (reprinted with permission from the *Bulletin of the Geological Society of America*). (A) Block diagram showing superficial anticlines formed over steps in fault surface. (B) Block diagram showing steps in fault surface (hanging wall block removed). (C) Schematic cross sections along line A-A before and after thrusting.

meters (10 miles) of overlap of the southern two, is 200 kilometers (125 miles). The Murphrees Valley anticline is unique in that its asymmetry is reversed; the associated fault, which throws Upper Cambrian rocks (Knox group) against Carboniferous (Lee group), cuts the steep southeast flank of the fold and dips northwest, but there is no reason to believe that its mechanics is different from that of the other two or of the Sequatchie anticline. Assuming the same mechanics, all record thrusting that followed the weak Cambrian (Conasauga) shale, presumably near its top (Fig. 6).

Summary

As already mentioned, the folds and faults of the Appalachian Plateau province have been interpreted in two quite different ways, as basement tectonics and as cover tectonics. One group of geologists, mainly those familiar with the gentle structures of the main Appalachian coal basin, has contended that the folds and faults seen at the surface reflect folds in the upper surface of the basement beneath and are localized by zones of weakness in that basement, the forces being transmitted upward from below as they would be in an experimental pressure box if slats at the bottom of the box were differentially moved. The other group, mainly those familiar with the structures of the Cumberland Mountains and Plateau, has contended that the faults and folds seen at the surface reflect thrust faults following weak zones within the sedimentary column and are localized where those thrust faults cut across the strata from one weak zone to another (or to the surface), as they would in an experimental pressure box if a piston on one side moved relative to the bottom and opposite side. The same difference of opinion is apparent in recent discussions of the Jura Plateau and many other areas, including the Appalachian Valley and Ridge province, as discussed in Chapter 3. The relations should, however, be clearer in the Plateau province than in the Valley and Ridge, because of the relative simplicity and individuality of the structures and because of the greater amount of subsurface information.

One must, I believe, interpret as basement tectonics the irregular structures on the northwest flank of the main coal basin, because of their similarity to and in some cases apparent continuity with structures on the central platform of the continent, of which this flank is merely the eastern margin. Certainly the Kentucky River fault zone and perhaps the associated folds seem to be most readily explained in this manner. On the other hand, one virtually must interpret as cover tec-

tonics the Pine Mountain fault and the folds and faults of the Cumberland Plateau, in view of the accurate control provided in several places by the associated windows and by wells. I am further convinced that the same interpretation best explains the folding on the southeast flank of the main basin from New York to West Virginia, including the Burning Springs anticline; the evidence here has been less complete but is now reasonably unequivocal (Gwinn, 1964; Prucha, 1968).

If cover tectonics is indeed the correct explanation of most of the structural features in the Plateau province, then one fundamental control of those features should be the distribution of weak layers in the sedimentary column, on which the various blocks slid relatively forward. Thus the large folds and faults of the southern part of the province all occur in the region where the Middle Cambrian and the lowest part of the Upper Cambrian in the adjacent Valley and Ridge province is a shale unit (Conasauga shale) 600 meters (2000 feet) or so thick; it is no accident therefore that Upper Cambrian strata are the lowest rocks exposed in each of these folds, except the shallow Cumberland Plateau thrust, if indeed it is an independent structure. The Cambrian shale unit thins and fingers out eastward and northeastward; already at Big A Mountain at the east corner of the Pine Mountain block, only 130 meters (400 feet) of shale remains (Bates, 1936, p. 177). Similarly, the Devonian (Chattanooga) shale is present but very thin through Alabama and much of Tennessee, but it thickens northeastward into southwest Virginia where there is locally 300 meters (1000 feet) of black shale; farther east and northeast, however, the black shale grades laterally into sandy shale interbedded with sandstone. This shale appears to have been a plane of movement only where it is relatively thick, at the north end of the Sequatchie anticline, under the Middlesboro coal basin, and perhaps also under the Abbs Valley and Hurricane Ridge folds, but movement upon it seems to have been especially easy, for the block behind the Pine Mountain fault shows the largest movement of any structure on the Plateau.

Other weak layers may have been important locally; for example, the shale units between the Upper Carboniferous sandstone layers (Lee group) for the Cumberland Plateau thrust and perhaps some other smaller superficial structures, and shale (Reedsville or Martinsburg shale, Rockwood formation) close to the top of the Ordovician or at the base of the Silurian in Tennessee at the southwest end of the Pine Mountain block and in West Virginia and Maryland as far west as the Browns Mountain (Pocahontas) and Elkins

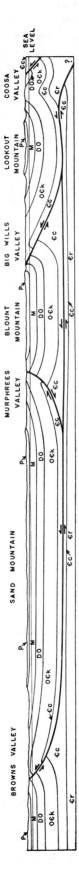

FIGURE 6. Interpretative cross section of Appalachian Plateau in northeastern Alabama. Stratigraphic units (top to bottom): Pennsylvanian; Mississippian; Devonian to Middle Ordovician; Knox group (Lower Ordovician and Upper Cambrian); Conasauga shale (Upper and Middle Cambrian); Rome formation (Lower Cambrian). From Rodgers, 1950, Fig. 3c (reprinted with permission from the *Bulletin of the American Association of Petroleum Geologists*).

Valley-Briery Mountain anticlines. In the northern part of the province, however, the principal weak layer seems to have been the salt-bearing shale of the Upper Silurian (Salina group); if the cover tectonics interpretation is correct, the blocks that moved upon it are the largest in the province, although they did not move very far (Rodgers, 1963, p. 1535).

To recapitulate, the cover tectonics hypothesis assumes that the sedimentary layers on the Plateau were caught between the deformed rocks of the Valley and Ridge province on the southeast, which during their own deformation exerted lateral pressure all along the southeast edge of the Plateau, and the basement beneath and rising to the northwest along the Cincinnati arch, to which at least the lower Plateau strata were firmly attached (whether the "push" or "active force" came from the Valley and Ridge rocks or the basement is indeterminable and indeed irrelevant). Caught in this pressure box, relatively thin slices of the upper layers, 1 to 2 kilometers (on the order of a mile) thick, tended to shear northwestward along weak layers in the column, tearing loose at their lateral margins along strike-slip faults and buckling at their leading edges where the total frictional resistance became too great or the weak layers too thin. Or, to use a different analogy,

familiar at least to those living in cool temperate climates, they slid forward the way a blanket of heavy wet new snow slides forward over the sidewalk well ahead of the leading edge of the snow shovel.

The age of the Plateau structures is not very clearly defined. Presumably they are later than the youngest rocks present, which are perhaps Lower Permian (Dunkard group) in the main basin, the middle part of the Upper Carboniferous (base of Allegheny group) around the Pine Mountain fault, and the basal part of the Upper Carboniferous (Lee group) on the Cumberland Plateau. Probably they are older than Late Triassic, though they are tens of kilometers (many miles) from the nearest Triassic sediments (Newark group). I see no particular reason to doubt, despite lack of any proof, that they were all. produced in one "period of orogeny," whatever that means, presumably the same one that formed most or all the structures in the Valley and Ridge province from Pennsylvania south. This orogenic episode has in the past been called the Appalachian Revolution, but, since several other episodes were at least equally important in the Appalachians taken as a whole, it is better designated by Woodward's name, Alleghany orogeny (Woodward, 1957a; 1957b).*

*The Indian name is spelled Allegheny, Allegany, or Alleghany, as applied to different geographic features and political units; the first form is the ordinary one for the mountains and the Upper Carboniferous stratigraphic unit, but Woodward (1958) deliberately chose the last name as the name for the orogenic episode. It should also be noted that Woodward (1959, p. 1076) attributed some of the folding on the Plateau, especially the Burning Springs anticline and the tight folding elsewhere in the Devonian strata, not to this episode but to an episode of compression in the Triassic, an episode for which I see no compelling evidence.

CHAPTER 3

The Valley and Ridge province—
Central Pennsylvania to Central Alabama

Central Pennsylvania Sector

At the eastern margin of the Appalachian coal basin of western Pennsylvania, the dissected plateau landscape that prevails throughout the coal field gives way abruptly to very different country. The edge of the "plateau" is an east-facing escarpment or topographic front, the Allegheny Front, in many places 500 meters (1500 feet) high although the descent may be spread over several kilometers (miles). The land beyond the front is neither low nor flat, however. It consists of alternating linear valleys and ridges of fairly constant width and commonly of great length—the classical Appalachian landscape of the Valley and Ridge province, made famous by W.M. Davis and other physiographers. The higher ridges are generally narrow—1 kilometer ($\frac{1}{2}$ mile) wide or so—and have sharp but even crests; they are especially continuous, being broken only here and there where the larger streams cut through them in spectacular water gaps or where the ridges themselves double back abruptly at an acute angle. Some of the lesser ridges are equally narrow and sharp, but others are wider, more rolling, and less distinctly set off, though generally nearly as continuous. The valleys between also show a wide

variety; some are narrow and shut in by the ridges on either side, but others are wider and more open, though they in turn may be divided lengthwise by minor ridges. But ridges and valleys alike are characteristically linear and parallel, so that the country has a strong grain; the direction of this grain changes from north-northeast, near the south edge of Pennsylvania, through a broad arc to east-northeast or even east by north, east of the center of the state. The higher ridges stand 300 to 400 meters (1000 feet or so) above the valleys, so that the relief is considerable, but the average elevation of the province is a good deal lower than that of the Plateau to the west, as the valleys occupy a much larger proportion of the ground, and the ridges, in Pennsylvania at least, do not reach as high as the highest part of the Plateau. The smaller streams naturally follow the linear valleys, but the larger streams are more independent; they follow the grain of the country only locally, and overall they are mostly transverse.

This classical Appalachian landscape is underlain of course by the classical Appalachian structure, made famous by the Rogers brothers and their successors. The nearly flat-lying beds of the Plateau, warped into a few broad folds, give way eastward to folds of great height and steepness.

These folds, especially those in the northwestern part of the Valley and Ridge province, are long and parallel, and hence the Paleozoic strata that form them crop out in long narrow belts, which here and there double back across plunging fold axes. As the strata are of widely varying resistance to erosion, they produce the prominent linear ridges and valleys of the province. The most prominent ridges are held up by resistant sandstone units at the base of the Silurian (Tuscarora sandstone), of the Carboniferous (Pocono sandstone), and of the Upper Carboniferous (Pottsville sandstone); the widest valleys are underlain by thick Ordovician carbonate rocks or by Devonian shales, though both groups contain more resistant strata that form minor ridges within the valleys. (For a summary of the stratigraphy in the Valley and Ridge province, see Colton, 1970.) The grain of the country faithfully reflects the trend of the fold axes and of the resulting outcrop belts, which outline a broad arcuate salient in central Pennsylvania.

There is no transition here between the Plateau and the Valley and Ridge. The first fold east of the Plateau, the Nittany arch, is also the highest and steepest; it is less an anticline than an anticlinorium 15 kilometers (10 miles) or so across, which generally includes two and locally three parallel anticlinal axes separated by mostly relatively shallow synclines. A total of 7000 meters (20,000 feet) of strata below the Carboniferous beds of the Plateau are exposed in the fold, and Cambrian rocks come to the surface in places along one or another of the crest lines for a total strike distance of about 120 kilometers (75 miles), making a broad culmination in the center and western limb of the arcuate salient. Most of the Cambrian rocks exposed, like the Lower Ordovician rocks next above, are thick-bedded dolostone and limestone, the whole forming a thick competent unit (the Kittatinny group), but the very lowest are shaly limestone, shale, and thin-bedded shaly sandstone in the base of the Middle Cambrian and the top of the Lower Cambrian (Pleasant Hill and Waynesboro formations).

The northwest flank of the Nittany arch (and of its constituent anticlines) is very steep; commonly some of the beds are overturned; and southeast-dipping thrust faults are present in those parts of the fold where Cambrian rocks appear, although at the surface they do not seem to be very continuous along strike. Commonly only about 8 kilometers (5 miles) intervene between virtually horizontal Carboniferous beds in the Plateau and virtually vertical Ordovician beds on the northwest flank of the arch. This very sharp upturn and belt of vertical strata is the Appalachian or Allegheny structural front discussed in Chapter 2

(p. 19); it corresponds approximately to the topographic Allegheny Front.

Southeast of the Nittany arch, similar but somewhat lower folds form a belt 50 to 60 kilometers (30 to 40 miles) wide (Nickelsen, 1963). The most competent rock units—the Lower Ordovician dolostone and limestone (upper part of Kittatinny group), the basal Silurian (Tuscarora) sandstone, and the Carboniferous sandstone units (Pocono and Pottsville sandstones)—outline first-order folds whose wave length ranges from 3 to 10 kilometers (2 to 7 miles); the less competent beds between show smaller folds of all sizes but with a prevailing though not invariable asymmetry like that of the major folds, the northwest limbs of the anticlines being the steeper. The relief of the largest folds here is about 5000 meters (15,000 feet), but in the more ordinary first-order folds it is about half that. In the least competent beds, flowage and distortion are present, but on the whole the strata have merely been bent into concentric (parallel) folds; fossils are mostly undistorted, and the thicknesses are probably little changed. Nevertheless, strong disharmony between the small and large folds and also between the large first-order folds in the different competent units strongly suggests the presence of bedding-plane decollements in several particularly weak zones between the competent units. Such decollements have been observed in a few places in this region but are better displayed in the rocks in and around the anthracite coal basin to the east (Wood and Bergin, 1970; also Chapter 4, p. 66). One of the best documented west of the Susquehanna is the Tuscarora fault (Pierce and Armstrong, 1966; not shown on the tectonic map), which follows a Middle Ordovician graptolite shale bed (at the base of the Reedsville shale) just above the top of the thick Cambrian and Ordovician carbonate sequence (Kittatinny group and overlying Middle Ordovician limestone formations) and represents a decollement of the Middle Ordovician shale and overlying beds over the massive and competent carbonates. It resembles the decollements on the Appalachian Plateau (Chapter 2), but as it has clearly been folded as much as the enclosing strata, it must predate the main folding of the Valley and Ridge province. Pierce and Armstrong give reasons, both geologic and radiometric, for assigning it to the Acadian orogeny (Devonian or earliest Carboniferous), which was very strong in New England and farther northeast but whose presence has rarely been suspected in the Central Appalachians; in particular, rootless folds of that age (like the folds over the Plateau decollements) have not hitherto been recognized (but see Chapter 4, p. 67). Relatively few cross-cutting faults have been recognized in this region, again in contrast to the anthracite region to the east. Other faults are relatively rare; the largest is the Little Scrub Ridge thrust fault on the northwest flank of the short but prominent McConnellsburg anticline in the southeast part of the belt near its south edge, the only fold in this belt that exposes Cambrian rocks (Wilson, 1952, p. 310–312).

Along the axis of the arcuate salient, the rocks exposed are mainly Silurian and Devonian, but Ordovician strata appear in several large anticlines. Carboniferous rocks are lacking here for a strike distance of more than 50 kilometers (30 miles) across what amounts to a culmination (called the Pennsylvania culmination by Nickelsen, 1963, p. 13 and Fig. 1, and the Juniata culmination by Gwinn, 1970, p. 132 and Fig. 1), though the high points on the individual folds align only roughly and then in a zone trending a bit west of south, at about 45 degrees to the trend of the folds (the McConnellsburg anticline lies at the west edge of the southern continuation of this zone, far out on the south limb of the salient). Southwest of the culmination, the folds plunge generally south-southwestward into a broad basin of folded Devonian and Carboniferous strata including the small Broad Top semibituminous coal basin (as on the Plateau, the coal here is Upper Carboniferous); east of it, they plunge more regularly east-northeastward across the Susquehanna River into the great anthracite coal basin of eastern Pennsylvania, a deep depression whose axis trends about S35°W and is thus, like that of the culmination, at an angle to the fold trends instead of directly across them. Moreover, at the West Fork of the Susquehanna on the east limb of the salient, the constituent folds of the Nittany arch plunge down completely into an area of gentle Plateau structure, so that farther east the structural front disappears and the outermost great fold of the Valley and Ridge province is not an anticline but the Lackawanna syncline, containing the northern anthracite coal field.

The belt of folds just described, in which Silurian to Carboniferous rocks predominate at the present land surface, is succeeded to the southeast by another belt, 20 to 30 kilometers (12 to 18 miles) wide, in which only Cambrian and Ordovician rocks are exposed. The boundary between these two belts is a zone of vertical or overturned strata marking a structural front almost as pronounced as the one between the Valley and Ridge province and the Appalachian Plateau; it may be called the mid-province structural front. As the basal Silurian (Tuscarora) sandstone is the lowest mountain-forming unit in the

sequence above quartzite layers at the base of the Cambrian (Chilhowee group), the topography of this new belt is a single broad valley (diversified to be sure by lines of low hills over the shale units), the Great Appalachian Valley, here called the Lebanon or Cumberland Valley. Its northwestern margin is the abrupt, almost continuous ridge called Blue Mountain (*not* the Blue Ridge), upheld by the Silurian (Tuscarora) sandstone standing vertical or overturned within the structural front; its southeastern margin is another ridge or group of ridges called South Mountain, underlain by basal Cambrian (Chilhowee) quartzite brought up along a third structural front or zone of vertical and overturned strata that marks the boundary of the Valley and Ridge province with the Blue Ridge province to the southeast. This last structural front is the northwest flank of the major Blue Ridge anticlinorium that forms the latter province; in the anticlinorium, beneath the basal Cambrian quartzite, are exposed older clastics and volcanics and, farther to the south in Maryland, the true Precambrian basement—none of these rocks are exposed in the Valley and Ridge province. In Pennsylvania, the anticlinorium plunges northeast and its southeast flank is faulted out along the margin of one of the Triassic basins of the Piedmont province, so that for over 70 kilometers (45 miles) near Harrisburg, where the Susquehanna River flows through, these Lower Cambrian and older rocks are out of sight.

The deformation of the rocks in the Great Valley has been considerably more intense than in the belt to the northwest. The folds have a shorter wave length (rarely over 1 kilometer—half a mile), they seem to be less continuous along strike, they are generally similar rather than concentric, and many are nearly isoclinal, both limbs dipping southeast (commonly at fairly low angles, especially in eastern Pennsylvania). On a generalized geologic map the geology looks rather simple, the gross units succeeding each other southeastward in order of increasing age, but in detail it is very complex and, indeed, far from fully known. Some of the complexities were imposed by the late Ordovician orogeny that is recorded in eastern Pennsylvania and farther northeast by angular unconformity between lower Upper Ordovician (Martinsburg) shale on the northwest side of the Great Valley and the basal Silurian (Tuscarora) sandstone of Blue Mountain; the effects of this orogeny are treated in Chapter 4. There has been body distortion in practically all the rocks in the southeast part of this belt (Fellows, 1943), even in competent thick-bedded dolostone and limestone as shown by the distortion of oöids in oölite (Cloos, 1947) and of fossils, so that thicknesses as now measured across the beds may be quite different from original thicknesses (moreover, in some sections of limestone, the common stylolite seams show that a tenth to a fifth of the rock has been dissolved away). Furthermore, in places the rocks show incipient metamorphism, especially slaty cleavage in the shale and shaly limestone units (eastern Pennsylvania indeed includes an important slate quarry district).

To the southwest toward the Maryland border, folds of considerable length and continuity become obvious; here an anticline or anticlinorium to the northwest and a synclinorium (Massanutten synclinorium) to the southeast trend N20°E between the zones of vertical or overturned dips that mark the structural fronts at either edge of the Great Valley. The anticlinorium (expressed in the Kittatinny group) is almost exactly on the southern continuation of the axis of the culmination in the belt of folds northwest of the mid-province structural front; northward it plunges down, pinching out against that front or else disappearing beneath unconformable Silurian strata along it. The synclinorium, on the other hand, may turn more northeasterly; it merges with the belt of Middle and Upper Ordovician (Martinsburg) shale that lies next to the front across central and eastern Pennsylvania, where indeed a recumbent synclinorial structure has recently been recognized (Chapter 4, p. 69–70). Southward, the north end of what farther south is a major thrust fault (the Little North Mountain fault) appears just north of the state line along the mid-province structural front on the northwest flank of the anticlinorium; where it crosses into Maryland, it already cuts out most of the Ordovician. Other faults, mostly minor, are known almost everywhere in the Great Valley that detailed work has been done; some are thrust faults associated with the folds, but others are normal faults like those that bound the Triassic basin.

Thus the Valley and Ridge province in central Pennsylvania is characterized by folds rather than faults, much of it by folds so large and uncomplicated that they can easily be worked out from topographic maps alone, once the pattern is understood. The apparent simplicity of the folding coupled with the reasonably consistent asymmetry early led to a simple explanation: the folds are the result of a lateral push from the southeast, exerted against the edges of the pile of strata, the push dying out northwestward among the gentle folds of the Plateau. When gradually it was realized that the rocks, considered to scale, are far too weak to transmit the enormous force apparently demanded by the observed folding, it was suggested that the force was transmitted through the underlying basement, so that the individual folds (at least the first-order folds) represent individual upthrusts from the basement. In general, the absence of major continuous thrust faults, which are so prominent in the southern part of the Valley and Ridge province, made most geologists loath to think in terms of shallow folding over a zone of decollement, which would have to be a zone of large-scale thrusting.

Thrust faults of considerable throw do appear, however, precisely in those places northwest of the Great Valley where the oldest (Cambrian) rocks come to the surface. Perhaps the most instructive locality is around the village of Birmingham, Pennsylvania, on the crest of the outermost anticline of the Nittany arch (Fig. 7). That fold is here broken by a moderately steep thrust fault (the Birmingham fault of Fig. 7), which throws lower Upper Cambrian or Middle Cambrian strata along the crest of the fold over strongly overturned Upper Cambrian or Lower Ordovician strata on its northwest flank, a throw of 600 meters (2000 feet) or less (all these units are within the Kittatinny group). The fault can be traced 40 kilometers (25 miles) northeast along the strike from Birmingham but less than 5 kilometers (3 miles) southwest; in that direction it dies out, and somewhat farther on the fold itself plunges and dies out in Silurian and Devonian rocks that are clearly quite unfaulted (the crest of the Nittany arch is continued by another anticline a little farther southeast). Yet at Birmingham, immediately southeast of the trace of the Birmingham fault (in the bottom of a stream valley followed by the main line of the Pennsylvania Railroad, and also in another place $2\frac{1}{2}$ kilometers—$1\frac{1}{2}$ miles— to the northeast), beneath the Cambrian rocks in the core of the anticline there appear small areas, like windows, of Upper Ordovician and basal Silurian rocks (Reedsville shale and higher), separated from the Cambrian (Kittatinny) rocks by one or more thrust surfaces dipping at low angles (generally southeastward but somewhat warped), a total throw of at least 1500 to 2500 meters (5000 to 8000 feet).

Most earlier explanations of this curious occurrence of relatively young rocks in the core of an anticline made it a local anomaly—a small downfolded or down-faulted block pinched into the top of the fold and then locally overridden by the Birmingham fault (Butts, 1939, p. 77–78; Fox, 1950; see Fig. 4 in Moebs and Hoy, 1959). But drilling 1 to 4 kilometers ($\frac{1}{2}$ to $2\frac{1}{2}$ miles) southwest of Birmingham (Moebs and Hoy, 1959) has shown that the younger rocks lie beneath a flat fault (the Sinking Valley fault of Fig. 7), which underlies the whole crestal area of the fold both

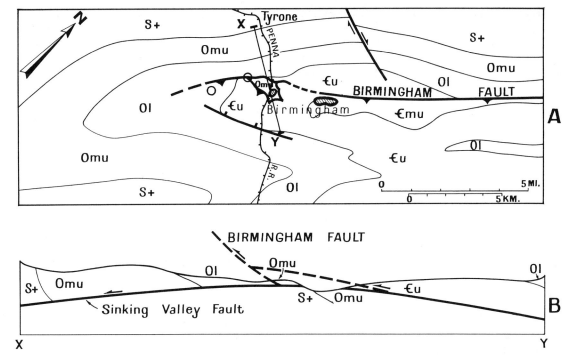

FIGURE 7. Geologic sketch map and cross-section of Birmingham area, Pennsylvania. **(A) Geologic sketch map after Fox, 1950, Fig. 3, with additions from Moebs and Hoy, 1959. Heavy lines are faults; ticks indicate downthrown side of steep fault (probably normal), triangles indicate upthrown side of thrust fault, arrows indicate relative movement along wrench fault; lined areas are windows through Sinking Valley fault. Large circles southwest of Birmingham indicate areas where drilling has reached Sinking Valley fault. Letter symbols indicate age of strata, as follows: S+ — Silurian and younger, Omu — Middle and Upper Ordovician. Ol — Lower Ordovician, Cu — Upper Cambrian, ∈mu — lower part of Upper Cambrian or Middle Cambrian. (B) Schematic cross section along line X-Y, at scale 5 times that of map. After Moebs and Hoy, 1959, Fig. 4E. Heavy lines are faults; arrows indicate relative movement of upper blocks. Letter symbols as on map.**

southeast and northwest of the trace of the Birmingham fault, and of which that fault is merely a steep branch. In the absence of drilling beyond the immediate area, the Sinking Valley fault cannot be traced; it is not known to appear at the surface anywhere to the northwest. Perhaps its place is taken there and its displacement accounted for by the structural front just to the northwest, along which the entire stratigraphic sequence is upended and much of it strongly overturned (to 30 degrees southeast, just northwest of the window at Birmingham), but more likely it descends to join the zone of decollement postulated in the Upper Silurian strata (Salina group) under the Appalachian Plateau (Chapter 2, p. 20); see also Gwinn, 1964, Fig. 13B, p. 882). A drill hole on the crest of the Nittany arch 40 kilometers (25 miles) to the northeast (Gwinn, 1970, p. 131–132) reached a similar fault at 335 meters (1100 feet) depth, passing from lower Upper Cambrian strata in the core of the surface anticline into nearly vertical Lower Ordovician beds; it then penetrated the latter to a subsurface depth of about 2637

meters (8650 feet), where it crossed another fault into virtually flat-lying Silurian strata, under which it penetrated a normal stratigraphic section down to the Middle Ordovician at the total depth of 4774 meters (15,662 feet). As the Silurian beds are at the same elevation as under the nearest syncline on the Appalachian Plateau to the northwest, the second fault is evidently laterally continuous with the Plateau decollement. Two other wells, 28 and 85 kilometers (17 and 53 miles) south-southwest of Birmingham, on the western anticline of the Nittany anticlinorium where it is lower than at Birmingham, also encountered fairly large thrust faults at relatively shallow depths but did not penetrate deep enough to reach the master decollement. Still other wells farther southeast in the Valley and Ridge province (including one on the McConnellsburg anticline; Gwinn, 1970, p. 132) cut similar thrusts.

The evidence of a major thrust fault in the Birmingham area and in the drill holes along strike from it, the general association of the biggest visible thrust faults in the province with the highest anticlines, and the entire absence in these same anticlines of any strata below the incompetent shaly beds (Waynesboro formation) at the top of the Lower Cambrian all suggest, to one familiar with the Pine Mountain fault and the other folds and faults of the southern arc of the Appalachians, that the Valley and Ridge folds of Pennsylvania are best explained as cover tectonics, the Paleozoic column having been stripped from the basement at the level of the upper Lower Cambrian shale, which is apparently the lowest incompetent bed in the column here, and folded independently. The Allegheny structural front would thus represent the northwestern limit of this wholesale stripping (beyond, any slipping along the beds took place at a higher level, in the Upper Silurian Salina group). Southeast of that front, in the northwestern belt of the Valley and Ridge province as far as Blue Mountain, the beds have folded in simple concentric (parallel) folds above the shaly zone like the rugs sliding over the floor in the usual analogy, distortion and flowage being confined to the least competent beds; thus the wavelength of the first-order folds is of the order of magnitude of the total thickness of strata involved. The mid-province structural front along Blue Mountain would mark the change from this type of folding to largely similar folding in which flowage and distortion affect all the beds and the first traces of metamorphism appear; as the mechanism of folding was different, the wave length ceases to have any simple relation to the total thickness of the folded sequence. Presumably differences in competence within the sedimentary sequence, so obvious in the folds to the northwest, were here nearly wiped out by the greater intensity of the deformation, perhaps because of slightly higher temperature, although the weak Cambrian shale zone beneath probably still served as an active slip plane, particularly in the earlier stages of deformation. Finally the third, South Mountain or Blue Ridge structural front may mark the limit where this zone, which is known to become less shaly and more dolomitic southeastward, ceased to be distinctly less competent than the surrounding beds and hence to be a major locus of slipping or where, with increasing temperature, the underlying basement was little if any less plastic than the overlying sedimentary rocks and therefore took part in the deformation; in any case, that front brings to the surface all the lower strata down to and including the basement.

Even if the Paleozoic strata were deformed independently of the basement, it does not necessarily follow that the basement surface was a smooth plane at the time (as I and others have generally assumed, but see Rodgers, 1964). The presence of the Pennsylvania culmination between the Broad Top and anthracite coal basins might suggest the contrary, that the basement surface was broadly arched in the area of the culmination along a trend somewhat east of north, obliquely to the folds that formed in the Paleozoic column in Pennsylvania though more nearly parallel to those in Maryland and the northern part of the Virginias. Whether any such arching would have taken place at the same time as the folding or earlier is not clear; perhaps more likely it would have been earlier, but in any case it would not have been the cause of the folding, although it might well have influenced the folding process. Gwinn (1970, p. 134 ff.), however, quotes unpublished geophysical evidence indicating that the basement is not arched under the culmination, but slopes regularly southeastward under the whole province.

Maryland-Central Virginia Sector (Potomac River to James River)

The different fronts and belts that can be recognized in central Pennsylvania can be followed along strike into central Virginia, but not without some changes. Of three anticlinal crests on the Nittany arch at the Pennsylvania-Maryland state line, only the western one, the Wills Mountain anticline, persists very far; it reaches the Potomac near Cumberland, Maryland, and continues in a nearly straight line south-southwestward for 200 kilometers (130 miles) across West Virginia and along the west edge of Virginia. It does not stand as high as the Nittany arch in Pennsylvania; along much of its extent in Maryland and West Virginia, the basal Silurian (Tuscarora) sandstone is exposed on the crest, forming a prominent anticlinal mountain locally breached by transverse streams. Farther south it rises somewhat higher; Ordovician rocks are exposed continuously for 100 kilometers (60 miles) on both sides of the West Virginia-Virginia border, and Lower Ordovician dolostone (upper Kittatinny group) appears in Virginia. Finally the fold plunges down again and almost but not quite loses its identity in folded Devonian shale around the western headwaters of the James River, just southeast of the high part of the Browns Mountain (Pocahontas) anticline and a little northeast of the point where the Valley and Ridge folds change trend from south-southwest to west-southwest. The northwest flank of this fold is here considered to be the southern continuation of the Allegheny topographic and structural fronts.

Most of the belt between the Wills Mountain anticline and the mid-province structural front, here represented by the Little North Mountain fault, is underlain by Devonian and Lower Carboniferous strata in relatively open folds with a wave length of 5 to 10 kilometers (3 to 7 miles), as in Pennsylvania; no large faults are known at the surface. The Lower Carboniferous beds contain a few rather poor coal seams, but there is no counterpart of the Broad Top coal field of Pennsylvania, where the richly coal-bearing Upper Carboniferous beds are still preserved. In West Virginia, Silurian rocks appear in several short anticlines not more than 20 kilometers (12 miles) southeast of the Wills Mountain anticline; these coalesce southward in Virginia into the more nearly continuous Warm Springs anticline, which brings up Lower Ordovician strata (upper Kittatinny) along two stretches (the southern of these is opposite the lowest part of the Wills Mountain anticline and contains the famous resort of Warm Springs). Together with the Wills Mountain anticline, these folds correspond to the Nittany anticlinorium of Pennsylvania. Silurian (and locally Upper Ordovician) rocks also reappear some 25 kilometers (15 miles) farther east along a prominent group of relatively short anticlines that together form the Cacapon Mountain anticlinorium (the first syllable of Cacapon is silent); it is highest in West Virginia, opposite the relatively low part of the Wills Mountain anticline, and plunges at both ends—southward not far from the mid-province structural front, and northward at about the Maryland-Pennsylvania line, but there it is relayed to the east by several folds in southern Pennsylvania, notably the McConnellsburg anticline.

The trend of the fold axes remains nearly constant throughout this belt, in contrast to the arcuate salient in central Pennsylvania and the recess formed by the sharp change in strike in central Virginia just to the south. The belt narrows southward, however, from 60 kilometers (40 miles) in Maryland to 35 kilometers (20 miles) near the James River as the structural front to the east gradually bevels across the folds (including the Cacapon Mountain anticlinorium). There are no obvious culminations and depressions; thus one of the two low parts of the Wills Mountain anticline lies opposite the high part of the Cacapon Mountain anticlinorium and the other opposite that of the Browns Mountain anticline. Yet in the Shenandoah synclinorium between, Carboniferous rocks disappear southward, the southernmost patch lying about 50 kilometers (30 miles) southwest of Harrisonburg, Virginia, and Silurian rocks appear in several minor anticlines between that patch and the James River. Remembering that the distinct culmination and depression in Pennsylvania do not trend directly across the

strike but at an angle, one might suggest a vague and low culmination trending nearly north-south (at only about 30 degrees to the strike), connecting this area with the high part of the Wills Mountain anticline on the Virginia-West Virginia line, between even vaguer depressions on either side, the one to the south trending diagonally across the angular recess north of Roanoke.

Looked at broadly, the folds in this belt seem open and simple, but detailed study (Gair, 1950; Cloos, 1951, p. 153–163; Cloos, 1964a) has shown a wealth of complexity, with innumerable minor faults and with coarse cleavage and locally distorted thicknesses in the weaker layers. Some of these minor features appear to antedate the main deformation of the Valley and Ridge province, and some may even be Acadian. Cloos states that in the folds in Maryland asymmetry is either inconsistent or absent.

The mid-province structural front, that is, the zone of vertical and overturned beds that in Pennsylvania underlies Blue Mountain at the northwestern margin of the Great Valley, is broken from southernmost Pennsylvania almost to the James River (290 kilometers—185 miles) by a major southeast-dipping thrust fault, the Little North Mountain fault. In places this fault throws Middle Cambrian (base of Kittatinny group) on Middle Devonian—a throw of 3500 meters (11,000 feet)—thereby concealing most of the zone of overturned beds, but for greater distances the Cambrian rocks are thrown against overturned Middle and Upper Ordovician (Martinsburg) shale—a throw of about 2000 meters (6000 feet). The uppermost Ordovician, Silurian, and Lower Devonian strata in the overturned zone next to the west in these stretches are locally drastically thinned or even cut out; both tectonic (Giles, 1927) and stratigraphic (Butts and Edmundson, 1939) thinning and pinch-out have been suggested to explain the facts (see also Brent, 1960, p. 96–99; Edmundson *in* Butts and Edmundson, 1966, p. 79 ff.). Similar thinning in the Upper Silurian and Lower Devonian, subject to the same controversy, is present along the Blue Mountain front just north of Harrisburg (here a thrust fault cuts out higher Devonian strata but apparently not the Lower Devonian; Wood and Kehn, 1961). If the stratigraphic theory is correct, then fault and front are located along and presumably controlled by an old positive axis, dating back at least to the Ordovician; if the tectonic theory is correct, the differences in thickness are simply the result of the extreme deformation along the structural front.

Southwestward toward the James River, the Little North Mountain fault gradually loses throw, though even here Bick (1960) has mapped a window of Lower Ordovician rocks extending about 3 kilometers (2 miles) southeast of the main fault trace. It finally dies out in Lower and Middle Ordovician strata (upper part of Kittatinny group and overlying units) in an area of complex folding and minor faulting not far north of the James (Spencer, 1968). The front also ceases to be a continuously separate zone of steep dips, but a general boundary between Cambrian and Ordovician rocks on the east and Silurian and Devonian rocks on the west can be traced to the James above Buchanan, Virginia.

The Great Appalachian Valley, called the Shenandoah Valley in West Virginia and northern Virginia, here ranges from 20 to 30 kilometers (12 to 20 miles) wide, as in Pennsylvania. The anticlinorium present in southern Pennsylvania swings against the Little North Mountain fault, which cuts out its northwest flank and crest near the Potomac River. About 90 kilometers (60 miles) farther on a fairly large anticline reappears, diverges from the fault, and continues 60 kilometers (35 miles) southwestward before plunging out close to Harrisonburg, Virginia. The Massanutten synclinorium, on the other hand, can be traced for 200 kilometers (120 miles) beyond the Potomac (for 60 kilometers—35 miles—beyond Harrisonburg), before it comes to a rather abrupt end opposite a prominent salient of the Blue Ridge to the east. In northern Virginia, for a strike distance of more than 70 kilometers (about 45 miles) northeast from Harrisonburg, the synclinorium deepens to include Silurian and Devonian strata; the resistant basal Silurian (Tuscarora or Massanutten) sandstone here forms a large isolated mountain group called Massanutten Mountain, splitting the Shenandoah Valley lengthwise. Some of America's most famous caverns are located in the Ordovician limestone on either flank of this synclinorium.

About 25 kilometers (15 miles) northeast of Harrisonburg and west of Massanutten Mountain, a north-plunging anticline relays to the east the south-plunging anticline mentioned above as diverging from the Little North Mountain fault. Beginning a few kilometers (miles) south of its northeast end, this anticline is cut by a major southeast-dipping thrust fault, here generally called the Staunton fault but in fact a northern extension of the very important Pulaski fault of the Southern Appalachian arc (Pulaski is over 100 kilometers—nearly 70 miles—southwest of the James River). Except northeast of Harrisonburg, Middle Cambrian (base of Kittatinny group) or possibly uppermost Lower Cambrian strata on the southeast side of this fault are thrust against various units in the Ordovician on the northwest.

Over most of this distance (almost 25 kilometers—about 80 miles—from Harrisonburg to Buchanan on the James), the shaly Cambrian strata close to the fault are intensely crumpled and brecciated and slightly metamorphosed, as they commonly are along other faults of the Pulaski system, but rarely along other thrust faults in the Valley and Ridge province. Horses several miles long along the fault show that it is a complex fault zone, and klippen as much as 7 kilometers ($4\frac{1}{2}$ miles) to the northwest show that it has been folded, again like the main Pulaski fault farther southwest.

The belt between the Staunton-Pulaski fault, which dies out northeastward, and the Little North Mountain fault, which dies out southwestward, is rather irregularly but not too tightly folded; this belt narrows irregularly southwestward from 18 kilometers (over 10 miles) near Harrisonburg to as little as 6 kilometers (4 miles) near the James River. The belt southeast of the Staunton-Pulaski fault is dominated to the north by the Massanutten synclinorium, which ends southward between the Staunton fault and a southeastern branch (the Fairfield fault). Farther south the fault gradually approaches the Blue Ridge structural (and topographic) front, separated only by a shallow syncline that locally contains Lower Ordovician (upper Kittatinny group) strata, as at the famous Natural Bridge of Virginia, 16 kilometers (10 miles) northeast of Buchanan, and this belt also narrows southwestward, from 8 to 3 kilometers (5 to 2 miles). Thus the whole structural and topographic belt of the Great Valley, between the two structural fronts and their topographic expressions, narrows to a few kilometers (miles) close to Buchanan.

North and east of Massanutten Mountain, the general structure in the Shenandoah Valley is not unlike that in the Great Valley in Pennsylvania. The folds are of relatively short wave length, though they are grouped into the major Massanutten synclinorium between the southeast dips off the Little North Mountain fault on the northwest and the nearly vertical or overturned dips in the Blue Ridge structural front on the southeast; faults are probably fairly common but none are of great throw or extent, and the rocks show much distortion and flowage and the beginnings of metamorphism. In the Silurian sandstone forming the mountain itself, however, the wave length of the folds is about 2 to 3 kilometers (1 to 2 miles), and in the competent Upper Cambrian and Lower Ordovician carbonate rocks to the west and southwest, it is the same or even larger (though the less competent beds above and below continue to show tight folds of all sizes), and there is far less body distortion of the folded rocks. It is as though the deformation, which farther north produced tight, small-scale structures over the whole belt, was here largely concentrated in a few major faults, especially the Staunton-Pulaski fault, along which its action was very intense, but between which it produced only rather open folds, not unlike the folds northwest of the Little North Mountain fault though expressed at the surface in lower strata.

The southeast margin of the Great Valley is the third, South Mountain or Blue Ridge structural front, which brings up the entire section down to the true "granitic" basement. This front is broken by thrust faults at several places—thus in Virginia east of the north part of Massanutten Mountain, such a fault brings Precambrian basement over Lower Ordovician rocks, a throw of about 3500 meters (more than 10,000 feet)—but the faults are not continuous north of the James River (though so shown on some general maps). The front shows several sharp swings in strike outlining shallow salients and recesses with a "wave length" of 30 to 40 kilometers (20 to 30 miles) or so; there is a particularly prominent salient opposite the south end of the Massanutten Mountain synclinorium. Several of these swings in strike seem to be associated with diagonal faults, probably combining thrust and dextral strike-slip movement. The rocks along the front and for a short distance northwest show strong cleavage and incipient metamorphism. The front and the anticlinorium southeast of it have been interpreted as a great slip fold by Cloos (1947); the matter is discussed more fully in the chapter on the Blue Ridge province (p. 166–167).

The persistence with which the Little North Mountain and Staunton-Pulaski faults bring up the weak shaly layers at the base of the Middle Cambrian (base of the Kittatinny group) and the intense deformation those layers show along the latter fault suggest a decollement along them beneath the Great Valley. In the northwest part of the province no beds are exposed older than the Lower Ordovician strata at the top of the thick and competent dolostone unit (Kittatinny group) that overlies those shaly layers, but the Sponaugle well (Perry, 1964), about 4000 meters (13,000 feet) deep, which began in the Upper Ordovician (Martinsburg) shale a little east of the crest of the Wills Mountain anticline just north of the Virginia-West Virginia state line, encountered the full thickness of the dolostone unit (nearly 2500 meters—over 7500 feet) and then passed through a complex fault zone back into the same Ordovician shale in which it began, at an elevation comparable to what that shale should have to the west under the Plateau. The evidence of this well is a strong argument that the folds in this sector, like those in central Pennsylvania, should be explained as cover tectonics.

If the stratigraphic theory for the thinning of beds along the mid-province structural front is correct, then that front and the Little North Mountain fault that follows it may here be controlled less by a change in style and intensity of deformation than by preexisting irregularities in the sedimentary sequence, especially a pronounced thinning of the competent basal Silurian (Tuscarora) sandstone.

Roanoke Sector—Transition from the Central Appalachian to the Southern Appalachian Arc

In a strike distance of about 50 kilometers (30 miles), from the vicinity of the upper James River to that of Roanoke (Woodward, 1932), the structure of the Valley and Ridge province undergoes a profound change. The strike changes fairly abruptly from S30–35°W to S55–60°W and the change is made by intersection and interdigitation of trends rather than by smooth curvature. Northeast of the James River in the Central Appalachian arc, folds dominate the structure and certain of them are of great length—the Wills Mountain-Nittany anticlinorium and the Massanutten synclinorium can both be traced into the heart of the arc in Pennsylvania—whereas there are only two thrust faults of any considerable length, both on the southeast side of the province and neither extending to the center of the arc. Southwest of Roanoke in the Southern Appalachian arc, on the other hand, major southeast-dipping thrust faults dominate the whole width of the province and a few of them can be traced entirely through the curve of the arc across Tennessee into Georgia, whereas folds are relatively less important and less continuous. Already in the western part of the Roanoke sector, one crosses six major thrust faults from the one at the Plateau border to the one at the edge of the Blue Ridge, and two of these are the north ends of faults over 600 kilometers (350 miles) long.

Where the south end of the Wills Mountain anticline at the Allegheny front crosses the headwaters of the James River, it is a low fold or group of folds in Devonian rocks and trends S30°W; only a few kilometers (miles) to the south it abuts against the end of a slightly higher anticline that plunges about N60°E into Upper Devonian shale. In the opposite direction, however, this second anticline rises rapidly, and where it crosses the Virginia-West Virginia state line south of White Sulphur Springs, West Virginia, only 20 kilometers (13 miles) from its northeast end, it is cut by a southeast-dipping thrust fault that throws Lower Ordovician strata on its crest or southeast limb against Lower Devonian strata on its overturned northwest limb, a throw of about 750 meters (2500 feet); the throw increases southwestward as more and more units on the overturned limb are overridden. This overturned limb is in effect the Allegheny structural front, traceable from the Susquehanna River in central Pennsylvania to this area, beyond which its surface expression changes from a belt of vertical or overturned strata to a single thrust fault of great throw, called the St. Clair fault for a locality 110 kilometers (65 miles) west-southwest of White Sulphur Springs.

East of the Wills Mountain anticline, the Warm Springs anticline—the other half, so to speak, of the Nittany anticlinorial belt—plunges S30°W and abuts against the Rich Patch anticline, which likewise plunges N55°E into a synclinorium of Upper Devonian shale. On the other side of the Rich Patch anticline, a low anticline appears on the same trend as the Warm Springs anticline; thus these three anticlines form a flattened ×, with the arms intersecting at about 25 degrees and each of the angles between containing Upper Devonian shale. At the intersection, the N55°E trend clearly dominates (Lesure, 1957). Traced to the west-southwest, the Rich Patch anticline persists as a distinct entity across a southeastern projection of West Virginia (though the plunge reverses several times and the axis is offset en echelon once or twice). On reentering Virginia, it in its turn picks up a thrust fault on its northwest flank, comparable to the St. Clair fault on the anticline to the north though neither so large nor so continuous; this fault is called the Narrows fault for the Narrows of the New River not far beyond. The Narrows fault and Rich Patch anticline bear much the same relation to the St. Clair fault and its accompanying anticline 5 to 10 kilometers (3 to 6 miles) to the northwest that the Warm Springs anticline and associated folds farther northeast bear to the Wills Mountain anticline; one can think of each pair of structures as having together the same significance as the Nittany arch in Pennsylvania—the first major uplift southeast of the Allegheny structural front. All these anticlines show a pronounced asymmetry, the northwest flank being steeper even where it is not cut by a southeast-dipping thrust fault.

The low compound anticline that makes the south-southwest bar of the × extends another 20 kilometers (12 miles) S40°W and there, like the Wills Mountain and Warm Springs anticlines, abuts against still another anticline that plunges N60°E into Upper Devonian shale; once again, as the new anticline is traced in the opposite direction, a thrust fault appears on its northwest limb. This thrust fault, named the Saltville fault for a locality 160 kilometers (100 miles) to the westsouthwest, can be traced continuously from here Georgia, and one or more of its continuations or branches may persist to the Coastal Plain overlap in Alabama 800 kilometers (500 miles) away. In this area, however, it is not as prominent as farther southwest; it throws Upper Cambrian on Ordovician or at most Lower Silurian strata, a throw of 1000 meters or less (2000 to 3000 feet). Its distance from the Rich Patch anticline and Narrows fault is about 10 kilometers (6 miles) at its northeast end but increases to about 15 kilometers (9 miles) southwestward, and it seems to represent an independent major uplift, like the Cacapon Mountain anticlinorium of northeastern West Virginia and Maryland. It is not on the same strike, however, for the belt of strata next southeast of it seems to be a narrowed continuation of the synclinorium next northwest of the Cacapon Mountain anticlinorium. Only the northwest half of this synclinorium is exposed southeast of the Saltville fault, forming a homocline dipping southeast under the next major thrust fault (the Catawba-Pulaski fault discussed below); Carboniferous rocks appear in the synclinorium a few kilometers (miles) east of the northeast end of the anticline, having been absent for about 80 kilometers (50 miles) across the James River "culmination."

Even more striking changes take place in the southeast part of the province. As noted above, the space between the second and third structural fronts, and with it the Great Valley, narrows at Buchanan, the narrowest point in the Great Valley in the entire Appalachian chain, except perhaps at Quebec City. Just west of Buchanan, however, the main trace of the Pulaski fault turns abruptly northwestward and cuts nearly 15 kilometers (10 miles) across strike, then turns as abruptly southwestward along strike again (Spencer, 1968). Northeast of the transverse portion of the fault is the confused area in which the Little North Mountain fault dies out and the associated mid-province structural front is vague; northwest of the longitudinal portion beyond, the beds dip northwest on the southeast limb of the synclinorium mentioned in the last paragraph, but southwestward the fault encroaches entirely across this limb until it throws Upper Cambrian rocks on Lower Carboniferous rocks in the core of the synclinorium; here the fault has a stratigraphic throw of over 2000 meters (7500 feet) and a probable total displacement of at least 15 kilometers (10 miles). In other words, this branch of the Pulaski fault system laps entirely over the mid-province structural front, and thus in effect takes the place of that front as the St. Clair fault takes the place of the Allegheny front.

The Pulaski thrust sheet brought forward on this fault is probably rather shallow for 25 kilometers (15 miles) southwest of Buchanan—deformed Cambrian rocks are exposed over a wide area and surround a basin of Lower and Middle Ordovician strata. Significant faults may indeed be concealed within the deformed rocks; in particular, it seems probable that a fault, perhaps a southerly branch of the Pulaski fault, strikes directly southwest from Buchanan, separating deformed Middle Cambrian thin-bedded, partly shaly carbonate rock (Elbrook formation, base of Kittatinny group) from even more deformed Lower Cambrian shale and thin-bedded carbonate rock (Waynesboro or Rome formation). Moreover, this area is partly overlapped by the Blue Ridge thrust fault, which emerges from the core of the Blue Ridge about where the James River cuts through and continues southwestward along the northwest face of the ridge, taking the place of the third, South Mountain or Blue Ridge structural front. At Fullhardt Knob, however, 20 kilometers (13 miles) southwest of Buchanan and 15 kilometers (10 miles) northeast of Roanoke, this higher thrust fault doubles back around the large Goose Creek half-window, revealing a wide area of deformed Lower and Middle Cambrian shale and carbonate rock belonging to the Pulaski thrust sheet or sheets. West of the throat of this half-window just south of Fullhardt Knob is an inner window, 7 kilometers (4 miles) long, doubtless cut through the main Pulaski fault, for the Ordovician to Devonian rocks within it are comparable to those north of Buchanan inside the angle made there by the fault. Apparently the possible southerly branch of the Pulaski fault mentioned above may skirt the south side of this window, but in the badly deformed rocks around the window it is difficult to trace.

About 15 kilometers (10 miles) north of Roanoke and west of the wide area of deformed Cambrian rocks southwest of Buchanan appears the blunt northeast end of the Catawba or Salem synclinorium, a roughly rectangular basin 40 kilometers (25 miles) long and 6 or 7 kilometers (about 4 miles) across (the dimensions are measured on the basal Silurian [Tuscarora or Clinch] sandstone, which forms Catawba Mountain on the northwest flank but is cut out along about half the southeast flank); its homoclinal northwest flank is thrust over the homocline southeast of the Saltville fault along the Catawba thrust fault. This fault is directly on strike with, has about the same stratigraphic throw as, and seems like a continuation of the frontal Pulaski fault just to the northeast. The synclinorium behind it contains a full succession of strata up to the Lower Carboniferous, but some parts, notably the Middle Ordovician, are in a different facies from the corresponding strata on the homocline northwest of the Catawba fault. Furthermore, the strata along the vertical southeast flank exhibit thinning like that along the Little North Mountain fault in northern Virginia; Cooper (1961, esp. p. 105–108; 1964, p. 92–93) and Lowry (1960, p. 5 ff.) consider this thinning stratigraphic—evidence that the synclinorium was already a distinct basin during deposition. This flank is also complicated by several minor faults, and it is cut off on the southeast by a major fault of the Pulaski system, the Salem fault (named for Salem, 10 kilometers—6 miles—west of Roanoke), which brings deformed Middle Cambrian rocks (Elbrook formation) against various units as high as Upper Devonian. A few kilometers (miles) farther southeast, these Middle Cambrian rocks are succeeded by equally or worse deformed Lower Cambrian rocks (Rome formation) along the southerly branch of the Pulaski, here called the Christiansburg fault for Christiansburg, 50 kilometers (30 miles) west-southwest of Roanoke. Finally the Blue Ridge fault, having recovered from its setbacks east of and around Roanoke, brings the crystalline basement out over these Lower Cambrian rocks only 10 kilometers (6 miles) southwest of Roanoke, a stratigraphic throw of not less than 1500 meters (4500 feet) and a total displacement, to judge by the sinuosity of the fault trace, of not less than 13 kilometers (8 miles). All these faults extend southwestward beyond the Roanoke sector.

To the northeast, the Salem fault becomes hard to trace as it enters the wide area of deformed rocks east of the synclinorium; either it or an older fault it cuts off may turn sharply north and cut transversely across to the Catawba-Pulaski fault, separating the shallow part of the Pulaski thrust sheet from the deep Catawba synclinorium. Cooper (1961, Pl. 21; Cooper and Cashion, 1970, p. 394) indeed believes that in this area the Salem fault is the northwestern boundary of the Pulaski thrust sheet; in that case, the Catawba synclinorium would be a reentrant cut in the front of the thrust sheet and the Catawba fault northwest of it would be an unrelated fault merely overridden by the Pulaski. Like most other workers, I have preferred to consider that the Catawba fault is the continuation of the frontal Pulaski fault and the synclinorium is an especially deep part of the sheet, though admitting that nowhere else on the entire Pulaski thrust sheet southwest of the south end of the Massanutten synclinorium are there any strata younger than Middle Ordovician, and that the facies of the Middle Ordovician in the synclinorium resemble those to the northwest at least as much as those elsewhere on the Pulaski thrust sheet.

The country underlain by the Pulaski thrust sheet is both topographically and structurally the continuation southwestward of the Great Valley of northern Virginia. Topographically, the Valley is here much more irregular; both its borders show sharp offsets, and the mountains upheld by the Silurian and higher rocks in the Catawba synclinorium narrow and divide it as those in the Massanutten synclinorium narrow and divide the Shenandoah Valley (though that valley is wider on either side of the mountains). At the western edge of the Roanoke region, furthermore, the main drainage divide of the Appalachians crosses the Valley, and because of the much greater distance to the sea via the New, Ohio, and Mississippi Rivers than via the Roanoke River, the valley floor along the New River to the west stands 400 meters (1300 feet) higher than the valley floor along the Roanoke River around Roanoke. Naturally the western headwaters of the Roanoke River are busily cutting back into the higher valley floor and diverting its drainage directly to the Atlantic; already they reach within 15 kilometers (10 miles) of the New River itself, and subterranean drainage encroaches even closer. Structurally, the highly deformed Cambrian rocks near the Blue Ridge and along the various faults of the Pulaski system resemble the highly deformed rocks in the Great Valley in northern Virginia and northeastward, but the higher strata are much more simply deformed, no more indeed that the rocks northwest of the Catawba-Pulaski fault.

To summarize, in this transitional area, the structural style of the Valley and Ridge province undergoes an abrupt change. Beginning here, the major folds are all cut by continuous thrust faults of large throw; not far to the southwest, many of the fold crests and troughs disappear from the land surface, engulfed by the thrust faulting. In particular, the structural fronts of the Central Appalachians are replaced by the largest and most continuous of the thrust faults. One major fault, the Pulaski, extends through the transition, but it too changes character, becoming the sole of a complexly faulted thrust sheet not less than 15 kilometers (10 miles) across. Finally, the transition marks one of the sharpest recesses in the whole Appalachian chain, and the change of strike is not smooth but angular (20 to 30 degrees), folds of the two trends intersecting and interfering instead of curving evenly from one trend into the other.

This abrupt change in structural style suggests that there must be significant differences in the mechanics of deformation of the two arcs that here meet. Several possibilities present themselves, and they are not mutually exclusive:

(1) Many years ago, Willis (1893, p. 263 ff.) suggested that the Central Appalachians are folded because the thick and competent Cambrian and Ordovician carbonate rocks were near the bottom of the sedimentary column, underlain by no great thickness of incompetent shale but overlain by a great thickness of clastic rock whose weight promoted continuous deformation, whereas the Southern Appalachians are faulted because the competent carbonate rocks were in or above the middle of the column, underlain by a thick, incompetent shale zone but overlain by a relatively thinner body of clastic rocks. The contrasts are probably not as strong, however, as Willis thought; the incompetent zone below seems to be present as far north as central Pennsylvania, and it does not thin abruptly along strike near Roanoke but generally across strike or at some intermediate angle over a large part of the province to the southwest. The Silurian and especially the Devonian clastics do thin greatly (but steadily) southwestward from a maximum in eastern Pennsylvania, but this thinning may have been in part compensated by an increasing thickness of Carboniferous rocks southwestward into Alabama; Carboniferous rocks are now largely absent on the southeast side of the province, but the few belts of Lower Carboniferous rocks still preserved suggest an originally continuous cover.

(2) One might postulate mainly cover tectonics in one arc and mainly basement tectonics in the other. The entire absence of basement and the repeated appearance of the weak shales near the Lower-Middle Cambrian boundary in the cores of the anticlines of the central arc and along the thrust faults of the southern render any such great difference unlikely.

(3) Perhaps the amount of shortening is greater in the southern arc than in the central. Kay (1942, p. 1647−1649) has suggested that the Saltville fault, appearing suddenly near Roanoke yet continuing from there to the Coastal Plain, marks the edge of a far-traveled Appalachian allochthone that swung on a hinge in the Roanoke area. I find it impossible to consider the Saltville fault unique in this way, for the

contrast in structural style across it seems to me like the contrast in style across the mid-province structural front in the Central Appalachians and unrelated to the difference in style between the two arcs, a difference that can be recognized on both sides of the mid-province front and Saltville fault. Nevertheless, the sum of the throws of the Southern Appalachian thrust faults, even omitting those at the edge of the Blue Ridge or Piedmont, must be very large and may be considerably greater than the shortening recorded by the Central Appalachian folds and the few faults associated with them. The difference in style may therefore result from greater shortening or greater compression.

(4) The two arcs may have been deformed at different times. In the Central Appalachians the highest beds known to have been deformed are highest Carboniferous or lowest Permian (Dunkard group); in the Southern Appalachians they are below the middle of the Upper Carboniferous (lower Allegheny group, approximately Westphalian C). Furthermore, the nature of the intersection in the Roanoke sector suggests that the folds of the southern arc may have formed before those of the central.

Southwestern Virginia Sector

Once the basic pattern of dominant thrust faulting is established in the Roanoke sector, it persists southwestward throughout the southern arc of the Valley and Ridge province, but many changes are rung upon it. In southwestern Virginia (except south of the Pine Mountain thrust sheet), it takes the form of three major faults—the St. Clair, Saltville, and Pulaski faults, all of which throw Cambrian on Carboniferous along at least part of their course—plus the major fault at the southeast margin of the province; in the belts between these faults, however, folds are still at least as prominent as additional thrust faults. The main difference in tectonic style across the province here takes place at the northwest fault of the Pulaski system, which thus plays the role of the mid-province—Blue Mountain or Little North Mountain—structural front of the central arc.

The northwestern—Nittany arch—uplift is represented, as explained above, by the St. Clair fault and the Narrows fault (or the anticlines along its trend). The throw on the St. Clair fault increases southwestward as the fault overlaps the Allegheny structural front, especially after the fault reenters Virginia near Bluefield. At the state line near its northeast end, it throws Lower

Ordovician on Lower Devonian, whereas on either side of Big A Mountain at the southeast corner of the Pine Mountain thrust block, 170 kilometers (110 miles) to the southwest, it throws Lower Cambrian on Lower Carboniferous, a total throw of over 2500 meters (over 8500 feet).

On both sides of Big A Mountain, however, where the transverse Russell Fork meets the longitudinal St. Clair fault, there are complicated subordinate fault slices in front of the main St. Clair fault (Cross Creek fault of Bates, 1936); Big A Mountain itself is the topographic expression of a syncline containing the resistant basal Silurian (Clinch) sandstone on a slice only 7 kilometers (4 miles) long, which has been thrust nearly 5 kilometers (3 miles) northwestward between two tear faults over the Upper Carboniferous strata at the southeast corner of the Middlesboro basin. Furthermore, the St. Clair fault itself becomes double, the two faults (Hunter Valley and Clinchport faults) extending for many kilometers (miles) southwestward only 1 to 8 kilometers ($\frac{1}{2}$ mile to 5 miles) apart. As mentioned in Chapter 2 (p. 18), the Abbs Valley anticline and Richlands fault on the Plateau enter the east part of this complicated area and are bevelled by a northwest branch of the St. Clair fault 11 kilometers (7 miles) east of Big A Mountain.

Throughout its length northeast of Big A Mountain, the rocks next southeast of the St. Clair fault are folded into one or more synclines that become generally shallower southwestward until only basal Silurian and Upper Ordovician rocks are preserved; behind them is a single continuous anticline, in effect the Rich Patch anticline. These folds show the typical Appalachian asymmetry. The Narrows fault breaks but never completely covers the northwest flank of the anticline for about 100 kilometers (60 miles)—the name comes from the Narrows where the New River breaks through the syncline to the north; then for about 30 kilometers (20 miles) to the west-southwest the fold is unbroken. The lowest beds exposed in the anticline are Upper Cambrian (lower part of Knox group) or locally upper Middle Cambrian (Honaker dolostone) where the Narrows fault is present, Lower Ordovician (upper part of Knox group) where it is not. Finally, southeast of Big A Mountain, another thrust fault, the Copper Creek fault (named for the stream it follows some kilometers—miles—to the southwest) appears on the fold, and this fault increases rapidly in throw southwestward until in 25 kilometers (16 miles) it has cut out the whole northwest limb of the anticline and reduced the syncline to the north to a southeast-dipping homocline 6 kilometers (4 miles) wide in which the youngest rocks preserved are Middle Ordovician.

Between the Rich Patch anticline and its faults and the Saltville fault roughly 15 kilometers (9 miles) to the southeast, the structure is no simple syncline or homocline but is diversified by large domes and basins, alternating along strike; these folds show no consistent asymmetry. On the crest of the largest dome, the Bane dome close to the New River, a shale unit (Rome formation) at the top of the Lower Cambrian is exposed, though neither Lower Cambrian nor lower Middle Cambrian strata come to the surface along the St. Clair fault for 65 kilometers (40 miles) to the west nor along the Copper Creek fault till 120 kilometers (70 miles) to the southwest. A drill hole on this dome (Cooper, 1961, p. 92, 157; 1964, p. 97) passed through an unusually small thickness of the shale unit and encountered 350 meters (about 1200 feet) of dolostone and sandy dolostone, which may be the next underlying Lower Cambrian unit (Shady dolostone) or higher strata repeated by faulting. North and south of this dome, the highest beds still preserved between the Narrows and Saltville faults are Middle Ordovician (thus here the New River can cross the belt without meeting the resistant basal Silurian [Clinch] sandstone), yet about 30 kilometers (20 miles) along strike on either side are equally large basins of Upper Devonian shale, and Lower Carboniferous rocks are preserved on the south side of the western basin against the Saltville fault. The eastern basin (John Creek syncline) extends northeastward to the × of folds near the James River, pinching out in its sharp southwest angle. Beyond the western (Kimberling) basin is the almost perfect Burkes Garden dome (Cooper, 1944); the lowest beds exposed are Lower Ordovician (upper part of Knox group), but a well in it reached the Lower Cambrian shale unit (Rome formation) and then encountered considerable anhydrite (Cooper, 1961, p. 109–110). Anhydrite, but of a somewhat different character, is otherwise reported in southwest Virginia only in the Lower Carboniferous (Maccrady formation); the anhydrite in the well might belong to that unit, but more likely it is an unusual facies of the Lower Cambrian. Beneath the anhydrite is more dolostone; Cooper interprets this as in sequence (Shady dolostone), but Griffiths (personal communication) considers it Upper Cambrian (lower part of Knox group) repeated by faulting beneath the anhydrite zone.

Farther westward are several more domes and basins, but the domes are lower and the basins shallower; the last low dome is hardly more

than a prominent nose plunging eastward from a kink in the Copper Creek fault at the point, southwest of Big A Mountain, where Lower Cambrian strata (Rome formation) first appear along it. Beyond this point, the belt between the Copper Creek and Saltville faults is simply a southeast-dipping homocline exposing the entire section from Lower Cambrian to Lower Carboniferous, except that close to the Saltville fault a syncline (the Greendale syncline) plunges gently southwest preserving an especially thick and complete Lower Carboniferous sequence over 2000 meters (some 7500 feet) thick (Cooper, 1948, p. 261–262).

The throw on the Saltville fault increases southwestward, though not very regularly. Near the New River, Upper Cambrian lies against Middle Ordovician; not far to the west, Middle Cambrian lies against Upper Devonian or lower Lower Carboniferous; and south-southwest of Big A Mountain, Lower Cambrian rocks (Rome formation) appear (almost due south of where they appear on the Copper Creek fault) against the highest Lower Carboniferous strata in the Greendale syncline, a total throw of 5000 meters (15,000 feet), nearly twice that on the St. Clair fault near Big A Mountain because the Paleozoic section is about that much thicker along the Saltville fault. There are no major complications nor prominent branches along this part of the Saltville fault though there are a few slices; complications begin, however, where the Lower Cambrian rocks appear. The belt southeast of the Saltville fault is a relatively simple southeast-dipping homocline with only minimal complications, except for those directly connected with the Pulaski fault to the southeast.

The Pulaski fault system, on the other hand, reaches its maximum complexity in this sector. As described above, in the Roanoke sector it consists of two and probably three major thrust faults, the Catawba and Salem faults on either side of the prominent Catawba synclinorium, and the Christiansburg fault between Middle and Lower Cambrian rocks farther southeast. The synclinorium ends southwestward almost as abruptly as it begins on the northeast, and beyond for 40 kilometers (25 miles), the belt 11 kilometers (7 miles) wide between the Pulaski and Salem faults is again a shallow thrust sheet consisting mostly of intensely crumpled and brecciated Lower and Middle Cambrian rocks (mainly Elbrook formation), through which, near the New River, three windows 5 to 13 kilometers (3 to 8 miles) long have been eroded, one along the Salem fault and the others to the north. In the northeastern window an anticline of Lower Carboniferous rocks (type of Price formation) is exposed; a well 3000 meters (almost 10,000 feet) deep drilled on the crest of this anticline encountered an excess thickness of Devonian and Ordovician shale that is more than enough to account for the structural relief of the anticline. Cooper (1961, p. 105, and Pl. 34, p. 148, but apparently *not* 1968, Fig. 7, p. 43) maintains, however, that all or most of this thickening is stratigraphic, a conclusion I find difficult to accept in this area of obviously intense deformation. West of the windows a shallow syncline preserves Upper Cambrian strata (lower part of Knox group). This whole shallow part of the thrust sheet appears to be separated from the Catawba synclinorium by a transverse branch fault of the Pulaski system or, if Cooper is correct in excluding the synclinorium from the thrust sheet, by the main Pulaski fault itself.

At the southwest end of this area, at Pulaski, Virginia, the Pulaski fault doubles back abruptly across the strike for nearly 15 kilometers (10 miles) to join the Salem and Christiansburg faults, and then swings back southwest, west, and west-northwest around the complicated Draper Mountain half-window (Cooper, 1939). This half-window is 20 kilometers (12 miles) wide at the back (southeast side) and 30 kilometers (20 miles) at the throat (northwest side), where the rocks within it are separated from the homocline southeast of the Saltville fault by another thrust fault, the Tract Mountain fault (equated to the Catawba fault by Cooper, 1961, Pl. 21), which locally throws Middle Cambrian on Lower Carboniferous but disappears under the Pulaski fault at each side of the half-window. Broadly the rocks in the half-window outline a strongly overturned syncline, with Cambrian on both flanks and Lower Carboniferous in the middle, but there are many complexities. The overturned southeast limb of this syncline may represent the northwest limb of the anticline out of which the Pulaski fault developed; it may also represent the mid-province structural front of the Central Appalachians, last seen near Buchanan, but on the other hand so may the Tract Mountain fault at the throat of the half-window. In any case, the half-window, like the windows to the east, prove that, as near Buchanan, the Pulaski thrust sheet has moved forward at least 15 kilometers (10 miles).

Around the half-window, especially on its southwest side, the Pulaski fault appears to be a wide fault zone of intensely crumpled and brecciated rock. Cooper (1939, p. 55 ff.; 1946, p. 95) has distinguished a lower and an upper fault in the zone, the upper marked by as much as 50 meters (150 feet) of extraordinary breccia with smaller amounts of mylonite and pulverized shale (Max Meadows

breccia of Cooper and Haff, 1940). The rocks between the two faults are mainly Middle Cambrian thin-bedded carbonate rock (Elbrook formation); the rocks above the upper fault (here called the Max Meadows fault and probably a continuation of the Christiansburg fault) are upper Lower Cambrian shale and thin-bedded carbonate rock (Rome formation), but fragments of still older Lower Cambrian quartzite (Chilhowee group) have been found in the breccia (this quartzite is exposed not far to the southwest—see below).

West of the half-window, the northwestern fault of the Pulaski system is well marked (Middle Cambrian against Upper Devonian and Lower Carboniferous); 3 to 6 kilometers (2 to 4 miles) to the southeast another fault, perhaps the Max Meadows fault, brings up Lower Cambrian, but it has not been continuously mapped. The small Kent window (Marshall, *in* Cooper, 1961, Pl. 24) lies along its trace a short distance southwest of the half-window. Between the two faults is a tight syncline containing strata up to Middle Ordovician, beyond which they nearly meet again. At Marion, Virginia, 70 kilometers (43 miles) west-southwest of Pulaski, is another small, complicated area (Cooper, 1936), a badly faulted dome with faults on each side. The northwest fault has not been traced past the dome, but the southeast fault swings around its south side and continues beyond, dividing in two. Cooper, following Butts, originally considered that only the northwest fault east of the dome is the "true" Pulaski fault, which would therefore end here, and he called the one south of the dome the Seven Springs fault (for a locality 25 kilometers—15 miles—west of Marion), but more recent work (Cooper and Cashion, 1970) showed that the southeast fault is the real continuation of the Pulaski fault. Its northern branch west of Marion is entirely comparable to the northwest fault of the system east of Marion; hence it may be called the Seven Springs-Pulaski fault. The southern branch extends southwest at least 30 kilometers (20 miles) along a narrow but relatively high anticline in the synclinorium southwest of Marion (see below).

The stratigraphic throw on the frontal fault of the Pulaski system (here the Seven Springs fault), which is 4000 meters (13,000 feet; Lower Cambrian against Lower Carboniferous) north of Pulaski, is still 2500 meters (over 8500 feet) just west of the Marion dome, but it decreases rapidly to about 700 meters (about 2000 feet; Middle Cambrian against Lower Ordovician) 40 kilometers (25 miles) west of Marion; it then remains nearly constant for many tens of kilometers (tens of miles) to the southwest, and Lower Cambrian rocks never reappear along it. Butts and Edmundson (1943) have shown that some of the disappearance of strata results from a disconformity in the homocline to the northwest, which brings Middle or Lower Devonian strata down on Upper Ordovician strata, cutting out the entire Silurian, especially the competent and mountain-forming basal (Clinch) sandstone. The same beds are also absent just north of the dome at Marion but are present, though locally rather thin, in the Draper Mountain half-window near Pulaski and in the Catawba synclinorium; they are present in full thickness north of the Saltville fault, both here and for 200 kilometers (120 miles) west-southwest into Tennessee, but are absent at the only place in Tennessee southeast of the Saltville fault where post-Ordovician strata are preserved. It may be suggested that the elimination of the competent basal Silurian (Clinch) sandstone from the section is the reason for the rapid decrease in throw in the Pulaski fault here.

Thus although each of the three major faults northwest of the Pulaski (counting the Narrows and Copper Creek faults as one) increases in throw, though irregularly, southwestward and finally brings up Lower Cambrian beds (Rome formation) in that direction, the Pulaski fault has its greatest throw from Buchanan to Pulaski and decreases in throw away from that area, though persisting for 250 kilometers (150 miles) in either direction from Pulaski. Probably, west of Marion, the steadily growing Saltville fault takes over from the Pulaski fault the function of representing the mid-province structural front and separating the somewhat different tectonic styles of the northwest and southeast parts of the Valley and Ridge province.

East of Pulaski, the southeastern fault of the Pulaski system, the Christiansburg fault, is separated from the thrust fault or faults (e.g., Poplar Camp fault) at the edge of the Blue Ridge province by 3 to 6 kilometers (2 to 4 miles) of intensely crumpled upper Lower Cambrian shale and shaly carbonate rock (Rome formation), commonly showing considerable slaty cleavage. South of Pulaski, these faults diverge to about 13 kilometers (8 miles), and they continue roughly this distance apart southwestward to Tennessee. In the part of the belt between Pulaski and Marion, however, strata appear that are lower than the upper Lower Cambrian shale unit (Rome formation) that almost everywhere else in the Valley and Ridge province is the lowest unit exposed; these lower strata include massive carbonate rock above (Shady dolostone) and quartzite, siltstone, and shale or slate below (upper part of Chilhowee group), the latter including about half of the thick (2000 meters— 6000 feet) clastic sequence that forms the base of the Paleozoic section and is known to rest on the Precambrian granitic basement nearby

in the Blue Ridge province. These rocks are seen in two different structural positions within the belt.

In the main part of the belt, what appear to be two anticlinoria composed of imbricate thrust slices of the basal clastic sequence, especially the quartzite, form two mountain groups about 25 kilometers (15 miles) long and 5 to 7 kilometers (3 to 4 miles) wide, called from prominent members the Lick Mountain and Glade Mountain groups. The individual thrust slices are $\frac{1}{2}$ to 1 kilometer $\frac{1}{4}$ to $\frac{1}{2}$ mile) wide, mainly homoclinal but locally anticlinal at the ends; the anticlines generally have steeper northwest flanks and the thrust faults generally dip southeast, but there are exceptions. Around and between the slices of quartzite, the massive Lower Cambrian carbonate unit (Shady dolostone) is exposed, and the anticlinoria are set in a sea of tightly crumpled upper Lower Cambrian shale and thin-bedded carbonate rock (Rome formation) underlying lower but hilly ground.

Some geologists have interpreted these masses not as anticlinoria but as great klippen of the older rocks thrust out over the crumpled shale from the edge of the Blue Ridge province, but detailed mapping of the two mountain groups (Stead and Stose, 1943; Miller, 1944), undertaken to study the manganese deposits that occur in residual clay over the massive (Shady) dolostone, has confirmed the anticlinorial hypothesis, though at the north edge of each anticlinorium fairly low-angle thrust faults are present. It follows that in this belt the fault beneath the Pulaski thrust sheet lies not in or above the upper Lower Cambrian shale (Rome formation), as east of Pulaski and probably west of Marion, but deep in the basal clastic sequence (Chilhowee group).

South of these mountain groups, the older rocks appear again in a thrust slice 3 to 8 kilometers (2 to 5 miles) wide just in front of the Poplar Camp thrust fault at the edge of the Blue Ridge province. The total exposed length of this slice is about 65 kilometers (40 miles), but its continuity is broken for 5 kilometers (3 miles) about midway of its length across a minor culmination (the faults bounding the two parts are called the Laswell and Sugar Grove faults). The rocks in the slice are mainly the Lower Cambrian shale and massive carbonate units (Rome formation and Shady dolostone) folded into a syncline, simple and shallow to the west in the Sugar Grove thrust sheet, more complex and split by an anticline and associated thrust faults to the east in the Laswell thrust sheet, where important zinc deposits occur in the carbonate unit (Currier, 1935). Quartzite at the top of the basal clastic sequence (Chilhowee group) appears along the thrust faults within the slice and locally along the bounding fault.

South of Marion, the older rocks disappear from the belt, for the anticlinoria trend at a low angle into, and presumably under, the Poplar Camp fault at the Blue Ridge front. Farther southwest on the Pulaski sheet, instead of anticlinoria there appear several synclinoria of higher Cambrian and Ordovician strata, cut by some small thrust and strike-slip faults.

The general strike of folds and faults in this sector is N65°E, though it ranges through 10 or 15 degrees. On the Pulaski thrust sheet west of Pulaski, the strike swings around almost to east-west for a few kilometers (miles), and a weaker swing can be detected in the belts farther north. Structural axes seem to rise and fall entirely independently in the individual belts between the main thrust faults, so that one cannot speak of culminations or depressions in the province or even a part of it. Only the southwestward increase in the throw along the faults northwest of the Pulaski fault may be considered consistent, and it is somewhat contradicted by the appearance of Lower Cambrian strata (Rome formation) on the crest of the Bane dome near the New River many kilometers (miles) east of their appearance on the faults. The southwestward deepening of the Greendale syncline contrasts with the shallowing of the syncline between the St. Clair and Narrows faults and with the disappearance of higher strata southwestward in the belt just north of the Pulaski fault. On the Pulaski sheet itself, the highest part appears to be the Lick Mountain and Glade Mountain anticlinoria; both east and west the basal strata present are upper Lower Cambrian or younger, and the highest are Middle Ordovician (until one reaches the Catawba synclinorium).

The facts suggest that, if a zone of decollement exists beneath this part of the Valley and Ridge province, it follows mainly the shale unit athwart the Lower-Middle Cambrian boundary (Rome formation and immediately overlying beds). Except between Pulaski and Marion, where it has brought forward older rocks, the Pulaski fault evidently reaches down only to the top of this unit; northwest of the Pulaski fault, however, the unit reaches the surface only near the southwest edge of the sector and in the Bane dome. The extreme deformation and brecciation of the lowest beds along the faults of the Pulaski system (exposed over wide areas where the thrust sheet is thin, as around the windows east of the New River) suggested to Rodgers (1970) an analogy with tectonic salt-bearing breccias (Haselgebirge) in the Austrian Alps, and on the basis of this analogy and the known presence of anhydrite in the Burkes Garden

well (p. 44) and also in the Sponaugle well in the northern Virginia sector he postulated that the shale unit in question contained evaporites, anhydrite or gypsum generally and salt in the area where the Pulaski fault system later developed, greatly facilitating if not guiding the decollement. Cooper (1970) has rebutted this idea, however.

In this and the Roanoke sector, Lowry (1957; 1960) and Cooper (1961; 1964) have amassed a wealth of thickness measurements to show that many individual stratigraphic units thicken and thin across strike, being thinner generally on the crests of anticlines and on their steep northwest flanks and thicker on the gentler southeast flanks and especially in the troughs of the synclines. Some of the measurements seem suspect to me because no account was taken of possible tectonic distortion of thicknesses by crumpling, by minor thrust faults, and by cleavage (which is present in the weaker shale and limy shale units in much of the area); both minor faults and cleavage would tend to increase the apparent thickness in the southeast-dipping homoclines southeast of the anticlines and to decrease it, perhaps drastically, on the steep or overturned limbs. Some of the data are more convincing, however, notably evidence that the Lower Ordovician and older strata (Knox group) were gently folded before the Middle Ordovician was deposited; a pronounced disconformity separates the two series in many if not most parts of the Valley and Ridge province south of northern Virginia (cf. Bridge, 1955), and evidence that it bevels the underlying strata is beginning to accumulate in several parts of the Southern Appalachians (cf. also Laurence, 1960, p. 174; Oder and Ricketts, 1961, p. 5-6).

Northeastern Tennessee Sector (Sector behind Pine Mountain Thrust Block)

Beyond Big A Mountain, the belt of thrust faulting is in effect widened by the addition of the Pine Mountain thrust fault northwest of the St. Clair fault and its continuations. As mentioned above, the St. Clair fault becomes double near Big A Mountain, and to the southwest it is represented by a sort of imbricate fault zone, generally 5 to 6 kilometers (3 to 4 miles) wide; in some places this zone is a fairly simple syncline between two well marked thrust faults (at one place, Rye Cove, Middle Ordovician rocks are preserved), but in others Lower and Middle Cambrian strata are repeated several times. The northwestern fault of the zone, called the Hunter Valley (or St. Paul) fault, throws Cambrian, generally Lower (Rome formation), on younger strata, mainly on Devonian or Lower Carboniferous for 75 kilometers (47 miles) from Big A Mountain, on Ordovician or Silurian beyond that. The southeastern fault is called the Clinchport (or Honaker) fault (all these names were given in southwest Virginia). The maximum complexity of the fault zone is close to the Virginia-Tennessee state line where there must be six or seven imbricate faults in all; not far beyond, however, they converge, and farther southwest the imbricate zone is discontinuous and finally disappears altogether, the faults all merging into a single fault.

For 55 kilometers (34 miles) west of Big A Mountain, nearly flat-lying Upper Carboniferous strata form the whole of the Pine Mountain thrust block, except for a kilometer or two (a mile or so) of folded and faulted rocks along the borders, but farther on the Powell Valley anticline rises (see p. 22 and Fig. 4), separating the main Middlesboro basin on the northwest from a prong of relatively flat-lying Carboniferous rocks 20 kilometers (13 miles) long on the southeast. Precisely on strike with the rather abrupt blunt end of this prong, a prominent anticline appears (Harris and Miller, 1958); the northwest flank of this anticline and, a few kilometers (miles) to the southwest, its crest are cut out by a new major thrust fault, the Wallen Valley fault (named some kilometers—miles—to the southwest). From the point where the crest is cut out, this fault separates two southeast-dipping homoclines, throwing Upper Cambrian strata (top of the Conasauga shale or base of the Knox group) in the southern one against Silurian strata in the northern one, which is the southeast flank of the Powell Valley anticline. Farther southwest, the Silurian rocks are cut out for two stretches of some 20 kilometers (15 miles or so) each (the basal Silurian rocks around the Powell Valley anticline are not so resistant to erosion as the basal Silurian [Clinch] sandstone farther east and northeast in the province and hence do not make such prominent ridges).

At the second place where Silurian rocks are cut out, in Tennessee due south of the western tip of Virginia, Lower Cambrian beds (Rome formation) finally appear on the southeast side of the Wallen Valley fault, and the competent Lower Ordovician and Upper Cambrian dolostone (Knox group) on the northwest side is thrown into isoclinal folds nearly 1 kilometer ($\frac{1}{2}$ mile) across and is mineralized with zinc and lead (Straight Creek district). The belt of isoclinal folding is only about 10 kilometers (6 miles) long; it appears to lie roughly at the apex of a triangular sub-block of the Pine thrust sheet, whose base is the Pine Mountain thrust fault and whose sides are two of the transverse belts of disturbed rocks that cross the Middlesboro basin (Chapter 2, p. 22), as though it reflected the lagging behind of the sub-block relative to the rest of the thrust sheet. Drilling shows that Lower Cambrian strata (Rome formation) are present under the Powell Valley anticline next above the Pine Mountain fault here and as far northeast as the state line, though they are not present around the windows along the anticline only a short distance beyond the line in Virginia. Finally, 130 kilometers (about 80 miles) from its northeast end, and just opposite the Jacksboro fault at the southwest end of the main Pine Mountain thrust block, the Wallen Valley fault merges with or disappears under the Hunter Valley-Clinchport fault, forming the Whiteoak Mountain fault, which persists southwestward across Tennessee into Georgia.

The belt between the Wallen Valley and Hunter Valley faults is mainly a homocline but along its southeast side the structure is more complicated. For 40 kilometers (25 miles), beginning in Virginia but mainly in Tennessee, the homocline dips into a deep syncline containing Lower Carboniferous strata; to the northeast the syncline can be traced with difficulty, because of minor thrust faults, to the end of the prong of Upper Carboniferous rocks southeast of the northeast end of the Powell Valley anticline. The southeast flank of this syncline is a belt of short anticlines and imbricate thrust sheets in Silurian and Devonian rocks, 4 kilometers ($2\frac{1}{2}$ miles) wide at a maximum but largely overlapped by the imbricate sheets of Cambrian rocks above the Hunter Valley fault; there are few more complicated belts in the Valley and Ridge province. Southwest of the end of the Lower Carboniferous rocks, however, the structure becomes simpler; a few kilometers (miles) farther on the ridge-making Silurian (Clinch) sandstone is also cut off, and the belt gradually narrows southwestward until it disappears where the Wallen Valley and Hunter Valley faults merge.

The Copper Creek fault, which first appears southeast of Big A Mountain, continues across the entire sector with remarkably little change; everywhere it separates two relatively simple monoclines, the one to the northwest exposing beds from Lower Cambrian to Middle Ordovician, the one to the southeast from Lower Cambrian to Lower Carboniferous—the basal Silurian (Clinch) sandstone in this belt forms the persistent ridge of Clinch Mountain. In a few places the Cambrian rocks next southeast of the fault are intensely imbricated, notably about 25 kilometers (15 miles) north of Knoxville, Tennessee. Directly southeast of this imbricated area, the outcrops of Silurian, Devonian, and Lower Carboniferous rocks in the Greendale syncline (the southeastern of the two homoclines), and also Clinch Mountain and its associated ridges, which are their topographic expression, terminate abruptly, and a new thrust fault (the Beaver Valley fault, named for a locality just north of Knoxville) as abruptly appears, changing the structure of the belt from one homocline (Lower Cambrian to Lower Carboniferous) to two (each Lower Cambrian to Middle Ordovician). The situation here closely parallels that at the northeast end of the Wallen Valley fault, where the southeast flank of the Powell Valley anticline is in effect doubled. With the disappearance in the longitude of Knoxville of all post-Ordovician rocks (except the discontinuous belt along the Wallen Valley fault), the topographic character of the Valley and Ridge province changes somewhat; one can no longer distinguish a Great Valley on the southeast from a belt of narrower valleys with intervening mountains on the northwest, for the whole province takes on the aspect of a single Great Valley, with only subordinate ridges diversifying its floor.

The Saltville fault is also continuous across this sector, but it is accompanied by far greater complications than the Copper Creek fault; here indeed it attains its greatest complexity and its greatest throw. Where it approaches the Virginia-Tennessee state line, it changes trend rather abruptly by about 30 degrees and strikes almost due west for 35 kilometers (24 miles) before resuming its normal S60°W trend; the change in strike reflects east-west right-handed strike-slip movement, which is still more clearly expressed by a zone of right-handed wrench faults southeast of the Pulaski fault and a single larger wrench fault (Cross Mountain fault) at the edge of the Blue Ridge province. A smaller thrust fault (the Carter Valley fault), hardly more than a large-scale imbrication, branches from the Saltville fault about midway of the east-west stretch and extends west-southwestward, lying about 4 kilometers (2½ miles) southeast of the Saltville fault where that fault resumes its normal trend.

About 20 kilometers (13 miles) into Tennessee, however, the Saltville fault is abruptly deflected about 6 kilometers (4 miles) to the southeast around a shallow embayment 25 kilometers (15 miles) long, beyond which it as abruptly resumes its former trend. The Greendale syncline of Lower Carboniferous rocks, which here lies close to the Saltville fault, does not share the deflection, so that in the embayment the entire southeast limb of the syncline (presumably the northwest limb of the anticline out of which the Saltville fault developed) is exposed down to the Lower Ordovician, strongly overturned and complicated by minor faults and folds (Sanders, ms. 1953). The whole

structure is reminiscent of the Draper Mountain half-window, though the embayment is shallower. Along the southeast side of the embayment, the Cambrian rocks above the Saltville fault are intensely imbricated for a width of 2 to 4 kilometers (about 2 miles); the Carter Valley fault enters the northeast end of this imbricate belt, and a fairly large anticline and a couple of thrust faults diverge southwestward from its southwest end. Beyond the embayment, the Saltville fault itself shows only minor complications as far as the vicinity of Knoxville, although, as mentioned above, the post-Ordovician rocks northwest of it end abruptly about 25 kilometers (15 miles) northeast of Knoxville, and the Beaver Valley thrust fault appears.

The larger thrust fault that emerges from the southwest end of the imbricate zone southeast of the embayment appears to cut diagonally upward across the southeast limb of the associated anticline and to connect with a prominent fault of flat dip and sinuous trace in the Tennessee zinc district east of Knoxville. This fault, called the Rocky Valley fault, is especially well known because of detailed surface mapping (Bridge, 1956) and subsurface drilling for zinc (Bumgarner and others, 1964), and its mechanics is clear; it illustrates on a smaller scale the intimate interrelation of faulting and folding so well displayed by the Pine Mountain fault in the Plateau province (indeed Rich, 1934, p. 1591, recognized the similarity between the two faults when the modern detailed work had barely begun). At the present land surface, it appears to be cutting upward from shale near the Lower-Middle Cambrian boundary (Rome formation and base of Conasauga group) across massive Upper Cambrian and Lower Ordovician carbonate strata (Knox group) to shale in the Middle Ordovician (Ottosee shale). Large bodies of rather low-grade but pure sphalerite ore occur in the Lower Ordovician rocks beneath the fault, especially around the southwest-plunging end of the anticline mentioned above, localized by brecciation associated with minor folds and faults (Bridge, 1956, p. 70–72; Brokaw and Jones, 1946; Brokaw, 1950; Oder and Ricketts, 1961). The fault can be traced about 30 kilometers (20 miles) across the zinc district, disappearing beyond in a mass of crumpled Middle Ordovician shale, but just east of Knoxville another thrust fault (the Knoxville fault) appears on roughly the same strike, and this fault can be traced continuously southwest to Georgia.

In this sector, one may speak of a Saltville system of faults, including the Beaver Valley, Saltville, Carter Valley, Rocky Valley, and Knoxville thrust faults, which appears to mark a boundary within the Valley and Ridge province. Stratigraphically notable facies changes take place across it, and structurally it separates a belt of imbricate thrust faults separated by southeast-dipping homoclines from a belt of folds cut by some thrust faults. Apparently, therefore, in this part of the province the Saltville system rather than the Pulaski system represents the second or mid-province structural front of the Central Appalachians, insofar as one can recognize such a front at all. Similarly, the first or Allegheny front appears to be displaced in this sector from the St. Clair-Hunter Valley fault trend to the Powell Valley anticline, or rather to the belt of steeply dipping rocks exposed in the windows along that anticline; farther southwest beyond the end of the main Pine Mountain thrust block, it would be represented by the sharply upturned rocks at the southeast edge of the Cumberland Plateau.

Where the frontal fault of the Pulaski system, the Seven Springs-Pulaski fault, enters Tennessee, it lies only 5 kilometers (3 miles) southeast of the Saltville fault, separated from it by a simple homocline (Middle Cambrian to Lower Ordovician). Like the Saltville fault, its trend changes near the state line, but the west strike persists less than 10 kilometers (6 miles), and the fault then turns nearly 45 degrees to a southwest trend and rapidly diverges from the Saltville fault system. In the angle between appears a broad synclinorium, filled with a thick sequence of Middle Ordovician shale and sandstone (Sevier shale, s.l.) and called the Bays Mountain synclinorium for a group of mountains upheld by resistant Middle Ordovician sandstone (part of Bays formation) preserved in its deepest part north of Greeneville, Tennessee; the mountains form an isolated group in the Great Valley comparable to the Massanutten Mountain group in northern Virginia. The synclinorium is here nearly 25 kilometers (15 miles) wide and consists of major folds with a wave length of 2 or 3 kilometers (1 or 2 miles) and of innumerable minor folds, but no large faults are known. West of Greeneville and roughly 75 kilometers (40 miles) from the northeast end of the synclinorium, this deepest part is brought to an end by a group of en echelon domelike uplifts, 5 to 15 kilometers (3 to 10 miles) long, of Lower Ordovician and Upper Cambrian carbonate rock (Knox group), but beyond them the synclinorium persists for another 175 kilometers (100 miles) to the southwest.

On the northwest flank of the synclinorium, the westernmost of the domelike uplifts rises southwestward to become a narrow anticlinorium cut by one or several thrust faults that bring up Middle Cambrian (Conasauga group) and locally Lower Cambrian (Rome formation). The principal fault on the northwest flank of the anticlinorium (called

the Dumplin Valley fault for a locality southeast of the zinc district) lies about 2 kilometers (barely 1½ miles) southeast of the Rocky Valley fault at one point, but they diverge southwestward; a smaller synclinorium of Middle Ordovician shale appears between them and becomes 11 kilometers (7 miles) wide southeast of Knoxville (Red Hills synclinorium). Certain layers and lenses of hematitic reef limestone and inter-reef fragmental limestone interbedded with the shale in this synclinorium furnish the well known "Tennessee marble."

Along much of the southeast flank of the Bays Mountain synclinorium there is a zone 1 to 2 kilometers (barely a mile) wide of close imbrication in Lower and Middle Ordovician rocks, with at least 4 or 5 thrust faults to the kilometer (6 or 8 to the mile). Northeast of Greeneville, it lies next to the frontal (Greeneville) fault of the Pulaski system (a curious flap of which spreads across it at one place), but southwest of Greeneville, where the fault doubles back (see below), the imbricate zone continues undeflected until it is finally overlapped by the Great Smoky thrust fault at the front of the Blue Ridge province.

The synclinoria of Middle Ordovician shale that lie southeast of the Seven Springs-Pulaski fault southwest of Marion extend into Tennessee as far as a north-south line 15 kilometers (10 miles) west of Elizabethton; the zone of wrench faulting mentioned above displaces them 1 kilometer (1 mile) or so to the right. Farther west the structure changes again, however; at about the point where the Seven Springs-Pulaski fault enters its short east-west trending segment, it splits, sending off two major branches to the southwest, and the three faults diverge until they are spaced roughly 9 kilometers (6 miles) apart. The three faults are called the Greeneville-Pulaski, Dunham Ridge, and Spurgeon faults; the Spurgeon fault may not be physically connected with the Seven Springs fault at the present land surface, but it is certainly a member of the Pulaski system. The rocks between these faults and also southeast of them are folded into practically upright isoclinal folds with a wave length of 1 to 3 kilometers (1 to 2 miles); they are mainly fairly massive Middle Cambrian to Lower Ordovician carbonate rocks (Honaker dolostone, Knox group), but a little Middle Ordovician shale is pinched into the tight synclines, and shale or shaly dolostone at the base of the Middle Cambrian (but nothing lower) is exposed along all the faults, displaying in many places the same intense crumpling that it shows along the faults of the Pulaski system throughout Virginia.

The three faults of the Pulaski system in the Valley strike S30—40°W in this belt, whereas the faults at the edge of the mountainous Blue Ridge province* strike S55–60°W, so that the latter trend bevels the former. The Spurgeon fault on the southeast is lost in unmapped and poorly exposed country near the mountain front, but the other two can be traced for 80 kilometers from the point where they split to a point 23 kilometers (14 miles) southwest of Greeneville, where the Greeneville-Pulaski fault doubles back to the southeast for 7 kilometers (4 miles) and merges with the Dunham Ridge fault; it then appears to run against the mountain front about 10 kilometers (6 miles) farther on.

The average strike in this sector is about N60°E (N40°E southeast of the Bays Mountain synclinorium), whereas in most of southwest Virginia it is nearer N65° or 70°E. It is not easy to recognize more than very local culminations and depressions, but the gradual disappearance of post-Ordovician rocks southwestward suggests a rise to a general culmination somewhat beyond Knoxville. All the major faults northwest of the Bays Mountain synclinorium bring up the shaly unit at the top of the Lower Cambrian (Rome formation), the lowest incompetent layer known in the Paleozoic section, but within Tennessee at least the faults of the Pulaski system bring up only the next higher unit (shale at the base of Honaker dolostone); where the Lower Cambrian (Rome) unit reappears at the edge of the Blue Ridge province, it is more dolomitic and less shaly, though still fairly incompetent. Perhaps therefore the Pulaski system cuts a bit less deeply here than it does in Virginia or than the faults to the northwest do in this sector.

This sector is notable for the increase in the number of major thrust faults across it; a cross-section west of Marion would encounter three major faults within the province, whereas one through Greeneville would encounter seven, plus the Pine Mountain fault on the Plateau beyond. The faults group themselves, however, into three systems: a Whiteoak Mountain system embracing the Wallen Valley, Hunter Valley, Clinchport, and Copper Creek faults (and thus continuing in a vague way the Nittany arch uplift), the Saltville system, and the Pulaski system. Apparently these systems correspond roughly to single major faults in southwest Virginia and to major anticlinoria in Pennyslvania. Probably the faults of each system are related as gigantesque imbricate slices arising from a single master fault; whether the different master faults rise separately from the basement or are themselves imbrications arising from a single underlying plane of decollement near the top of the Lower Cambrian (in the Rome formation) depends of course on whether the deformation of the whole province is basement or cover tectonics, a question discussed again at the end of this chapter. Where the dip of the faults can be observed, in this and the two adjoining sectors, it is mostly about 30 degrees, but both steeper and flatter dips are well attested; parts of certain faults are known to be almost horizontal (e.g., the Rocky Valley fault in the zinc district or the Pulaski from Pulaski eastward), whereas the straight stretches of the faults of the Pulaski system near and east of Greeneville must be nearly vertical, at least at the land surface, to judge by the dips in the associated isoclinal folds. As the dip is known to change drastically along the strike of a single fault, however, or even in places down the dip, it is of little significance for the question of the ultimate downward course of the faults toward the basement.

Southeastern Tennessee Sector

As noted above, at the northeast end of the Pine Mountain thrust block the Russell Fork cross fault meets the St. Clair-Hunter Valley thrust fault, which in effect forms the southeast margin of the block. At the southwest end, on the other hand, the Jacksboro cross fault, after cutting off the Powell Valley anticline (which here is broadest and rises to its highest point, exposing the top of the Lower Cambrian, the Rome formation), swings through an arc of 75 degrees until it is parallel to the regional strike and assumes the character of an ordinary thrust fault, like the Whiteoak Mountain fault about 7 kilometers (4 miles) to the southeast. It marks to be sure the boundary between the Appalachian Plateau and the Valley and Ridge province, throwing southeast-dipping Lower Cambrian beds (Rome formation) against northwest-dipping or vertical beds as high as the base of the Upper Carboniferous (Lee group); within the 75 degree arc indeed the whole section from Lower Ordovician to Upper Carboniferous is exposed standing vertical and doubtless representing the structural front at the province boundary (probably the Allegheny front, displaced from the St. Clair-Hunter Valley to the Powell Valley trend).

*North of Elizabethton and for nearly 50 kilometers (30 miles) to the southwest, the frontal thrust fault—the Holston Mountain fault—of the Blue Ridge province does not bring up the resistant quartzite and other rocks of the basal clastic sequence (Chilhowee group), as it does farther northeast and as other faults do to the southeast and southwest; hence topographically the area next southeast of it belongs to the Great Valley, but structurally it should still be reckoned to the Blue Ridge province, with which it is discussed in Chapter 8 (p. 169).

The block between this part of the Jacksboro fault and the Whiteoak Mountain fault contains strata from Lower Cambrian to Silurian in a homocline, duplicated by a minor thrust fault, that is simply the southwestward continuation of the southeast flank of the Powell Valley anticline; it thus represents a part of the Pine Mountain thrust sheet where the Pine Mountain-Jacksboro fault failed to follow the Devonian black shale (Chattanooga shale) but broke directly from Lower Cambrian to Carboniferous strata, as did, apparently, most of the thrust faults in the Valley and Ridge province proper. Southwestward the minor fault on the homocline increases in throw and becomes involved in an imbricate zone behind the Jacksboro fault; 30 kilometers (20 miles) southwest of the point where the Jacksboro fault begins to turn parallel to the regional strike, Lower Cambrian strata (Rome formation) appear along this new fault and it takes its place among the major faults of the area, the homocline in effect having become two. The northern homocline preserves rocks as high as Silurian 40 kilometers (25 miles) to the southwest; the two faults bounding it, which presumably take the place of the single Jacksboro fault and which can apparently be traced from here to the Georgia state line, are called the Chattanooga and Kingston faults (Kingston is about 50 kilometers—30 miles—from the transverse stretch of the Jacksboro fault, but Chattanooga is just north of Georgia).

Due west of the point where the Chattanooga and Kingston faults become individualized is the east edge of the "Harriman corner," the area where the tear faults of the Emory River line cut across the vertical strata that form the front at the Plateau border and meet the Chattanooga fault. The structure here is similar to that at Big A Mountain, where the Russell Fork fault meets the St. Clair-Hunter Valley fault, but if anything more complicated (Milici, 1962); a wedge of the rocks along the front, 10 kilometers (6 miles) wide at the base, has been pushed 2 or 3 kilometers (1 or 2 miles) relatively northwestward. According to Milici, a new thrust fault, the Rockwood fault (Rockwood is 15 kilometers—9 miles—southwest of Harriman at the west edge of the corner), appears here in front of the Chattanooga fault, which continues southwest behind the wedge, and it has brought a thrust sheet of vertical or overturned mainly pre-Carboniferous strata forward into or over the base of the wedge. This sheet in its turn has been cut by faults, and erosion has worn windows through it.

Beyond the tear fault at the west edge of the Harriman corner, the Rockwood fault continues to cut the vertical strata along the Plateau front, which it follows for about 80 kilometers (50 miles) southwest of Harriman to a point somewhat beyond Dayton (Swingle, 1961). The forward trace of this fault lies up to 5 kilometers (up to 3 miles) northwest of the Chattanooga fault but is quite irregular, enclosing several half-windows; moreover, two lines of windows appear in the northern half of the belt between the two faults. The several windows of the western line (the longest is 5 kilometers—3 miles—long) lie within a kilometer (a mile) of the trace of the Rockwood fault and are evidently eroded through its thin leading edge; both windows and half-windows expose crumpled Upper Carboniferous strata (Lee group) and are surrounded by the vertical strata brought forward by the fault, apparently displaced northwestward at least a kilometer (nearly a mile). The eastern line consists of two windows, 4½ and 7½ kilometers (about 3 and 5 miles) long, lying against the Chattanooga fault, which forms their southeastern sides (Post Oak and Rhea Springs windows—see Tiedemann, 1956; these are the windows recognized as such by Rodgers, 1950, p. 680—see Chapter 2, p. 26). They expose nearly vertical strata from Middle Ordovician (Chickamauga group) to Upper Devonian (Chattanooga shale) and in the larger window also Lower Carboniferous (Fort Payne chert), all displaced 2½ to 4 kilometers (1½ to 2½ miles) southeast relatively to their position in the structural front above the Rockwood fault. Swingle and Tiedemann interpret the fault on the northwest sides of these windows as the Rockwood fault, but the greater displacement suggests that it is a larger fault of which the Rockwood is only an imbrication, probably the Sequatchie Valley or Cumberland Plateau fault.

Near Dayton the Rockwood fault approaches the Chattanooga fault, and somewhat farther on it either dies out or is overridden by that fault. Just to the northwest, the Plateau border is displaced westward 3 kilometers (2 miles) around the northern end of an anticline cut in its turn by a southeast-dipping thrust fault (Cranmore Cove anticline and fault); the fault continues southwest for at least 60 kilometers (at least 40 miles) past Chattanooga. The main belt of vertical and overturned strata (the structural front) is not deflected, however, but remains southeast of the Cranmore Cove fault, practically disappearing under the Chattanooga fault locally where the two faults approach within 300 meters (1000 feet) of each other.

Near Chattanooga the border of the Plateau northwest of the Chattanooga fault displays not a simple upturn but three anticlines, complicated by some faulting and exposing beds down to the Middle Ordovician (Chickamauga group). The northwesternmost fold is the Lookout Valley anticline, the northeastern of the three long en echelon anticlines that split the southeastern part of the Plateau in Georgia and Alabama southeast of the Sequatchie anticline (Chapter 2, p. 26). The middle fold represents the Cranmore Cove anticline, for the Cranmore Cove fault follows its crest; fold and fault appear to die out in Georgia on the southeast flank of the Lookout Valley anticline, on the west side of Lookout Mountain, which commands Chattanooga and is upheld by the north end of the body of flat-lying Upper Carboniferous strata east of the Lookout Valley anticline. The southeastern fold is a short, doubly-plunging anticline that appears only at Chattanooga from beneath the Chattanooga fault; its northwest flank appears to represent the structural front, and the steep strata along it continue south into Georgia at the east edge of Lookout Mountain, although the anticline plunges down and dies out. Furthermore, the Chattanooga fault itself splits at Chattanooga into two branches, and each in turn, one on each side of the state line, cuts westward and upward into the steep strata of the structural front and appears to die out there as a bedding-plane fault in the Mississippian beds; where the southern branch cuts westward, its place along the strike of the main fault is taken by a sharply asymmetrical south-plunging anticline, the steep northwest flank of which becomes the structural front. The effect of all these complications is to displace the Plateau border and the structural front along it 5 kilometers (3 miles) eastward from the east side of Walden Ridge north of the Tennessee River to the east side of Lookout Mountain south of the River.

As far southwest as the Rhea Springs window— 25 kilometers (15 miles) northeast of Dayton— the Chattanooga fault brings up Lower Cambrian strata (Rome formation), but farther southwest the lowest beds exposed are high in the Upper Cambrian (Knox group). Along the Kingston fault, Lower Cambrian rocks (Rome formation) persist to the latitude of Dayton, and the overlying Middle and Upper Cambrian shale (Conasauga group) continues to and across Georgia, though in Georgia it is exposed in an anticline just southeast of the fault rather than along the fault itself. The block between the two faults contains beds higher than Lower Ordovician (top of the Knox group) for 50 kilometers (30 miles) northeast from the latitude of Dayton and again near Chattanooga; in the former area, Silurian rocks are preserved in a short strip and also reappear in a window behind a long slice of

older rocks northwest of the main Kingston fault.

Near Chattanooga this block is split by another thrust fault, the Missionary Ridge fault, which throws Upper Cambrian against Middle Ordovician to (in Georgia) Silurian strata (Missionary Ridge is at the eastern edge of Chattanooga, and like Lookout Mountain played a strategic role in the struggle for the city during the Civil War). The fault appears from beneath the Kingston fault 25 kilometers (15 miles) northeast of Chattanooga and extends south-southwest into Georgia, but about 8 kilometers (5 miles) south of the state line (Cressler, 1964) it doubles back across the south-plunging anticline on strike with the main Chattanooga fault, which has evidently folded the Missionary Ridge fault and the beds above and below it. On the west flank of the anticline just south of the state line, the Missionary Ridge fault is cut off abruptly by the southern branch of the Chattanooga fault. These relations seem to demand that the Missionary Ridge fault is an older fault, roughly parallel to bedding, that has been dismembered by later thrusting along the Chattanooga and Kingston faults, and indeed it may be the southeastern extension of the fault that presumably underlies the Plateau to the west and emerges along the Sequatchie anticline as the Sequatchie Valley fault (as well as on the northwest sides of the Post Oak and Rhea Springs windows); the displacements along it would be compatible with this interpretation. If so, the entire area from the point where the Missionary Ridge fault doubles back across the anticline south of Chattanooga northward between the Chattanooga fault on one side and the Missionary Ridge and Kingston faults on the other would be a gigantic window or half-window, up to 150 kilometers (100 miles) long.

The anticline in question continues to plunge southward beyond the point where it is crossed by the Missionary Ridge fault, and it finally disappears under the Plateau 40 kilometers (25 miles) south of the state line, so that the Plateau border and structural front are again displaced 10 kilometers (6 miles) eastward into the Valley and Ridge province, as far as the line of the Kingston fault, which there throws Upper Cambrian (lower part of Knox group) against Middle Ordovician (Chickamauga group), steep or overturned at the Plateau border.

In the central part of the sector here considered, seven parallel strike thrust faults, all with at least 1000 meters (3000 feet) of stratigraphic throw and several with twice that or more, are packed within a width of 30 kilometers (18 miles), separated by six homoclinal belts with only relatively minor complications such as asymmetrical synclines next northwest of the faults, slices along them, or narrow imbricate zones southeast of them. Both faults and homoclines dip southeast at moderate angles, generally between 20 and 35 degrees; the stratigraphic section that they repeat consists of a middle unit, 800 meters (2500 feet) thick, of competent siliceous Upper Cambrian and Lower Ordovician dolostone (Knox group) flanked by units of better bedded limestone and of shale, commonly sandy (Conasauga group and Rome formation below, Chickamauga limestone and higher units above). The faults can be classed into three systems. The first system consists of the Chattanooga and Kingston faults, both related to the Jacksboro fault as noted above and hence to the Pine Mountain fault; the Rockwood and Missionary Ridge faults may also belong to this system or they may be more closely related to the Sequatchie Valley or Cumberland Plateau fault on the Plateau to the west. The second system consists of the Whiteoak Mountain fault, itself formed by the merging of the Wallen Valley and Hunter Valley faults, and the Copper Creek fault; thus this system continues the St. Clair and Narrows fault trends, which in turn appear to correspond to the Nittany arch of the Central Appalachians. The third system is the Saltville fault system.

In Tennessee in this sector, only one of the homoclinal belts still preserves post-Ordovician beds (save for the short strip of Silurian rocks in the belt northwest of the Kingston fault); it is the one next northwest of the Whiteoak Mountain fault and is of course continuous with the belt northwest of the Wallen Valley fault, the southeast flank of the Powell Valley anticline, which likewise preserves these higher strata. This belt widens steadily southwestward, as the Whiteoak Mountain fault diverges from the Kingston fault, and it contains Silurian rocks for more than half its extent in Tennessee, Devonian and Lower Carboniferous rocks here and there to the southwest, notably for 50 kilometers (30 miles) athwart the Georgia state line, and basal Upper Carboniferous rocks (Lee group) in two or three small patches on either side of the state line (the Whiteoak Mountain fault here has a stratigraphic throw of not less than 3000 meters—9000 feet). Near the Tennessee-Georgia line, the basal Silurian sandstone (here the Whiteoak Mountain sandstone) regains its competence and resistance to erosion, in contrast to its character northeast along this belt of northwest at the Plateau border (Rockwood formation); it therefore holds up a ridge similar to but lower than Clinch Mountain, called Whiteoak Mountain.

Next southeast of the Whiteoak Mountain fault (or the Hunter Valley fault), Lower Cambrian strata (Rome formation), commonly strongly imbricated, are exposed continuously across Tennessee and for some kilometers (miles) in either direction. Thus the Whiteoak Mountain fault, like the Hunter Valley and St. Clair faults of which it is the extension, has one of the largest stratigraphic throws in the Valley and Ridge province. Southeast of it the Copper Creek fault maintains its throw (Lower Cambrian against Middle Ordovician, roughly 2000 meters— 6000 feet) most of the way across the state, but some 40 kilometers (25 miles) north of the Georgia line the throw begins to decrease, and somewhat farther on the fault enters the imbricate zone behind the Whiteoak Mountain fault and loses its individuality. At the Georgia line, there is a lesser fault (the Pine Hill fault) along the same trend, but this fault dies out in an anticline about 20 kilometers (10 miles) into Georgia.

The third or Saltville system of faults here consists of the Beaver Valley, Saltville, and Knoxville faults; as mentioned above, the post-Ordovician rocks along the Saltville fault are cut off abruptly a bit northeast of Knoxville, where the Beaver Valley fault appears, and from that point southwest the three faults are subequal in throw, bringing Cambrian on Ordovician. Lower Cambrian strata (Rome formation) extend along the Saltville fault only as far as Knoxville, along the Beaver Valley fault only 30 kilometers (20 miles) farther west-southwest; they are nowhere exposed along the Knoxville fault. Across Tennessee the three faults gradually converge; the homoclines between average 5 kilometers (3 miles) wide near Knoxville but only 2 kilometers (1½ miles) wide near the Georgia line, and little of the difference can be accounted for by increase in dip. Around Dalton, Georgia, 23 kilometers (14 miles) south of the state line, the Saltville and Knoxville faults, their throw decreasing considerably, approach one another very closely (Munyan, 1951, p. 92–93) if they do not actually merge, whereas northwest of the Beaver Valley fault Silurian, Devonian, and Carboniferous rocks reappear. About 13 kilometers (8 miles) south of Dalton, all three faults appear to merge into one larger fault, the Rome fault (named for Rome, Georgia, 50 kilometers—30 miles—farther south), which throws Middle Cambrian (Conasauga group) and locally Lower Cambrian (Rome formation) against Lower Carboniferous (Floyd shale), a throw of about 2500 meters (7500 feet).

Southeast of the Saltville fault system, which appears to represent the mid-province structural front in this sector, the structure is no longer dominated by thrust faults but consists of the two

synclinoria and the intervening faulted anticlinorium that appear between the Saltville and
Pulaski fault systems in the northeastern Tennessee
sector (see above, p. 50). The overall wave length
of these major folds is about 15 kilometers (10
miles), but they are formed of smaller and less
continuous folds of all sizes, from fairly large
simple folds, locally broken by thrust faults, in
the dolostone and sandstone units to tight
crumples in the shale. The larger folds and most
of the smaller ones show the typical Appalachian
asymmetry. The northwestern (Red Hills)
synclinorium contains 1000 meters or so (3000 to
4000 feet) of Middle Ordovician shale for much
of its length, but it ends about 13 kilometers
(8 miles) north of the Georgia line and is replaced
along strike by a broad belt of tightly crumpled
Cambrian strata. The anticlinorium is cut by
several thrust faults, mainly along its northwest
flank, but no one fault is continuous across the
sector; its core exposes Middle Cambrian
(Conasauga) shale, and Lower Cambrian strata
(Rome formation) are present locally along the
Dumplin Valley fault southeast of Knoxville and
along minor folds and faults at a few other spots.
The southeastern (Bays Mountain) synclinorium,
which is somewhat interrupted by the en echelon
domes west of Greeneville, Tennessee, deepens
again southwestward until due south of Knoxville
its northwest flank displays 2500 meters (7500
feet) of Middle Ordovician shale and sandstone
(Sevier and Bays formations) overlain disconformably by about 700 meters (2300 feet) of
Devonian and Lower Carboniferous strata, the
only patch of post-Ordovician rocks southeast of the Saltville fault in Tennessee. Farther
southwestward the syncline again shallows,
and the Middle Ordovician rocks in its core
are interrupted for about 13 kilometers (8
miles) somewhat north of the Georgia line, but
they reappear beyond and continue about 20
kilometers (12 miles) into Georgia, where
a thickness of about 1000 meters (3500 feet) is
preserved.

Much of the southeast flank of this synclinorium
is partly or wholly covered by the Great Smoky
thrust sheet at the front of the Blue Ridge province, but it reappears, commonly cut by several
thrust faults, in reentrants between the salients
of the mountain front and also, within the foothills of the Great Smoky Mountains, in windows
through the Great Smoky thrust sheet. Except in
the reentrants and windows, the rocks in this
part of the Valley and Ridge province show no
signs of metamorphism, except local poor cleavage. Within one reentrant (Tellico Plains area),
west-southwest of Knoxville and west of the Great

Smoky Mountains proper, a fault southeast of
the synclinorium brings up the basal Lower
Cambrian quartzite strata (Chilhowee group) in
tight faulted anticlines, much smaller than but
otherwise rather like the Lick Mountain and
Glade Mountain anticlinoria of southwestern
Virginia. One is tempted therefore to consider
that fault a southwestward reappearance of the
Pulaski fault, last seen 120 kilometers (70 miles)
farther northeast, but it may instead belong to the
system of faults at the mountain front. Similar
questions are raised by the appearance of strata
lower than the shaly unit at the top of the Lower
Cambrian (Shady dolostone and upper part of
Chilhowee group, below Rome formation) in two
places, one 23 kilometers (14 miles) north and
one 20 kilometers (12 miles) south of the Tennessee-
Georgia state line, but both close to the Great
Smoky fault.

The strike in this sector swings smoothly from
about S60°W at Knoxville to about S20°W at the
Georgia line, forming the apex of the main
Southern Appalachian salient. The sector also
represents somewhat of a culmination, for post-
Ordovician strata are absent from the central
part of the province for about 200 kilometers
(120 miles), from northeast of Knoxville to near
Dalton, Georgia, except along the Kingston,
Wallen Valley, and Whiteoak Mountain faults, and
even there they are discontinuous. Cambrian
rocks occur throughout on the upthrown sides
of faults and in the cores of anticlines, but Lower
Cambrian strata (Rome formation) disappear
southwestward along most of the major faults
except those of the Whiteoak Mountain system
(along the Whiteoak Mountain fault, they finally
disappear about 28 kilometers—17 miles—
south of the Georgia line). The synclinoria on the
southeast side of the province, however, have
their deepest spots south of Knoxville on the
east side of the salient and become shallower
southwestward. Possibly the axis of the culmination here, as in central Pennsylvania, crosses
the strike at 45 degrees or so instead of 90 degrees,
from the southwest corner of the Pine Mountain
block to a point on the mountain front near the
Georgia line; a parallel line north-northeastward
from the patch of Carboniferous rocks still preserved against the mountain front south of Knoxville might represent a vague depression or the
western margin of one.

The thrust structure of the Southern Appalachians
reaches its acme in the northwestern part of this
sector; the seven parallel thrust faults suggest a
giant imbricate zone above a sole fault, presumably a zone of decollement in the incompetent
Lower and Middle Cambrian strata (Rome forma-

tion and Conasauga shale). The overlying competent dolostone unit (Knox group) seems to have broken into long slabs that acted as stiff struts or backbones for the homoclines, preventing the development of large folds. The grouping of the faults into distinct systems, with the youngest strata appearing only along one fault of each system, further necessitates two levels of imbrication, if one tries to draw cross sections on the basis of the decollement hypothesis, for the faults of each system must merge downward into a single flat fault, which then turns downward again to the master sole fault or basal decollement zone. This necessity appears very clearly northeast of Knoxville where the Saltville fault halves its throw just as the Beaver Valley fault appears at one side. The Greendale syncline between the Saltville and Copper Creek faults farther northeast contains a stratigraphic sequence not less than 4000 meters (13,000 feet) thick, so that the basal decollement there must lie at least that deep. But where the Beaver Valley fault is intercalated, there are two superposed sequences about half that thick, of which the northwestern lies above the Copper Creek fault, itself fairly clearly a large-scale imbrication on the back of the Whiteoak Mountain fault. The basal decollement surely does not rise here to half the depth; it must remain beneath the northwestern homoclinal sequence following the first weak beds above the basement, which would be roughly at the same level under the Valley and Ridge province as under the Plateau, or deeper because of the steady thickening southeastward of the whole Paleozoic column, whereas the southeastern sequence would be thrust over the northwestern one at the higher level.

In the southeastern part of the sector, however, the beds above the Lower and Middle Cambrian have mostly been folded instead of broken; here the Middle Ordovician is very thick and mainly shale instead of thinner and mostly limestone, and the underlying Lower Ordovician and Upper Cambrian Strata (Knox group) are as much limestone as dolostone, and hence a bit less competent than the siliceous dolostone to the northwest. As the weak shaly unit at the top of the Lower Cambrian (Rome formation) is rarely visible, it may lie lower here, and the thicker and perhaps more plastic body of rocks above may therefore have failed to imbricate. The distinction between the two parts of the province is less sharp here, however, than in Pennsylvania or even in southwestern Virginia, and, as noted above, metamorphism is virtually absent (through it reappears down the strike in Georgia). At the edge of the Blue Ridge province, in any case, the Lower Cambrian reappears, though only locally is it visible beneath the Great Smoky thrust sheet, composed of mostly still older strata of the Blue Ridge province.

Northwestern Georgia Sector

The structural front and the edge of the Plateau province is offset considerably to the east in northwesternmost Georgia (as noted above, p. 53) around a sort of inverse salient of the Plateau that projects into the Valley and Ridge province; this southeastward-projecting salient is precisely that part of the Plateau cut off from the rest by the Lookout Valley and Big Wills Valley anticlines. The biggest part of the offset in the Plateau border occurs where the anticline associated with the Chattanooga fault (the one that folds the Missionary Ridge fault) dies out in the flat-lying Carboniferous strata of the Plateau; this offset lies opposite the en echelon shift from the relatively low Lookout Valley anticline, apparently unfaulted at the surface, to the higher Big Wills Valley anticline, which is cut by a thrust fault along almost its entire northwest flank. South of the offset, the Plateau front lies along the Kingston fault instead of the Chattanooga fault; the front is continuous and straight or gently concave to the northwest as far southwest as Gadsden, Alabama, but the fault may not be continuous beyond the Georgia-Alabama state line, and the anticline behind it becomes lower there, though it still brings up high Upper Cambrian dolostone (lower part of Knox group). At Gadsden, the inverse salient is abruptly terminated by a major transverse fault (Gadsden fault) that is part of the Rome fault system (see below), and just to the west the Big Wills Valley anticline is replaced en echelon by the Murphrees Valley anticline (with some strike overlap); thus the en echelon arrangement of the three anticlines on the Plateau roughly parallels, at a distance of about 15 kilometers (about 10 miles) the offsets in the Plateau front that define the inverse salient.

East of this inverse salient, the belt that is dominated by thrust faults in Tennessee is characterized instead by large-scale folding in Georgia, the folds plunging generally southward. Of the Tennessee fault systems, the Saltville system faults combine to form the Rome fault, the Pine Mountain or Jacksboro system is represented only by the Kingston fault at the Plateau border, and the Whiteoak Mountain system between reduces a few kilometers (miles) south of the Tennessee line to the single Whiteoak Mountain fault, which persists with decreasing throw to a point about

65 kilometers (40 miles) south of the state line, where it dies out in Lower Carboniferous (Floyd) shale in the heart of the Floyd synclinorium, an irregular basin of only mildly deformed Carboniferous rocks northwest of Rome, Georgia (named for Floyd County, of which Rome is the seat). The Floyd synclinorium sends out arms in various directions—two long ones northward on either side of the anticline followed by the Whiteoak Mountain fault, and several shorter ones westward, separated by short anticlines plunging east-northeast. West of the Floyd synclinorium, between it and the anticline behind the Kingston fault, lie a pair of north-northeast-trending folds, an anticline faulted on its northwest flank and exposing the Middle Cambrian (Conasauga) shale and a syncline northwest of it; these folds have no counterparts in southeastern Tennessee. Where they and the Whiteoak Mountain fault meet the east-northeast-plunging anticlines, the two trends intersect in flat x's like the one formed by the Rich Patch and associated anticlines near the James River at the similar intersection of trends in the Roanoke recess.

The east and south sides of the Floyd synclinorium are overlapped by the Rome thrust fault, which throws mainly Middle Cambrian (Conasauga) shale over the Lower Carboniferous (Floyd) shale in the synclinorium, a throw of 2500 meters (7500 feet). Both north and west of Rome, the fault has evidently been folded with the synclinorium, for tongues of the Cambrian shale up to 10 kilometers (6 miles) long are preserved in the cores of individual synclines of both east-northeast and north-northeast trends. Just west of Rome, the Cambrian shale is also thrust over the end of a small faulted east-north-east-trending anticline and rests locally on beds as low as Ordovician. About 40 kilometers (25 miles) north-northeast of Rome, 3 kilometers (2 miles) east of the main fault trace, Carboniferous rocks reappear in a window surrounded by the Cambrian (Conasauga) shale.

Thus the Rome fault around Rome differs greatly from the faults of the Saltville system in southeastern Tennessee, by whose merging it is formed not far south of Dalton. Whereas they are typically nearly straight and plane, dipping 20 to 35 degrees southeast parallel to the homoclinal beds on either side, it is evidently not far from horizontal and is strongly folded. It was indeed the first great low-angle "overthrust" recognized in the Appalachians (Hayes, 1891). More than any other fault in the Appalachians, it resembles the Pulaski fault, especially that part in the general vicinity of Pulaski and Roanoke; it is probably no coincidence that these two thrust faults reach their maximum

development in and near prominent recesses, although no other major fault within the Valley and Ridge province is continuous through those recesses. The relations of this part of the Rome fault to the faults of the Saltville system seem much like those of a sole fault to its overlying imbricate faults or schuppen, but in fact all the evidence suggests that the recess corresponds to a fairly deep depression, and one might therefore suggest that the faults of the Saltville system converge upward instead of downward to form the Rome fault, which would thus be less a "sole" than a "ceiling."

From Rome northward to Dalton, the trend of the Rome fault is roughly parallel to that of the folds on either side, though it gradually bevels the northeast arm of the Floyd synclinorium; from Rome westward into Alabama, however, the fault (which may be called here the Gadsden fault or the Gadsden branch of the Rome fault) cuts at a sharp angle across the Floyd synclinorium and the folds west of it until it approaches the front of the Plateau on the trend of the Kingston fault. There it makes a series of abrupt turns: first southwest parallel to the front for 35 kilometers (22 miles), then due west again for 15 kilometers (10 miles) past Gadsden, cutting across to the southeast flank of the Big Wills Valley anticline, and finally southwest once more. Throughout this stretch, a wide belt of intensely crumpled Middle and Upper Cambrian (Conasauga) shale lies on the south side of the fault, replacing entirely the Floyd synclinorium and the folds west of it, and thrown against various strata up to Upper Carboniferous. In effect, the fault and the shale belt to the south cut east-west diagonally across the entire northwest half of the Valley and Ridge province and a part of the Plateau province, a width across strike of 60 kilometers (35 miles), to produce an arrangement unique in the Valley and Ridge province.

Within the rocks above the Rome fault near and south of Rome is a zone of rather close-spaced imbricate faults, 1 or 2 kilometers ($\frac{1}{2}$ to 1 mile) apart, which bring upper Lower Cambrian strata (type area of the Rome formation) to the surface. Apparently the northwest margin of the imbricate belt is a larger thrust fault, a major split from the Rome fault, separating the imbricate zone with its Lower Cambrian strata from the intensely crumpled Middle and Upper Cambrian rocks next the Rome fault. It is called the Coosa fault, for the Coosa Valley, whose southern margin it follows, and it seems to play the same role relative to the Rome fault that the Christianburg and Max Meadows faults play to the Pulaski fault in Virginia. At Rome it actually merges with the

Rome fault for 3 or 4 kilometers (2 or 3 miles), but the two faults diverge in both directions. To the northeast, the Coosa fault may extend as far as the window mentioned above (on whose southeast side Lower Cambrian rocks are again thrown on Lower Carboniferous); to the southwest it continues beyond the Alabama line and splits, its northern branch extending to Weisner Mountain, about 30 kilometers (20 miles) due east of Gadsden. In Weisner Mountain and in several smaller hills within 10 kilometers (6 miles) both east and south, basal Lower Cambrian quartzite strata (Weisner formation or Chilhowee group) appear along this branch of the Coosa fault, thrown over the Middle Cambrian (Conasauga) shale south of the main Rome fault; here again is a point of similarity to the Pulaski thrust sheet, which contains the only other exposures of these basal strata more than a few kilometers (miles) away from the southeast edge of the Valley and Ridge province.

The belt from the Rome and Coosa faults to the southeast edge of the province, corresponding to the southeast half of the province in Tennessee, is 25 to 40 kilometers (15 to 25 miles) wide in Georgia, but narrows to less than 15 kilometers (10 miles) as it enters Alabama. The well marked synclinoria that characterize it in Tennessee fade out in northernmost Georgia, and the belt comes to resemble the corresponding southeast part of the province in Pennsylvania more than any intervening stretch. Cambrian and Lower Ordovician rocks, mainly shale below (Rome and Conasauga formations) and carbonate above (Knox group), are folded in small, relatively discontinuous folds with a wave length of 1 kilometer (1 mile) or less. All the shaly rocks are tightly crumpled, and those near the mountain front show slaty cleavage and incipient metamorphism as well. South of a vague culmination southeast of Dalton, the outcrop belts outline an irregular, south-plunging synclinorium, lying between belts of older rocks along the Rome and Coosa faults on the west and along the mountain front on the east; mostly the youngest beds exposed are Lower Ordovician carbonate (Knox group) or Middle Ordovician shale (Rockmart slate, in part), but south and southeast of Rome several patches of Devonian and Lower Carboniferous shale or slate rest disconformably on the Ordovician strata.

From the Tennessee-Georgia line, the southeast margin of the Valley and Ridge province runs almost due south for 100 kilometers (60 miles) to the vicinity of Cartersville, Georgia, marked by the prominent Great Smoky or Cartersville thrust fault, which throws phyllite or schist of the Blue Ridge and Piedmont provinces on mildly

metamorphosed Cambrian shale and limestone (also on Middle Ordovician shale close to the Tennessee line—Salisbury, 1961, p. 49); 20 kilometers (12 miles) south of the line, a lesser fault appears from beneath the Great Smoky fault and brings up the basal Cambrian quartzite (Chilhowee group or Weisner formation) for a strike distance of about 8 kilometers (5 miles), forming a short mountain within the Valley and Ridge province (mentioned above, p. 55, in connection with similar exposures of the quartzite in Tennessee; Munyan, 1951, p. 15–18). Just southwest of Cartersville, the Piedmont border turns abruptly west-southwest toward and into Alabama; the thrust fault along it bevels completely across the synclinorium mentioned above and throws phyllite or schist of unknown age against various Paleozoic strata from Middle Cambrian to Lower Carboniferous. In the Cartersville district at the very pit of the recess, however, anticlinal ridges of the basal Lower Cambrian (Weisner) quartzite appear west of the Piedmont border, and as all the rocks in this district are considerably metamorphosed (chlorite has formed where the composition permitted), the fault itself becomes very difficult to trace. After detailed study of the district, Kesler (1950, p. 30–32) denied the very existence of the fault, and it is possible that in the deepest part of the recess the thrust displacement, which is clearly demonstrated by recent work north of Cartersville (Salisbury, 1961) and is probably equally important to the southwest, was partly or wholly taken up by folding along the Blue Ridge structural front, perhaps uncovered again here in the recess, or was distributed along planes of cleavage or schistosity associated with the metamorphism, which here reaches its highest rank in the sector, if not in the entire Southern Appalachian part of the Valley and Ridge province.

Close to the Alabama line, a thrust sheet of the basal Lower Cambrian rocks (Weisner formation and Shady dolostone) appears above a fault (called the Indian Mountain thrust fault for a mountain at the state line) at the edge of the Piedmont province, overlapping a large part of the belt between that province and the Coosa fault; southwestward into Alabama, there are several such sheets covering a belt up to 10 kilometers (6 miles) wide between the Valley and Ridge and Piedmont provinces proper. This belt probably corresponds to the belt of thrust sheets in similar strata at the northwest edge of the Blue Ridge province in northeastern Tennessee and southwestern Virginia (p. 167–170), but the geology is very poorly known. Its southeastern edge, the northwestern edge of the slate and phyllite of the

Talladega belt of the Piedmont, has traditionally been considered the southwestern continuation of the Cartersville fault, but in central Alabama at least it is equally probably an unconformity (Chapter 8, p. 181), and if the unconformity interpretation be extended as far northeast as the Georgia state line, then the Indian Mountain fault would be the true continuation of the Cartersville fault.

The change in strike through the Rome or Cartersville recess in northwestern Georgia is even greater than that around Roanoke, Virginia; north and northeast of Rome the strike ranges from S25°W to due south, whereas to the west and southwest it averages about S55°W. The change is most abrupt along the southeast border of the province at Cartersville; the northwest border and the folds nearest to it, in contrast, swing around gradually. The Carboniferous rocks in the Floyd synclinorium mark a rather deep depression in the northwest part of the province corresponding almost exactly to the recess; the Lower Carboniferous rocks at the south end of the synclinorium southeast of Rome may indicate the position of this depression in the southeast part of the province.

The present sinuous trace of the Rome fault near Rome implies that it was originally nearly flat, following the weak Middle Cambrian (Conasauga) shale which it brought over various strata as high as the Lower Carboniferous. The meaning of the transverse Gadsden fault, bevelling across all the structure within the northwest part of the province and even across an outlying part of the Plateau province, is much less clear (but see below, p. 61); both north and south of the transverse fault the same shale is the lowest rock exposed, and presumably therefore it forms the zone of decollement under the northwest part of the province. Lower Cambrian rocks (Rome formation) are entirely missing at the surface here for a strike distance of about 150 kilometers (nearly 100 miles), from a point on the Whiteoak Mountain fault in north Georgia, about 50 kilometers (30 miles) north of Rome, to an undetermined point on the Helena fault in central Alabama east of Birmingham.

On the other hand, the appearance of Lower Cambrian rocks (Rome formation) along the Coosa fault across most of the sector shows that in the southeast part of the province the zone of decollement must be at least that low, and further suggests that, southwest of Rome at least, the Coosa rather than the Rome or Gadsden fault represents the mid-province structural front. The importance of the Coosa fault is further emphasized by the presence of the basal Lower

Cambrian (Weisner) quartzite along its northern branch at Weisner Mountain in eastern Alabama, as well as in folds and fault slices at the southeast edge of the province in both Georgia and Alabama. The similarities between the Rome-Coosa fault system in this sector and the Pulaski fault system in Virginia are considerable, but the transverse fault from Rome to Gadsden has no parallel elsewhere in the Appalachians.

Central Alabama Sector

At the latitude of Gadsden, Alabama, the entire northwest part of the Valley and Ridge province, between the upturned beds along the front of the Appalachian Plateau and the basal Cambrian (Weisner) quartzite strata on Weisner Mountain above the Coosa fault, is underlain by crumpled Middle and Upper Cambrian (Conasauga) shale south of the Gadsden fault. Not far to the south, however, this shale belt splits into two arms, each dipping southeast under a homocline of higher strata; the two homoclines are separated by a major thrust fault, called the Helena fault for a locality 105 kilometers (65 miles) southwest of Gadsden. The Helena fault can be traced northeastward to a point only 5 kilometers (3 miles) south of Gadsden and the Gadsden fault, but there it runs out into the crumpled (and poorly exposed) shale, and a connection with the Gadsden fault is uncertain, though not unlikely. Southwestward it can be traced to the Coastal Plain, 150 kilometers (95 miles) from Gadsden. In that direction, the two homoclines become synclinoria, though generally their southeast flanks are partly cut out by thrust faults, and each contains a thick succession of Upper Carboniferous coal measures—the Cahaba and Coosa coal basins. On the other hand, the two arms of Cambrian (Conasauga) shale end rather abruptly about 50 kilometers (30 miles) southwest of Gadsden.

Farther southwest, between the Cahaba coal basin and the Appalachian Plateau (here the Black Warrior coal basin beyond the southwest ends of the Murphrees Valley and Sequatchie anticlines), the Birmingham anticlinorium forms the en echelon continuation of the northwestern of the two shale arms. The oldest beds exposed in the anticlinorium are Upper Cambrian limestone (upper part of Conasauga group); along much of its northwest flank, a fault (Opossum Valley fault) brings them against beds as high as Upper Carboniferous. The city of Birmingham, Alabama, situated in the valley eroded in this anticlinorium, owes its industrial importance to the fortunate juxtaposition of Cambrian limestone, Silurian iron ore, and Carboniferous coal. The Opossum Valley fault is the local representative of the structural front at the northwest edge of the Valley and Ridge province; it may indeed be continuous with the southwest end of the Gadsden fault, which plays the same role. Southwest of Birmingham, the Opossum Valley fault splits into at least two strands; one trends toward an outer anticline (Yolande anticline), which may be a miniature Sequatchie anticline only 6 kilometers (4 miles) out in the Carboniferous rocks of the Plateau, whereas the other appears to die out in irregularities on the steep northwest flank of the main anticlinorium, where the available mapping suggests such complications as northwest-dipping thrust faults or small windows. Where the anticlinorium goes under the overlapping Cretaceous strata of the Coastal Plain, 65 kilometers (40 miles) southwest of Birmingham, it is again rather complex.

The belt of older rocks along the Helena fault, between the Cahaba and Coosa coal basins, continues the trend of the other arm of Cambrian shale; it is mostly a simple homocline, and only at the southwest end near the Coastal Plain are there major complexities. Near Helena, 25 kilometers (15 miles) south of Birmingham, the belt makes an S-curve between a projection of the Cahaba coal basin and the south end of the Coosa coal basin; it then turns southwest again and, sliced by several parallel thrust faults, disappears under the Cretaceous cover. In this area and for an indeterminate but probably not great distance to the north, the Helena fault brings up Lower Cambrian strata (Rome formation). The S-curve appears to be the western end of an east-west belt of irregular curves in strike that extends across much of the Valley and Ridge province and the Talladega belt of the Piedmont province.

The southeast side of the Coosa coal basin and the area beyond are complex and poorly known. The northern branch of the Coosa fault cuts off the northeast end of the belt of Lower Carboniferous rocks northeast of the coal basin, but at the same point the Lower and Middle Cambrian rocks along it disappear; farther southwest available maps show a complex of relatively small thrust faults among which its course is uncertain. Carboniferous rocks also appear southeast of it here, cut off eastward by the southeastern branch of the Coosa fault, along which Lower Cambrian rocks (Rome formation) persist some kilometers (miles) farther south than along the northern branch. The rocks between the two branches are especially complexly faulted (Warman and Causey, 1962;

Cloud, 1967). The southeastern branch of the Coosa fault, here called the Pell City fault for a locality southeast of the Coosa coal basin, is by far the largest and most persistent of all these faults, but it too is lost southwestward in complex and poorly known structure northeast of Columbiana, Alabama, in the east-west belt of irregular strikes. The belt next east of it is much like the belt east of the Rome and Coosa faults in Georgia— small folds and faults with relatively little continuity and considerable low-grade metamorphism. Presumably, therefore, the Pell City fault represents the continuation of the mid-province structural front. Throughout this area, and also in the southern end of the belt next west (along the Helena fault), Silurian rocks are absent, and only a thin unit of Devonian sandstone and shale (Frog Mountain formation) separates the Carboniferous from the Middle Ordovician; this is the same disconformity as that mentioned above along the southeast side of the province in Georgia, southeastern Tennessee, and southwestern Virginia.

The thrust sheets of basal Cambrian quartzite, associated shale or slate, and overlying dolostone (Weisner formation and Shady dolostone) that appear along the southeast border of the Valley and Ridge province at the Georgia-Alabama state line persist with increasing complexity southwestward. The details of this belt are very poorly known, but the basal unit of quartzite and slate (Weisner formation) is present discontinuously as far as Columbiana. East and south of Columbiana, it thickens enormously (lower part of Talladega slate of Butts, 1926, p. 49–53; 1940, p. 2–4; an estimated 3000 meters—10,000 feet— thick) and is thrust over the Valley and Ridge rocks on the Columbiana fault, which may be the southwestern continuation of the Indian Mountain and hence of the Cartersville fault. In this area, in and south of the east-west belt of irregular strikes mentioned above, the trace of the Columbiana fault makes a great Z-like loop; the "horizontal" bars of the Z strike northeast, and the upper corner (Columbiana Mountain, just east of Columbiana) lies on the trend of the Pell City fault, so that the thrust sheet above completely overlaps the belt of Cambrian and Ordovician rocks southeast of that fault and rests on Lower Carboniferous (Floyd) shale belonging to the same fault block as the Coosa coal basin.

Inside the lower angle of the Z is a remarkable dome (Kelley Mountain anticline). Upper Cambrian rocks (lower part of Knox group) in its core are surrounded by outcrop belts of Ordovician, Devonian, and Lower Carboniferous strata, and these again by Ordovician; the Columbiana fault and the quartzite and slate (Weisner formation) in the thrust sheet above surround the last in turn on three sides. An interpretation as a domed recumbent syncline with a core of Carboniferous shale, lying beneath the domed thrust sheet (Rodgers, 1953b, p. 159), has yet to be checked by field work.

In general, the strikes in this sector change gradually from no more than S55°W near Gadsden to no less than S40°W at the Coastal Plain; the east-west belt of S-curves and other irregularities in strike is the chief exception. The two great coal basins, whose only match within the Valley and Ridge province is the anthracite coal basin at its other end in eastern Pennsylvania, mark a depression, separated from the one in the Rome recess (Floyd synclinorium) by the transverse belt of Cambrian shale around Gadsden. The southeast part of the province is too little known to afford much evidence of culminations or depressions, but the manner in which it is completely cut off southwestward by the forward encroachment of the Columbiana thrust fault suggests that axes are plunging generally southwest in that area. Cambrian rocks are present along all the principal thrusts in the sector; only Upper Cambrian limestone (upper part of Conasauga group) is exposed in the Birmingham anticlinorium, but the upper Lower Cambrian shaly unit (Rome formation) appears along parts of the Helena fault and both branches of the Coosa fault, and the basal Lower Cambrian (Weisner quartzite) appears along the northern branch of the latter as well as along the faults nearest the southeast edge of the province. The east-west transverse belt of Middle and Upper Cambrian (Conasauga) shale between Gadsden and Rome may reflect the southern edge of the thick shale body of that age, for farther south the correlative strata seem to be mainly carbonate rock, though some shale is interbedded—enough perhaps to have influenced the structure. The top of the Lower Cambrian (Rome formation) remains shale, however, and has probably been the main zone of decollement, at least on the southeastern side of the province.

All the strata in the Alabama sector of the Valley and Ridge province, as in those to the north, seem to have been folded together, including beds as young as Upper Carboniferous (Westphalian) in the coal basins. On the other hand, a flood of clastic sediment (Floyd shale and Parkwood formation) appears considerably earlier in the Carboniferous in central Alabama than anywhere to the north as far as Pennsylvania (lower Meramec or lower Viséan instead of mid-Chester or lower Namurian) but contemporaneously with the major flood of clastics in the Ouachita Mountains of Arkansas and Oklahoma (Stanley shale and Jackfork formation), suggesting major uplift and perhaps orogeny in an east-west belt south of both the Ouachitas and the southernmost Appalachians before the beginning of the Alleghany orogenic episode that ultimately folded the Valley and Ridge province. As noted above, this southern part of the Appalachians is distinguished by two east-west transverse belts of unusual structure—one marked by the Gadsden fault and the accompanying transverse belt of Cambrian shale, the other by S-curves and other marked irregularities in strike from the Helena fault into the Piedmont. These belts are unusual, not to say unique, in the Appalachians, and perhaps they reflect east-west irregularities that predated the main Alleghany deformation. If so, they may have begun as mild outlying folds in front of the Lower Carboniferous uplift south of the Ouachitas and Appalachians, like the mild folds produced by the Alleghany orogeny in the Appalachian Plateau province. Prominent folds of this sort have not been reported from the Black Warrior coal basin to the west, however, where Alleghany deformation was minimal.

Summary

The Valley and Ridge province of the Appalachians possesses a strongly characterized individuality; it contrasts sharply with the other parts of the mountain chain and is separated from them (except at its northeast end) by abrupt boundaries marked by striking changes in structural style across readily observed structural fronts. Moreover, no other part displays in such detail or perfection the classical Appalachian features—the persistent, narrow, parallel mountains and valleys, and the consistent, closely spaced, parallel folds and faults that are responsible for them. A few features in the Appalachian Plateau, especially in its southern part, have some of the same characteristics, but they are generally isolated in the midst of flat-lying strata. Valley and Ridge features also persist northward along the west edge of New England as far as the Canadian border (see Chapter 4), but there they are less regular and consistent and are spread over a much narrower belt. In the other provinces, the rocks are mostly metamorphosed and they build grosser features, both structural and topographic; a few of these features show equal continuity along but none a comparable density across strike.

There are also differences, to be sure, between various parts of the Valley and Ridge province.

First is the obvious separation at Roanoke into Central and Southern Appalachians, which not only form distinct arcuate salients but have different structural styles—mainly asymmetric folding in the central, southeast-dipping thrust faults in the southern arc. (Possible explanations for this difference are discussed above, p. 42–43). Within the two arcs, moreover, there appear to be culminations and depressions, the highest culminations coinciding roughly with the centers of the salients and the deepest depressions with the recesses, though there is a persistent suggestion that the axes of both culminations and depressions cut diagonal instead of perpendicular to the strike of the individual folds and faults. Yet many structural features, particularly the largest ones, can be traced from culmination into depression, from salient into recess, and even from one arc into the other.

There is also the less obvious but nevertheless persistent difference between a northwestern and a southeastern part of the province. The northwestern part generally shows relatively regular, large-scale deformation expressed, except in Tennessee, mainly in Middle and Upper Paleozoic rocks; the southeastern part generally shows irregular, smaller-scale but more intense deformation expressed in Lower Paleozoic rocks, and also in many places slaty cleavage and other evidence of incipient metamorphism. The two parts can be recognized in every sector of the province, although the boundary separating them, called the mid-province structural front in the preceding descriptions, shifts across strike somewhat from sector to sector. Within the two parts of the province, moreover, there are other features that persist along strike, especially uplifts (whether anticlinoria or thrust faults of large throw), notably the uplift that follows the structural front at the northwest border of the province nearly everywhere, though again it shifts across strike where the Pine Mountain or Jacksboro fault enters the province from the Plateau. Table 1 summarizes the relations and emphasizes the continuity of these uplifts (the intervening synclinoria, though some of them extend hundreds of kilometers— miles—along strike, do not seem to be as persistent or as significant).

Like that of the Appalachian Plateau, the structure of the Valley and Ridge province is currently interpreted in two quite different ways:

(a) The deformation was essentially in the underlying basement, the structure we see in the sedimentary rocks being merely a reflection of that in the basement (Cooper, 1961, p. 100–118; 1964; 1968).

(b) The deformation was essentially in the cover, which was sheared off the basement along a zone of decollement at a certain level (generally near the Lower-Middle Cambrian boundary) by tangential pressure exerted on the cover itself, whether because of lateral shove by a plungerlike mass (Rodgers, 1953b, p. 164) or because of lateral creep away from an uplifted mass (Bucher, 1956; Gwinn, 1964); in either case the mass is conceived to be the Blue Ridge anticlinorium.

The principal arguments in favor of the theory of basement deformation (a) are:

(1) The incompetence of the cover rocks to transmit laterally, through the required distance, the stress needed to deform them across the whole province, let alone to move them laterally as far as the cover deformation theory demands.

(2) The absence of evidence of large-scale faulting in the Central Appalachians, especially in Pennsylvania, and prevailing moderate rather than flat dip of thrust faults in the Southern Appalachians (exceptions to both rules are granted).

(3) Indications that the folds, including those that later broke to form thrust faults, began forming long before the end of the Paleozoic, perhaps as early as the Ordovician (see esp. Lowry, 1957, and Cooper, 1961, p. 103 ff.; 1964; 1968).

(4) Analogy with the folds in the Appalachian Plateau of Pennsylvania, which were presumed to persist downward to the basement.

The principal arguments in favor of the theory of cover deformation (b) are:

(1) The consistency with which the folds and faults bring up Cambrian strata, commonly the upper part of the Lower Cambrian (Waynesboro or Rome formation) or slightly higher beds, but never the basement.

(2) The strong parallelism of folds and faults in individual sectors, supposed to be unlikely if they merely reflect deformation of a presumably heterogeneous basement.

(3) The consistent asymmetry of folds and faults, supposed to be more readily explained by the action of a lateral plunger on the cover than by deformation mainly in the basement.

(4) The existence of at least a few roughly horizontal faults, and analogy with the horizontal thrust faults of the Cumberland Plateau and the Pine Mountain fault.

(5) Geophysical data suggesting that the basement is depressed, not elevated, under the Valley and Ridge province, notably under the Nittany arch in Pennsylvania.

Attempts to apply the two theories to carefully

TABLE 1 Principal Uplifts in the Valley and Ridge province of the Central and Southern Appalachians.

ALABAMA	GEORGIA	TENNESSEE	VIRGINIA	PENNSYLVANIA
Birmingham anticlinorium	Kingston fault	Chattanooga and Kingston faults	St. Clair and Narrows faults	Nittany anticlinorium
		(Pine Mountain fault on the Plateau)	Wills Mountain and associated anticlines	
Helena fault	Whiteoak Mountain fault	Whiteoak Mountain fault system		Blue Mountain front
Gadsden fault (of Rome system)		Hunter Valley and Copper Creek faults	Cacapon anticlinorium	
Pell City and Coosa faults	Rome and Coosa faults	Saltville fault system	Saltville fault	
		(Anticlinorium with Dumplin Valley fault)	Little North Mountain fault	
		Pulaski fault system	Staunton-Pulaski fault	
	Faults bringing up basal Cambrian (Weisner) quartzite		Pulaski fault system	
		Faults at Blue Ridge front	Faults at Blue Ridge front	
Columbiana fault	Cartersville fault	Great Smoky fault	Blue Ridge front	South Mountain Front

Province bands (left side): PLATEAU; VALLEY AND RIDGE; PIEDMONT.
Province bands (right side): APPALACHIAN PLATEAU; V and R; BLUE RIDGE.

BLUE RIDGE / PIEDMONT

63

drawn cross sections and to deduce the consequences have been rather few in the Appalachians; my own attempt (Rodgers, 1953b, Figs. 2 and 3) is crude and hardly indicates more than that the cover theory is geometrically tenable, though not easy to work out consistently and quantitatively by taking account, as I did not, of the third dimension and reconstructing the original position of the strata. Vinton E. Gwinn's last paper (1970) provides a more satisfactory analysis, and an estimate of more than 80 kilometers (50 miles) of lateral shortening in Pennsylvania, nearly equal to the whole width of the province there. The first argument for the basement theory is greatly weakened for me by the demonstration (Hubbert and Rubey, 1959) that the force needed to move a large thrust sheet laterally may be much less than previously supposed because of excess fluid pressure beneath impermeable layers in the sequence, such as those supposed to have been the zones of decollement on the cover theory. The other arguments likewise do not seem very cogent; cover tectonics could well have begun in the Ordovician, when there seems to have been orogeny farther southeast in the chain (Chapters 9 and 11), and the evidence from the Burning Springs and other Plateau anticlines (see Chapter 2, p. 19—20) combats the conclusion that the folds of the Plateau in Pennsylvania and West Virginia persist to the basement. Furthermore, recent wells in the westernmost major anticline in the Central Appalachians strongly favor the second hypothesis for that fold, and geophysical data (Joesting, Keller, and King, 1949; Watkins, 1964; Sears, 1964; Gwinn, 1964, p. 887—889; 1970; Zietz, King, Geddes, and Lidiak, 1966, p. 1432—1433; Wood, Trexler, and Kehn, 1969, p. 115—116) support it for the rest of the province. Nevertheless, one must admit that data are still inadequate to decide the question once and for all.

The two theories might be further tested by using them to explain the structural fronts, of which two set the Valley and Ridge province off sharply from its neighbors and one persistently divides it into a more regular northwestern part and a less regular but more intensely deformed southeastern part. The Blue Ridge front at the southeast margin of the province, along the southeast side of which the basement is obviously involved, must on any theory be explained as the result of a sharp change in the nature of the basement deformation, either because of an actual difference in the materials composing the basement, or because the temperature and grade of metamorphism there rose high enough during the Paleozoic orogeny to permit body deformation

in the Precambrian crystalline rocks. For the others, which maintain a striking though not invariable parallelism with the Blue Ridge front, the basement theory demands similar sharp though perhaps lesser changes in basement deformability, peripheral to the observed change, but the nature of these changes is unspecified and in the present state of knowledge perhaps unspecifiable. On the cover theory, the two outer fronts must be explained as marking the limits of certain kinds of deformation in the cover, the outer one as the limit of simple gliding on the Cambrian zone of decollement (made possible by a lowered coefficient of friction or by increased fluid pressure at or under the gliding plane), the inner one (mid-province front) as the limit of body deformation in the rocks above that plane, a limit that should be reached more readily in the sedimentary rocks of the cover than in the underlying crystalline basement, which shows the same change at the Blue Ridge front. Both limits would on this theory necessarily be generally parallel to the Blue Ridge front, because the amount of work required to deform the sedimentary rocks in either way would be directly proportional to the width of the belt to be deformed, whereas such other factors as the thickness of the section deformed, the amount of shortening imposed, or the mechanical properties of the rocks, especially those of the gliding layer, should change only gradually across or along strike.

As Carboniferous rocks (lower Upper Carboniferous in the Southern Appalachians, upper Upper Carboniferous in the Central Appalachians) are obviously involved in typical and intense Valley and Ridge folding and faulting in many places from the anthracite coal basin of eastern Pennsylvania to the Cahaba coal basin of central Alabama, the climax of deformation in the province was late or post-Carboniferous. The presence of Lower Permian strata in the Georges Creek syncline just to the west of the province boundary in Maryland confirms this conclusion. Upper Triassic sedimentary rocks lap over deformed Ordovician rocks in eastern Pennsylvania and contain pebbles of Devonian rocks; presumably the deformation was over well before their deposition. This period of deformation, occurring in the Permian or perhaps continuing into the early Triassic, is the Alleghany orogeny of Woodward (1957b); apparently it formed most if not all the major structural features of the province, at least southwest of the Susquehanna River.

Cooper (1961, 1964, 1968), on the other hand, strongly denies that the presence of strongly deformed Carboniferous rocks can be taken as evidence that the main deformation was later; he believes, on the basis of thickness measurements of the sedimentary strata, that the folds and thrust faults of the Valley and Ridge province grew throughout the Paleozoic and were essentially completely formed by Early Carboniferous time (or locally even earlier) in the southeast part of the province and by early Late Carboniferous time at the northwest edge; for him, moreover, this history is an argument for the theory of basement deformation. That some of the folds may have begun to form as early as the Middle Ordovician I am quite willing to admit, and that orogeny is not a matter of sudden spasms separated by periods of complete calm, not a matter of years or even hundreds of thousands of years, I heartily agree, but the nearly perfect parallelism of all the Paleozoic strata in the most severe folds and thrust sheets in the province southwest of eastern Pennsylvania, except where the lack of parallelism obviously results from tectonic disharmony, coupled with the tectonic history that can be read from the facies of the sediments themselves (see Chapter 11), makes me insist that orogeny was very unevenly distributed through time and that it reached a major climax after the deposition of all or virtually all the sediments affected by it (Cooper's thickness differences

amount to a very few degrees except for overturned limbs and other places where tectonic thinning or thickening is to be expected). On the other hand, the appearance of coarse clastic sediments already in the upper Lower Carboniferous and upwards along the full length of the Valley and Ridge province (and apparently lower in the Southern than in the Central Appalachians) suggests that the orogenic unrest that finally culminated in the Alleghany orogeny may have begun early in the Carboniferous in the southern Piedmont province and gradually spread northwestward and northeastward.

The patterns of crossed anticlines found in the recesses near Roanoke (Rich Patch anticline and associated folds) and near Rome (folds in the Floyd synclinorium) suggest the possibility that the salients on either side were deformed at slightly different times within a general Alleghany orogenic period; if so, the southern salient was the earlier in each case, but the evidence is meager. Against this possibility, on the other hand, one might cite the continuity of the Pulaski and Rome fault system through these recesses (though they are virtually the only features known to carry through them, except the Big Wills Valley and Sequatchie anticlines on the Plateau northwest of the Rome recess).

CHAPTER 4

Northeastern Extension of the Valley and Ridge Province (Eastern Pennsylvania to the International Boundary); The Taconic Problem

Eastern Pennsylvania to Southeastern New York (Susquehanna River to Hudson River)

As mentioned in Chapter 3, the Nittany arch dies out near the West Fork of the Susquehanna River, plunging eastward into an area of gentle Plateau folding, but the folds southeast of it continue eastward, plunging into the deep depression of the anthracite coal basin in eastern Pennsylvania. Along the axis of this depression, which trends about N35°E at an angle of about 35 degrees to the trends of the folds, only Carboniferous rocks are now exposed, though none are still preserved on the axis of the Pennsylvania culmination west of the Susquehanna. The basal Carboniferous (Pocono) sandstone outlines relatively broad folds with a wave length of about 15 kilometers (10 miles), but the sandstone at the base of the Upper Carboniferous (Pottsville sandstone) forms folds with a wave length of barely 2 kilometers (a little more than a mile). The intervening shale (middle member of the Mauch Chunk formation)

is incompetently folded and, over much of the region, bounded above and below by through-going surfaces of decollement (Wood, Trexler, and Kehn, 1969, p. 95–99, 114–115), and the coal measures at the top of the preserved section exhibit extraordinary disharmonic folding and intricate faulting, which has greatly complicated the mining of the coal they contain (Darton, 1940; Wood and Bergin, 1970). One of the main coal beds, the Mammoth seam, which is normally over 3 meters (10 feet or more) thick where undisturbed, has been squeezed until it ranges from zero on the flanks of many folds (especially the steep or overturned north flanks of the anticlines) to 7 to 10 meters (20 or 30 feet) on the crests; in one place it formed a triangular prism 20 meters (60 feet) on a side along the crest of an anticline, as was shown by open-cut mining.

In several areas around the southwest corner of the anthracite coal basin, an angular unconformity has recently been mapped (Trexler, Wood, and Arndt, 1961) just above the base of the Carboniferous in the coarsest part of the Devonian-

Lower Carboniferous clastic wedge ("Catskill delta") that is the sedimentary reflection of the Acadian orogeny; otherwise the westernmost reported occurrence of an Acadian unconformity is in Rhode Island. Perhaps the unconformity will be found all around the anthracite basin as more careful mapping is done, or perhaps it is present only in a relatively restricted area where there was an outlying Acadian fold separated from the main Acadian folded belt by flat-lying strata, like the Alleghanian Sequatchie anticline in the southern Appalachian Plateau. If such a fold was formed by decollement, bedding-plane faults should be present in the flat-lying strata southeast of them; perhaps the Tuscarora fault of Pierce and Armstrong (1966; see Chapter 3, p. 32) is a fault of this kind. Hoskins (1970), however, denies the existence of this unconformity.

East of the anthracite depression, the axes of the folds rise again, but the folds rapidly become shallow and within 30 kilometers (20 miles) to the east they die out on the Pocono Plateau, a wide area of nearly flat-lying Upper Devonian and Lower Carboniferous rocks that topographically and structurally belong to the Appalachian Plateau province rather than to the Valley and Ridge. Along the southeast margin of the Pocono Plateau, however, the Devonian and older strata are turned up steeply, in apparent continuation of the Blue Mountain structural front south of the anthracite coal basin; that front is of course the mid-province structural front from Harrisburg southwestward, but at the east edge of Pennsylvania it marks the northwest margin of the Valley and Ridge province. Thus the entire northwest half of the province, continuous from the anthracite region to Alabama, disappears abruptly here by fading into the Plateau province, whereas the southeast half of the province disappears at the other end of the belt in Alabama under the Columbiana thrust fault at the edge of the Piedmont province. The line along which the anthracite folds die out eastward on the Pocono Plateau, hence the local "boundary" between the Valley and Ridge and the Appalachian Plateau, trends somewhat east of north, in a rough way parallel to the axis of the anthracite depression to the west.

Most of the fold axes in the anthracite basin and in the Plateau province north and east of it strike about N70°E, but the main axis of the Lackawanna syncline at the north edge of the basin forms a conspicuous exception, swinging in a wide arc from N70°E to N35°E and locally even to N10°E at its northeast tip. As shown by Darton (1940, Pl. 10) and reemphasized by Woodward (1957a, pp. 1436–1437), the minor folds on the flanks of the major syncline, especially on its southeast flank, retain the normal N70°E strike, so that they diverge from the major fold like the barbs or pinnules of a one-sided feather. In some respects, the intersection of trends here is like that in the Roanoke and Rome recesses, and here again it appears close to a pronounced recess in the Appalachian chain. Woodward considered the intersection to prove a difference in age between major and minor folds, and he believed that the major fold is the younger, probably Triassic in contrast to the Carboniferous or Permian (Alleghany orogeny) age of the minor folds. On the other hand, although it is roughly parallel to the trend of the Triassic basins and border faults, the Lackawanna syncline is utterly different from them in character (see Chapter 10)—it suggests compression, whereas they suggest extension. It seems improbable therefore that the syncline could have formed at the same time as the basins and more likely that the similar trends were inherited independently from previously established parallel trends. Moreover, the minor folds branch from the main synclinal axis instead of being warped by it, suggesting that they cannot be older.

The Carboniferous rocks preserved in the major synclinoria of the anthracite coal basin lie far below the level they would have had (before erosion) on the plateau to the north and to the east—on the order of 1 kilometer (3000 feet) below in the Lackawanna syncline, 3 kilometers (10,000 feet) in the southernmost or Minersville synclinorium. It is difficult therefore to escape the conclusion that the basement surface under the anthracite basin is depressed by the same amount below its position under the plateau, the axis of the basement trough striking about N35°E and rising northeastward. The Paleozoic strata here, as in the rest of the Valley and Ridge province, probably folded independently of the basement despite the irregularity of the basement surface (Wood, Trexler, and Kehn, 1969, p. 115–116, give the arguments for applying the decollement interpretation to the anthracite region); thus the folds trend across the depression at an angle, plunging into it from both sides, but only the outermost fold, the Lackawanna syncline, is deflected by it, following it for some tens of kilometers (a few tens of miles) northeastward out into the Plateau. The presence of the basement trough may also explain why here and here only the outermost large fold of the Valley and Ridge province is a syncline and not an anticline. The rapid dying out of the rest of the anthracite folds on the east flank of the trough still requires explanation, however (see below, p. 71).

The strike of the Blue Mountain structural front

also changes in this sector, making two fairly abrupt shifts. The first shift, from N60–65°E in Pennsylvania on the south side of the anthracite basin to N35°E in New Jersey and southeastern New York on the southeast side of the Pocono Plateau and the Catskill Mountains, takes place near the Delaware Water Gap in eastern Pennsylvania. West of the point where the strike shifts, the front is offset en echelon in two places by pairs of folds trending N70°E, at a low angle to the front. As the youngest beds turned up along the front from the Delaware Water Gap northeastward are Devonian, Woodward (1957a, p. 1435) has suggested that here the N35°E trend is an older one, perhaps pre-Carboniferous. On the other hand, the Lackawanna syncline, much of which has a similar trend, contains beds as high as Upper Carboniferous and cannot be that old; the Carboniferous strata in its northeast tip are the northeasternmost preserved in the entire Valley and Ridge province, the next to the east being those in the Narragansett basin in southeastern New England.

From a little beyond the Delaware Water Gap, the structural front proceeds N35°E in a nearly straight line almost to the Hudson River at Kingston, New York; it consists of steeply dipping but generally not overturned Silurian and Lower Devonian strata, locally showing some tight folds (there is weak cleavage in places in the shale beds). The basal Silurian (Tuscarora or Shawangunk) sandstone is here conglomeratic, and it becomes younger northeastward, being mainly Upper rather than Lower Silurian in New York State; it is resistant to erosion here as elsewhere in the province and holds up the nearly continuous mountain called Blue Mountain in Pennsylvania, Kittatinny Mountain in New Jersey, and Shawangunk Mountain (the second a and the k are silent) in New York. About 40 kilometers (25 miles) southwest of Kingston, folds appear in the Silurian rocks and the belt of steep dips widens; the folds trend N25–30°E at a low angle across the belt (which here trends a bit more easterly) but die out on its northwest side where they enter the less steep Middle Devonian strata. In the next 30 kilometers (20 miles) to the northeast, the basal Silurian (Shawangunk) sandstone unit, which is a competent and resistant mountain-making layer from here to Knoxville, Tennessee, thins out rather rapidly by overlap on the underlying Ordovician, and the folding in the remaining Silurian and Lower Devonian rocks decreases in wave length but greatly increases in complexity.

Just at Kingston, the belt of folding makes a second shift in trend, even more abrupt than the one near the Delaware Water Gap, from N45°E to N10–15°E, and from here north almost to Albany, New York, it exhibits extraordinary complications—small-scale but intricate imbricate thrusting and tight folding of thin thrust sheets—in a belt 70 kilometers (45 miles) long but nowhere more than 3 kilometers (2 miles) wide (Goldring, 1943, p. 295–306; Chadwick, 1944, p. 157–185); the area is deservedly classic for such structure. For the most part the folds are strongly overturned to the west, but they die out rapidly in that direction; the Middle Devonian rocks beyond have a simple west dip that falls rapidly to nothing within about 15 kilometers (10 miles). The rocks beyond are folded, if at all, only very gently on east-west axes, the last eastern traces of the Appalachian Plateau folds of central New York. One may readily suppose therefore (and it has frequently been suggested) that the intense north-south folding in the Hudson Valley between Kingston and Albany is unrelated to and older than the gentle east-west folding on the Plateau; as the latter is probably Carboniferous or Permian (Alleghany), the former would be early Carboniferous or Devonian (Acadian). Northward, the belt of deformed Silurian and Devonian rocks ends 13 kilometers (8 miles) southwest of Albany, where the basal contact of the Silurian swings away to the west on the north flank of the Appalachian Plateau or Allegheny synclinorium, the south side of the Adirondack Mountains dome.

The Blue Mountain structural front changes in more than trend northeastward from Harrisburg, for a major angular unconformity appears along it, roughly between the Silurian and Ordovician strata. Although this angular unconformity has been disparaged by many writers, who are unwilling for one reason or another to accept the unequivocal evidence it provides for a late Ordovician, Taconic orogeny, it is nevertheless a major feature; the rocks above and below stand at a high angle to each other almost everywhere they can be observed together from Albany to the Lehigh River 45 kilometers (28 miles) west of the Delaware Water Gap, a total distance of 250 kilometers (160 miles), and the unconformity probably extends nearly if not quite to the Susquehanna River (Stose, 1930; Willard and Cleaves, 1939; Willard, 1943). The rocks above it are mainly Silurian, increasingly high Silurian northeastward (near Albany, the lowest beds may indeed be lowest Devonian; Rickard, 1962); the rocks below it are Ordovician, upper Middle Ordovician in much of the area but lower Upper Ordovician in at least part of eastern Pennsylvania. Upper Upper Ordovician strata, which farther west include the coarsest beds in the Ordovician-Silurian clastic wedge ("Queenston delta") that is the sedimentary reflection of the Taconic orogeny, are not certainly known where the angular unconformity has been recognized, but coarse sandstone and conglomerate that may be of this age are present *above* it at a few places between the Delaware and the Susquehanna (Willard and Cleaves, 1939, p. 1181–1182; Platt, Loring, and Stephens, 1969). At the Susquehanna River near Harrisburg a disconformity, if not a low-angle unconformity, is found beneath the upper Upper Ordovician strata (a considerable thickness of beds may be missing), and those strata are conformable with the Silurian above. In my opinion, the disconformity is more likely than the conformable contact between Ordovician and Silurian to represent the distal extremity of the angular unconformity, but in any case I am far from believing that the Taconic orogeny took place in so small an interval of time as that recorded by either contact; more probably orogenic movement took place in the Hudson Valley region throughout the entire latter half of the Ordovician, spreading farthest southwestward, as far as Harrisburg, about the middle of the Late Ordovician and perhaps continuing in a waning and areally more restricted phase well into Silurian time.

The northwestern limit of pronounced Taconic deformation can also be located just west of Albany, where it lies a little west of the western limit of strong post-Devonian deformation; between this point and the vaguer limit east of the Susquehanna River, it is hidden beneath the later rocks of the Catskill Mountains and the Pocono Plateau. A line connecting these points would trend about N40°E, nearly along or a bit east of the axis of the anthracite depression; if it were somewhat concave to the west it would approximate the eastern limit of strong folding in the Carboniferous rocks north of the Blue Mountain structural front.

In the southeast part of the Valley and Ridge province, the Great Valley (here the Lebanon, Lehigh, Kittatinny, and Wallkill Valleys), mainly Cambrian and Ordovician rocks are exposed. The northwest part of the Valley, from the Susquehanna to the Hudson, is underlain by a thick sequence of Upper and Middle Ordovician (Martinsburg) shale or slate,* with many sandstone (graywacke) beds in the middle part and some thin limestone beds, mainly below, also more local bodies of cherty shale and volcanics. Estimates of the thickness of the shale have ranged from 1000 to 3500 meters (3000 to 12,000 feet);

the higher figure is confirmed by the most recent work (Drake and Epstein, 1967). The southeast part of the Valley is underlain by a thick sequence of Middle Ordovician to Lower Cambrian carbonate rock (Kittatinny group and overlying units), including considerable limestone above but mainly or entirely dolostone below (the shale zone present near the Lower Cambrian-Middle Cambrian contact through the whole Valley and Ridge province to the southwest apparently fades out in eastern Pennsylvania); this carbonate sequence is over 1000 meters (roughly 4000 feet) thick. Beneath it is a basal Lower Cambrian quartzite unit (Hardyston quartzite), not over 100 meters (300 feet) thick in this area though corresponding to the thick basal Paleozoic clastic sequence (Chilhowee group) present in the Blue Ridge province to the southwest and in the Piedmont province directly to the south; here it crops out at the southeast edge of the Great Valley or within the Highlands belt to the southeast, resting directly and unconformably on a Precambrian basement complex, mostly gneiss, which forms the Highlands belt, beginning near Reading, Pennsylvania, 80 kilometers (50 miles) east of Harrisburg, and continuing northeast to the Hudson River 50 kilometers (30 miles) below Kingston.

Recent detailed work around Lebanon, Pennsylvania, 40 kilometers (25 miles) east of Harrisburg (Geyer, Gray, McLaughlin, and Moseley, 1958; Gray, Geyer, and McLaughlin, 1958), suggests that at that longitude the overall structure of the Great Valley is a virtually recumbent east-west synclinorium (Lebanon Valley synclinorium), of which principally the overturned limb is exposed, the under limb being largely hidden under the post-Ordovician rocks to the north. The overturned limb is diversified by a great number of recumbent folds of all sizes, cut by irregular and discontinuous thrust faults. All the weaker rocks in the Lebanon area show strong slaty cleavage, nearly flat in the carbonate rock on the upper limb, but steeper in the shale near the axis.

Westward the course of this synclinorium is not clear. One possibility is that it remains entirely north of the northeast-plunging end of the Blue Ridge (South Mountain) anticlinorium (Chapter 3, p. 33), connecting with the north end of the (nonrecumbent) Massanutten synclinorium to the west, but more likely its axial surface rises southwestward and its deepest keel passes southeast of the plunging nose of the asymmetrical but by no means recumbent anticlinorium, disappearing under the Triassic basin to the south; the quite

---

*Anomalies in the stratigraphy of the slate sequence are discussed below (p. 89).

different stratigraphy of the Cambrian and Ordovician carbonates in the overturned limb of the recumbent synclinorium and around the plunging end of the anticlinorium supports this view. At the longitude of Lebanon, the south limit of the synclinorium is hidden under Triassic strata, but about 40 kilometers (25 miles) farther east, what may be parts of the core of the complementary recumbent anticlinorium appear as masses of Precambrian basement in the Reading Hills at the west end of the Highlands belt.

The structure of the Reading Hills has been controversial; Stose and Jonas (1935) interpreted them as mainly, though not entirely, a far-traveled thrust sheet and the many small areas of lower Paleozoic rocks within them as windows, but Miller (1944) adduced local field evidence to show that the faults present are steep and that the areas of Paleozoic rocks are down-folded or down-dropped by the faults. Probably, however, both high-angle and low-angle faults are present, the high-angle faults being the later. Repeatedly the northwest sides of individual Precambrian blocks are directly overlain by the unconformable Paleozoic, in places by the full Cambro-Ordovician sequence, but the southeast sides are generally faulted. It seems possible, therefore, using the down-structure method (Mackin, 1950) and assuming a general northeast plunge, to interpret the Precambrian masses as large digitations on the arch-bend of a very large, recumbent anticlinorium or nappe, the lower sides of some of the digitations being thrust faults now dipping north-northwest. Later, steeper, southeast-dipping thrust faults probably complicate the picture by cutting across the older faults and folds. The nose of one such digitation is exhibited in the outlying mass of Precambrian rocks 20 kilometers (12 miles) west of Reading, which is known from geophysical evidence to be rootless (Geyer and others, 1963, p. 48).

Near the Delaware River, the structure seems more complicated still (Drake, 1970). The Precambrian and Paleozoic rocks form alternate belts, but the Paleozoic belts appear to be antiformal, the Precambrian synformal, and klippen of Precambrian and windows of Paleozoic have been found. Apparently the entire section is here inverted on the overturned limb of the anticlinorium, and the Precambrian with the quartzite at the base of the Paleozoic is thrust northward over the Paleozoic carbonates (Musconetcong nappe of Drake, named for a locality in New Jersey 14 kilometers—9 miles—east of the Delaware where a window was first discovered), but after the thrusting the whole mass was folded again by more nearly upright folds (the

present antiforms and synforms) and cut by higher angle thrust faults.

To the north, between the Precambrian masses of the Highlands and the Silurian unconformity at the Delaware Water Gap, the Ordovician shale shows evidence of the same two deformations, of which the older produced major recumbent folds (Northampton nappe of Sherwood, 1964, p. 24 ff; see also Ryan and others, 1961, p. 21 ff., 41–43, 61 ff.; Drake, 1970, p. 286) and excellent slaty cleavage (Maxwell, 1962)—slate has been quarried commercially on a large scale from certain favorable beds—and the younger produced more upright folds and "fracture" cleavage. What appears to be the younger deformation can be found in the Silurian and Devonian rocks to the north, but the older one, during which the Lebanon Valley synclinorium and the Highlands anticlinorium were formed, is probably Taconic (Drake, Davis, and Alvord, 1960; for a contrary view, see Epstein and Epstein, 1969, p. 165–170).

The shale or slate belt continues northeastward across New Jersey into southeastern New York, where it widens considerably. In northernmost New Jersey and New York, however, stratigraphic units in both shale and underlying carbonate seem to succeed each other fairly regularly from southeast (older) to northwest (younger) without overturning or even excessively tight folding (Offield, 1967). Here, however, we are probably entirely on the upper upright limb of the recumbent anticlinorium, so that the structure is deceptively simple (Drake, 1970, p. 288); Isachsen (1964, p. 821–826) has marshalled the reasons for believing that the entire Highlands anticlinorium, at least as far east as the eastern border of New York State, is floating above the Valley and Ridge rocks, as in eastern Pennsylvania.

The exposed Precambrian on the southeast similarly widens northeastward as the edge of the Triassic recedes to the east; the overall trend of the anticlinorium seems to be about N50°E across New Jersey and into New York, but individual (commonly faulted) upfolds of Precambrian gneiss and downfolds of younger rock trend about N35°E. Two of three major (faulted and compound) upfolds in the belt of maximum complexity in northern New Jersey plunge down northeastward into the Great Valley just north of the New York state line, and only the third, the southeasternmost, continues to the Hudson, which breaks through it in a scenic fjord. On its northwest flank, in northeastern New Jersey and southeastern New York (west of the Hudson), a narrow, locally isoclinal but nearly upright faulted syncline, the Green Pond syncline (named for a locality 25 kilometers—15 miles—southwest of the state line), preserves a belt of Silurian and Devonian strata 80 kilometers (50 miles) long and up to 6 kilometers (4 miles) wide, lying more than 25 kilometers (15 miles) from the Silurian rocks along the Blue Mountain front northwest of the Great Valley. The basal Silurian formation (Green Pond conglomerate) in this syncline, again a competent ridge-forming unit, rests unconformably on all the older units from Ordovician shale and limestone at the ends of the belt to Precambrian gneiss along parts of its sides (Finks, 1968); thus here again there were at least two quite separate orogenic episodes. The N35°E trend of the syncline, evidently produced in the later orogeny (late Devonian or younger), suggests that the individual upfolds in the Highlands belt likewise result from the superposition of later folding and faulting at an angle across the main anticlinorial axis, presumably established in the Taconic orogeny late in the Ordovician. The apparently steep faults associated with the upfolds and with the Green Pond syncline have the same strike, roughly N35°E, but this is also the strike of part of the Triassic border fault on the east side of the Highlands; hence the faults may be as late as Triassic, or else both they and the border fault may first have formed at the time of the later folding and then been reactivated in the Triassic.

The sector between the Susquehanna and Hudson Rivers, like the Roanoke and Rome sectors farther south, corresponds to a recess in the general Appalachian trend, the strike swinging from N65°E on the eastern limb of the Central Appalachian arcuate salient to N35°E and then to N10°E on the southern limb of the Northern Appalachian salient. As in those recesses, intersecting fold trends appear in several areas, and here it seems very likely that they result from multiple deformation, though the details are far from clear. One of the deepest and most marked depressions in the entire chain, the anthracite coal basin, lies on the northwest side of the sector, but it lies asymmetrically to the west of the center of the recess and its axis is distinctly oblique to the axis of the recess. On the southeast side, there is no obvious depression, unless one so considers the gap between the Precambrian rocks of the Blue Ridge anticlinorium southwest of Harrisburg and those in the Highlands anticlinorium to the east; this gap lies on the continuation of the axis of the anthracite depression, but it may result merely from Triassic down-faulting of an originally continuous structural front or from bevelling by the Triassic faults of the recumbent Lebanon Valley synclinorium between the Blue Ridge and Highlands anticlinoria—as all these folds appear to plunge northeastward, the depression would lie

not in Pennsylvania but in southeastern New York. Possible this depression is also responsible for the preservation of the Green Pond syncline, in which case it was produced by the later orogeny.

As noted above, one of the unique features of the sector is the way the entire belt of folding north of the Blue Mountain front, a belt 50 kilometers (30 miles) wide, dies out eastward as it climbs out of the anthracite depression. The east side of that depression lies not far from the line connecting the western limits of strong Taconic deformation in the Cambrian and Ordovician strata near Albany, New York, and along Blue Mountain in Pennsylvania. It seems plausible to suggest that during the Alleghany orogeny, the already deformed strata to the east of that line were far more resistant to the later deformation than the undeformed Cambro-Ordovician strata to the west, that they therefore protected the post-Ordovician rocks overlying them from deformation, except in a narrow strongly deformed belt along the Blue Mountain structural front itself, and that their western edge determined the oblique trend of the basement trough under the anthracite depression and thus of the Lackawanna syncline at its north end.

Although the structure of the Great Valley is still incompletely known, we are beginning to unscramble the effects of the several orogenies it has clearly undergone; the differing trends that appear in several parts of the sector help to provide clues. The Alleghany orogeny is certainly responsible for the folds of the anthracite coal basin (including, it seems to me, the Lackawanna syncline) and for that part of the Blue Mountain structural front west of the Delaware River, and probably also for the weak folds on the Appalachian Plateau to the north and northeast, as far as the Catskill Mountains; thus, save for the Lackawanna syncline and the main axis of the anthracite depression itself, it seems to be characterized in this sector by strikes approximating N65°E or even more nearly east-west. Yet it is also responsible for the folds of central and south-central Pennsylvania, where the strike swings around as far as N25°E, including almost certainly the Massanutten synclinorium and its northern extension in the Great Valley west of Harrisburg. Whether the part of the Blue Mountain structural front that trends N35°E and the north-south folds in Silurian and Devonian strata between Kingston and Albany were also formed at this time or earlier is simply unknown. The discrepancy in trend rather favors their assignment, as frequently suggested, to the Acadian orogeny of the Northern Appalachians. If these structures are Acadian, so also is the Green Pond syncline, and presumably also the upfolds of Precambrian gneiss that diagonal across the Highlands anticlinorium. Finally, as noted above, the outer limit of Taconic orogeny appears to trend about N40°E, not far from parallel to several obviously later features (Green Pond and Lackawanna synclines, for example). On the other hand, the overall trend of the Highlands anticlinorium is now N50°E, and one might assume a similar trend for the Lebanon Valley synclinorium, both presumably originally Taconic structures, though their present trend might have been in part imposed by later (Alleghany?) deformation.

Valley of Lake Champlain

The central Hudson Valley and the hills east of it as far as the Taconic Mountains are mostly underlain by shale or slate continuous with the slate belt of eastern Pennsylvania and southeastern New York. The presence of Cambrian as well as Ordovician fossils within this slate shows, however, that the structure is far from simple, and the region has been indeed the scene of a major controversy, which is the subject of later sections of this chapter. Orthodox Valley and Ridge structure does not reappear northward until the vicinity of the low divide between the Hudson River and Lake Champlain; here begins a rather narrow belt of thrust faults that extends to the international border and at least a short distance beyond, a belt about 200 kilometers (120 miles) long and up to 20 kilometers (12 miles) wide.

On the west side of Lake Champlain rise the Adirondack Mountains, composed of Precambrian rocks like those in the Laurentian Highlands of Canada, surrounded and overlapped by a virtually flat-lying lower Paleozoic sequence. This sequence begins with an Upper Cambrian quartzite unit (Potsdam sandstone) overlain by Upper Cambrian and Lower Ordovician dolostone (Beekmantown group). Above a disconformity entirely comparable to the one present in the Central and Southern Appalachians at this level follow thin lower Middle Ordovician limestone (several thin units) and thick upper Middle Ordovician graptolite-bearing shale, black and free of sand below (Canajoharie shale), gray and full of graded beds of graywacke above (Schenectady formation). All the units below the shale thicken markedly from the region of the Mohawk Valley and Saratoga Springs at the southeast corner of the Adirondacks, where they aggregate about 150 meters (about 500 feet), into the Champlain Valley, on the west side of which they reach 750 meters (2500 feet).

On the north and west sides of the Adirondacks, these strata simply dip gently away from the Precambrian core, but on the east and south sides, Precambrian and Paleozoic rocks alike are broken by high-angle normal faults. Some of the faults are rather sinuous, but their trend is mainly north-northeast (except for certain cross faults); they are spaced from 1 to 20 kilometers (1 to 12 miles) apart and have throws up to 600 meters (2000 feet) in the Paleozoic rocks (some of them had considerably larger Precambrian throws). Most of them are downthrown on the east, and many of the blocks between have been tilted west, to judge by the attitude of the Paleozoic strata, but some have been tilted north and south; where the faults are downthrown on the west the blocks tend to be tilted east, as in the area from Whitehall, New York, to Lake George, which lies in a deep graben. The age of these faults is uncertain, except that they cut upper Middle Ordovician shale (Schenectady formation); on the south side of the Adirondacks they are lost in this shale in the Mohawk Valley before they reach the overlapping Silurian and Devonian rocks to the south, and no such faults are known to cut those younger rocks. In the Champlain Valley, most observers report that the normal faults cut the "Valley and Ridge" folds and thrust faults, but as the age of those features is not precisely known, that information helps but little.

The Precambrian rocks of the Adirondacks come down to the west shore of Lake Champlain in several places (just north of Whitehall they cross its southern tail into a projection of Vermont), but mostly the lake washes flat-lying Paleozoic strata in the various normal-fault blocks (widely hidden by a cover of Pleistocene lake and marine clay). Within a few kilometers (miles) to the east, however, and to the north on the eastern shore or on the islands in the lake, one finds that the Paleozoic rocks, mostly the Middle Ordovician (Canajoharie) shale, are crumpled and show strong slaty cleavage. Slaty cleavage also encroaches in places into the flat-lying and otherwise undeformed shale to the west, locally as much as 5 kilometers (3 miles) west of the present exposures of crumpled rocks. In a few places, small thrust slices of the underlying Middle Ordovician limestone appear within the crumpled shale.

The belt of crumpled shale is mostly rather narrow, but it widens to 15 kilometers (10 miles) on the islands at the north end of the lake (Hawley, 1957); on the other hand, it is entirely absent at the south end. On the east it is bordered by various low-angle thrust faults that bring up older beds. In the southern part of the Champlain Valley, the first fault is a relatively minor one, the Orwell fault and its probable continuations; along much of it Lower Ordovician dolostone (Beekmantown group) is brought over the Middle Ordovician (Canajoharie) shale, but Upper Cambrian dolostone and quartzite (base of Beekmantown group and Potsdam sandstone) are brought up for about 10 kilometers (6 miles) near Shoreham, Vermont, 18 kilometers (11 miles) southwest of Middlebury (here the throw of the fault is over 650 meters— 2000 feet), and also near Whitehall, though there the trace of the thrust fault or faults is so cut to pieces by the Adirondack normal faults that only relatively short stretches are exposed at the present land surface. This line of faulting can be traced about 17 kilometers (10 miles) south of Whitehall, and the belt of deformed carbonate rock can be traced about 10 kilometers (6 miles) farther before it disappears in the mass of slate that fills the Hudson Valley to the south. Mostly the belt next east of the Orwell fault seems to be a simple anticline or an east-dipping homocline, though the Middle Ordovician limestone and shale that follow to the east are generally tightly folded, sliced by small faults, and cleaved. At Shoreham, however, the presence of the competent Upper Cambrian quartzite (Potsdam or Danby formation) seems to have produced complications, notably two additional thrust faults that are only a few kilometers (miles) long but attain throws of 350 meters (1200 feet); the quartzite along one of them is bounded by faults on both sides and seems to have punched up through the overlying strata like a stiff board through laminated clay. No strata are exposed older than this quartzite, except possibly a bit of Middle (?) Cambrian dolostone close to Shoreham.

At the northern end of the Champlain Valley, a somewhat similar thrust sheet, the Highgate Springs slice (Kay, 1958), bounds the crumpled slate on the east, but it is nowhere more than 1 or 2 kilometers (a mile or so) wide and includes only Lower and Middle Ordovician rocks, somewhat different in facies from the rocks of the same age around the Adirondacks, for some of the Middle Ordovician limestone units become shaly and the Lower Ordovician dolostone units include much limestone. The slice is poorly exposed, and its structure appears to be rather complex in detail. At the international boundary and for a few kilometers (miles) north and south, another thrust sheet, the Philipsburg slice, overrides the Highgate Springs slice, bringing forward a rather simple north-northeast-plunging syncline of strata from Upper Cambrian to Middle Ordovician, in which the facies are altered a little more in the same sense. Northward both slices are lost in a broad slate terrain extensively covered by Pleistocene marine clay.

Behind these relatively minor slices or, where they are absent in the central part of the Champlain Valley, directly overriding the crumpled slate belt along the lake, is the major Champlain thrust fault. This fault brings up the upper part of the Lower Cambrian (Monkton and Dunham formations) for 120 kilometers (75 miles), from 6 kilometers (4 miles) north of the international boundary to the latitude of Middlebury, Vermont, and the slice behind it (generally called the Rosenberg slice) contains a full sequence up to the Middle Ordovician (Canajoharie or Morses Line) shale. The total thickness of the sequence is about 2000 meters (6000 feet); not only are the Upper Cambrian to Middle Ordovician strata about twice as thick as around the Adirondacks but beneath them are some 600 meters (2000 feet) of older rocks not present there. The facies show considerable change not only from the Adirondack border to the slice but also along the strike of the slice; eastward and northeastward limestone increasingly displaces dolostone, and along a line cutting diagonally across the slice some 40 kilometers (25 miles) south of the border, the carbonate units change abruptly into partly limy, partly black shale containing lenses of lime-breccia. This line was interpreted by Shaw (1958, Fig. 6) as the south edge of an unstable cross-axis, the lime-breccia lenses being considered as evidence of numerous subaerial disconformities, but it may rather mark the change from a shallow carbonate bank to a deeper shale basin, the breccia lenses having accumulated at the foot of the steep face of the bank; if so, the edge of the central platform of the continent, as it existed during the Cambrian and part of the Ordovician, is here preserved on a single thrust slice (Rodgers, 1968, p. 144).

In general the structure of this slice is synclinorial and shows a remarkable symmetry north and south of a strong double culmination in the synclinorial axis, opposite the stretch where the fault directly overrides the crumpled slate belt near the lake. Between the two crests of the culmination is a relatively shallow basin of Lower Ordovician rocks (Beekmantown group) 40 kilometers (25 miles) long, called the Hinesburg synclinorium; it is separated, by stretches 25 and 15 kilometers (15 and 10 miles) long where all Ordovician rocks have been removed, from deeper synclinoria to the north (St. Albans synclinorium; Shaw, 1958) and south (Middlebury synclinorium; Cady, 1945). These plunge away from the culmination until they are filled with Middle Ordovician slate (called Morses Line slate to the north; Canajoharie slate to the south); beyond, in each direction, the Champlain fault cuts up across the west limb into the core and is lost there, so that the slate in the synclinoria is no longer separated from the slate of the same age on the Philipsburg and Orwell slices. Finally those slices themselves are lost in wide slate terrains both north and south, the Philipsburg slice some 11 kilometers (7 miles) north of the international border, and the Orwell slice, as noted above, beyond Whitehall. An outlying sliver of the Highgate Springs slice, the St. Dominique slice, appears about 60 kilometers (40 miles) north of the border, between masses of slate.

The steep or overturned east flanks of these synclinoria mark in effect a structural front, the west flank of the major Green Mountains anticlinorium, which, like the Blue Ridge anticlinorium or front in the Central and Southern Appalachians, marks the east edge of the Valley and Ridge province and brings up a basal Cambrian clastic sequence, ranging up to 1500 meters (1 mile) thick, from beneath the upper Lower Cambrian strata that are the lowest exposed along the Champlain fault west of the synclinoria. Behind the Hinesburg and St. Albans synclinoria, this front is diversified by minor folds and broken into slices by one or more thrust faults (Hinesburg and Oak Hill thrusts of Cady, 1945; Arrowhead, Fairfield Pond, and Brigham Hill thrusts of Booth, 1950); klippen attest displacements up to 3 kilometers (2 miles), but the total need not have been much more, for the facies of the Lower Cambrian strata involved do not change markedly, though the basal clastic sequence continues to thicken eastward. The east flank of the Middlebury synclinorium is only locally broken by faults, but it is strongly overturned, so that the synclinorium is nearly isoclinal and locally semirecumbent. Moreover, metamorphism sets in all along the east flanks of the synclinoria; the shale units are reconstituted to sericite phyllite and the carbonate rocks to marble, especially south of Middlebury where the marble is quarried commercially. East of the Middlebury synclinorium, the Precambrian basement complex (Mt. Holly complex, resembling the Precambrian rocks of the Adirondacks in some respects) is exposed beneath the basal clastic sequence in the core of the Green Mountains anticlinorium, but northward it plunges out of sight beneath the ever-thickening clastic sequence, and it is not seen again along strike short of Newfoundland.

The general strike in most of the Champlain Valley is almost north-south, roughly parallel to the Adirondack border, but between 40 and 25 kilometers (25 and 15 miles) south of the international boundary, directly opposite the north end of the Adirondacks, it swings to about N30°E;

this trend continues for some tens of kilometers (tens of miles) into Quebec. The Champlain Valley sector thus marks the south limb of the great Quebec salient of the Northern Appalachians. The culmination in the synclinorial axis on the Champlain thrust sheet lies south of this turn in strike, roughly opposite the highest part of the Adirondacks, and the St. Albans synclinorium plunges northeastward past it toward the center of the Quebec salient. On the other hand, the zone where limestone breccias are most abundant (Shaw, 1958) lies close to the turn in strike, which may reflect the edge of the platform. The Green Mountains anticlinorium likewise plunges northward toward the salient, being highest considerably farther south. Thus the culminations are more probably related to the presence of the Adirondacks to the west than to the presence of salient and recess north and south.

It is a remarkable coincidence that the Champlain thrust, the one major thrust in this sector, should, like so many thrust faults in the Southern Appalachians, reach down to the upper part of the Lower Cambrian but no lower. It is difficult to interpret this fact in the same terms, however, for the units next above the Champlain fault are dolostone or quartzite (Dunham dolostone and Monkton quartzite), never shale, and to the north, where a shale unit reappears along the Lower Cambrian-Middle Cambrian boundary, it lies mostly a few hundred meters (several hundred to a thousand feet) above the fault. Nevertheless, the Champlain fault and its smaller companions to the west, the Orwell, Highgate Springs, and Philipsburg faults, are probably confined to the sedimentary column, at least west of the synclinorial axis.

The age of the deformation in the Champlain Valley is quite uncertain. Middle Ordovician rocks are involved; certain probably Cretaceous intrusive stocks in southern Quebec are not. The relations down strike to the south suggest a Taconic age, for the strike is not unlike that of the known Taconic folding near Albany (but it is also not unlike that of the known later folding between Albany and Kingston), and the normal faults that clearly cut the deformed rocks in the southern Champlain Valley do not cut the post-Ordovician rocks in the Mohawk Valley (but they have not been traced as far as the post-Ordovician unconformity). The relations across strike to the east on the other hand suggest an Acadian age, for the metamorphism increases fairly steadily eastward across the Green Mountains anticlinorium into the rocks beyond, where the staurolite grade is reached in post-Ordovician strata. There may well have been two separate periods of metamorphism in central Vermont, however (Albee, 1968; p. 329–331; see also p. 96).

The Taconic Controversy

In the preceding sections, I have passed over the great mass of shale and slate that underlies the central Hudson Valley and makes up the Taconic Mountains along the western border of New England and their foothills west to the Hudson River. This mass could be explained readily if only it could be interpreted as entirely Middle Ordovician or younger shale, lying in stratigraphic continuity over the Lower and Middle Ordovician carbonate strata that dip under it on various sides, though more intensely crumpled than they because of its incompetence, and increasingly metamorphosed eastward. This simple interpretation has been put forward repeatedly and challenged as repeatedly, and the resulting debates, now spread over more than a century, constitute the Taconic controversy. Because I agree with all its main arguments, I believe that the summing-up of Taconic geology by Zen (1967) will finally put an end to the major current controversy, although doubtless lesser points will be argued for many more years.

The first phase of the Taconic controversy was initiated in 1842 by Ebenezer Emmons; it may be called the Wernerian phase. Emmons was familiar both with the flat-lying black (Canajoharie) shale (now assigned to the upper Middle Ordovician), which overlies equally flat-flying fossiliferous limestone (now assigned to the lower Middle Ordovician and older) in the Mohawk Valley west of Albany, and with the intensely crumpled and considerably metamorphosed slate and phyllite associated with marble in the hills between Albany and Williamstown, Massachusetts, where he taught at Williams College for years, and he could not conceive that these two groups of rocks are of the same age. The strongly tilted slate, phyllite, and marble, as well as some associated quartzite, seemed to him obviously older than the flat-lying shale and limestone, and also older than the sandstone (Potsdam sandstone, now assigned to the Upper Cambrian) at the base of the flat-lying sequence, although both groups of rocks are clearly younger than the ancient (Precambrian) gneisses of the Green Mountains and the Adirondacks on which they respectively rest. Accordingly, he proposed (Emmons, 1842, p. 135 ff.) to recognize the deformed rocks as a "Taconic System," distinctly older than the flat-lying "New York System" (now recognized as Upper Cambrian to Devonian) then being surveyed for the state of New York by a group of leading geologists of whom Emmons was one. His colleagues in general refused to accept this idea, believing that the one sequence was in fact simply the deformed and metamorphosed equivalent of the other, and a bitter personal controversy ensued, which ended in the more or less forced withdrawal of Emmons from the New York group and his removal to North Carolina, where he continued for the rest of his life to insist on the validity and separateness of the system he had named, to which he also assigned relatively low-grade metamorphic rocks in North Carolina, Rhode Island, Maine, the Lake Superior region, and elsewhere.

The geologists of the New York Survey understood the stratigraphic value of fossils and quickly recognized that their "New York System" correlated with the Silurian system erected by Murchison in Great Britain only a few years before (that its upper part was Devonian they realized only a little later). Emmons therefore argued that the "Taconic System" was older than the Silurian and in face equivalent to the Lower Cambrian of Sedgwick (Sedgwick's Upper Cambrian being recognized as equivalent to part of Murchison's Silurian). In 1844 (Emmons, 1844, p. 19–21), he announced the discovery of two trilobites in the "Taconic System" close to Bald Mountain, 21 kilometers (13 miles) east of Saratoga Springs, New York, which he maintained were not like those in the "New York System," but his opponents argued the contrary, and Emmons himself repeatedly stated that the "Taconic System" was based not on fossils but on the superposition of strata. The fossils therefore played only a minor part in the first phase of the controversy.

A second, faunal, phase of the controversy opened with the announcement in 1860 by Joachim Barrande (transmitted to America by Jules Marcou) that Emmons' fossils, and others that had more recently been discovered in northwestern Vermont and southeastern Quebec, belong to the "primordial" (Cambrian) fauna and are indeed older than the faunas of the "New York System" (which are mainly "second fauna," i.e., Ordovician, and younger, though including at the base the highest "primordial," i.e., Upper Cambrian). The importance of this discovery was debated for over a decade, especially as other fossil discoveries showed that at least some of the limestone in Emmons' original "Taconic System" contains younger (Ordovician) fossils. Beginning in 1871, however, S.W. Ford, a jeweler in Troy, New York, published a series of careful descriptions of fossils from Troy and vicinity that left no doubt of the existence of a "primordial" (we would now say Lower Cambrian) fauna in the heart of the

Taconic area. The controversy again became very bitter, notably between Marcou and J. D. Dana; finally C. D. Walcott, already recognized as the leading American student of Cambrian faunas, was sent by the U.S. Geological Survey to study the Taconic area. Walcott spent two field seasons in the region, and finally reached the conclusion (Walcott, 1888) that although, as the fossils showed, Emmons had been right in asserting that rocks older than the base of the flat-lying sequence are present in the deformed belt, he had been wrong in believing that all the deformed rocks are older than all the flat-lying rocks, since both Lower Cambrian and Lower and Middle Ordovician faunas are present in the Taconic slate, and entirely wrong in the sequence he had recognized in his "Taconic System," and therefore that the "Taconic System" had been misbegotten. Dana followed up this article with a famous "Brief history of Taconic ideas" (Dana, 1888), culminating in an obituary notice of the Taconic system, and the matter was generally considered closed.

The third phase of the Taconic controversy began in the early part of the twentieth century and is hardly over today; it concerns chiefly the structural position of the Taconic slate mass rather than its overall stratigraphic age and may be called the tectonic phase, though of course stratigraphy continues to be basic to the argument. The existence of Lower Cambrian fossils at many localities along the west side of the slate mass, from the north end of the Taconic Range to the vicinity of Albany 135 kilometers (85 miles) away, prevented, for that part of the belt at least, a return to the simple original structural interpretation of the whole mass as a great synclinorium of Middle Ordovician shale (such an interpretation has been repeatedly favored by some, however, for the more metamorphosed eastern part of the slate mass, where no Lower Cambrian fossils are known). Even before Walcott's work, it was recognized that a major thrust fault must be located along the western margin of the Lower Cambrian part of the slate; this fault was considered part of the great fault that Sir William Logan had found at the edge of the Appalachian deformed belt in Quebec and was generally called Logan's line. It is not, however, physically connected with Logan's fault, and I propose to call it Emmons' line, although Emmons himself thought it was an unconformity rather than a fault. The necessity for postulating such a fault only increased with further detailed study of the slate belt, especially as the painstaking mapping of T. N. Dale and the thorough revision of the graptolite faunas of New York by Rudolf Ruedemann showed that the Taconic slate sequence contains not only Lower Cambrian strata older than any to the west but also Lower and lower Middle Ordovician shale older than the upper Middle Ordovician (Canajoharie) shale there and equivalent instead to the underlying carbonate units in the flat-lying sequence. The Taconic slate mass was even further isolated stratigraphically by the discovery, made by Walcott and confirmed by later work, that the marble sequence *east* of it includes not only Lower Ordovician and Upper Cambrian carbonate strata equivalent to those to the west, though metamorphosed, but also at its base Lower Cambrian (Dunham) dolostone overlying Lower Cambrian (Cheshire) quartzite. In other words, the Taconic slate sequence, ranging in age from Lower Cambrian to Middle Ordovician, now lies between extensive outcrop belts of a carbonate sequence of the same age range, in which shaly or slaty rocks appear only at the very top (upper Middle Ordovician) or at the very bottom (in the basal clastic sequence, between the known Lower Cambrian quartzite and the Precambrian gneissic basement).

In 1909, Ruedemann published a paper describing various types of inliers in New York State, and in this paper he refers, almost incidentally, to a map by Dale (1904, p. 187, footnote, and Pl. 11) of the area near Sudbury, Vermont, where the northern tip of the Taconic slate mass is surrounded on three sides by rocks of the carbonate sequence. The map also shows a small area of Ordovician carbonate rock just within the Taconic slate, which Dale interpreted as a downfolded outlier. Ruedemann (1909, p. 190–191) mentioned that he and Ulrich had independently come to the conclusion that the slate mass here must be thrust entirely over the carbonate rocks, from unspecified roots to the east, so that the small area of carbonate rock would not be an outlier but an inlier, a window in the thrust sheet. Ruedemann (1909, p. 189) also suggested the possibility that the entire slate belt of eastern New York is a great thrust sheet, an idea he later reiterated in reports on mapping along its western edge around Albany, though there he does not seem to have sought to derive it from roots east of the eastern carbonate (marble) belt.

Dale reacted vigorously to Ruedemann's suggestion, trying to disprove it by more detailed study and even by excavation and drilling around the alleged window. Shortly thereafter, however, Arthur Keith began mapping in the northern end of the Taconic Range, assisted in later years by Allyn Swinnerton, and he reaffirmed the thrusting hypothesis, postulating roots in the Green Mountains to the east; unfortunately he published only abstracts until 20 years later (Keith, 1912; 1913;

1932, p. 364 ff.). In the next two decades, the idea that the entire Taconic slate mass is a great thrust sheet was also applied further south along the belt by Ruedemann, L. M. Prindle, and E. B. Knopf (Prindle and Knopf, 1932); the contrary opinion was upheld by Dale and Robert Balk.

Stratigraphy of the Taconic Region

The Lower Paleozoic sequence on the south and east sides of the Adirondacks and in the Middlebury synclinorium has been described above; it shows many close similarities to the Lower Paleozoic sequence in the Valley and Ridge province from Pennsylvania to Alabama. As carbonate rocks dominate it except at the bottom (basal Cambrian clastic sequence—Mendon group and Cheshire quartzite) and the top (Canajoharie shale and Schenectady formation), it may be called the carbonate sequence.* From the east flank of the Middlebury synclinorium around Middlebury, it can be traced continuously along the "marble belt" or Vermont Valley between the Taconic Range and the Green Mountains past Rutland (Brace, 1953; Thompson, 1967) and as far as Bennington in the southwest corner of Vermont (MacFadyen, 1956). There are relatively few changes in the sequence in this belt, one of the most notable being a steady decrease in the ratio of quartzite to dolostone in the basal Upper Cambrian and upper Lower Cambrian quartzitic units (Potsdam or Danby formation and Monkton formation); both units finally lose their identity near Bennington. In an area near Rutland, however, the Middle Ordovician shale, with limestone and locally a thin volcanic unit at its base, bevels down unconformably across the whole of the sequence and comes to rest on the Precambrian basement and across a fault (normal?) separating the basement from Ordovician limestone (Thompson, 1959; 1967, p. 81, 87–88).

Just north of the Vermont-Massachusetts state line south of Bennington, the outcrop of the carbonate rocks is interrupted for not more than 4 kilometers (3 miles), apparently because the overlying Middle Ordovician slate bevels down to rest unconformably on the basal Cambrian clastic units, but beyond that point it can be traced as a continuous anastomosing belt across western Massachusetts and northwestern Connecticut into the eastern edge of Dutchess County, New York (whose county seat is Poughkeepsie), lying between a series of separated Precambrian gneiss

anticlinoria (Berkshire, Housatonic, and Hudson Highlands) on the east and south and the main Taconic slate mass (here largely schist) on the west. Because of widespread glacial cover, metamorphism, and the absence of the distinctive quartzite units within the carbonate section, the stratigraphy here has been harder to decipher, but Zen (1964c; 1969a, p. 12–14; Zen and Hartshorn, 1966), Ratcliffe (ms. 1965), and Waldbaum (1963) have shown that it remains the same and that even individual units can be recognized from the Champlain Valley to Dutchess County. The basal clastic sequence thins southwestward above the basal unconformity; it is represented by only about 100 meters (300 feet) of fairly clean (Poughquag) quartzite in Dutchess County. The carbonate section proper (Stockbridge limestone) shows a threefold division—clean white dolostone below (mainly Lower Cambrian), gray dolostone with some sandy and silty layers in the middle (mainly Middle and Upper Cambrian), and limestone with some dolostone above (mainly Lower Ordovician)—and a total thickness on the order of 1000 meters (3500 feet), though tectonic thickening and thinning make accurate measurements impossible. Unconformably above, a discontinuous and mostly thin bluish limestone unit (lower Middle Ordovician) grades upward into black phyllite or schist (Walloomsac formation, part of Berkshire schist s.l.). According to Ratcliffe (ms. 1965; 1969b; but see Zen, 1969a, p. 6–33), the underlying carbonates had been severely folded as well as faulted before the Middle Ordovician beds were laid down. In any case, here as near Rutland, Vermont, considerable deformation preceded the deposition of the Middle Ordovician strata.

From the easternmost belt of carbonate rock in Dutchess County, bands of the carbonate sequence extend north and west into the southern part of the Taconic slate mass, and here the grade of metamorphism drops rapidly so that around Stissing Mountain, an isolated area of Precambrian gneiss in northern Dutchess County, a more detailed stratigraphy based on fairly adequate faunas has been established, the most detailed in the carbonate sequence south of Vermont and Saratoga Springs (Knopf, 1927, p. 433 ff.; 1946; 1956; 1962). Above a basal (Poughquag) quartzite, roughly 100 meters (300 feet) thick, lies a conformable carbonate section (Wappinger limestone) on the order of 1000 meters (3000 feet) thick, containing Lower Cambrian, Upper Cambrian, and Lower Ordovician faunas, and having many similarities to the carbonate sequence in the

---

*Zen (1961, 1967) and Bird (1969) call it the synclinorium sequence, but they generally exclude from it the upper Middle Ordovician clastic strata at the top, which they class instead as part of the Taconic sequence (see p. 78 ff.), although they agree that those strata were not deposited upon the main body of that sequence in its original home but upon the carbonate rocks.

Middlebury synclinorium at the other end of the Taconic region.

Farther south in Dutchess County, the carbonate sequence reappears on the north flank of the Hudson Highlands, in precisely the same structural position as the carbonate belt on the other side of the Hudson River in the Wallkill Valley of New York State and across New Jersey into Pennsylvania (p. 69, 70); in New York close to the New Jersey line, the sequence of units recognized around Stissing Mountain has been found (Offield, 1967, p. 43–48).

Considering the region as a whole, therefore, the carbonate sequence presents a unified and consistent picture of stratigraphic relationships. Thin and relatively incomplete in the Mohawk Valley, it expands steadily eastward, partly by the thickening of units already present, partly by the addition of older units at the base. The bulk of the sequence is carbonate, mainly dolostone, but limestone is prominent in the Lower Ordovician, especially to the east; the chief noncarbonate intercalations in this part of the section are lower Upper Cambrian and upper Lower Cambrian quartzite units (Potsdam and Monkton formations) that fade out eastward and southward, strongly suggesting a source of the quartz sand in the Adirondacks or at least on the continental platform northwest of the Appalachian belt.* Below the carbonate part of the section lie clastic rocks, thin and mostly pure quartzite to the southwest and west, thick and heterogeneous to the northeast, though pure quartzite is present here also just under the carbonate rocks. Near the top of the sequence, a pronounced disconformity (the only well-documented one within the sequence, except for small ones along the Adirondack border) underlies Middle Ordovician strata, and in the eastern part of the region, on the west flank of the Green Mountains anticlinorium and farther south, it becomes an angular unconformity, recording a significant period of deformation (characterized by Zen, 1968, p. 133–134, as a period of high-angle faulting producing horsts and grabens). The base of the Middle Ordovician is generally limestone, but upward this limestone gives way fairly abruptly to black shale (or slate or phyllite); evidently, during Middle Ordovician time there was a fairly sudden westward invasion of mud from some uplifted area to the east into what had been clear shallow seas. In the present discussion, the rocks

younger than the limestone-shale contact are called upper Middle Ordovician, those older but above the disconformity are called lower Middle Ordovician. In the Mohawk, upper Hudson, and Champlain Valleys, this contact is closely dated by both the shelly faunas in the limestone and the graptolites in the shale; it lies at the top of the Shoreham portion of the Trentonian series of Kay (1937 and other papers), near the base of the Barneveld stage of Fisher (1962; "Trenton" stage of Cooper, 1956, p. 9 and chart opp. p. 130), and within the zone of *Orthograptus truncatus* var. *intermedius* of Berry (1960 and other papers; equivalent to zone of *Climacograptus wilsoni* in the Caradoc series of Great Britain). To the east and south, however, the base of the shale appears to be somewhat older (zone of *Climacograptus bicornis* of Berry; equivalent to zone of *C. peltifer* in Great Britain, Wilderness stage of Cooper, lower Trentonian [Rockland] or upper Bolarian of Kay). In any case, the consistent stratigraphy of the carbonate sequence wherever it is exposed, from Saratoga Springs northeast to Middlebury and then south along the marble belt to Stissing Mountain and the Hudson Highlands, implies that the entire region had a consistent history from the Early Cambrian to the Middle Ordovician; through most of this time it would have been a shallow bank (Rodgers, 1968) along the eastern margin of the central platform of the continent, receiving limy deposits and occasionally quartz sand like the Florida or Yucatán Banks of today.

Nevertheless, framed within the almost continuous belt of carbonate rock just described lie the Taconic rocks, mainly shale, slate, or phyllite, shown by fossils to form a sequence of strata ranging through precisely the same time interval— Early Cambrian to Middle Ordovician. The stratigraphy of the Taconic sequence has been much more difficult to unscramble than that of the carbonate sequence, but in recent years great strides have been made, and a general consensus has now been reached, even among workers who differ fundamentally in their structural interpretations. Facies changes are present, so that the sequence shows some variation from area to area, and different stratigraphic names have been applied in different parts of the region (see Zen, 1964b), but the basic pattern is now fairly clear (see summary in Zen, 1967, p. 14–17, 23–27).

The bulk of the Taconic sequence consists of argillaceous strata, either gray to black (com-

*Zen (1968, p. 135, 131; the central paragraph in column 1, page 135, is out of place and, with its headings, belongs at the foot of column 1, page 131) interprets argillaceous material in the Middle Cambrian (Winooski dolostone) and Lower Ordovician (Bascom formation) carbonates as derived from the east, from the same source as the Taconic sequence. This interpretation seems unnecessary to me; clay as well as sand could come from the continental platform to the northwest, as it did to form the Conasauga shale in the Middle and Upper Cambrian of the southern Appalachian Valley and Ridge province (Rodgers, 1953a, p. 47 and Fig. 3).

monly pyritic) or else greenish but with locally prominent purple or red. The types of shale recur in different parts of the sequence, but highly siliceous argillite is mostly and bedded chert perhaps entirely confined to the Ordovician; some of the chert contains considerable disseminated feldspar (probably mainly albite) and weathers with a distinctive white crust—it is probably tuffaceous. To add to the stratigraphic difficulties, the shaly rocks are folded on all scales from tight crumples to large-scale isoclinal or recumbent folds, and slaty cleavage is virtually ubiquitous, commonly obscuring the bedding of at least the greenish varieties. Eastward the grade of metamorphism rises, and in the easternmost and southeasternmost parts of the region garnet and staurolite are present, though locally retrograded to chlorite and muscovite.

The coarser clastic rocks are more distinctive stratigraphically. They include fairly thick units of slaty siltstone (Bomoseen "grit"), impure quartzite (Zion Hill quartzite), and coarse graywacke or graywacke conglomerate (Rensselaer graywacke) associated with Lower Cambrian greenish slate (Bull and Nassau formations), beds of coarse quartz sandstone with dolomitic or ankeritic cement associated with Cambrian, especially Upper Cambrian, black slate (West Castleton and especially Hatch Hill formations), and thick commonly graded beds of coarse graywacke associated with Middle Ordovician graptolite slate in the uppermost unit of the sequence (Austin Glen graywacke). Thin purer silty quartzite beds appear in green slate in several parts of the sequence. Thin layers of limestone (rarely dolostone) occur interbedded in certain of the black slate units, and layers and lenses of lime-breccia and lime-conglomerate are known here and there almost throughout the sequence, being especially common along the western side of the Taconic region. Some of the breccias in the Cambrian units are monomict, and the fragments appear to be simply limestone beds pulled apart shortly after deposition, perhaps during penecontemporaneous slumping, but most are definitely polymict; Lowman (1961) has likened these to the brecciolas of the northern Appenines. Detailed study of the fragments in some of the Ordovician breccias (Ruedemann, 1901, p. 7–10, 89 ff.; Ross, 1949) has shown that they become more varied upward and include recognizable, commonly fossiliferous pieces from units of the carbonate sequence.

Igneous rocks are known in a few places in the southern part of the region; they include layers of tuff, masses of pillow lava, and dikes of albite basalt, but their relations to the surrounding rocks are not clear. The feldspar-bearing chert mentioned above also indicates igneous activity.

Aside from fossils in the carbonate-sequence blocks in the lime-breccias, fossils in the Taconic sequence are fairly rare; they are found only in the western part of the Taconic region, for farther east the grade of metamorphism rises and they have been destroyed. They fall into two groups: Cambrian (mainly Lower Cambrian) faunas consisting of trilobites, inarticulate brachiopods, and hyolithellids and the like, which differ considerably from the Cambrian faunas found in the carbonate sequence (Lochman, 1956; Fisher, 1961; Bird and Rasetti, 1968; Theokritoff, 1968), and several graptolite faunas ranging from Upper Cambrian to Middle Ordovician (Berry, 1961, 1962b, 1963b, 1968). Before the recent discovery of Upper Cambrian graptolites by Theokritoff and, of both Middle and Upper Cambrian trilobites by Rasetti and Bird, a disconformity was assumed between Lower Ordovician and Lower Cambrian, but those discoveries made a disconformity unlikely, and probably deposition was essentially continuous into the Middle Ordovician. An unconformity has recently been demonstrated within the Middle Ordovician, on the other hand (Shumaker, 1967, p. 31; Zen, 1961, p. 308; 1964a, p. 28–29; Berry, 1962b, p. 712–713), in the northern part of the Taconic region beneath the unit containing the graywacke at the top of the sequence (Pawlet or Austin Glen graywacke) or beneath a subjacent unit of black slate and chert, but it appears to be absent farther south. This unconformity and the base of the graywacke above it lie within the graptolite zone of *Climacograptus bicornis* and are thus older than the first appearance of shale (or of graywacke) at the top of the carbonate sequence west of the Taconic region but younger than the disconformity beneath the Middle Ordovician limestone in that sequence.

Both the sediments and the faunas in the Taconic sequence imply fairly deep water, extending at least below wave base. The sediments seem to be derived from several sources; the mud and some of the carbonate settled or precipitated out of the overlying sea water, the impure quartz sand came from some landmass of siliceous rock (probably a granitic terrain in the Cambrian but a sedimentary, volcanic, or low-rank metamorphic terrain in the Ordovician), from which it was brought, in the Middle Ordovician at least, by turbidity currents, and the fragments in the lime-breccia layers came from the shallow bank nearby, where the carbonate sequence was being contemporaneously deposited. The graptolite faunas were probably mainly pelagic, and the Cambrian trilobite faunas may likewise record deeper water than the Cambrian faunas in the carbonate sequence (Lochman, 1956, p. 1348–1349; Theokritoff, 1968, p. 18–19). Platt (1969) has accumulated evidence that the bottom on which the sediments were deposited sloped eastward, at least in the western part of the area.

Thus the Taconic slate mass, shown by its fossils to be contemporaneous with the carbonate sequence though quite different in facies, and lying in the very center of the region outlined by the outcrop belts of the latter, clearly contradicts the consistent geologic history deduced above from the stratigraphy of that sequence. There have been several solutions for this dilemma, depending on which link in the chain of argument that leads to the dilemma is doubted or denied. One hypothesis, the oldest and perhaps the simplest, has been to deny or ignore the age assignment of the Taconic rocks, considering them all Middle Ordovician or younger conformably overlying the carbonate sequence, yet without totally ignoring or impugning the fossil evidence, one cannot apply this hypothesis to the region as a whole. It can and has been applied, however, in those parts of the region where no fossils have been found in the slate, phyllite, or schist; thus Dale (1899 and other papers) considered the whole eastern part of the Taconic mass Middle Ordovician (Berkshire schist), and he has been followed in recent years by Balk (1936), MacFadyen (1956), Weaver (1957, for the high-grade rocks in his area), and Hewitt (1961, p. 68–75). But this solution would be tenable only if a boundary could be drawn between the slate or schist thus assigned to the upper Middle Ordovician and that shown by its fossils to be older, for which one of the other hypotheses must be adopted. Relatively few attempts have been made to find such a boundary, and at least some of the boundaries chosen, for example those of Dale and Hewitt, are in effect metamorphic and not stratigraphic, the eastern edge of rocks still preserving recognizable fossils or the western edge of phyllite or schist (the higher grade rocks being considered the younger).

A second hypothesis accepts the general age assignments of the Taconic rocks but denies that individual slate units in the Taconic sequence are contemporaneous with individual carbonate units in the carbonate sequence, deposits in one sequence corresponding in general to disconformities in the other. Such a solution was partially endorsed by Ruedemann (1930, Fig. 8, p. 131; Cushing and Ruedemann, 1914, Fig. 15, p. 140), who, under the influence of Ulrich, suggested that the two sequences accumulated in completely separate parallel troughs, in which deposition more or less alternated. More thoroughgoing in this direction is the hypothesis advocated by Craddock (1957) and endorsed by Bucher (1957); according to them, the Lower Cambrian strata in the Taconic sequence correlate mainly or entirely with the basal Cambrian clastic strata at the base of the carbonate sequence, which include rock types not unlike the unfossiliferous siltstone and impure quartzite units near the base of the Taconic sequence, whereas the Ordovician rocks in the Taconic sequence are all younger than the youngest Lower Ordovician carbonate unit but older than the Middle Ordovician limestone that disconformably overlies it. The carbonate units are not found between the Cambrian and Ordovician parts of the Taconic sequence, and the Ordovician Taconic strata are not found between the Lower and Middle Ordovician parts of the carbonate sequence, either because they were not deposited there (thus the Taconic area is thought to have been an island, but shedding no sediment, onto which the Upper Cambrian and Lower Ordovician carbonate units lapped uncomformably) or because, having been deposited there, they were eroded when the next unconformity was produced. Unfortunately, not only is there little or no stratigraphic evidence for either the required alternation of units or the required unconformities (excepting the well-established one beneath the Middle Ordovician limestone in the carbonate sequence), but the faunal evidence does not support the alleged lack of contemporaneity of the two sequences; as more and more faunas have been found, the strict contemporaneity of the two sequences has become apparent and the hypothesis has become untenable.

The third hypothesis, which can be combined with either of the first two, accepts the Taconic sequence or the main body of it as contemporaneous with the carbonate sequence and denies instead the simple picture of stratigraphic relationships and geologic history deduced from the latter. This was apparently Dale's solution, at least for the fossiliferous part of the Taconic mass, and it has been carefully worked out by Lochman (1956, Pl. 10). The Taconic sequence is considered a relatively deep-water facies, deposited roughly where it now lies in a basin almost completely surrounded by a shelf on which the shallow-water carbonate sequence accumulated—a modern analogy would be the Tongue of the Ocean within the Great Bahama Bank, which may have persisted since the Cretaceous, but siliceous clastics must be virtually absent within it. This interpretation has the advantage of explaining the present distribution of rocks and faunas with a minimum of structural postulates, but the disadvantage (besides requiring the abandonment of the attractive if simple picture of the carbonate sequence) that, although in many areas the carbonate and slate sequences are now close together (as at the north end of the Taconic Range) and in some areas along the east side of the mass their outcrop belts interdigitate (if the slate or schist in those areas is really Taconic and not upper Middle Ordovician), yet nowhere has evidence of a truly transitional facies been reported, so that the postulate of a facies change all around the Taconic mass rests solely on the present distribution of the rocks, without independent support.

The fourth hypothesis accepts the deduced picture of the carbonate sequence as valid and cuts the Gordian knot by simply denying that the Taconic mass belongs where it now lies. Instead it is considered allochthonous, a possibly compound klippe at least 220 kilometers (140 miles) long and in places as much as 50 kilometers (30 miles) wide, brought into its present position by tens of kilometers (tens of miles) of tectonic movement from a source area to the east. Not only does movement from the east best fit the general asymmetry of Appalachian deformation (at least along the west side of the Appalachian belt), but in our present state of knowledge the relatively thin Taconic sequence can reasonably be interpreted as transitional between the thick carbonate sequence west of the Green Mountains and the even thicker Lower Paleozoic clastic-volcanic sequence (now highly metamorphosed) east of them. It is also not unlike the sequence of shale with lime-breccia lenses in the St. Albans synclinorium of northwestern Vermont (p. 73) and northeastward in Canada, and the lowest part resembles strata on the east flank of that synclinorium, especially east of the Hinesburg and related thrust faults (p. 74), in a similar transitional position (Zen, 1968, p. 131). Paleogeographically, the Taconic sequence would represent the deposits on the slope between the foot of the carbonate bank (slides and slumps from which would provide the lime-breccia and lime-conglomerate in the western part of the Taconic mass) and the center of a trough in which the clastic-volcanic sequence was deposited; its relative thinness would thus reflect not relative uplift but relative starvation, for clastic materials could reach it in abundance only in the Early Cambrian, before the growth of the bank cut it off from the Precambrian shield areas to the west and northwest, and in the Middle Ordovician, when Taconic deformation was beginning in areas to the east.

The problems facing the klippe hypothesis are no less severe than those facing the autochthonous hypotheses, however; they concern the boundaries, the roots, and the mechanics of emplacement of the supposed klippe. Keith (1913, 1932) and Ruedemann, at least in part, interpreted the klippe as an erosional remnant of a great thrust sheet, brought forward above an orthodox low-angle thrust fault—like the Champlain and related faults to the north (which were being studied at about the same time) though larger and involving different strata—from a root to the east where the thrust fault finally disappears below the present land surface; Keith appears to have included in the klippe virtually all the deformed shale, slate, and schist in the region, so that for him the boundary was approximately the limestone-shale contact. Later work has shown, however, that at least some of the shale, etc., around the edges of the main Taconic mass must be interpreted as belonging at the top of the carbonate sequence, and proponents of the klippe hypothesis have been little if any more successful than their rivals in finding a satisfactory boundary between autochthonous and Taconic slate. Equally serious has been the root problem; no thrust fault has been found in the supposed root area east of the Green Mountains anticlinorium (Hawkes, 1941), and most attempts to resolve the problem seem to be as *ad hoc* as the arguments about unconformities or facies changes in the autochthonous hypotheses. Finally, many geologists have simply not been prepared to believe in the tectonic transport over tens of kilometers (tens of miles) of a thrust sheet composed of incompetent shaly rock, though in this regard the Taconic thrust sheet is hardly unique— both the Roberts Mountains thrust sheet of Nevada and the Simmendecke of the Swiss Prealps are made of equally weak materials and have probably traveled farther—and much of the difficulty is alleviated by the demonstration (Hubbert and Rubey, 1959) that fluid pressure in the sediments can vastly reduce frictional resistance to thrusting (Cady, 1968).

A fifth, also allochthonous hypothesis for the Taconic mass has been developing in recent years. Cady (1945, p. 570, 578) suggested an analogy with tar and, quoting White, questioned whether the klippe had remained attached to a root. Thompson (Billings and others, 1952, p. 20) more explicitly suggested gravity gliding off the Green Mountains anticlinorium just to the east at the time of the known Middle Ordovician uplift in that area; thus no orthodox root-zone thrust fault would be needed, and the incompetence of the material would be no bar to its movement. Rodgers, influenced by new ideas on the Pre-Rif nappe of northern Morocco and the argille scagliose ("Liguride nappe") of north-central Italy (see Rodgers and Neale, 1963, p. 726–727), and Zen (1961, p. 328–330) further suggested that the mass or masses slid off the anticlinorium into the Middle Ordovician sea to the west *during* the deposition of the shale at the top of the carbonate sequence, presumably into relatively deep water in a depression complementary to the anticlinorial uplift. Deposition of shale and sandstone may well have continued, locally at least, even after the arrival of the sliding mass; moreover, several workers (see summary in Zen, 1967, p. 35—40; see also below, p. 84) have found breccias containing blocks of Taconic rocks in autochthonous shale close to the edge of and just below the allochthonous mass. The difficulty in locating the actual contact, which would lie mainly or entirely within now metamorphosed shale, would thus be the natural result of the arrival of the klippe during the deposition of mud in part derived from its own erosion. It should be mentioned that a closely similar hypothesis was independently developed by Henderson (1958) for the corresponding rocks in southern Quebec (p. 118).

Essentially, then, in interpreting the stratigraphy of the Taconic region, one is faced with a choice between a solution or solutions that accept a simple and consistent stratigraphic picture but require *ad hoc* structural postulates (a conventional thrust fault that is difficult to locate or a gravity slide from an uplift to the east), and a solution or solutions that accept a relatively simple structural picture but require *ad hoc* stratigraphic postulates (rapid unexposed facies changes or overlapping unconformities).

Structure of the Taconic Region

Concerning the factual stratigraphy of the Taconic region, in both the carbonate and the Taconic sequences, a general agreement has been reached, although differences of opinion as to details still abound, and although the paleogeographic reasons behind the stratigraphic facts remain the subject of vigorous controversy. But concerning the structure of the region, there has been almost total lack of agreement on the data, let alone the interpretation. In one and the same area one observer sees extensive large-scale recumbent folding where another sees only minor tight crumpling in a relatively simple synclinorium, or one sees great far-traveled thrust sheets where another categorically states that the only thrust faults present are high-angle and of relatively limited throw. Almost the only major points on which argument has been reached (and even on these it is not unanimous) are that the west side of the Taconic slate mass, or at least the west side

of the fossiliferous Cambrian slate (what is here called Emmons' line), is marked by an important fault, probably an east-dipping thrust fault, for many kilometers (miles) on either side of Albany and Troy, whereas along the east and southeast sides of the mass and at the north end, especially where the outcrop belts of carbonate rock and of slate or schist interdigitate, the slate or schist lies geometrically above the carbonate rock in probably complex synclinoria. Even about apparently factual observations there are serious disagreements (see Prologue in Zen, 1967); observers have been influenced not only in their interpretation of the observations but also in their selection of what to observe and perhaps in the observation itself by the general view they have had of the problem, by whether they emphasized stratigraphy or details of structure or the general tectonic relations, by what kinds of data they considered inherently more informative and what kinds of explanation inherently more likely. Under these circumstances it is incumbent on me to admit my own biases in favor of broad generalizing explanations in general and of the klippe hypotheses in the particular case, and to emphasize that this summary was written from the point of view of the hypothesis (the fifth above) that the Taconic slate mass was emplaced piecemeal as a series of large gravity slides from a source area to the east, roughly in the vicinity of the present Green Mountains and Berkshire Highlands anticlinoria.

One of the most significant contributions to Taconic structure in recent decades is the work of E-an Zen (1961) in Vermont at the north end of the Taconic slate mass, including the northern 25 kilometers (15 miles) of the Taconic Range proper and also the foothills to the west toward the Vermont-New York state line. Building on painstaking but unpublished work by Swinnerton, which had also been available to Keith when he wrote his later papers on the area, Zen was able to construct a consistent stratigraphic column, containing not only a recognizable sequence of major units (mainly Cambrian) but also a number of somewhat discontinuous but traceable and distinctive key beds. Given the stratigraphy, the structure could be deciphered.

The northern end of the Taconic mass is surrounded on three sides by the carbonate sequence folded into the south-plunging and nearly isoclinal Middlebury synclinorium, and the Taconic slate seems to lie on top of that sequence, folded with it into the same synclinorium and preserved there by the continuing southward plunge. There has indeed been considerable disagreement on just where the black slate at the top of the carbonate sequence stops and the Taconic slate (also black in general next the contact) begins; both are tightly crumpled by minor folds and cut by axial-plane cleavage entirely consistent with the synclinorial pattern, and the axes of the minor folds and the intersections of cleavage and bedding in both plunge gently south.

Now Zen showed that within the Taconic slate, as one proceeds southward and hence upward across the strata in the core of the synclinorium, one crosses the stratigraphic sequence four to six times, the order of the sequence reversing with each repetition (except that one inverted sequence is cut out along part of its trace, presumably by a thrust fault); in places indeed he was able to trace individual key beds where they double back from an inverted to a normal limb. In other words, before the strata that are now the Taconic slate were folded into the synclinorium, crumpled, cut by cleavage, and metamorphosed, they had already been thrown into great recumbent folds with a half-wave length approximating the total thickness of the sequence involved, an unknown but certainly not small amplitude, and an axial length measured at least in kilometers (miles). The original direction of the axes of the recumbent folds is difficult to reconstruct because of the intense later deformation; it may have been east-west or northeast-southwest, with the anticlinal noses of the folds facing north or northwest. At least as a general rule, Zen's mapping indicated that the lowest recognizable sequence is inverted, so that Cambrian or lower Ordovician black slate at the *top* of the local Taconic sequence, upside-down, lies in contact with and above upper Middle Ordovician black slate at the *top* of the carbonate sequence, right-side-up; because the two black slates look much alike and both are considerably metamorphosed, the contact is difficult to locate. (That the lowest Taconic slates are inverted has not been accepted by all observers; cf. Zen, 1963; Doll and others, 1963; Zen, 1967, p. 95 97; Thompson, 1967, p. 84—85).

Traced east and west from the axial region of the synclinorium, the strike of the strata and hence presumably the axial planes of the folds turn more and more nearly parallel to the axial plane of the nearly isoclinal synclinorium. On the east flank the grade of metamorphism rises and it becomes increasingly difficult to trace the units; in the absence of fossils, indeed, Dale and Hewitt have excluded the rock here from the Taconic sequence and classed it instead as phyllite at the top of the carbonate sequence, but no sharp boundary can be found, and bodies of distinctive Taconic rock and even some of the key beds crop out for many kilometers (miles) southward along this

flank. On the west flank, on the other hand, near and beyond the Poultney River along the Vermont-New York state line, the grade of metamorphism falls, fossil localities become relatively more abundant, and the stratigraphy is completed at the top as far as the lower Middle Ordovician. The rocks are folded isoclinally into 4 to 6 folds, but because the strike is roughly parallel to that of the main synclinorium, it would be difficult to determine here whether the folds were formed at the same time as the synclinorium itself or as the earlier recumbent folding in its core. More probably they formed with the latter, for at least the eastern folds here can apparently be traced back into the recumbent folds of Zen's area. On this flank, moreover, the westernmost limb (presumably the lowest) appears to be normal rather than inverted, and the contact between the green slate at the bottom of the Taconic sequence and the underlying black slate at the top of the carbonate sequence is relatively sharp; this contact is Emmons' line. Where along the edge of the Taconic mass the change from a normal to an inverted limb takes place, or whether it takes place several times, is not yet known.

Several conclusions follow from the structural pattern discovered by Zen. First, here at least the Taconic slate mass can hardly be in place. If it was deposited where it now lies, within the horseshoe-shaped frame of the more competent carbonate sequence, it must owe its present structure to compression within that frame; a fan anticline or anticlinorium, overturned toward the frame on all sides, is conceivable, but the observed large-scale recumbent folding is both qualitatively and quantitatively incompatible with the assumed boundary conditions. For if one tries to imagine the rocks restored to their position before deformation, one must first flatten out the Middlebury synclinorium, which affects both sequences, and then unfold the recumbent folds in the Taconic sequence; evidently its strata would then cover far more area than those of the carbonate sequence, whereas if it is in place they must fit inside the frame of the carbonate sequence (restored to its position before deformation), with due allowance for the invisible transitional facies.

Second, the Taconic mass must have moved into the area from the east or southeast and probably originally lay above what is now the core of the Green Mountains anticlinorium, between the carbonate sequence on its western flank and an almost entirely clastic but more highly metamorphosed sequence on its eastern flank. There is a "room problem" here too, but if one takes into account the shortening involved in the formation of the individual folds of the Green Mountains anticlinorium and in the folding and meta-morphism of the rocks of its east flank, it is pos-sible to believe that there was originally enough area here to accomodate the strata now forming the recumbent folds in the Taconics. If the mass did not come from here, it must have come from many kilometers (miles) farther east, from an area where the Cambro-Ordovician rocks are now covered with later strata and are apparently of the wrong facies (they contain virtually no car-bonate and large amounts of metavolcanic rocks).

Third, the Taconic strata moved into place not during the main orogenic episode that deformed and metamorphosed the rocks of the carbonate sequence and produced the Middlebury synclin-orium but earlier, probably *during* the deposition of the upper Middle Ordovician shale at the top of that sequence, gliding probably by gravity off an arch that was already forming on the present site of the Green Mountains into the basin of deposition to the west. As noted above (p. 000), on the west flank of the Green Mountains the unconformity beneath the lower Middle Ordo-vician limestone bevels down across all the underlying units of the carbonate sequence, showing that uplift there had begun early in the Middle Ordovician. Many of the anomalous features of the Taconic klippe, if it is a klippe—for example, the almost invariable presence of autochthonous shale beneath it and the difficulty in distinguishing autochthonous from allochthon-ous slate—are more readily explained if the allochthonous strata arrived while the auto-chthonous strata were still being deposited than if it was emplaced above a conventional subsurface thrust fault. If so, the Taconic mass need not have been a single coherent block but probably arrived in several detached masses. An example is the small isolated or virtually isolated Sunset Lake area of Taconic slate, which lies about 10 kilo-meters (6 miles) west of the north end of the Taconic Range in a subsidiary synclinorium on the west flank of the Middlebury synclinorium, south-east of the Orwell fault but southwest of where the Champlain fault dies out in the main synclin-orium; this mass shows the same pattern of recum-bent folds, apparently rotated, however, relative to the main mass. Carrying this reasoning further, Zen (1967) has divided the "main mass" into seven slices, and some of these may well be further divided as work progresses. Furthermore, one would expect to find quasisedimentary breccias in the autochthonous shale, made of fragments of all sizes of slate and other Taconic rocks; fragments of slate in slate would be hard to recognize in this area where all the rocks are now highly cleaved, but such breccias—the "Wild-flysch-type conglomerate" of Bird (1963, p. 17—20; 1969, p. 671 ff.) and Zen (1967; Forbes Hill con-glomerate of Zen, 1961, p. 311)—do exist and have now been recognized all along the west side of the main mass from near the Sunset Lake mass south to the vicinity of Poughkeepsie and Newburgh, and also around its northern end and locally on the east side (Potter, 1963, p. 62—63, 43—45; Potter and Lane, 1969, p. 14—15), not to mention similar brec-cia at the top of the Middle Ordovician shale at the north end of Lake Champlain (Hathaway forma-tion of Hawley, 1957). Apparently, all that was necessary to observe these breccias was to realize that they ought to exist. (The area in which such breccias are presently known or suspected is shown with a separate pattern on the tectonic map of the Appalachians accompanying this book—Pl. 1.)

One set of facts perhaps less favorable to the hypothesis of emplacement by preorogenic gliding remains to be mentioned. Cady (1945, p. 570) and Kay (1959) have shown that around Sudbury, Vermont, at the north tip of the Taconic slate mass, a 10-kilometer (6-mile) plate (the "Sudbury nappe") of lower Middle and upper Lower Ordo-vician limestone of the carbonate sequence, folded into recumbent folds of smaller scale than those in the Taconic rocks (wave length measured in tens or hundreds of meters—tens of hundreds of feet) overlaps the main autochthonous slate core of the Middlebury synclinorium but underlies the north margin of the Taconic mass. If the "nappe" roots on the strongly overturned east flank of the synclinorium, its presence seems more compatible with a "conventional" thrust fault (acting as traineau écraseur for the "Sudbury nappe") than with a preorogenic gravity slide, but possibly it too was emplaced by gravity sliding off the west flank of the rising Green Mountains arch. A similar large slice of carbonate rock is known at Dorset Mountain 60 kilometers (40 miles) to the south on the east side of the main Taconic mass (Thomp-son, 1967, p. 90—92), and smaller bodies occur here and there along the west side, where they appear to grade into blocks isolated in the autochthonous shale, as at Bald Mountain (see below, p. 86).

Dale (1899) traced the isoclinal folds on the west side of the Taconic mass from east of White-hall south nearly to the Hoosic River, 70 kilometers (45 miles) away, where the pattern of folds apparently changes. The higher-grade rocks, phyl-lite or schist, on the east side of the mass continue southward a like distance until they are cut off by a westward projection of the carbonate sequence around Hoosick Falls, New York, west of Benning-ton, but they reappear southwest of Bennington and continue south (interruptedly) along the

Massachusetts-New York state line in the original Taconic Range, apparently as a large synclinorium. The Green Mountains anticlinorium to the east plunges down just inside Massachusetts, and on its strike lies the Mt. Greylock (Saddle Mountain) mass, a nearly isolated synclinorium of schist east of the Taconic Range proper, but the Green Mountains are relayed to the east by the Berkshire Highlands, which also have a Precambrian core. Between these various masses of schist and gneiss, the carbonate sequence crops out in a rough H, with Williamstown at the west end of the crossbar.

West of the Taconic Range is the broad Rensselaer Plateau, underlain by a mass of unusually coarse graywacke interbedded with green and red slate (Rensselaer graywacke); the rocks are coarsest and locally conglomeratic to the west (Balk, 1953, p. 826). The rock is unfossiliferous, except for some possible tracks, but the stratigraphic relations of smaller bodies of similar rock elsewhere in the region link it to the lowest part of the Taconic sequence. This fairly competent rock mass appears to form a shallow and only slightly folded basin and has been considered Silurian (Dale, 1893, p. 330 ff.) or even Devonian (Ruedemann, 1930, p. 123−130), resting unconformably across the apparently more deformed Taconic rocks, but recent workers, notably Balk, Bird, and Potter (Potter, 1963), have recognized that it is thrust over them, forming a separate slice above the main Taconic slate mass or masses.

West of the Rensselaer Plateau, more ordinary Taconic rocks underlie lower hills almost to the Hudson River near Troy and Albany. East of Emmons' line in this region, Ordovician rocks appear only in patches, one of which, northeast of Troy, contains the type Deepkill fossil locality. The published maps here give little or no structural information and do not indicate whether the folding of the rocks is merely minor crumpling or includes large-scale isoclinal or recumbent anticlines and synclines like those farther north.

Emmons' line can apparently be traced continuously from the Vermont-New York state line 110 kilometers (70 miles) south to Albany and at least 20 kilometers (12 miles) beyond; as noted above it has generally been interpreted as a major thrust fault along the west side of the main Taconic slate mass (Ruedemann indeed suggested that the patch of Ordovician slate containing the type Deepkill locality is a window through the fault). Except for a few stretches—the longest, north of the Hoosic River, is 8 kilometers (5 miles) long— Cambrian slate adjoins the line on the east. To the west is dark Ordovician slate, deformed by intense but apparently entirely small-scale crumpling

through a belt 10 to 15 kilometers (5 to 10 miles) wide, beyond which lies the nearly horizontal shale of the Mohawk Valley. Much of the deformed slate has upper Middle Ordovician fossils (zone of *Orthograptus truncatus* var. *intermedius*) and is clearly autochthonous or parautochthonous, but some of it contains graptolites of the next older zone (zone of *Climacograptus bicornis*) and hence is contemporaneous on the one hand with comparable slate at the top of the normal Taconic sequence and on the other with limestone on the margin of the Adirondacks not far to the northwest (one body of such slate, just south of Albany, contains the type Normanskill fossil locality). Furthermore, some of the younger slate contains visible blocks of all sizes of various members of the Taconic sequence, especially close to Emmons' line (the "blocks-in-shale" unit of Elam; see Berry, 1962b, p. 713, 715; 1963a). Perhaps the bodies of older slate, none of which lies more than 12 kilometers (7 miles) west of Emmons' line, are simply large blocks of the same sort and originally lay above the Cambrian slate that now crops out east of the line, where the amount of Ordovician Taconic slate is now conspicuously small, and either slid off the source area ahead of the main mass or perhaps traveled with it most of the way before becoming structurally independent. Southward both the outer front of deformation and the outer limit of the older Ordovician strata west of Emmons' line disappear under unconformably overlapping Silurian and Devonian rocks, implying that the deformation of the slate west of the line, and probably that of the main Taconic slate mass as well, is Taconic in age.

The presence of layers and lenses of lime-breccia and lime-conglomerate in the Taconic slate sequence, especially along the west side of the main Taconic mass, is mentioned above (p. 79); blocks of such lime-breccia have been found within a kilometer (a mile) west of Emmons' line, notably near Albany but also as far north as the Sunset Lake outlier, included in the autochthonous upper Middle Ordovician slate, along with blocks of other Taconic rock types and, in places, blocks from the carbonate sequence. The type Rysedorph Hill conglomerate of Ruedemann (1901), on the east side of the Hudson River opposite Albany, is a block of such Taconic lime-breccia within the deformed autochthonous slate, the blocks in the breccia themselves being fragments of the carbonate strata that now underlie the slate.

Bald Mountain, 21 kilometers (13 miles) east of Saratoga Springs and 55 kilometers (35 miles) north of Albany, is a classical and important locality, but evidently a complicated one; indeed it illustrates very well the remark made above that in the Taconic region observers cannot even agree on factual observations, let along on their interpretation. Some consensus is now possible, however; it is agreed that the mountain itself is made of Cambrian Taconic slate, that the glacial lake plain to the west is underlain by dark Ordovician slate (probably mainly upper Middle Ordovician and hence autochthonous), and hence that Emmons' line lies near the west foot of the mountain. Carbonate rock, evidently similar to that in the carbonate sequence though perhaps more like that to the east than that in the nearest outcrop belts to the west, crops out in places in a narrow north-south belt between the two main slate bodies, however; Lower and lower Middle Ordovician strata are certainly present and Cambrian strata may be. Two large quarries have been opened in limestone masses at the west foot of the mountain, yet dark slate surrounds each of the limestone masses that were quarried, separating them from other parts of the carbonate outcrop belt, and close to them it contains considerable sand and many pebbles and cobbles of limestone and dolostone.

Through the years since Emmons and Fitch (Emmons, 1844, p. 19—21) found the first "Primordial" (Lower Cambrian) fossils in America close to the mountain, the relations have been variously interpreted. Emmons (1844, p. 45—46) considered that the carbonate rock rested unconformably on the Taconic slate. Walcott (1888, p. 317) recognized that the Taconic slate is thrust over the other rocks and described the carbonate rocks as "interbedded in the shales" beneath the thrust fault. Ruedemann (Cushing and Ruedemann, 1914, p. 80, 83—84, sections on colored plate) considered the carbonate rocks to be slices along the fault and called the slate containing pebbles a mylonite. Rodgers (in Billings, Rodgers, and Thompson, 1952, p. 49), on the other hand, suggested that the quarried masses of limestone were simply mammoth boulders in the pebbly slate, but he agreed that the rest of the carbonate rock is a thrust slice. Sanders, Platt, and Powers (1961 and personal communication) considered that the pebbly slate unconformably overlies the quarry limestone, and that all the carbonate rock is autochthonous, brought up from below along a normal fault; like Rodgers, however, they accepted Walcott's view that Emmons' line is a major thrust fault.

Finally, detailed mapping by Rodgers, Bird, and Fisher (unpublished) showed that *all* the carbonate rock is in blocks in the (presumably autochthonous) slate, and that blocks of Taconic sequence rocks are mixed in; reconnaissance further showed similar blocks of the carbonate sequence here and there along Emmons' line as far north as the Whitehall region (where Rodgers had mapped some of them three decades before but had completely misunderstood their relations), and probably beyond to the north end of the Taconic slate mass. Ironically, the area of carbonate rock near Sudbury, which Ruedemann originally interpreted as a window when he first proposed a great Taconic thrust sheet (p. 76), may well be such a block, and indeed the whole "Sudbury nappe" may be simply a very large mass of the same sort.

In view of the general lack of structural information through much of the central part of the Taconic region and the disagreements between the various published reports, one can place little confidence in any general conclusions one might be tempted to draw. The great width of the slate mass here (45 kilometers—28 miles—from the east edge of the Greylock slice to Emmons' line) leaves more room for an autochthonous Taconic basin between the non-Taconic rocks on either side, yet it intensifies the room problem in the source area for the klippe hypothesis. The problem is made worse by the en echelon arrangement of the Green Mountains and Berkshire Highlands Precambrian anticlinoria, between which the carbonate sequence in the H-shaped area around Williamstown and the clastic sequence east of the anticlinoria are in contact along the Hoosic thrust fault (Herz, 1961), and the room available for the Taconic sequence is only that hidden by the fault or faults. Zen (1967, p. 58—61, Fig. 13) has suggested, however, that the Hoosic fault bifurcates northward, and that the rocks between, originally thought by Skehan (1961, p. 25, 45—62) to be a separate late Precambrian sequence lying unconformably between the Paleozoic clastic sequence east of the Green Mountains anticlinorium and the Precambrian gneissic basement in its core, are actually a piece of the Taconic sequence barely moved from its original position; this would be a satisfactory solution. One might further speculate that the main mass of Taconic slate to the west consists of several separate slid masses, one or more from each anticlinorium, now in contact along the zone of structural irregularities in the vicinity of the Hoosic River, but recent mapping appears to give little support to this speculation.

South of the latitude of Albany, the problems of Taconic structure are further compounded. For one thing, fossil localities are fewer so that the age of large bodies of slate is unknown, even along the western side of the region; for another, Emmons' line, which is both continuous and unique from Vermont past Albany, becomes hard to follow and is flanked by other similar contacts between Cambrian slate on the east and Ordovician slate on the west. Maps of four adjacent 15-minute quadrangles have been published in this area by four different geologists (Ruedemann, 1942; Goldring, 1943; Weaver, 1957; Craddock, 1957); not only the interpretations but also the age assignments and even the geological contacts show serious discrepancies from quadrangle to quadrangle. Farther south and southeast, work has been done by still others in recent years (Knopf, 1962; Warthin, quoted in Bird and others, 1963, p. 2–3, 28–29, 55–57; Carroll, ms. 1952), but the discrepancies are almost equally great.

The difficulties about Emmons' line may be considered first. The line is reasonably clear (and checked by fossil localities on both sides) as far south as Schodack Landing 20 kilometers (12 miles) south of Albany, but then it disappears under the kilometer-wide (mile-wide) estuary of the Hudson River; a similar contact reappears out of the estuary at Hudson, 25 kilometers (15 miles) farther south, runs under the Becraft Mountain outlier of Devonian and highest Silurian rocks, proving its Taconic or pre-Taconic age, and finally is lost in Ordovician shale covered with lake clays 10 kilometers (6 miles) south-southeast of Hudson. The rocks east of the line near Hudson are not certainly Cambrian, however; thus R. H. Flower found Lower Ordovician graptolites at one locality mapped by Ruedemann as Lower Cambrian, and Weaver and Craddock deny the presence of any Cambrian in this belt altogether. Southwest of Becraft Mountain, on the other hand, are several strips about 6 kilometers (4 miles) long of Cambrian strata arranged roughly en echelon and apparently entirely surrounded by lower Middle Ordovician strata; the east side of each strip appears to show a normal succession from Cambrian into Ordovician, the west side is a sharp contact exactly like Emmons' line, and the ends are ambiguous. If these strips are along thrust faults, the faults are short and without known continuations, though they could easily be lost in the thick and monotonous Ordovician slate; they might also be separate slid masses of Taconic rock—great exotic blocks in the autochthonous slate.

East of Emmons' line lies the Chatham thrust of Craddock, which brings probably Lower Cambrian green slate on the east (Weaver calls this slate Upper Cambrian and Lower Ordovician but he is probably wrong) against a broad belt of poorly exposed slate extending west to Emmons' line, which has been assigned three different ages by the four different geologists. Craddock's detailed work indicates a considerable stratigraphic sequence here, and evidently it extends from lower Middle Ordovician at the top to Lower Cambrian at the base (see Fisher, 1961; Craddock called it all Ordovician); this sequence is folded isoclinally, much like the sequence next east of Emmons' line in the northern part of the Taconic region.

The Chatham thrust or line itself is evidently at least as important a feature in this area as Emmons' line; moreover, bodies of carbonate rock from the carbonate sequence are present along it here and there for a distance of 30 kilometers (20 miles). They much resemble the body of carbonate rock along Emmons' line at Bald Mountain, and opinions on their structural position vary almost as widely; thus Craddock has interpreted them *à la* Emmons as unconformable upon the adjacent Cambrian slate, others interpret them as ordinary slices along the thrust fault, and one might also suggest that they are sedimentary fragments in autochthonous Ordovician slate caught between separate slid masses. The Chatham thrust can be traced south-southwest to south of the area where Emmons' line becomes difficult to follow; it may well merge with that line or at least assume the same functions, bringing Cambrian green slate on the east against Middle Ordovician slate on the west. As a sharp contact, however, it has been traced only to a point 45 kilometers (28 miles) south of Hudson, for there the Cambrian rocks to the east apparently come to an end.

The eastern contact of this Cambrian green slate belt is crucial for the interpretation of the region; it runs diagonally southwest across Weaver's quadrangle (which lies between Becraft Mountain and the state line) and is the northwest edge of a belt of black slate 3 to 8 kilometers (2 to 5 miles) wide. At the southeast edge of the latter belt black slate with beds of blue Middle Ordovician limestone at its base rests unconformably on a large area of the carbonate sequence, in the southern part of which (see above, p. 77) Mrs. Knopf worked out the complete carbonate sequence from the Lower Ordovician down to the Precambrian basement exposed in Stissing Mountain. Weaver, recognizing that on the southeast side of the belt black slate rests unconformably on the Cambro-Ordovician carbonate sequence and is therefore in part at least Middle Ordovician, believes that on the northwest side also it rests unconformably on the Cambrian green slate, the transition between the two Cambrian facies, possibly shortened by preunconformity thrusting, being concealed beneath the black slate belt.

Some of the facts Weaver has assembled suggest an alternative interpretation. First, the two supposedly equivalent unconformable contacts are not at all alike; the Middle Ordovician limestone bodies attesting to the unconformity along the southeast contact are entirely missing along the northwest contact, which Weaver states is transitional and difficult to draw. Second, the very dip of the latter contact is uncertain; if Weaver is correct it should dip southeast, but the data in his report (dips of bedding, deflection by stream valleys) suggest that it may rather dip northwest, the black slate structurally underlying instead of overlying the green. Third, in the western part of the black slate belt are lenses of quartzite of typically Taconic (Cambrian) aspect, as Weaver recognizes; he explains them as the tops of hills almost buried by the unconformably overlapping Ordovician slate, but elsewhere in the Taconic slate mass such quartzite is interbedded with black slate in a normal Cambrian assemblage. Thus this black slate belt probably includes both Cambrian and Ordovician black slate; if so, an as yet unobserved boundary must be assumed to separate them, but this explanation seems no more *ad hoc* than the alleged unconformity around the hill tops, and similar relations seem inescapable in the northern Taconics.

South of the published quadrangles and west of Stissing Mountain, A.S. Warthin has worked out the stratigraphy of certain belts of slate; he finds the slate sequence in regular order above the lower Middle Ordovician limestone which in turn rests unconformably on the main carbonate sequence (Lower Ordovician to Lower Cambrian). For those units of slate with Middle Ordovician graptolites, this view may be tenable, but others exhibit rock associations (but no fossils as yet) that farther north in the Taconic region are Lower Ordovician or Cambrian. Here again therefore bodies of Taconic strata probably arrived in the depositional basin of Middle Ordovician shale.

Eastward and southward from these areas toward southwestern Massachusetts and northwestern Connecticut, the grade of metamorphism rises (Balk, 1936; Barth, 1936); the larger valleys are underlain by the carbonate sequence with its characteristic stratigraphy and the intervening hilly belts by synclinoria of phyllite or schist until the Precambrian anticlinoria forming the various "Highlands" belts are reached (carbonate sequence and overlying schist also extend between and behind the Hudson and Housatonic Highlands). Where present above the regional unconformity, the (locally fossiliferous) Middle Ordovician limestone at the top of the carbonate sequence grades up into black phyllite or schist, but higher up green phyllite or schist appears. Most earlier observers assumed a simple stratigraphic gradation from black up into green phyllite (classing

them together as the Berkshire schist of Middle or Late Ordovician age), but Carroll (ms. 1952), mapping around the southwest end of the Housatonic Highlands, confirmed the discovery of Knopf (1927, p. 454–457) and Agar (1932, p. 38–48) that the green phyllite shows retrograde metamorphism in this belt (staurolite altering to muscovite and garnet to chlorite; see also Zen, 1969b), and he became convinced that it is separated from the black phyllite below and to the west by a thrust fault. More recently, Zen and Ratcliffe (1966) have shown that the contact is marked in many places by slivers of carbonate rock and is undoubtedly tectonic, and they interpret it as the base of the Taconic klippe.

Recently published reports on this part of the Taconic region that have rejected the allochthonous theory for the Taconic slate mass have explained it instead by a combination of facies changes and unconformities (Bucher, 1957); the difficulties of this hypothesis have been discussed above (p. 80). An allochthonous explanation also has its difficulties, however, at least in the present state of knowledge. The boundary between what is allochthonous and what autochthonous is not everywhere obvious, especially where Emmon's line breaks down, and the multiplicity of "lines" in this area is a serious drawback to the theory of a single orthodox thrust sheet, at least. Furthermore, the possible source area lies even farther away from the final resting place than in the central part of the Taconic region; from the Connecticut portion of the Berkshire Highlands, the nearest place were a source area seems to be available, to the westernmost body of Taconic Cambrian rocks near the Hudson River is over 50 kilometers (over 30 miles). Thinking of the allochthonous slate not as a coherent thrust sheet but as a group of sliding masses alleviates a bit the difficulties about the boundary and the multiple "lines" but not the one about the distance of travel, for almost the whole distance would have been depositional basin at the time of the postulated sliding.

The southern limit of the Taconic slate mass is not as clear as its abrupt northern termination near Sudbury in the Middlebury synclinorium. Cambrian fossils are last recorded near Hudson, and continuous masses of the accompanying rock types in northwestern Dutchess County west of Stissing Mountain, and Zen (1967) has drawn the limit of the allochthonous mass here. Blocks of "Taconic" rock types of various sizes, up to a kilometer or two (a mile or so) across, can be found still farther south, however, as far as the *west* bank of the Hudson River at Newburgh, New York.

Southwest from Newburgh, the belt of Middle

Ordovician shale northwest of the Highlands shows no Taconic-type rocks or fossils for some 160 kilometers (100 miles) across New Jersey and into Pennsylvania, but both do appear *south* of the Highlands in a shale outlier at Jutland, New Jersey, 120 kilometers (75 miles) from New-burgh. Here Lower Ordovician graptolites occur associated with "Taconic" rock types in shale overlying Middle Ordovician limestone, itself resting disconformably on a Lower Ordovician and older carbonate sequence (Harry N. Dodge, Robert B. Neuman, and William B. N. Berry, personal communications; also observations on a field trip conducted by Dodge and Neuman in 1964). Actually, the rocks at Jutland are roughly on strike with the last Taconic-type rocks at New-burgh, owing to the discrepancy between the over-all trend of the Highlands and the trends of the individual blocks (p. 70).

In Pennsylvania, on the other hand, both rocks and fossils of Taconic type reappear in the Ordo-vician shale belt north of the Highlands trend, in the core of the Lebanon Valley synclinorium. Such rocks are widespread in this belt for at least 110 kilo-meters (70 miles) along strike, from the Sus-quehanna River at Harrisburg more than halfway east to the Delaware; they include chert, lime-breccia and graded lime-sandstone, red shale, coarse sandstone and graywacke, and volcanics, the last especially around Jonestown, 9 kilo-meters (6 miles) northwest of Lebanon, and in at least some areas they occur in a Taconic-type stratigraphic order that includes rock types characteristic of the Upper Cambrian part of the typical Taconic sequence as well as those charac-teristic of the Ordovician part. Furthermore, the boulder breccia ("Wildflysch-type" conglomerate) has now been found in the region (Alterman, 1969). Lower Ordovician graptolites have been found in these rocks only in the vicinity of Harris-burg (Stose, 1930, p. 640—641; Platt, p. 9—16, *in* Carswell, Hollowell, and Platt, 1968, and personal communication). Yet upper Middle Ordovician faunas are known here and there from the Hudson to the Susquehanna and, as mentioned above (p. 68), lower Upper Ordovician faunas are present in Pennsylvania.

If our understanding of the faunas is correct, the older Ordovician faunas in these areas are as anomalous as the Cambrian and Lower Ordovi-cian faunas in the Taconic slates east of the Hudson, and naturally the same solutions can be proposed. One can ignore the fossils or postulate that they persisted after the change from limestone to shale deposition in the Middle Ordovician; this solution has probably been the commonest, for in the absence of Cambrian fossils the dilemma has not been so apparent as in the Taconic region. One can postulate a rapid facies change or balancing unconformities, for which no evidence is visible except the distribution of graptolites. Or one can suppose that the shale containing the anomalous faunas was thrust or slid into place from some un-disclosed source area to the southeast, now con-veniently hidden under the Triassic basin or obscured by metamorphism. Kay (1941) was apparently the first to see the acuteness of the dilemma and also the first to apply the klippe solution in Pennsylvania; later Stose (1946) at-tempted to draw the boundaries of the klippe, but his boundaries were not based on sufficient field mapping and they appear to exclude at least some of the slate with anomalous fossils, so that they are not consistent with the hypothesis. Platt's mapping suggests on the other hand that the Taconic-type rocks do not form a single large mass but are scattered as exotic blocks up to 8 kilo-meters (5 miles) long in the autochthonous Middle Ordovician shale and graywacke. If one accepts an allochthonous hypothesis for the slate masses in the main Taconic area in eastern New York and vicinity, therefore, one is forced to conclude that a fragment of a "Taconic" slide mass is preserved at Jutland and a large group of such masses in Pennsylvania, extending as far west as the Sus-quehanna River and probably including Cambrian as well as Ordovician strata.

The strike in the Taconic region averages about N10°E; only near the south end does it swing more to the northeast, paralleling the recess outlined by the post-Devonian folds at Kingston just to the west (the same recess is even more evident in the trends of the Precambrian anticlinoria to the east; see Chapter 5, p. 93). On almost any theory, the presence of the great mass of slate suggests a major depression in the region, south of the cul-mination in the Champlain Valley; how far south or southwest it reaches is much less clear, but probably it extends at least past the axis of the recess.

The evidence southwest of Albany and at Becraft Mountain seems to show unequivocally that strong deformation and at least some low-grade metamorphism of the Taconic rocks took place between the deposition of the upper Middle Ordovician and Upper Silurian strata, and the continuity of the deformation southwestward to eastern Pennsylvania suggests that it reached its climax during the late Ordovician; the very name Taconic orogeny reflects this line of reason-ing. Some have suggested that the main deforma-tion took place during Middle Ordovician time, when the unconformity beneath the Middle Ordovician strata was formed and the older rocks deformed and bevelled, but in general the rocks above and below were later folded together and metamorphosed alike, as in the Middlebury synclinorium; the Middle Ordovician movement, though real, was apparently less than that in the Late Ordovician, at least in the region here considered. Others have suggested that the major deformation was later—during or at the end of the Silurian—but there seems no reason to doubt that the unconformity under the Devonian and highest Silurian rocks of Becraft Mountain, where it overlaps what appears to be Emmons' line, is the same as the unconformity that can be traced southwestward across New Jersey into Pennsylvania, where it underlies Lower Silurian and perhaps upper Upper Ordovician strata. How far to the east the Taconic deformation extended is not known; in that direction later deformation and metamorphism are certainly present and largely obscure evidence of Ordovician orogeny.

It seems reasonable to suppose, however, that where retrogressive metamorphism has been observed in the southeastern Taconic region, the earlier high-grade metamorphism was Taconic and only the later Acadian; this interpretation would jibe with Ordovician radiometric ages in this area (Long, 1962) and also south of the Hudson Highlands (p. 96).

CHAPTER 5

New England (except Maine)

I turn now from the mostly unmetamorphosed sedimentary rocks of the western Appalachian provinces to the metamorphic and plutonic rocks of the eastern provinces, beginning in central New England, because there it is possible to make a tectonic cross section whose broad outlines are reasonably clear (e.g., Billings and others, 1952), though to be sure many major problems remain unsolved. At the west, Precambrian gneiss appears from under the Paleozoic rocks along the east side of the Valley and Ridge province, and in the nineteenth century it was therefore natural to regard all or most of the high-grade metamorphic rocks farther east as also Precambrian; this view is still expressed on the Geologic Map of the United States dated 1932. Several fossil localities were found in central New England in the nineteenth century, however, especially near the Connecticut River, and already at the end of that century Emerson (1898, 1917) called most of the rocks in Massachusetts Paleozoic. The careful work of Marland Billings and his students and colleagues, beginning from the known fossil localities and working outward, has entirely confirmed this view, and it is now clear that Precambrian rocks are exposed in New England only in certain restricted anticlinorial belts, the most important of which is precisely the one just east of the Valley and Ridge province.

Green Mountains and Related Anticlinoria along the West Side of New England

The structural front that forms the eastern boundary of the Valley and Ridge province in the Champlain Valley is at once the east flank of the Middlebury, Hinesburg, and St. Albans synclinoria and the west flank of the major anticlinorium underlying the Green Mountains, which form the orographic backbone of the state of Vermont and indeed have given their name to it. As suggested in Chapter 1 (p. 7), these mountains and this anticlinorium are a link in a chain that can be traced more or less continuously from the northern Long Range of northwestern Newfoundland to the south end of the Blue Ridge in Georgia; likewise the structural front is entirely comparable to the structural front that in the Central and Southern Appalachians separates the Valley and Ridge from the Blue Ridge (the third front encountered in central Pennsylvania; Chapter 3, p. 33). Precambrian basement is exposed along the Green Mountains anticlinorium for 150 kilometers (95 miles) in central and southern Vermont, from northeast of Middlebury to just south of the Massachusetts border. Recent studies in this basement (e.g., Brace, 1953; Skehan, 1961; others unpublished) show that the largest part of it consists of high-grade metamorphic rocks, with many similarities to the Precambrian rocks of the Adirondacks, and radiometry confirms the correlation (Faul and others, 1963, p. 3). The structural trends in the basement are markedly discordant to the trend of the anticlinorium itself, except near the margin where they were evidently reoriented during the formation of the anticlinorium; additional unequivocal evidence of the redeformation is provided by pervasive retrogressive metamorphism of the high-grade rocks (epidotization of plagioclase, chloritization of biotite and garnet). At a point 16 kilometers (10 miles) southeast of Rutland a small stock of alkaline rocks cuts the basement rocks; it appears to be the westernmost representative of the Mesozoic White Mountain plutonic series of New Hampshire, discussed below (p. 106), and hence quite irrelevant to the anticlinorium.

The basement rocks are unconformably overlain and areally surrounded by a Paleozoic metasedimentary cover, beginning with clastic, commonly somewhat conglomeratic, strata. On the west flank of the anticlinorium, these strata are precisely the basal Cambrian clastic sequence at the base of the Paleozoic carbonate sequence of the Middlebury synclinorium and the Taconic region (Chapter 4, p. 74, 77). The basal sequence apparently thickens steadily northward along the west side of the anticlinorium, and to the north, where the Precambrian basement plunges under, it must be several kilometers (1 to 2 miles) thick; from here northward it forms a wide belt along the axis of the anticlinorium (Camels Hump and Oak Hill groups), extending to the international border and for some tens of kilometers (tens of miles) beyond (Cady, 1960). On both sides of the border, mafic volcanic rocks (Tibbit Hill volcanics) appear along the axis, lying conformably beneath or within the clastic strata. (The complex history of deformation in this region has been investigated especially in southern Quebec and is discussed below, p. 119–120). On the east flank of the anticlinorium, on the other hand, the basal clastic strata form the base of an immensely thick, mainly clastic but in part volcanic sequence (described in the next section of this chapter); beds well up in this sequence are reasonably well dated as Middle Ordovician. The basal clastic beds are everywhere metamorphosed, mainly to the biotite grade (garnet appears on the east side, especially to the south); the volcanic rocks at the Canadian border are in the greenschist facies.

Within the Paleozoic strata in northern Vermont and southern Quebec, the anticlinorium is double, the two major crests being 4 to 13 kilometers (3 to 8 miles) apart; where it brings up the

Precambrian, however, the double crest cannot be followed continuously. The west flank is locally a simple (generally overturned) monocline, but more commonly there are one or two subsidiary tightly appressed folds (wave length 1 or 2 kilometers—about a mile), and in places, especially in northern Vermont and southernmost Quebec, this flank is broken by thrust faults dipping east, generally at a low angle. Close to Rutland, one such fault (Pine Hill thrust) brings up the basement once again, thrusting it locally over Middle Ordovician slate at the top of the carbonate sequence; the faults farther north reduplicate the sedimentary cover, especially its lower part. The east flank is apparently everywhere tightly folded on a relatively small scale, but only locally are there larger folds (wave length of 3 kilometers—2 miles), and faults are rare or absent.

Southward the Green Mountains anticlinorium plunges abruptly just inside the state of Massachusetts, and along its strike lies the easternmost synclinorium (Greylock slice) of the Taconic phyllites or schists, but only 8 kilometers (5 miles) en echelon to the southeast appears the comparable anticlinorium of the Berkshire Highlands. Although its limits are still imperfectly known, especially around the southern end in Connecticut, the Precambrian basement is exposed for about 100 kilometers (60 miles) along the axis of this anticlinorium, widening generally southward to a maximum of about 25 kilometers (15 miles) near the state line; it consists of a varied series of high-grade metamorphic rocks much like the basement in the Green Mountains. The cover on the west is the normal Cambrian and Ordovician carbonate sequence of the Taconic region, here with a rather thin basal clastic unit (Dalton and Cheshire formations), but the west side of the anticlinorium is very irregular and presents no continuous structural front; instead the section is completely overturned in several areas, so that basement rocks now overlie Paleozoic strata, partly in thrust relation (Hoosac nappe of Christensen, 1963; Norton, 1969; Ratcliffe, ms. 1965; 1969a). On the east side, the clastic-volcanic sequence from the east side of the Green Mountains continues south, here in the amphibolite facies with garnet and, to the south, staurolite. These two contrasting Paleozoic facies are very near together, if not in contact, in the saddle between the north end of the Berkshire Highlands and the south end of the Green Mountains. Several theories have been proposed to explain this sharp contrast: a very rapid facies change (Pumpelly, Wolff, and Dale, 1894, p. 9–19; Herz, 1961); an unconformity on which the entire clastic-volcanic sequence overlies the western carbonate sequence, or at least its Lower Ordovician and older strata (Thompson *in* Billings and others, 1952, p. 18); a major thrust fault or faults bringing originally distant facies together, the thrusting being related to the emplacement of the Taconic klippe (Prindle and Knopf, p. 293–298 and Fig. 2; Zen, 1967, p. 58–62). Quite possibly facies change, unconformity, and fault are all present, but the base of the clastic-volcanic sequence is almost certainly Cambrian and hence cannot overlie the carbonate sequence unconformably. Probably the major structure is a thrust fault or faults (Hoosic fault of Herz, 1961; Hoosac fault of Skehan, 1961, Fig. 30); as suggested by Zen (1967, p. 60; see also Chapter 4, p. 86), a remnant of the Taconic sequence may be present in a thrust slice between the other two sequences.

A gap about 40 kilometers (25 miles) wide separates the south end of the Berkshire Highlands from the east end of the Hudson Highlands. As shown above (p. 70), the Hudson Highlands and their western continuation across New Jersey into Pennsylvania are clearly an anticlinorium of Precambrian rocks, mainly gneiss of various sorts, including considerable granite and much metasedimentary rock, probably in large part overturned over the Paleozoic rocks to the northwest and also broken by and in part at least uplifted along a series of relatively steep, mainly southeast-dipping reverse and normal faults, which, however, trend at an angle to the general trend of the Highlands anticlinorium (the southeast border west of the Hudson is formed by normal faults that bound the adjacent Triassic basin).

The east end of the Hudson Highlands and the south end of the Berkshire Highlands trend at a considerable angle to the general regional strike and almost at right angles to each other, so that the gap between them is wedge-shaped, flaring to the northwest. Within the gap are several bodies of high-grade gneiss and schist of various sizes, for example Stissing Mountain and the Housatonic Highlands. In the northwest part of the gap, the rock succession is that of the southern part of the Taconic region; unconformably above the Precambrian basement gneiss and schist comes a thin unit of pure quartzite (Poughquag quartzite, Lower Cambrian), then a thick and readily subdivisible sequence of carbonate rocks (Wappinger or Stockbridge limestone, Lower Cambrian to Middle Ordovician), and finally a great mass of argillaceous rock with some more quartzose zones ("Hudson River" terrain). Whether the last is *stratigraphically* in sequence, in whole or in part, above the carbonate rocks is precisely the Taconic problem discussed in the last chapter; for the present discussion, however, the question can be bypassed. In any case, these argillaceous rocks exhibit a Barrovian progression of metamorphic grades (Balk, 1936; Barth, 1936) from barely altered slate along the Hudson River to sillimanite schist and gneiss with bodies of pegmatite and granitoid gneiss along the Housatonic River. The isograds strike about N25°E across the gap, at an angle to the trends of both the Hudson and Berkshire Highlands but roughly parallel to the broader regional trend.

Unfortunately, as the metamorphism rises, the rock sequence, and with it our evidence for even the gross structure, becomes difficult to decipher. Around Stissing Mountain and along the northwest front of the Hudson Highlands near and west of the Hudson, the high-grade Precambrian gneiss and schist contrast strongly with the unconformably overlying lower-grade Paleozoic metasedimentary rocks, even where faulting has seriously disturbed the relations. But already in places along the northwest side of the Housatonic Highlands, in the throat of the gap, deformation and metamorphism have proceeded far enough to wipe out the evidence for the unconformity (Balk, 1936, p. 732–736), and farther east and south the schist and gneiss at the top of the sequence converge petrographically with those at the bottom. Where first quartzite and then marble is found beside a given gneiss body, the presumption is that the gneiss is Precambrian, but otherwise no unequivocal criteria remain, for even along the border of known Precambrian gneiss bodies, the carbonate rocks and especially the quartzite may fail, cut out by faulting, unconformity, or facies change. For several gneiss masses in this area, it simply is not known whether they are anticlinal or synclinal, and uncertainty similarly clouds the borders of the Berkshire and Hudson Highlands on either side of the gap. In particular, outcrops of the pure basal quartzite, probably the most useful structural clue in the area, become increasingly rare to the southeast. Perhaps this is merely because the quartzite is especially prone to be eliminated tectonically, but perhaps there are stratigraphic changes as well. Both to the north in Vermont and to the southwest in Pennsylvania (beyond the Triassic basin that interrupts the continuity of the Paleozoic rocks), the rocks next above the Precambrian basement grade eastward or southeastward from a relatively thin unit of pure quartzite into a thick sequence of very heterogeneous clastic rocks (the basal Cambrian clastic sequence already mentioned), in which pure quartzite is present only near the summit. A similar change may well take place here also; in the sillimanite grade of metamorphism, such a sequence would likewise converge with the basement gneiss and the superjacent argillaceous rocks.

On the east side of the Hudson south of the Hudson Highlands—in Westchester County, New York, and southward into New York City—one finds again an assemblage of rocks much like the most highly metamorphosed rocks in the gap and probably continuous with them around the east end of the Hudson Highlands (Clarke, 1958). A threefold sequence (New York City group) is generally recognized (Prucha, 1956): from below upward, banded gneiss ranging from granitoid gneiss to amphibolite (Fordham gneiss), marble (Inwood marble), and rather massive sillimanite schist and gneiss (Manhattan schist) with some bodies of granitic gneiss; a quartzite (Lowerre quartzite) occurs in places between the banded gneiss and the marble. In addition to the generally concordant granitic and granitoid gneisses, the sequence is intruded by a late discordant stock of noritic rocks (Cortlandt complex) in northwestern Westchester County (Balk, 1927; Shand, 1942; smaller bodies of similar rock are known to the northeast as far as west-central Connecticut).

Although some observers have considered this a conformable sequence unique to the area (either entirely Precambrian or entirely Paleozoic), others (beginning with Mather—1843, p. 464) have correlated it with the Precambrian and overlying Lower Paleozoic rocks north of the Highlands, and this point of view has now been virtually proved by the work of Hall (1968a; 1968b) and Ratcliffe (1968a; Ratcliffe and Knowles, 1969). Hall has recognized within the marble unit the full stratigraphy of the carbonate sequence in the eastern Taconic region (marble belt of Vermont and Massachusetts) and has demonstrated angular unconformities at the base of the marble (beneath the quartzite where it is present) and close to its top, beneath a discontinuous unit of blue limestone or marble from which Ratcliffe and Knowles obtained probably Middle Ordovician fossils; clearly these unconformities are the same as those above the Precambrian basement and beneath the Middle Ordovician in the carbonate sequence of the Taconic region. Furthermore, Hall and Ratcliffe suggest that a persistent change in the uppermost unit from graphitic schist below to quartzose schostose gneiss above is the base of the Taconic sequence, which here as in the Taconic region would be allochthonous; if so, the possibly Taconic rocks would form a link between the slid masses in the southern end of the Taconic region and those at Jutland, New Jersey, and in Pennsylvania (Chapter 4, p. 89), although the high degree of metamorphism prevents recognition of the characteristic Taconic rock types and stratigraphy.

In southern Westchester County and New York City, the sequence described above outlines several parallel steep isoclinal folds with variable plunges; the present wave length ranges from 2 to 8 kilometers (1 to 5 miles) (there are also, of course, innumerable folds of much smaller size). Moreover, some of these folds were themselves later folded into a large steep anticline (Scotford, 1956; Hall, 1968a), the northeast end of which plunges northeast past the east end of the Hudson Highlands, whose southeast boundary is here a fairly steep north- or northwest-dipping reverse fault (Fluhr, 1950, p. 182; Clarke, 1958, p. 42—44; Prucha, Scotford, and Sneider, 1968, p. 20—21). The whole deformation (save for the reverse fault, which may be late) was very plastic; schistosity and foliation are everywhere parallel to the contacts of the rock units and swing smoothly around the later anticline, yet recrystallization was clearly syn- or post-tectonic.

The rather heterogeneous assemblage of marble, schist, and gneiss that fills the gap northeast of the Hudson Highlands and extends southward to New York City appears to give way eastward abruptly to another assemblage, virtually free of marble and characterized by more quartzitic schist (Hartland schist; Hutchinson River group). The grade of metamorphism is perhaps a bit lower (abundant garnet, staurolite, and kyanite, but sillimanite only along the western border and to the south near Long Island Sound); bodies of granite, granite-gneiss, and dioritic gneiss abound. The contrast between the two assemblages has been particularly emphasized by workers in west-central Connecticut (Agar, 1927, p. 16 ff.; Cameron, 1951, p. 8—11; Gates, 1952, p. 20—21), and the contact between them there is presumably an important tectonic line (perhaps a steep west-dipping reverse fault or zone of reverse movement; it has been informally called "Cameron's line" by workers in the region). Much of the course of the contact is not yet well known, however; in places it appears to follow the easternmost major marble belt, but elsewhere it must lie within the schists. In a gross way, the rocks east of the line seem to correspond to the sequence east of the Berkshire Highlands and the Green Mountains, but their stratigraphy and correlation are still in debate; the matter is further discussed in the next section.

Taken as a whole, the anticlinoria described in this section form a somewhat sinuous belt along the entire west side of New England and indeed for many kilometers (miles) beyond both northeast and southwest, a belt that contrasts in several ways with the Valley and Ridge province (including the Taconic region) to the west. To the north, the boundary between is a well marked though not entirely continuous structural front, locally but by no means universally broken by thrust faults, but to the south, the anticlinoria are overturned and pushed several kilometers (miles) westward until they overlie the eastern part of the Valley and Ridge belt, as in Pennsylvania and New York (see also Chapter 4, p. 70); this superposition is confirmed by geophysical data (Griscom and Bromery, 1968, p. 433). To the east in the anticlinoria, the rocks exposed are mostly the Precambrian basement or the overlying heterogeneous basal clastic unit, whereas to the west these rocks are nowhere visible and seem to have taken no part in the folding and faulting that affected the higher Paleozoic sedimentary rocks (unless the bottom of the Taconic sequence, including the Rensselaer graywacke, corresponds to part of the basal clastic unit), and they only reappear in the Adirondacks, entirely beyond the belt of Appalachian deformation. The uplift of the basement represented by the structural front can hardly be less than 3 kilometers (2 miles) and is probably nearer 10 (6), especially in the middle part of the Taconic region, for on the one hand an unknown thickness of basement has been eroded from parts of the anticlinorial crests, and on the other the Taconic rocks just to the west, probably isoclinally folded, lie in synclinoria overlying the "normal" Paleozoic carbonate sequence, itself on the order of 2 kilometers (over a mile) thick. Moreover, the Green Mountains anticlinorium follows a pronounced linear gravity high, or else the gradient between that high and a linear low to the west, strongly suggesting a major uplift of lower layers of the crust or even of the mantle beneath it (Diment, 1968, p. 407–408). Metamorphism, which is incipient in the Valley and Ridge province (slaty cleavage almost throughout the belt here, formation of new sericite and chlorite and locally of biotite to the east), increases to the east across the various anticlinoria, reaching the garnet grade or locally even the sillimanite grade on their east flanks.

Much the most conspicuous irregularity in the belt of anticlinoria is the angular recess and gap between the east end of the Hudson Highlands, trending about N60°E, and the south end of the Berkshire Highlands, trending about S5°E. Here the Paleozoic rocks penetrate entirely across the belt, and the Precambrian basement reaches the surface only in patches. The anticlinorial axes revert to more normal Appalachian trends on each side of the gap — on the south side about at the Hudson River, on the north side at the south end of the Green Mountains on the Massachusetts-Vermont line. Between these two points one finds no distinct structural front like that present to the north, but the N25°E line connecting them passes through Stissing Mountain, the outermost fragment of Precambrian in the gap, and moveover it is roughly parallel both to the larger structural trends in the Paleozoic rocks of the southern Taconic region and to the isograds. Yet the angle made by the anticlinorial axes here seems to be reflected in the shallower angle made by the trends of folding in the Silurian and Devonian rocks at Kingston, New York. Furthermore, the gap lies in the center of an area where instead of a thick heterogeneous basal clastic unit, as to the north in Vermont and to the southwest in southeastern Pennsylvania, a thin quartzite forms the base of the Paleozoic column, as though the area had been positive from the beginning of Paleozoic time.

North and southwest of the gap, the trends of the Highlands anticlinoria swing more gradually. To the southwest, beyond offsets caused by the slightly diagonal high-angle faults that break the Hudson and New Jersey Highlands, they parallel fairly closely the Blue Mountain front, which lies to the northwest across the Great Valley. Thus they show a minor recess south of the Delaware Water Gap and would probably outline a pronounced salient south of Harrisburg, if anticlinoria and structural front were not cut off diagonally by normal faults bounding the Triassic basin to the southeast and south. Where Precambrian rocks appear beyond, at the north tip of the Blue Ridge province in south-central Pennsylvania, they are very different; as noted above (p. 69–70), they may lie on the opposite side of the Lebanon Valley synclinorium from those in the Highlands anticlinoria.

To the north of the gap, the general strike of the anticlinoria appears more independent and outlines two salients and an intervening shallow recess. About N5°W across Massachusetts, it swings to N20°E in southern Vermont, to N15°W in central Vermont, and then in a broad arc to about N30°E at the international boundary. The recess lies opposite the southern part of the Adirondack Mountains and appears at first sight related to them, but the salient to the north shows no such influence and presses to within 25 kilometers (15 miles) of their Precambrian core, reducing the Valley and Ridge province proper to about 15 kilometers (10 miles) in width. In a rough way the basement surface along the crest of the anticlinoria seems to be higher near the angular gap and to fall off irregularly to the north and perhaps also to the southwest, but this may only reflect the increasing thickness of the basal clastic unit away from the gap, for the absence of exposures of that unit in the Valley and Ridge province suggests that, though stratigraphically a part of the cover, it may have acted tectonically as part of the basement.

If one accepts the theory that folding and faulting in the Valley and Ridge province (and the Taconic region) are entirely cover tectonics, the great belt of anticlinoria to the east is readily explained as the western margin of true basement deformation. It is then no coincidence that the western limit of metamorphism and the isograds to the east (at least up to the garnet isograd) are in general parallel to the belt, locally even following its sinuosities (see Plate 3, p. 6, in Billings and others, 1952, or metamorphic map on state geologic map of Vermont, Doll and others, 1961), for precisely the same conditions of temperature and pressure that produced the metamorphism made it possible for the basement to deform. Where the belt is broken by the angular gap, the isograds continue across the gap, but even here the westernmost Precambrian outlier lies within the zone of sericite phyllite. To the west, where metamorphism was weak or absent, the basement was relatively rigid and took no part in the deformation. Along the west side of the anticlinoria, where the metamorphism was epizonal, the basement was less rigid and it buckled upward 5 kilometers (3 miles) or more and westward an unknown amount, though it broke in many places along steeper or flatter reverse faults; precisely this upward and westward movement may have caused the deformation in the Paleozoic cover to the west. Along the east side of the anticlinoria (and in the gap), where the metamorphism was mesozonal, the basement was quite plastic and was molded along with the cover into large isoclinal folds; indeed the distinction between cover and basement was there mechanically meaningless, and locally it is difficult even to locate the boundary, petrographically or stratigraphically.

There is clear evidence in the retrogressive metamorphism of the Precambrian basement of the anticlinoria that there have been at least two major orogenies in the area—one Precambrian and the other Paleozoic. Only the latter was specifically Appalachian because confined to the Appalachian belt, but its age is in debate. As in the folded and faulted belt next to the west in the Champlain Valley, one can argue for either a Taconic or an Acadian orogeny; from the evidence in the Hudson Valley it is probably that both occurred. The angular unconformity beneath the Middle Ordovician on the west side of the anticlinoria in both Vermont and Massachusetts suggests that those anticlinoria had already begun to rise at that time; if so, the argument in the preceding paragraph would imply that metamorphism also had already begun there. Furthermore, radiometry suggests that sillimanite was produced in the schists south of the Hudson Highlands and these were then cut by the Cortlandt norite complex before the end of the Ordovician, that is, during the Taconic orogeny (Long and Kulp, 1962, p. 982; Ratcliffe, 1968b). On the other hand, kyanite-grade metamorphism in the Connecticut Valley synclinorium to the east affects Silurian and Devonian rocks and must be Acadian, at the earliest. The boundary between the two metamorphisms is not clear, but evidence suggests that the metamorphism in and west of the anticlinorial belt is mainly Taconic, though with some Acadian retrogression (Albee, 1968, p. 329–331; Harper, 1968; see also above, p. 88, 90), as far as the east flank of the anticlinoria, where in places the grade falls off somewhat, and is mainly Acadian only beyond. Thus Osberg (1952, p. 96 ff.) found that in central Vermont distinctly later minor folds have been superposed on folds congruent with the main Green Mountains anticlinorium, but only on its east flank, and Rosenfeld (1968, p. 196) reports that, a little farther south, rotated garnets on the same flank record two periods of growth, probably with a long interruption between.

Connecticut Valley Synclinorium

From the east edge of the Precambrian basement in the core of the Green Mountains anticlinorium in Vermont, one proceeds eastward across a wide belt of mesozonal metamorphic rocks, the foliation of which dips steadily eastward or passes through the vertical to dip steeply westward. Although small isoclinal folds abound, detailed mapping of the reasonably distinct stratigraphic units present shows that the sequence is grossly homoclinal, the units succeeding each other in regular order eastward through a belt that, in part of the area at least, is 25 to 40 kilometers (15 to 25 miles) wide. In east-central Vermont, White and Jahns (1950, p. 190–191) calculated an apparent thickness for the sequence of 30 kilometers (19 miles), which they considered to be less than twice the original thickness; in southeastern Vermont, Thompson (Billings and others, 1952, p. 17–18, 39–41) calculated about 9 kilometers (6 miles) but reported that in certain structural positions the thickness is further reduced, presumably tectonically. As the small isoclinal folds prove tectonic thickening, whereas stretched pebbles in conglomerates (Brace, 1955) prove tectonic thinning, the original stratigraphic thickness is unrecoverable, but it must obviously have been large.

The sequence falls into two main parts, separated by an unconformity or disconformity of major importance. The lower two-thirds is largely mica schist and mica quartzite; lenses of greenstone schist or amphibolite are common throughout, though few are traceable for any distance. Carbonate rock is rare and occurs mostly near the base of the sequence. At the base lenses of feldspathic conglomerate rest unconformably upon the Precambrian basement, and a lens high in this part of the sequence in northern Vermont (Umbrella Hill conglomerate; Cady, Albee, and Chidester, 1963, p. B25—B27) records a lesser unconformity. The uppermost unit in this part of the sequence, a particularly heterogeneous unit (Cram Hill formation) characterized, however, by graphitic pyritic or pyrrhotitic schist (sooty but rusty-weathering) can be traced northward along strike to Magog, Quebec, where it is dated by graptolites as Middle Ordovician (Berry, 1962a). The age of the strata below is less certain, but according to recent work (Osberg, 1956; 1969, p. 695; Cady, 1960), the lower part can be traced around the north-plunging end of the Green Mountains anticlinorium in Quebec into Cambrian rocks on the west flank. In any case, this part of the sequence represents an immense thickness of clastic sediments interspersed with volcanics, deposited during the Early Paleozoic east of the carbonate sequence of the Champlain Valley and the Taconic region, which is also fairly thick, and presumably also east of the Taconic sequence, which is apparently thinner than either of the others but whose composition can be thought of as intermediate between them (see paleogeographic interpretation of the three sequences, p. 81).

The upper third of the sequence (St. Francis group—name from southern Quebec) begins with a unit containing a distinctive quartz conglomerate but also lenses of marble, schist, and metavolcanic rocks (Shaw Mountain formation), but the rest consists of dark gray graphitic phyllite, either alone or, more commonly, interstratified with quartzose and micaceous recrystallized limestone, or with fine-grained generally laminated mica quartzite (originally shaly siltstone), or with both. The limestone and mica quartzite dominate in different units in the phyllite sequence, the limestone mainly to the west, the quartzite to the east; whether the limestone-phyllite (Waits River formation) or the quartzite-phyllite (Gile Mountain formation) unit is stratigraphically the higher has been in debate (see below, p. 98—99). Volcanic rocks are relatively rare, but one persistent zone in the eastern part of the outcrop belt, roughly at the contact between limestone and quartzite there, has proved very useful (Standing Pond amphibolite).

The age of these upper strata was long debated, opinions being divided between correlation with fossiliferous Silurian and Lower Devonian strata in western New Hampshire and in southern Quebec and correlation with presumably Ordovician strata beneath, but recent fossil discoveries have proved the former correlation. Accordingly, the sequence east of the Green Mountains extends from Lower Cambrian to Lower Devonian, with one unconformity between Ordovician and Silurian and probably others in the Ordovician below.

The homocline that exhibits this stratigraphic sequence forms the relatively simple west flank, or better the western part of the west flank, of the Connecticut Valley synclinorium, and appears to be disturbed only here and there by folds of more than a few tens of meters (a few tens of feet) wave length; faults are virtually unknown. All the folds here, whether large or small, are tightly appressed or isoclinal and show the standard relation of minor folds to larger master folds (the master folds here being the Green Mountains anticlinorium and the Connecticut Valley synclinorium); despite the metamorphism, the shear sense recorded by the minor folds is that to be expected in ordinary concentric (parallel) folding of the master folds—the higher beds have moved toward the anticlinorial axis relative to the lower beds.

The trough of the synclinorium, on the other hand, is very complex. Two outstanding pieces of work have been done here, that by White and Jahns (1950) and that by Thompson and Rosenfeld (unfortunately mostly unpublished, but see Thompson and Rosenfeld, 1951; Billings and others, 1952, p. 20, 21; Doll and others, 1961, esp. cross section E-E'; Rosenfeld, 1968). In the trough, apparently a little to the west of its deepest part and encroaching on the west flank, is a series of remarkable domes, those to the south exposing cores of possibly Precambrian gneiss surrounded by the entire synclinorial sequence, complete but greatly thinned, those to the north not exposing rocks below the extremely plastic limestone-phyllite mixture in the upper third of the sequence.

White and Jahns (1950, p. 210—213) studied particularly the Strafford dome in east-central Vermont and the area to the north; this dome is the northernmost complete dome in the synclinorium and exposes only the upper third of the stratigraphic sequence. Using the persistent volcanic layer (Standing Pond amphibolite) mentioned above, they showed that the rocks had already been isoclinally folded, with a wave length of perhaps 1 kilometer ($\frac{1}{2}$ mile), before they were domed. Furthermore, they found means for distinguishing between minor isoclinal folds formed during two periods of folding (which were not necessarily far apart in time). They interpreted the folds of the earlier period as ordinary parasitic folds showing the normal shear sense for the west flank of a synclinorium, the folds of the later period (including the domed isoclinal folds) as drag folds produced by the upwelling of the plastic limestone-phyllite unit from beneath the quartzite-phyllite unit to form the dome, their shear sense being reversed relative to that of the earlier folds on the east limb of the dome but not on the west.

Later work in this part of Vermont has fully confirmed the existence of the two periods of folding, but the dome itself must be differently interpreted. Gravity surveys (Bean, 1953) have shown that the rocks deep in the core of the Strafford dome are not heavy (limestone and phyllite) but light (gneiss), and hence that this dome differs from its neighbors to the south only in depth of erosion. Thus the primary upwelling that caused the dome was not in the limestone-phyllite unit but in gneiss beneath and may even have been produced by the density difference between the gneiss and the overlying sediments. That the gneiss did well up is virtually proved by the observations of Thompson and Rosenfeld around the Chester dome in southeastern Vermont, where the isoclinal folds of the second period, some of them with wave lengths and amplitudes measured in kilometers (miles), swing completely around the north end of the dome from one limb to the other, like the overhang of a mushroom or the limbs of a spruce tree (see also Skehan, 1961, p. 110 ff., for similar structure on domes farther southwest in Vermont). In these folds younger rocks appear in the cores of apparent anticlines (antiforms) and older in the cores of apparent synclines (synforms), so that the folds of this second period are exactly opposite to the older "normal" minor folds, whether their shear sense is the same or not. Finally, by detailed microscopic study, Rosenfeld (1968) has shown that the snowball garnets common in the rocks around the Chester dome record in sequence the shear senses of the different periods of folding, confirming the upwelling of the gneiss in the later period but suggesting that in the earlier period the plastic limestone-phyllite mixture was squeezed out westward between underlying and overlying strata (so

that only in the underlying strata is the shear sense "normal"); Rosenfeld considered that all these strata were then in normal stratigraphic order, only later being upended and folded during the rise of the domes. The garnets also prove that metamorphic recrystallization was going on all during deformation (of both periods), and they provide a minimum measure of the amount of shearing (the maximum simple shear recorded was over 20 for the first period, about $3\frac{1}{2}$ for the second; Rosenfeld, 1968, p. 192).

As noted above, the stratigraphic order of the highest units in the synclinorium has been in debate, for the sequence appears quite different on the two flanks of the synclinorium in Vermont; most explanations have therefore required that a rapid facies change be hidden in the synclinorial core. The standard view has been that the quartzite-phyllite unit (Gile Mountain formation) lies stratigraphically above the limestone-phyllite unit (Waits River formation), because it does lie structurally above in the Strafford dome and in the core of the Willoughby foliation-anticline, which extends 100 kilometers (60 miles) on to the north-northeast, although admittedly these are second-period folds and the first period had already produced isoclinal folding. Murthy (1957, 1958) reinterpreted the data in terms of two limestone-phyllite units separated by a quartzite-phyllite unit, postulating facies changes along strike at the present land surface in two areas, but the supposed facies changes turned out to be fold closures, one at the north end of the Willoughby foliation-anticline and the other at the south end of a foliation-syncline to the west. Goodwin (1962; 1963, p. 98–101, Pl. 3) and Ern (1963, p. 67, 72–75, Fig. 5; 1964) suggested instead that the quartzite-phyllite unit in the foliation syncline is in the nose of a great (first-period) recumbent fold or nappe* and hence stratigraphically underlies the limestone-phyllite unit. This explanation is entirely consonant with evidence for major first-period recumbent folds elsewhere on the east flank of the synclinorium and especially over the Bronson Hill anticlinorium, the next major tectonic unity to the east (see p. 103–104), and it would also place the axial plane of the underlying recumbent syncline exactly where Rosenfeld's garnets show a reversal in the shear sense of their first-period rotation, where, as Rosenfeld has shown (1968, p. 196–197), two stratigraphic zones containing those garnets (on the two limbs of the proposed syncline) diverge with an angle of about

---

*Goodwin and Ern placed the root of their nappe *within* the east part of the synclinorium, for they considered that the Meetinghouse or Northfield slate lies above the Gile Mountain formation, but if, as is more probable, it lies beneath, at the base of the Silurian section, then the core lies farther east in the pre-Silurian rocks on or even east of the Bronson Hill anticlinorium, as suggested in the text. The concept of a recumbent fold here was first suggested by Eric and Dennis (1958, p. 61), but they rejected it.

10 degrees; it is therefore a very attractive hypothesis, although it cannot yet be considered proved. The requisite "hidden" facies change, from phyllite to quartzite-phyllite beneath the limestone-phyllite unit, has, moreover, been described down the strike in western Massachusetts by Hatch, Schnabel, and Norton (1968, p. 181).

The structure of the east flank of the Connecticut Valley synclinorium, which lies more or less along the Connecticut River between the states of Vermont and New Hampshire, has also been controversial. Under the interpretation that the upper third of the sequence in eastern Vermont is Ordovician, several west-dipping, mainly premetamorphic thrust faults had to be postulated to separate these Ordovician rocks from the Silurian and Lower Devonian strata that surround the domes along the Bronson Hill anticlinorium. Now that the strata in question have been shown by fossils to be Silurian and Devonian, the faults are unnecessary and the east flank of the Connecticut Valley synclinorium merges with the west flank of the Bronson Hill anticlinorium, both being folded into isoclinal recumbent folds, some of them quite large.

At least one of the faults, the Ammonoosuc fault, certainly exists, however; it is postmetamorphic and hence can be traced by the offset of the metamorphic isograds for 150 kilometers (almost 100 miles) with an average strike of N25°E. This fault dips to the west at a fairly low angle (average perhaps 40 degrees) and is well exposed at several places, being locally accompanied by strong silicification of the wall rocks. Now the lower metamorphic grades and in general the younger rocks lie in its west or hanging wall; hence if it is a thrust fault, it brings younger, lower-grade rocks over older, higher-grade rocks, which is possible if it intersected an already folded terrain (which is likely) in which the surfaces of equal metamorphic grade were steep (which is less certain). It is also possible, however, that it is a normal fault; indeed a large, late normal fault with similar attitude (although the dip is steeper) and similar silicification forms the eastern boundary of the Triassic basin in northern Massachusetts and can be traced north into southern New Hampshire to within a few kilometers (miles) of the south end of the Ammonoosuc fault, and other late faults of the same kind are known in the intervening area and may interconnect them. If the Ammonoosuc fault can thus be disposed of as a Triassic normal fault, the only evidence adduced for the others, which in any case would be premetamorphic as they do not displace the isograds, is stratigraphic and can be otherwise interpreted. Indeed no other faults of

appreciable size (other than obviously late faults like those mentioned above) are known anywhere in eastern Vermont, despite a large amount of recent detailed mapping; evidently during their deformation and metamorphism the rocks were too plastic to break.

The metamorphic grade of the rocks on the west flank of the Connecticut Valley synclinorium in central and southern Vermont increases eastward to a maximum along the line of domes; here kyanite is common in rocks of the right composition, and the metavolcanics are amphibolite or plagioclase gneiss. On the far side of the line of domes, the grade drops off rapidly to a narrow but persistent belt (mostly about 3 or 4 kilometers—2 or 3 miles—wide) of chlorite-zone greenschist-facies rocks; this belt lies a bit east of the trough of the synclinorium close to the Connecticut River. Its east margin is the Ammonoosuc fault where that fault is present, and east of the fault the metamorphism jumps back up to the mesozone; even south of the mapped end of the fault, the belt continues narrow and straight until it disappears under the Triassic rocks in northern Massachusetts.

Intrusive rocks of several kinds are present in the synclinorium in eastern Vermont. Many ultramafic bodies, mostly small and now largely serpentine (asbestos and talc are quarried locally), cut the units below the major unconformity on the west flank of the synclinorium (and locally in the domes) but are known nowhere above that unconformity (Chidester, 1968). They are associated especially, though not exclusively, with the mafic metavolcanics (greenstone or amphibolite) and are certainly older than the last major deformation and metamorphism and hence probably all pre-Silurian; indeed, up strike in Quebec similar rocks appear to be pre-Middle Ordovician (Chapter 6, p. 119), and perhaps in Vermont the bodies now found in presumed Middle Ordovician rocks have been reintruded (protruded) after their initial emplacement. A number of bodies of granite (petrographically mainly quartz monzonite and granodiorite) are present, especially in the rocks above the unconformity; they are partly discordant but seem to have been emplaced during or shortly after the climax of deformation and regional metamorphism (sillimanite and cordierite are found in mostly narrow zones around them). They are probably outliers of the mainly syntectonic New Hampshire plutonic series of New Hampshire (see below). Finally, the utterly discordant and disharmonic stock of Ascutney Mountain, formed of alkalic syenite, diorite, and gabbro, and including small amounts of related volcanics, cuts the east side of the Chester dome;

Daly (1903) used it as a type example for his theory of piecemeal magmatic stoping, but it is now considered an outlier of the White Mountain plutonic series (see below), the stocks of which according to Billings (1945) were mostly emplaced by cauldron subsidence.

The Connecticut Valley synclinorium is perhaps best known in central and southern Vermont, but it can be traced far in both directions. In northern Vermont it widens greatly behind the salient in the Green Mountains anticlinorium to the west; the belt of Silurian and Devonian rocks in its core, which is nowhere more than 25 kilometers (15 miles) wide in southern Vermont, widens to 40 kilometers (25 miles) north of the middle of the state and to 60 kilometers (35 miles) at the international border. North of the Strafford dome it contains no more full domes, but the north-plunging Willoughby foliation anticline can be traced nearly to the border (Dennis, 1956, p. 36–37; Hall, 1959, p. 76–77; Goodwin, 1963, p. 18). Granitic rocks become more abundant northward, but the grade of metamorphism remains about the same, except that for about 50 kilometers (35 miles) south of the border andalusite replaces kyanite in rocks of appropriate grade. The general strike, which averages perhaps N15°E in southern Vermont, swings to about N30°E at the border.

To the south, the synclinorium can be followed nearly across Massachusetts; its west flank is well displayed and was long ago carefully described by Emerson (1898; 1917, p. 40–49), but the east flank largely disappears under the Triassic basin along the Connecticut River. The line of domes is here continued by two prominent domes, one with a gneiss core (Shelburne Falls dome); this gneiss was interpreted as an early intrusive by Balk (1946), but it may be simply a pile of felsic volcanics within the Lower Paleozoic sequence, remobilized during metamorphism so that it rose through the heavier metasediments. Near the south border of the state, however, almost all the stratigraphic units turn southeast and disappear under the Triassic strata, the belt abruptly narrows to about 10 kilometers (6 miles), and only the lower part of the sequence appears to continue into Connecticut. Intrusive rocks, mostly granite and pegmatite, abound in south-central Massachusetts, and the metamorphism is largely mesozonal, though at one point a narrow strip of the lower-grade belt to the east appears for a few kilometers (miles) from under the Triassic rocks.

In northern Connecticut, the relations are still imperfectly known, and even the contact of the Paleozoic sequence with the Precambrian core of the Berkshire Highlands to the west has not yet been precisely located. South of the end of the Berkshire Highlands, what is probably the same sequence swells out into a belt 40 kilometers (25 miles) wide; it here forms the more quartzitic assemblage (Hartland formation) mentioned above (p. 94) as lying to the east of and contrasting with the assemblage of higher-grade metamorphic rocks in the angular gap between the Berkshire and Hudson Highlands anticlinoria (from which it is separated by the tectonic line—"Cameron's line"—mentioned on p. 94). The general dip of the foliation here is not east, however, as on the east flank of the Green Mountains and the Berkshire Highlands in Vermont and Massachusetts, but west and northwest, off a line of gneiss domes, probably part of the same line as those in Vermont and northern Massachusetts; some of the domes indeed show the same inverse ("spruce-tree") minor folding as the domes in Vermont. In Connecticut, the line of domes trends S25–30°W to the Waterbury dome and may continue to Long Island Sound; the general strike in the rocks to the northwest is about the same, but a prominent salient, convex to the northwest, fits neatly into the rear of the angular gap between the Highlands anticlinoria, the strike swinging from S75°W somewhat southwest of the Berkshire Highlands to S15°E east of the Hudson Highlands. Farther southwest, this assemblage can be followed, with increasingly steep northwest dips, to the shores of Long Island Sound and with vertical or even southeast dips across southeastern Westchester County into New York City, where, however, it has not generally been distinguished from the assemblage to the west (where it has, it is called the Hutchinson River group).

The stratigraphic sequence in this region, its correlation with the sequence in western Massachusetts and eastern Vermont, and even which end of it is up have been quite uncertain, and ideas have been changing rapidly as new pieces of detailed work have added evidence. When the line of domes was first recognized, the section was thought to become younger fairly regularly away from the domes both to the northwest and to the southeast (Gates and Rodgers *in* Rodgers, Gates, and Rosenfeld, 1959, p. 14–15), although correlation of the two flanks was not at all obvious. The stratigraphic position of the gneiss in the domes themselves is not clear; they all share a distinctive, partly metavolcanic unit (Collinsville formation), probably conformable with the covering metasediments, but in the core of the Waterbury dome a still older complex of gneiss appears (Waterbury gneiss, s.s.), which is possibly a fragment of Precambrian basement (though radiometry makes it dubious). Southeast of the domes, Fritts (1962) mapped out a major syncline, containing, in its core, strata (Orange or Wepawaug phyllite) that had already been recognized as correlative with the top of the eastern Vermont section (Waits River formation) and hence Siluro-Devonian. Subsequent work in the underlying rocks showed that large lenticular bodies of felsic volcanics are present (Crowley, 1968; they had previously been considered intrusive granitoid gneiss), complicating the correlations, and that parts of the section near the domes are completely inverted overhangs of the partly metavolcanic unit from within the domes, as in Vermont (first suggested by Rosenfeld, personal communication, 1955). This area has now been synthesized by Dieterich (ms. 1968; 1968), who has shown the presence of three periods of synmetamorphic folding (each producing a strong schistosity in some places at least), the first two identical with those in eastern Vermont, the third related to further uplift of the domes and tightening of the syncline to the east. (A fourth, unrelated, period of folding produced kink-bands of all sizes striking roughly east-west across the regional northeast-southwest trend produced by the earlier periods.) The total effect of the three periods was to produce a belt of "jelly-roll" folding between the domes and the eastern syncline, bedding planes in the core of the roll having been rotated up to 180 degrees in one direction during the early recumbent folding and then up to 270 degrees in the other during the rise and overfolding of the domes.

Northwest of the domes, stratigraphic sequences were worked out in several areas (Gates, 1959; Martin, ms. 1962; Stanley, 1964), generally on the assumption that the rocks become younger northwestward, at least near the domes; original discrepancies in the various sequences recognized are now being ironed out. Gates and Martin (1967, p. 25) suggested, however, that the partly metavolcanic unit in the domes reappeared in the lower part of this sequence, and Stanley (1969, Hatch and Stanley, 1970) has further suggested that the west-dipping sequence is largely inverted, west of a sinuous syncline (of The Straits schist) threading its way between the domes; this disposition would in fact square better with the known situation in Vermont and Massachusetts, where the domes appear in the deepest part of the Connecticut Valley synclinorium.

Considering the Connecticut Valley synclinorium from the international boundary to Long Island Sound, one observes an irregular but unmistakeable southward narrowing of the synclinorium between the tectonic unities on either side and a parallel increase in the height of the domes; it is as if, just opposite the sharply angular recess in the belt of anticlinoria to the west, these tendencies had finished by turning the synclinorium inside out.

The grade of metamorphism is metazonal in most of this belt in western Connecticut; staurolite and kyanite are widely distributed, and sillimanite occurs near the contact with the assemblage to the west, close to the Berkshire Highlands, and near Long Island Sound. There is no evidence that the grade is especially high along the line of domes, but to the southeast toward New Haven, especially near and southeast of the axis of the major syncline, the grade drops off to the chlorite zone, greenschist facies, evidently a reappearance of the low-grade belt that follows the Connecticut River between New Hampshire and Vermont and disappears under the Triassic in northern Massachusetts. The east side of the belt here is probably the normal fault on the east side of the Triassic basin, beyond which the rocks contain sillimanite; at the south end of that basin, low-grade and high-grade rocks face each other across the mouth of New Haven Harbor, only about 4 kilometers ($2\frac{1}{2}$ miles) apart.

Plutonic bodies are abundant in western Connecticut; though they have not yet been classified into plutonic series like those of New Hampshire (p. 102—104), a number of different groups and types are known: amphibolitic metagabbros, dioritic and granodioritic gneisses (but some of these may turn out to be piles of felsic metavolcanics), granitic gneisses, late pegmatitic granites, even later dikes of aplitic granite, and one small, very late plug of rhyolite porphyry.

If the Precambrian anticlinoria to the west represent the upbuckling of the basement at the western limit of metamorphism severe enough to render it somewhat plastic, the Connecticut Valley synclinorium represents down-buckling of an immense pile of clastic sediments, including considerable amounts of volcanics, under conditions of metamorphism where both cover and basement were entirely plastic, so that faults did not form and flow was universal. The snowball garnets show, moreover, that recrystallization and flow went on together; recrystallization was probably the mechanism of flow. This flow greatly distorted the thicknesses of the stratigraphic units, thinning them in some places and thickening them in others, and produced isoclinal folds, some of which, in the core of the synclinorium, are large enough to be called "nappes." Kyanite is ubiquitous, except in northern Vermont, and thus the whole synclinorium, along with large parts of the flanking anticlinoria, was probably depressed some 15 kilometers (10 miles) below the Earth's surface (Thompson and Norton, 1968,

p. 324). At a late stage in the downbuckling, great bodies of gneiss, some probably from the underlying basement and some originating in piles of felsic volcanics within the sequence, rose like bubbles through the overlying metamorphosed sediments. Probably, like the salt in salt domes, the gneiss rose because it was lighter and perhaps also more plastic than the sediments; the higher grade of metamorphism around the domes in eastern Vermont suggests that, rising out of the downwarped part of the synclinorium, it was also hotter. More orthodox plutonic rocks also found their way into the sediments at various stages of the metamorphism, but they seem mostly to have avoided the gneiss domes. The alignment of the domes and of their long axes along the regional strike suggests that when they rose the region was still under stress, presumably a compressive stress with the major compressive axis roughly WNW-ESE and horizontal.

The age of the principal deformation and metamorphism in the Connecticut Valley synclinorium in Vermont is evidently Acadian, that is, some time between the Early Devonian and the Late Carboniferous, the two limits assigned by the available fossil evidence in central and southern New England. Moreover, the metamorphism shows no discontinuity from the east flank of the Green Mountains anticlinorium to the Bronson Hill anticlinorium, except along the Ammonoosuc fault, which is obviously late whatever its character. Further south, there is simply no convincing evidence of the age, for none of the rocks are at all accurately dated; all one can say is that no field evidence has yet been found there for two Paleozoic orogenies such as exists in the Hudson Valley to the west. Radiometry is also moderately equivocal, indicating Acadian orogeny over much of the area but recording a late Paleozoic "event" in southern Connecticut (Clark and Kulp, 1968). Even in Vermont, evidence for the Taconic orogeny is provided only by the unconformities within the Paleozoic sequence (at the top of and probably also within the Ordovician) and by the apparent restriction of the ultramafic rocks to the beds below the principal unconformity.

Bronson Hill Anticlinorium

As mentioned above, east of the Connecticut Valley synclinorium lies the Bronson Hill anticlinorium, which can be readily followed from the Maine-New Hampshire border northeast of Mount Washington across and down the west side of New Hampshire and then across Massachusetts and Connecticut, just east of the Triassic basin, to Long Island Sound, a distance of 400 kilometers (250 miles). It is rather different from the anticlinorial belt on the opposite side of the synclinorium; whereas that consists of a few large elongated anticlinal masses of Precambrian gneiss, the Bronson Hill anticlinorium consists of a large number of individual droplike domes separated by deep, tightly pinched to isoclinal synclines, which anastomose between the domes. The domes are aligned and elongated roughly parallel to the regional strike, in places in two or even three more or less parallel lines; certain of them lie en echelon, their axes cocked somewhat to the left of the general strike. In New Hampshire they are fairly short (only one is more than 40 kilometers—25 miles—long), but in Massachusetts and northern Connecticut they are mostly long, narrow, and parallel.

The cores of these domes are formed by the granitoid rocks of Billings' Oliverian plutonic series (Billings, 1956, p. 48–53), rocks that range from quartz diorite to granite and that are commonly but not invariably gneissic, especially toward the concordant borders. Granulation and granoblastic texture show that these rocks have been metamorphosed with the surrounding rocks since their emplacement. The series is distinguished from the other plutonic series in New Hampshire partly by its rather homogeneous chemistry (generally rather sodic but saturated with silica—in this respect it does not differ from the Highlandcroft series, discussed below) but principally by its tectonic occurrence, for it is not known outside the cores of these domes, whereas the New Hampshire and White Mountain series are emplaced in the cover rocks of the domes and especially in the Merrimack synclinorium to the east in central New Hampshire and to the south.

Above the Oliverian rocks in the cores of these domes follows a distinctive sequence of stratigraphic units that was first worked out by Billings (1937) in northern New Hampshire and that has now been followed along strike to southern Connecticut. Next to the gneiss in most of the domes is a unit of mafic metavolcanics (greenstone to amphibolite depending on the metamorphic facies), commonly mixed with felsic metavolcanics and metasediments (Ammonoosuc volcanics in New Hampshire, Middletown formation in Connecticut); above this is a rather variable unit (Partridge formation in New Hampshire, Brimfield schist in Massachusetts and Connecticut) characterized by graphitic, commonly pyrrhotitic (sooty and rusty) slate to schist but containing, locally at least, calcareous beds (now largely calc-silicate rock), spessartine quartzite (originally manganiferous chert), and zones of volcanics.

An unconformity has been reported between these two units in Connecticut, but much more important is the unconformity above them, for it bevels down across them and in places brings the quartzite-conglomerate únit (Clough quartzite) next above it directly against the granitoid gneiss in the cores of the domes; opinion was divided as to whether the quartzite unit is altered by the gneiss or overlies it unconformably, but the latter view now prevails.

Above this unit, which is thin and locally discontinuous, comes a vast thickness of mainly clastic rocks (slate and sandstone to mica schist and mica quartzite, depending on grade); carbonate rocks, mostly impure and including calc-silicate rocks in the higher metamorphic zones, are important and locally even dominant in the lowest part of the sequence (Fitch formation) but are rare farther up (Littleton schist). In addition, relatively thin members of quartzite and of metavolcanics occur here and there throughout, and some are mappable. The rocks above the principal unconformity are dated by fossils and range in age from Early Silurian to Early Devonian; those below have furnished no fossils in New Hampshire but are presumably Ordovician. (The trace of the unconformity around the domes—taken mostly from Thompson and others, 1968, Pl. 1a—has been generalized on the accompanying map (Pl. 1), for it is repeated so many times between the elongate domes and along the nearly paralled limbs of isoclinal and recumbent folds that it could not be completely represented at this scale.)

The Ammonoosuc fault lies mostly west of the Bronson Hill anticlinorium but encroaches upon it near Littleton in northern New Hampshire. Northwest of the fault in this region the metamorphic grade is especially low; it was here that the first fossils were discovered (nearly a century ago) and that Billings was able to establish the stratigraphy. Here the unit of mafic volcanics at the bottom of the sequence described above contains an especially large proportion of felsic volcanics; furthermore, it is underlain by a thick unit of slate and impure quartzite (or mica schist and mica quartzite—Albee formation), and both are intruded by Billings' Highlandcroft plutonic series, a series of granitoid rocks ranging from diorite to quartz monzonite, which in turn is clearly overlain unconformably by the basal Silurian (Clough quartzite). Older quartzose metasediments (Plainfield formation) also appear at the other end of the anticlinorium in the Stony Creek dome just east of New Haven, Connecticut, beneath a unit of gneisses of Oliverian type (Monson formation), and in one of the domes in Massachusetts.

The stratigraphic sequence on the Bronson Hill anticlinorium is much like the upper half or so of that on the west flank of the Connecticut Valley synclinorium, especially if one overlooks the volcanics as relatively local phenomena; in each a unit of quartzite and quartzite-conglomerate (Clough and Shaw Mountain formations) at the base of a thick, clastic Silurian-Devonian sequence overlies unconformably a unit of rusty-sooty schist (Partridge and Cram Hill formations). Fossils in southern Quebec date the latter as Middle Ordovician on the west flank of the synclinorium (p. 97), but no fossils are known below the unconformity on the Bronson Hill anticlinorium. Perhaps the most significant difference in the rocks in the two belts is the presence of the pre-Silurian Highlandcroft series of acid intrusive rocks east of the synclinorium, at least in the area northwest of the Ammonoosuc fault.

At first sight, the attitude of the mantle rocks in the main part of the anticlinorium seems simply to reflect the domes, but recent work has uncovered much more complicated structures. In southwestern New Hampshire and adjacent Vermont near Bellows Falls, Thompson (1956) discovered a large, west-facing recumbent fold or nappe (Skitchewaug nappe) with an amplitude measured in kilometers (miles), which is older than the domes and was folded by them. Further work has shown that the Skitchewaug nappe is the middle one of three such nappes (Thompson and others, 1968, p. 210–214); it has a present horizontal width (after intense later folding and shortening) of about 24 kilometers (15 miles) in northern Massachusetts and southern New Hampshire, as measured at the Silurian-Ordovician unconformity, but decreases in size north of Bellows Falls. It seems to root along the easternmost domes of the anticlinorium or along their eastern flanks, losing displacement northward about where the line of domes becomes single. The Cornish nappe beneath it, on the other hand, roots on a more western line of domes and increases in size northward; it is insignificant south of Bellows Falls but reaches a present width (again as measured at the Silurian-Ordovician unconformity) of 15 to 20 kilometers (10 to 13 miles) in west-central New Hampshire. The Fall Mountain nappe above (named for the mountain east of Bellows Falls) is preserved on the anticlinorium in two down-faulted pockets in saddles among the western domes, one east of Bellows Falls and one just north of the state line; these remnants indicate minimum widths of 20 and 15 kilometers (13 and 10 miles). The roots of the nappe lie east of the domes, where, however, mapping is still incomplete. Because the Ammonoosuc fault intervenes, it is not clear which of these might be the core of the large nappe postulated above (p. 98—99) in the Connecticut Valley synclinorium; the Cornish nappe seems the most likely candidate.

A similar recumbent fold or nappe has now been recognized in eastern Connecticut (p. 109), but it seems to face east instead of west and to lap over into the Merrimack synclinorium. Whether these opposite facings are topologically compatible has been under debate between the geologists working in Massachusetts and those working in Connecticut, but even in Massachusetts, old eastward-facing if relatively minor recumbent folds have been recognized (Thompson and others, 1968, p. 215), along with younger domes (in some cases cylinders or even mushrooms) overturned in almost every direction. In the kind of plastic deformation here recorded, weak, presumably lighter material being forced up from deep in the anticlinorium apparently flopped over irregularly in whatever direction was temporarily easiest; one can perhaps compare the process to the very slow bubbling of thick, greasy soup.

The plutonic rocks of the New Hampshire series, widely distributed in the Merrimack synclinorium to the east, encroach also onto the Bronson Hill anticlinorium in several places. The older members of this series (diorite to quartz monzonite) are concordant and syntectonic; a large, sill-like body in the Devonian schist along the eastern flank of the anticlinorium in New Hampshire is 125 kilometers (nearly 80 miles) along, and smaller masses in the same schist west of the eastern domes are clearly what remains of tongues of this body that extended across the domes and were folded by them. These tongues are, moreover, involved in the nappe structure mentioned above. Accordingly, Thompson and others (1968, p. 208) suggest that these rocks are not intrusive but metavolcanic. The younger members of the series (quartz monzonite to granite) are, however, more stocklike and may cut any part of the stratigraphic sequence or the core rocks of the domes. The White Mountain plutonic series also lies mainly to the east in New Hampshire, but some of its characteristic ring dikes and stocks cut discordantly the northeasternmost dome on the anticlinorium.

As noted above (p. 99), the grade of metamorphism jumps up across the Ammonoosuc fault, and it continues to rise eastward across the Bronson Hill anticlinorium, which in New Hampshire definitely does not mark a belt of maximum intensity. Across New Hampshire the sillimanite isograd lies along or just east of the crests of the eastern domes, encroaching westward in the saddles, the isograds being inverted

there under the higher nappes, and in Massachusetts and northern Connecticut it lies within the anticlinorium, swinging in southern Connecticut against the Triassic border fault, despite strong local retrogression (accompanied by silicification) along that fault. In New Hampshire, all the dome cores containing Oliverian rocks lie above the garnet isograd and most above the staurolite isograd; on the other hand, the outcrop areas of the Highlandcroft series west of the Ammonoosuc fault are mostly below the biotite isograd, rising above it only at the northeast end of the belt, where the fault is dying out.

North of the point where the Ammonoosuc fault encroaches on the anticlinorium in the vicinity of Littleton, New Hampshire, the east flank of the Connecticut Valley synclinorium is formed not by domes with Oliverian cores but by more continuous conventional anticlines. Indeed the anticlinorium they form has not generally been considered part of the Bronson Hill anticlinorium, which has been restricted to the belt of domes with Oliverian cores and hence would come to an end at the New Hampshire-Maine border northeast of Mount Washington; instead it has been called the Gardner Mountain anticline (west of Littleton), the Coos (two syllables) anticlinorium in northernmost New Hampshire, and the Boundary Mountains anticlinorium along the Maine-Quebec border (Green and Guidotti, 1968). There is little doubt, however, that these structures continue the line of uplift of the Bronson Hill anticlinorium, and the recent state map of Vermont (Doll and others, 1961, see cross sections) groups them all as the Bronson Hill-Boundary Mountain anticlinorium. Their continuation northeast of New Hampshire is discussed in Chapter 6.

The trend of the Bronson Hill anticlinorium varies between N–S and N20°E from Long Island Sound nearly to Littleton, vaguely outlining shallow salients (convex to the west) in southern Connecticut and southern New Hampshire and a complementary recess about at the Massachusetts-Connecticut state line. Just south of Littleton, however, the anticlinorium turns rather sharply and broadens out; the last of the Oliverian domes extends N50°E from Littleton almost to the Maine border, whereas the anticlines northwest of the Ammonoosuc fault trend N30°E across northernmost New Hampshire into the Boundary Mountains. The Ammonoosuc fault also changes to a more easterly strike, but apparently it dies out halfway to the Maine border. The sharp swing in strike reflects in part the general arc of the Northern Appalachians but also in part the northward widening of the Connecticut Valley synclinorium.

It is not possible to recognize culminations and depressions along the crest of the anticlinorium which, being formed by the individual domes, is mostly very irregular. The largest dome containing Oliverian rocks in New Hampshire is precisely the northeasternmost, lying entirely east of the swing in strike near Littleton, and the long narrow domes of Massachusetts and northern Connecticut are continuous through the shallow recess there. The decrease in the proportion of Siluro-Devonian rocks to the south (they finally disappear opposite Middletown, Connecticut) and the suggestion of a southward increase in metamorphic grade (and in coarseness of grain size) imply, however, a rough overall northward plunge for the anticlinorium.

The key problem in the tectonics of the Bronson Hill anticlinorium is the relation of the Oliverian granitoid rocks in the cores of the domes to their metasedimentary and metavolcanic mantle. Feldspathization and pegmatite intrusion have been reported in the rocks around their borders, notably where they are in contact with the basal Silurian (Clough) quartzite, but later work has not confirmed the report. On the other hand, in many domes the granitoid rocks are entirely concordant with the overlying unit of mafic volcanics (Ammonoosuc volcanics) and seem to be interstratified with it; narrow but persistent and concordant bands of amphibolite can be found far below the main mass of the volcanic unit, particularly where the core rocks are gneissic and granodioritic or quartz-dioritic. Billings (1956, p. 123−124, 147−148) has firmly maintained that the Oliverian rocks were intruded as magma after the deposition of the Silurian and Lower Devonian sediments but during an early phase of the subsequent orogeny, either as a great sill now exposed only in the domes or as a series of laccoliths that formed them. Others have proposed various kinds of granitization by the addition of alkalis to preexisting rocks. A more radical suggestion (first made in the nineteenth century by C.H. Hitchcock) is that the Oliverian rocks are simply a unit of metamorphosed felsic volcanics that underlay and interfingered with the mafic volcanics (see Naylor, 1968); this explanation accounts very well for the interlayering of quartz diorite or granodiorite and amphibolitic gneiss observed in many places but is less successful for the more potassic rocks, which are more massive and uniform and rather irregularly distributed within their respective domes, though still mainly concordant in detail.

Following a specific suggestion by Eskola (1949, p. 470−472), Rosenfeld and Eaton (1956; Eaton and Rosenfeld, 1960, p. 170−172) have interpreted the Oliverian domes in southern Connecticut as mantled gneiss domes, that is, as older granitoid rocks formed in an earlier orogeny, covered unconformably by a sedimentary mantle, and metamorphosed with it in a later orogeny and perhaps partially melted so that they intruded rocks younger than themselves. The original character of the granitoid rocks (magmatic, metasomatic, or simply metamorphic) would naturally be thoroughly masked by their later history, but Rosenfeld and Eaton found some evidence suggesting that the more potassic rocks at least had intruded the mafic volcanic unit. Further, Bernold (ms. 1962), studying the southwesternmost dome on the anticlinorium, the Stony Creek dome just east of New Haven, found evidence for two origins for the granitoid gneisses there—the more sodic being metamorphosed felsic volcanics (Monson formation) from which potash has been removed (it now appears in the abundant associated pegmatites), the more potassic being intrusive and magmatic (Stony Creek granite), the magma itself produced by the extreme metamorphism of older sediments underlying the volcanic rocks. Thus the Oliverian series probably includes rocks of three different origins: altered volcanics, metamorphosed older intrusives (as in Eskola's picture), and magma derived from sediments by partial melting of their more fusible components. In the New Hampshire domes, Naylor (1968, 1969) has found petrologic and radiometric evidence for the first two origins but not for the third; in southern Connecticut, Hills and Dasch (1969) have interpreted granite of the third type as perhaps derived from late Precambrian sediments or volcanics.

It would be consistent with these ideas about the Oliverian plutonic series to see in the area west of the Ammonoosuc fault in northern New Hampshire the same rocks unaffected by such remobilization and reintrusion, which would have occurred only in those areas subject to mesozonal metamorphism. Here the felsic volcanics are still preserved along with the mafic; fairly quartzose sediments underlie both; and all are intruded by the Highlandcroft plutonic series. The distinction between the two plutonic series was based on their obviously different tectonic history; the Highlandcroft series is unconformably overlain by Silurian rocks, whereas the Oliverian series was metamorphosed along with them. But this difference in history can be adequately explained by the difference in metamorphic grade on the two sides of the Ammonoosuc fault; in chemistry and mineralogy the two series are quite similar. Unfortunately we cannot test this hypothesis by finding the intermediate steps, for no bodies of these rocks seem to be present in the critical area beyond the northeast end of the Ammonoosuc fault.

Thus the main part of the Bronson Hill anticlinorium seems to represent a long belt where preexisting granitoid rocks were extensively remobilized, lying between two synclinoria filled with a thick Silurian and Devonian sequence where they were not, whether because the overburden prevented it or because the granitoid rocks were absent. Nevertheless, the parallelism of the anticlinorium with the other major structural elements in the region and the more normally anticlinal character of the part that, lying northwest of the Ammonoosuc fault, has been less severely metamorphosed, suggest that the belt would have been anticlinorial in any case, and that the mantled gneiss dome tectonics has simply modified it. The general though by no means complete parallelism of the individual domes to the regional strike suggests further that they were formed under orogenic pressure, a view confirmed by the character of the gneisses in their cores. The en echelon arrangement of certain of the domes and steeply plunging late folds in some areas suggest that a left-handed horizontal couple was also present.

It seems probable that the line of the Bronson Hill anticlinorium was marked out early. Metavolcanics appear to reach a maximum along it, especially in the pre-Silurian part of the sequence, and it may have been a line of volcanoes, a volcanic island arc, in the Ordovician sea, east of the deep trough in which the clastic-volcanic sequence of the Connecticut Valley synclinorium was deposited. The mechanics of its domes may have been like that of the domes in the synclinorium to the west—the upwelling of relatively lighter gneiss through relatively heavier metasediments under conditions of metamorphism where both were plastic—but whereas the gneiss cores in the synclinorium may be partly Precambrian basement from beneath the Paleozoic sequence, those on the anticlinorium seem to have been intrusions into the pre-Silurian part of that sequence or piles of volcanics within it. Perhaps therefore the Bronson Hill anticlinorium marks the metamorphic and plutonic axis of the Taconic orogeny, which farther west produced deformation and at least some metamorphism across the present Green Mountains-Berkshire Highlands anticlinorium and the Hudson Valley as far as a line from Albany to eastern Pennsylvania; the Highlandcroft plutonic series is evidence that granitoid rocks were intruded at that time at the north end of the belt, and Rosenfeld and Eaton's evidence suggests the same for the south end. Later during the Acadian orogeny, whose metamorphic and plutonic axis seems to have been rather in the Merrimack syn-

clinorium to the east, metamorphism spread over a wide belt on both sides of the old axis, blotting out the evidence for Taconic metamorphism but remobilizing the gneiss along the older axis to produce the Bronson Hill anticlinorium as we see it today.

Merrimack Synclinorium

The rocks in the central part of New Hampshire, east of the Bronson Hill anticlinorium and extending southeast to within 25 kilometers (15 miles) of the coast, are highly metamorphosed sediments—mica schist, mica quartzite, and biotite gneiss, all with sillimanite—intruded by granitoid rocks that belong to two different plutonic series and occupy nearly half the area. The metasediments also include layers and lenses of quartzite, calc-silicate rock, and metavolcanics, but these have so far been traced only locally and no consistent stratigraphic sequence has been reported. As the rocks are continuous with the Devonian strata at the top of the sequence of the Bronson Hill anticlinorium, the whole mass, probably thousands of meters (well over 10,000 feet) thick, is considered Devonian (Littleton schist), preserved in a great synclinorium called the Merrimack synclinorium for the principal river in central New Hampshire. It is likely indeed that older units are present within this mass, but if so they have not yet been distinguished as such in this high-grade terrain, and the boundary between the Devonian and older rocks has not been traced out.

The plutonic rocks belonging to the New Hampshire plutonic series range from gneissic granodiorite and quartz monzonite in great concordant sill-like batholiths along the two sides of the synclinorium to massive two-mica granite in stock-like bodies that are more discordant and more irregularly distributed. Magmatic, metasomatic, and metavolcanic origins have all been proposed for these rocks. On the other hand, the rocks of the obviously magmatic White Mountain series, ranging from gabbro to granite but all distinctly alkalic, occur entirely in utterly discordant bodies—ring dikes, circular stocks, and a major batholith—that evidently mark the sites of a series of calderas arranged in an irregular belt trending about N10°W; indeed in several places lavas of the same magmatic series are still preserved inside the ring-dike complexes. These rocks underlie many of the high peaks of the White Mountains, but the highest range, including Mount Washington, the culminating point of the whole Northern Appalachians, is underlain by sillimanitic mica quartzite.

On the southeast side of this high-grade area, just beyond an elongate batholith of the New Hampshire series that extends for 140 kilometers (more than 80 miles) along strike from the Maine border across New Hampshire and far into Massachusetts, the grade drops off very abruptly, so that one crosses the sillimanite, staurolite, and garnet isograds, and locally even the biotite isograd, in not more than a couple of kilometers (a mile or less). Moreover, parallel with the isograds if not exactly along them lies the Flint Hill silicified zone (Freedman, 1950, p. 479–480), which extends for 25 kilometers (15 miles) N30°E, parallel to the strike of the strata; it is thus one of the straightest and longest zones of silicification in New Hampshire (there are others with similar trends just to the east in the lower-grade rocks and also to the west well within the sillimanite zone). The situation is exactly like that along the Ammonoosuc fault, which forms part of the east boundary of the low-grade zone near the Connecticut River, and one is tempted therefore to postulate a major fault zone here also—perhaps a Triassic normal fault trending northeast but downthrown to the southeast and thus comparable not to the fault on the east side of the Triassic basin along the lower Connecticut but to the fault on the northwest side of the Triassic basin in the Bay of Fundy and eastern Gulf of Maine. The sharp drop in grade can be followed from the Maine border across both New Hampshire and Massachusetts, and brecciation, silicification, and other evidence of faulting have been found along this trend almost as far as Worcester, Massachusetts (Novotny, 1961).

Except for the difference in grade, however, the rocks appear to be about the same in the low-grade zone as in the high; furthermore, they resemble the top third of the sequence in the Connecticut Valley synclinorium, though they are somewhat less calcareous. Despite poor exposures and the absence of fossils, a sequence of units has been worked out here in the area along the Maine border, and it shows that these strata form the southeast flank of the Merrimack synclinorium. Almost at the coast, one reaches the base of this slate-siltstone-calcareous slate or mica schist-mica quartzite-calc-silicate granulite sequence, and its basal unit of rather impure quartzite rests on an older and more varied group of rocks including metavolcanics (largely amphibolite) and metasediments (largely feldspathic mica schist). Probably we see here once again the Silurian-Ordovician contact (which may or may not be an unconformity here); nothing contradicts this view, but there is no fossil evidence to prove it. In this area (called the Rockingham anticlinorium), the grade of metamorphism again rises

rapidly (but continuously) into the sillimanite zone. As in the Connecticut Valley therefore the belt of low-grade metamorphism follows neither an anticlinorial nor a synclinorial axis but lies in between, on the southeast flank of the synclinorium. The low-grade belt in southeastern New Hampshire is much wider, however—roughly 25 kilometers (15 miles). Relatively small, sill-like bodies of rock ranging from diorite to granite and assigned (with some doubt) to the New Hampshire plutonic series intrude all these units, even where the metamorphic grade is lowest, and a few small outlying stocks of rocks like those of the White Mountain series are also present on both sides of the Flint Hill fault.

The strike of the beds on the southeast side of the Merrimack synclinorium in New Hampshire swings as far around as N45°E, whereas its west side is the nearly north-south Bronson Hill anticlinorium; the synclinorium therefore widens greatly north-northeastward toward Maine, flaring from a width of 70 kilometers (45 miles) at the Massachusetts border to 140 kilometers (90 miles) on a line southeast from Littleton, New Hampshire. Only to the southwest in central Massachusetts does the strike along the east side swing more nearly north-south.

In Massachusetts, the rocks in the belt east of the Bronson Hill anticlinorium are much like those in New Hampshire—high-grade mica schist, mica quartzite, and mica gneiss intruded by large, concordant bodies of granitoid rocks (the White Mountain series is completely missing here). In the west half of the belt, much of the mica schist is markedly pyrrhotitic and graphitic and weathers rusty and sooty (Brimfield schist), reminding one of the strata next below the basal Silurian quartzite on the Bronson Hill anticlinorium. Farther east similar schist is associated with larger amounts of more quartzose schist (Paxton quartz schist), some of it rich in diopside or other lime silicates. Along the east side of the belt, the zone of low-grade rocks can be traced from southeastern New Hampshire across Massachusetts (passing by Worcester) into the northeastern corner of Connecticut, but it narrows steadily southward and the metamorphic contrast diminishes. Here the rocks are phyllite (Worcester phyllite) and impure quartzite (Oakdale quartzite); in particular there is a quartzite unit (Merrimack or Vaughan Hills quartzite), locally associated with conglomerate (Harvard conglomerate), along the east side of the low-grade belt, beyond which are more varied high-grade rocks (Nashoba formation), largely gneiss but including amphibolite and also rusty schist like that farther west. Many of the contacts in this area are probably northwest-dipping thrust faults, however (see p. 112–113, also Skehan, 1968).

Coming from New Hampshire, one is naturally tempted to consider the zone of quartzite and conglomerate as the base of the Silurian on the east flank of the main synclinorium, but workers in Massachusetts (Jahns, 1941; Currier and Jahns, 1952; Hansen, 1956) have held that the high-grade rocks to the east (Nashoba formation) are at the *top* of the local sequence and that the quartzite appears from beneath in the cores of isoclinal anticlines, the conglomerate perhaps resting unconformably upon it. Moreover, they have called all the rocks in the region Upper Carboniferous (except possibly the quartzite), because of the discovery more than half a century ago of fossil plants within the low-grade belt at Worcester, Massachusetts.

This age assignment is obviously in flat contradiction to the age assignment of the same rocks in New Hampshire, which is based on correlation across the strike from the dated sequence on the Bronson Hill anticlinorium. Several solutions to the contradiction have been proposed; presumably one of them (or a variant) must be correct. One is to deny that the reported plants were really fossils; certainly metamorphic structures have been mistaken for fossils in New England as elsewhere, and most of the original specimens have been lost, but new unequivocal fossils have recently been collected from the original locality. A second is to deny the present age assignment of the fossils, which is low Upper Carboniferous, a bit older than the Carboniferous beds in the nearby basin in eastern Rhode Island and southeastern Massachusetts; if the plants were really Lower Carboniferous (or Upper Devonian) the beds containing them could perhaps represent the uppermost part of the New Hampshire stratigraphic sequence, though if so the "Acadian" orogeny in southern and central New England was considerably younger than in eastern Maine and the Maritime Provinces (Acadia) where the principal phase appears to have been during the Middle Devonian. Examination of the newly discovered fossils (Grew, Mamay, and Barghoorn, 1970) confirms, however, the original age assignment. A third is to suppose the fossiliferous beds are in fact a tiny outlier of the Rhode Island Carboniferous basin resting entirely unconformably on the surrounding rocks, which could then be Devonian or older; this view has been upheld by a persistent minority since the discovery of the fossils, but those who have mapped around Worcester in the past have generally rejected it. A fourth solution is to suppose that the deformation and metamorphism in central Massachusetts, New Hamp-

shire, and eastern Vermont is not Acadian at all but Alleghany, though the evidence in eastern Rhode Island and southeastern Massachusetts, where those orogenies are distinguishable, shows clearly that the older orogeny was the principal one, and radiometric results (Zartman and others, 1965, p. D7–D9) make this solution unlikely, even in the Worcester area. For my part I have always preferred the third and entirely rejected the fourth solution and hence the Carboniferous age assignment of the rocks of the Merrimack synclinorium, save for the plant-bearing beds themselves; the latest work in the Worcester area (Grew, 1970) seems to be bearing out this solution to the dilemma.

The same belt of rocks continues southward across much of eastern Connecticut, and a tentative stratigraphy has been established there by recent workers (Lundgren, 1962; Dixon and Lundgren, 1968, p. 220–221). The top of the sequence is a unit of mica schist (Scotland schist) pinched in one or more synclines near or east of the center of the belt, along strike with the phyllite in the low-grade zone around Worcester. Next below are two persistent mappable units, one dominantly of calc-silicate rock (including diopside-quartz granulite and calcite-biotite schist—Hebron formation), the other dominantly two-mica schist, commonly rusty and sooty (Brimfield or Tatnic Hill schist), though each contains smaller bodies of the other rock type. Below these are more varied gneisses and schists, some at least metavolcanic. Other granitoid gneisses (e.g., Canterbury gneiss) are also present in the area, and some seem curiously tied to the stratigraphy and may also be altered extrusive rocks instead of intrusives. Lenses of quartzite near the base of the highest schist unit perhaps represent the quartzite in or along the east side of the low-grade belt in Massachusetts and New Hampshire. The rocks are in the sillimanite zone, except in the cores of the major synclines, or where retrograded close to late faults, and cordierite and hypersthene appear in a limited area to the southeast.

No fossils are present but, except for the appearance of the calc-silicate unit (Hebron formation), the sequence fits rather well the sequence in New Hampshire, especially that along the Bronson Hill anticline, whereas it is inverted relative to the sequence proposed for central Massachusetts. If the correlation with New Hampshire is accepted, the upper schist is probably Devonian and the rusty-sooty schist Middle Ordovician; the underlying gneiss unit would correspond to the mafic volcanic unit (Ammonoosuc volcanics) in the Ordovician and probably also to part of the Oliverian gneiss. Further, if the quartzite lenses were the base of the Silurian, the calc-silicate unit beneath would be Upper or Middle Ordovician; even if it is Silurian, more than half the rocks exposed in the Merrimack synclinorium in Connecticut would be pre-Silurian.

Use of this stratigraphy has shown that in the Devils Hopyard basin, a shallow structural basin 25 kilometers (15 miles) southwest of Willimantic, Connecticut, the rocks are in reality entirely upside-down and therefore represent the upper limb of a recumbent syncline or the lower limb of a nappe (Colchester nappe of Dixon and others, 1963) 25 kilometers (16 miles) wide, probably rooting near or along the narrow eastern anticline of the Bronson Hill anticlinorium and extending east halfway across the Merrimack synclinorium, of which the deepest fold would be the recumbent syncline beneath the nappe. Around Willimantic, a dome has lifted the overturned limb above the land surface, but to the north it may descend again, involving an unknown amount of the schists in northern Connecticut and southern Massachusetts. A tunnel section in central Massachusetts (Callaghan, 1931) found a wide extent of nearly flat-lying schists and can indeed be interpreted in terms of an arched recumbent syncline; it is not impossible that the overturned limb extends as far east as the west edge of the low-grade belt near Worcester. As noted above, however (p. 103), the nappes recently recognized across the Bronson Hill anticline in northern Massachusetts and southwestern New Hampshire, although they also root along the east side of the anticlinorium, face west into the Connecticut Valley synclinorium.

The Merrimack synclinorium retains a width of about 40 kilometers (25 miles) from central Massachusetts to within 25 kilometers (15 miles) of Long Island Sound, but there it is abruptly cut off by the major Honey Hill fault (Lundgren, Goldsmith, and Snyder, 1958; Dixon and Lundgren, 1968, p. 225ff). The main part of this fault trends for 48 kilometers (30 miles) generally east-west across the regional trends, but the strike is somewhat sinuous; the dip is north at a moderate angle, in part under the Devils Hopyard basin. At each end, however, the fault bends abruptly to the left into the regional strike; at the western bend indeed the fault surface swings around a north-plunging axis until it is dipping back to the east-northeast. The metamorphic rocks along the fault are converted to mylonite or blastomylonite in a zone up to $\frac{3}{4}$ kilometer ($\frac{1}{2}$ mile) thick, and at least a good deal of movement must have been late, but movement may well have been concentrated in this zone during the main deformation as well (Lundgren, 1969).

At the Honey Hill fault, the structure changes

abruptly. Between the fault and Long Island Sound lies a striplike area of gneiss domes and reclined gneiss anticlines, somewhat like the Bronson Hill anticlinorium (if anything, more complicated) and continuous with it at its south end but trending roughly east, following the sinuosities of the Honey Hill fault into the southeast corner of Connecticut. The rocks are those of the south end of the anticlinorium—not only mafic metavolcanics (Middletown formation) and Oliverian gneisses (Monson formation), but also underlying quartzose metasediments with a unit or units of pure quartzite (Plainfield formation), cut by pink granite and granitic-gneiss (Sterling plutonic series) that may be the result of partial melting of the metasediments (Bernold, ms. 1962; Goldsmith and Dixon, 1968; see also above, p. 105). At the western bend of the Honey Hill fault, the higher units of the Merrimack synclinorium can be traced into a narrow, completely isoclinal, intensely sheared syncline (Chester syncline), not more than a few hundred meters (yards) wide, evidently the root of the recumbent syncline under the Devils Hopyard basin to the north, which extends southward along the east side of the Bronson Hill anticlinorium and then becomes part of an anastomosing network of tightly pinched synclines between the domes on either side. An eastward extension (Hunts Brook syncline) from the south end of this syncline makes a spectacular reverse-S in the area northwest of New London, Connecticut, having been refolded on an axis that now plunges moderately northeast (Goldsmith, 1961). The whole area lies in the sillimanite zone, and in much of it muscovite has broken down to form orthoclase; mylonite and other evidence of shearing disappears about where this breakdown occurs. Cutting indiscriminately across all the other rocks and structures are dikes, commonly striking east-west and dipping south, of undeformed aplitic granite (Westerly granite) related to undeformed granite that farther east in Rhode Island cuts Upper Carboniferous strata (Feininger, 1968).

This extraordinary east-west strip forms a bridge of older rocks from the Bronson Hill anticlinorium around the south end of the Merrimack synclinorium to the granitic region of western Rhode Island; its origin must be tied up with the no less extraordinary Honey Hill fault that marks its northern boundary. That fault appears at first sight to be a right-handed wrench fault, and the map pattern of the refolded fold near New London and of other similar features in the area suggests the same movement. As the fault bends abruptly at both ends, however, and as the Bronson Hill anticlinorium just to the west is completely unaffected, the wrench movement cannot have been significant at least during the later movement recorded by the mylonite along the fault. This later movement may have been normal, despite the rather low dip of the fault, the slip being roughly parallel to the north-plunging axis of the western bend and of the sinuosities; the combination of normal movement on the fault and the west dip of the units to the north could give the impression of right-handed wrench movement.

Another hypothesis is suggested by the rough parallelism of the fault surface and the axis of its bends and sinuosities with the axis of the refolded fold to the south and the axial surface and probably the axis of the recumbent syncline immediately to the north; a little farther north, on the other hand, the recumbent syncline becomes nearly horizontal beneath the Devils Hopyard basin. If one assumes that the axes and surfaces farther south were also nearly horizontal when formed and that they have only been tilted to the north at a later date, then the structural features in question all becomes consistent with the plastic movement of nappelike masses from the Bronson Hill anticlinorium eastward into the Merrimack synclinorium. The present abrupt termination of the synclinorium, which presumably originally continued on to the south, and the present east-west trend of the Honey Hill fault and of the gneiss anticlines south of it, together with the appearance of right-handed wrench movement, would thus be secondary, the result of uptilting south of an east-west axis and subsequent erosion; the present *map* of southeastern Connecticut south of the latitude of the Devils Hopyard basin would be in effect a *cross section* of the bottom of the synclinorium and of the gneiss folds in its floor as they existed at the end of the plastic part of the deformation. Thus the principal movement on the Honey Hill fault would have been thrust, the upper block moving east; it is curious that the thrust fault formed within the lower upright limb of the recumbent syncline instead of in the overturned limb, but minor thrust faults, some associated with mylonite, occur in the rocks above the fault up into the overturned limb (Dixon and Lundgren, 1968, p. 227). Finally, the coincidence of the trend of the tilting with that of the post-Carboniferous aplite dikes suggests that the tilting may be post-Carboniferous (though certainly pre-Upper Triassic); perhaps the late movement on the Honey Hill fault was associated with the tilting. It may be added that radiometric ages in this area, including those in the well known Middletown pegmatite district, probably one of the best dated group of rocks in the world, are not Acadian, as farther north and northwest, but late Paleozoic—

Alleghany (as in western Connecticut; see p. 102). Lundgren (1966, p. 450; 1968) has suggested indeed that not only the east-west strike but also the high-grade metamporphism of this coastal strip (sillimanite-orthoclase zone) were produced in the late Paleozoic, at the same time as the metamorphism and granite intrusion in the Upper Carboniferous rocks of southern Rhode Island (see below, p. 111).

From its eastern abrupt bend, the Honey Hill fault has been traced northward into southern Massachusetts, roughly parallel to both strike and dip in the enclosing rocks (their dip is 25° or less to the west); this stretch of the fault is known as the Lake Chargoggagoggmanchauggagoggchaubunagungamaugg fault. The Lake Char fault throws the metavolcanic rocks (Quinebaug formation, also an associated gabbro body) at the base of the sequence in the Merrimack synclinorium (p. 108) against the older metasediments (Plainfield formation) and the accompanying granitic gneisses (Sterling plutonic series) that underlie the area to the east in Rhode Island (see p. 113).

Except for the cross-structure formed by the Honey Hill fault and the strip south of it, the trend of the rocks in the Merrimack synclinorium roughly parallels that in the Bronson Hill anticlinorium to the west—N20°E in Connecticut, about N5°E in southern and central Massachusetts, and from N20°E to N50°E in New Hampshire. The swing to the northeast is less abrupt, however, than along the Bronson Hill anticlinorium; along the east side of the synclinorium indeed it takes place in central Massachusetts. In view of the dispute about the age and sequence of the beds and the possibility of large-scale recumbent folding, it is difficult to be sure of the longitudinal structure, but it seems as if the synclinorium deepens northward at least into east-central New Hampshire. Certainly the strip south of the Honey Hill fault now marks a major culmination.

The Merrimack synclinorium and its margins include the largest body of high-grade metamorphic rocks in the Northern Appalachians, and perhaps also the largest volume of syntectonic Paleozoic intrusives. It may therefore be considered to mark the metamorphic and plutonic axis of the chain, along which a vast thickness of Paleozoic sediments was downbuckled and subjected to the extremes of heat and pressure, probably (though not yet certainly) during the Acadian orogeny. Except for the Worcester plants, no fossils are known in the entire belt, and hence opinions on the age of the orogeny depend on the relative importance attached to the Carboniferous date given for the plants, which demands an

Alleghany age (presumably about Permian), and to the correlations with dated beds in the adjoining belts, which indicate an Acadian age (Middle Devonian or younger, possibly but not probably as late as Early Carboniferous). Only in the extreme south has evidence of more than one major deformation been found; here the later movement on the Honey Hill fault is clearly later than the metamorphism, yet the fault itself appears to be cut by steep faults, associated with silicification (e.g., Lantern Hill fault) that may well be Triassic, like the silicified zones in southern New Hampshire.

Whereas the New Hampshire plutonic series is syntectonic to the deformation, whatever its age, the White Mountain series is clearly later. Because somewhat similar alkalic rocks lie unconformably beneath Upper Carboniferous beds in the basins in southeastern Massachusetts and Rhode Island, the series was first dated as Lower Carboniferous, but more recently it has been assigned to the Jurassic and, in part, Cretaceous, on the basis of radiometry (see Toulmin, 1961; Foland, Quinn, and Giletti, 1970). It has also been commonly compared to the alkalic Monteregian stocks of southern Quebec, to which a Cretaceous age is now assigned. One might argue indeed that a pocket of highly alkalic magma has been present along a northwest-southeast belt from near Boston to near Montreal since the late Paleozoic, migrating northwestward to a present position under the Ottawa graben beyond Montreal; this whole belt is still characterized by many small earthquakes (Smith, 1957, Fig. 5). Chapman (1968), on the other hand, considers the alkalic rocks of eastern Massachusetts and Rhode Island part of a northeast-trending belt of mildly alkalic intrusives also exposed along the coast of southeastern Maine (p. 137).

Southeastern New England

Beyond the Merrimack synclinorium, it is even less easy to generalize about the geology than in that belt or farther west. One would expect an anticlinorium of some sort, but the presumably older rocks are mostly rather little known and very poorly dated; on them, however, rest several basins of younger rocks of various ages. Moreover, the area is one of rather low relief and heavy glacial cover, so that exposures are mostly inadequate.

Except for the ubiquitous glacial cover and for Tertiary and Cretaceous sediments, which underlie the offshore islands and Cape Cod and reach northward along the shore to within 40 kilometers (25 miles) of Boston, the youngest rocks present form the large Narragansett basin (Quinn and Oliver, 1962; Mutch, 1968; Quinn and Moore, 1968), 90 kilometers (55 miles) long and up to 40 kilometers (25 miles) wide, which underlies Narragansett Bay and its shores in eastern Rhode Island and extends northeast into Massachusetts, one arm reaching to a point about 17 kilometers (10 miles) south of Boston. The kilometers (miles) of strata within it are clastic, entirely continental sediments—conglomerate, graywacke, gray and red shale, and coal—and are dated by plants found near the base of the series as Upper Carboniferous (Knox, 1944); it is possible that the highest beds reach into the Lower Permian. Small patches of volcanics occur in one part of the basin. The basal beds rest unconformably on the surrounding rocks except where the contact is a fault (as along the western side of the basin north of Providence, Rhode Island; silicification along this fault suggests but certainly does not prove a Triassic age for it) or where, in the extreme southwest corner of the basin, they are intruded by granite and pegmatite (Nichols, 1956). Here metamorphism has altered the Carboniferous rocks to staurolite-garnet-mica schist, but elsewhere they are mildly or barely metamorphosed in contrast to the surrounding higher-grade rocks; they are severely deformed, however, and the coal is a graphitic anthracite, useful as a source of graphite rather than as a fuel. Two small basins of similar rocks, only 10 to 20 kilometers (5 to 10 miles) long, lie to the northwest in northern Rhode Island and adjacent Massachusetts; these rocks may indeed be older than those in the main basin, like those in the Boston basin (see below). The Worcester plant locality presumably records still another basin, but whether it is merely a tiny patch or includes most of the Merrimack synclinorium in Massachusetts is, as indicated above, in dispute.

Formerly it was believed that the granite and pegmatite that intrude the Carboniferous rocks in the southwest corner of the Narragansett basin are part of a large batholith of granitic gneiss extending over much of western Rhode Island and adjacent Connecticut, but recent work shows that that gneiss is older than the Carboniferous sediments and that the only younger intrusions are a batholith of medium- to coarse-grained granite (Narragansett Pier granite) extending along the shore of southwestern Rhode Island but barely reaching Connecticut, and dikes and stocks of aplitic granite (Westerly granite, quarried here and there for building stone), scattered across southwestern Rhode Island and southeastern Connecticut (in the latter state along the east-west strip of gneiss anticlines). Within the basin the belt of middle-grade metamorphism and intrusion is confined to the southwest corner; on the other hand, the trends of folding in the basin rocks are about N10°E in the south end of the basin, swinging to about N60°E in its northeastern part and even farther around in the arm south of Boston.

Around Boston, but separated from the nearby arm of the Narragansett basin by the Blue Hills, a ridge of alkalic plutonic rock (Quincy granite and associated rocks) only 5 kilometers (3 miles) wide, is another basin of dark, clastic, slightly metamorphosed sedimentary rocks, ranging from conglomerate to slate (Boston Bay group). The basal conglomerate unit in this basin includes the famous Squantum tillite (whether it is a tillite is in debate; see Dott, 1961). No coal is present and only a few poorly preserved plant impressions have been found. The sedimentary rocks are underlain by a thick series of mildly alkalic volcanics (Mattapan volcanic complex); an unconformity has been reported between but if present is probably minor, for in places sedimentary and volcanic rocks are interbedded. The folding of the basin has an average strike of about N75°E, but it is irregular and complex in detail, especially along the imbricated south margin (Billings, 1929). The north and south margins of the basin appear to be outward-dipping thrust faults.

The rocks here have generally been correlated with those of the Narragansett basin and hence assigned to the Upper Carboniferous (or Lower Permian; the tillite has sometimes been considered an argument for the latter age assignment). Some observers, however, have pointed out that, although the alkalic plutonic rock of the Blue Hills is very common as boulders in the basal conglomerate in the north arm of the Narragansett basin on the south side of the hills, it is not known in the conglomerate of the Boston basin on the north side, which does contain lenses as well as fragments of the possibly related alkalic volcanics, and they have therefore interpreted the sediments and associated volcanics as pre-Upper Carboniferous; Pollard (1965) has given reasons for assigning a Lower Carboniferous (mainly Mississippian) age.

In northeasternmost Massachusetts, roughly 30 and 50 kilometers (20 and 30 miles) north of Boston and only 5 to 15 kilometers (3 to 10 miles) southeast of the supposedly Silurian metasedimentary rocks on the southeast flank of the Merrimack synclinorium, lie two small isolated basins (Topsfield and Newbury basins) of mainly felsic volcanic rocks, each exposed over an area of only a few square kilometers (a few square miles), but here marine fossils have been found, suggesting an Early Devonian or Late Silurian age. These rocks are in strong contrast to those in the Merrimack synclinorium so short a distance across strike but resembled volcanics of similar age in southeastern Maine and adjacent New Brunswick (see below, p. 137), approximately along strike though separated by 225 kilometers (140 miles) of the waters of the Gulf of Maine. (A patch of volcanics just north of the Boston basin presumably belongs either to this group of volcanics or to those associated with the basin sediments.)

Finally, a few small patches of fossiliferous Cambrian slate are known in eastern Massachusetts, one in an inlier completely surrounded by the Carboniferous rocks of the Narragansett basin not far from Providence, and others as inclusions in the alkalic plutonic rocks of the Blue Hills and other intrusions near Boston. The marine faunas in these strata are much more like those of Europe (and of southeastern Newfoundland and southern New Brunswick; see Chapter 7, p. 161); Chapter 6, p. 137) than they are like those in the Valley and Ridge province on the other side of New England, only 200 kilometers (120 miles) away.

All the rest of the rocks exposed in the area southeast of the low-grade belt extending from southeastern New Hampshire past Worcester, Massachusetts, are either mesozonal metamorphic rocks or plutonic rocks. The apparently plutonic rocks predominate, except perhaps along the northwest margin of the area; large areas are underlain by granitic, granodioritic, and dioritic gneiss, and across these cut the Blue Hills mass and several other stocks of distinctly alkalic rocks, the largest of which, forming Cape Ann northeast of Boston, is at least 30 by 15 kilometers (18 by 9 miles) in surface area.

The dispute over the age of the rocks in the Merrimack synclinorium affects these rocks also. If the correlation to the New Hampshire stratigraphic sequence is accepted, and if the various quartzite (and conglomerate) units along the southeast flank of the synclinorium really represent the base of the Silurian, then at least the nonplutonic rocks farther southeast are Ordovician or older, but if the sequence proposed in Massachusetts is accepted and the quartzite is the oldest unit, appearing in anticlines, then presumably some part of these rocks is Upper Carboniferous, though no obvious line separates them from rocks farther southeast that clearly underlie unconformably the much less metamorphosed Silurian to Carboniferous rocks of the various basins. Recent investigations have emphasized the presence of many faults in eastern Massachusetts (Bell, 1968; Skehan, 1968), especially large thrust faults nearly parallel to the bedding (striking northeast and dipping northwest); apparently one of these faults (Clinton-Newbury fault) largely conceals the probable base of the Silurian in this region.

In the northwestern part of the area in question is a unit of quartzose metasediments (Westboro quartzite) that includes some pure quartzite and probably underlies more varied, partly metavolcanic rocks (Marlboro formation); apparently it can be followed, though with interruptions, from just north of the Boston basin (LaForge, 1932, p. 15—17) southwestward across east-central Massachusetts to northeastern Connecticut and into the quartzose metasedimentary unit (Plainfield formation) at the base of the local sequence in southeastern Connecticut, lying there beneath possibly Ordovician metavolconic rocks (Monson and Middletown formations). In northern Rhode Island near Providence, on the other hand, quartzite and other metasedimentary and metavolcanic rocks (Blackstone group) and plutonic rocks intruding them are clearly older than the Upper Carboniferous beds just to the east in the Narragansett basin (Quinn, Ray, and Seymour, 1949), and the considerably less metamorphosed Lower Cambrian beds in the outlier within the basin have been shown (Dowse, 1950) to rest unconformably on a granodiorite similar to that widely distributed in southeastern Massachusetts. Recent work by Charles E. Shaw, Jr., (personal communication) in Massachusetts just north of Rhode Island (see also Quinn and Moore, 1968, p. 271, 273) suggests that the two quartzite-bearing units are not the same, the second being more deformed than the first and intruded by what may be the same granodiorite. Unfortunately, the relations of the various plutonic rocks in this region are still very uncertain; radiometry suggests a very late Precambrian age (about 580 million years—distinctly post-Grenville—Fairbairn and others, 1967) for some of the granodiorite in southeastern Massachusetts and perhaps elsewhere, but in Rhode Island at least the bulk of the granitic rocks seems to be Devonian (apart from the known Carboniferous ones). Alkalic rocks are present in Rhode Island also (East Greenwich group), younger than these possibly Devonian granites but older than the Upper Carboniferous sediments, and they have generally been correlated with the alkalic rocks of the Blue Hills south of Boston. That all the alkalic rocks, intrusive and extrusive, in eastern Massachusetts and Rhode Island are contemporaneous is, however, an unproved assumption,

which radiometric determinations tend to discredit (Lyons and Faul, 1968, p. 311; Zartman, 1969).

If one is willing to reject the interpretation that part of these high-grade rocks must be Carboniferous, the rest of the lines of evidence, though mostly very tenuous, can be woven into a hypothetical history that has the possible virtue of being consistent with the somewhat better known history of the Kennebecasis anticlinorium along the coast of southern New Brunswick (Chapter 6, p. 136ff.), which lies along strike on the other side of the Gulf of Maine. Except for the alkalic rocks of the Blue Hills and comparable stocks, the plutonic rocks in the east part of the area would be the core of an anticlinorium, perhaps a late Precambrian geanticline, upon which sediments and volcanics were deposited in local basins at various times from the Lower Cambrian to the Upper Carboniferous, but which, unlike the belts farther west, was never deeply buried beneath thick bodies of marine sediments. The metamorphic rocks in the western part of the area would be Lower Paleozoic, forming the east flank of the Merrimack synclinorium but invaded by large bodies of mainly granitic plutonic rocks during either the Taconic or the Acadian orogeny or both; if Acadian, these plutonic rocks may belong to the New Hampshire plutonic series, but according to Currier (Currier and Jahns, 1952) at least some of them are metasomatic and not magmatic. The boundary between these Lower Paleozoic rocks and the anticlinorial "basement" might lie along the trend of the first, apparently younger, quartzite mentioned above, running roughly from the northeast corner of Rhode Island to the northeast corner of Massachusetts; it is shown with question marks on the map (Pl. 1.). The alkalic rocks, which all lie southeast of this boundary, used to be compared with the White Mountain series of New Hampshire, but they are certainly pre-Upper Carboniferous, whereas it is now assigned a Jurassic date (see above, p. 111). The core of the anticlinorium seems to have been little affected by the Acadian orogeny (unless the alkalic intrusions are considered its work), but the area was subjected to the Alleghany orogeny, which produced mesozonal metamorphism and granite intrusion in a narrow belt along the present coast of Rhode Island and perhaps eastern Connecticut, tight folding and incipient metamorphism as far north as Boston. It hardly needs to be emphasized that this hypothesis rests on very flimsy foundations; for example, the western boundary of the probably Precambrian rocks has not been recognized as such in the field.

Summary

A cross section of New England from Lake Champlain to the Atlantic Ocean displays three synclinoria and three anticlinoria. The western synclinorium, which represents the Valley and Ridge province here, is formed in thick Cambrian and Ordovician sedimentary rocks, mostly carbonate rock though the more clastic Taconic sequence lies nested enigmatically within its southern extension. The other two are filled with even thicker clastic metasediments ranging in age up to at least Devonian and are not unlike, though the western one seems to contain more metavolcanics, whereas the eastern one has been subjected to higher-grade metamorphism and to much more plutonism.

The three anticlinoria, on the other hand, are quite different. The westernmost, a line of great upbucklings of the Precambrian basement that corresponds to the Blue Ridge province farther south, was evidently once covered with Lower Paleozoic sediments; through much of the Cambrian and the lower half of the Ordovician the boundary between dominantly carbonate and dominantly clastic sedimentation, the edge of the carbonate bank, was located here (Rodgers, 1968). The region of the anticlinorium began to rise by early Middle Ordovician time, and shortly thereafter it was supplying clastic sediment to the Valley and Ridge province and to the platform to the west. It remained high during the Silurian, for the Silurian deposits in the Valley and Ridge province overlap progressively eastward toward it, till in the Hudson Valley the very highest beds of the Silurian or the base of the Devonian come to rest directly on deformed Ordovician rocks. Whether Lower Devonian strata extended across it is not known, but in any case it must by then have been quite low; during the Middle and Late Devonian, clastic sediments were transported across its eroded stumps into the Valley and Ridge province and beyond from new uplifts farther east.

In the middle anticlinorium, no Precambrian rocks are known; instead it seems to expose a belt of Taconic (Middle or Upper Ordovician) intrusions, which may follow an old volcanic island arc. On the other hand, Lower Silurian to Lower Devonian strata, which transgress unconformably over the presumed Ordovician rocks, show little change across it, except that they contain considerably more limestone to the west and perhaps more volcanics near its crest; thus it could then have had little surface expression except for a few remaining volcanoes.

We see only a fragment of the eastern anticlinorium; if we understand it correctly (which is rather doubtful), it was a persistent anticlinorium of very late Precambrian rocks throughout most of the Paleozoic, either as the southeastern edge of the complex trough or geosyncline in in which the thick Lower and Middle Paleozoic sediments were deposited or simply as one island in a nonvolcanic island chain within that trough, others of which appear in southern New Brunswick, Cape Breton Island, and southeastern Newfoundland (p. 139, 144, 161). The northwest border of this trough was the central platform of the continent, represented along our line of section by the Adirondack Mountains; thus only the western edge of the geosyncline lay in what is now the Valley and Ridge province, the main part, and the deepest, being in what is now the metamorphic region of New England. Linear uplifts or island arcs were present at certain times within the geosyncline, particularly during the period of unrest during the Ordovician that culminated in the Taconic orogeny.

One remarkable feature of the geology of central and southern New England is the southwestward convergence of these anticlinoria and synclinoria. From flat-lying Paleozoic rocks at the northwest corner of Vermont across strike to the Gulf of Maine, under which the southeastern Massachusetts anticlinorium is probably hidden, is 300 kilometers (200 miles), whereas from flat-lying Paleozoics in the Catskill Mountains to the edge of the same anticlinorium just north of Rhode Island is less than 200 (less than 120); on the other hand, from the north shore of Gaspé to southern New Brunswick is nearly 400 kilometers (250 miles). This convergence results from the southward narrowing particularly of the two eastern synclinoria, to a minor extent of the intervening Bronson Hill anticlinorium. It is hardly a coincidence that the grade of metamorphism (and in general the grain size of the metamorphic rocks) also increases southward along the strike of each belt, and in particular that andalusite, present in northern Vermont, much of New Hampshire, eastern Massachusetts, and central Rhode Island, gives way southwestward to kyanite, present in parts of eastern Vermont and western Massachusetts and especially widespread in Connecticut (Thompson and Norton, 1968, Fig. 1). In southwestern New England we are seeing deeper into the metamorphic core of the Appalachians than farther northeast; one might even suggest, viewing it by the down-structure method (Mackin, 1950), that the map of the Appalachians in New England and adjacent Canada is not far from an oblique cross section of that core, so that the southwestward convergence simply reflects its downward narrowing within the crust.

The orogenic history of New England is best displayed by considering the various angular unconformities in the stratigraphic sequence, upon each of which a new series of deposits transgressed across all previous rocks. Cambrian deposits, or clastic strata conformably underlying Cambrian deposits, lap over gneiss and other Precambrian rocks in the core of the Green Mountains and related anticlinoria, and probably also over very late Precambrian granodiorite and so forth in southeastern Massachusetts; thus there had already been orogeny and plutonism, probably more than once, before the beginning of the Paleozoic era. Silurian (or earliest Devonian) deposits lap over Lower Paleozoic rocks in many places from the Hudson Valley eastward as far as the Newbury basin, notably over the Highlandcroft plutonic rocks in northern New Hampshire and perhaps over intrusive Oliverian rocks elsewhere on the Bronson Hill anticlinorium. Probably the Taconic orogeny thus recorded was itself compound, to judge by unconformities in several places *beneath* the highest pre-Silurian units. Upper Carboniferous deposits (and possibly also Upper Devonian, depending on the age assignment of the rocks in the Boston basin) lap over metamorphosed rocks of various, mostly undetermined ages in southeastern New England, recording the Acadian orogeny, which was probably the most intense and widespread that affected New England, though unfortunately poorly dated here (in eastern Maine and in the Maritime Provinces—Acadia—it too is known to have been compound, but the principal unconformity lies between Lower or lower Middle Devonian and Upper Devonian strata; (see Chapter 6, p. 146). The older metamorphic and plutonic rocks (and in the Maritime Provinces also Carboniferous strata) are overlapped by Upper Triassic deposits and cut by apparently associated faults accompanied by silicification, providing an upper age limit for the Alleghany orogeny, which appears to have affected only the southern edge of New England. The Triassic rocks in their tilted and downfaulted basins are overlapped in turn by the Cretaceous and Cenozoic strata of the Atlantic Coastal Plain, now present only on the extreme southern fringe of New England, which was apparently being slowly uplifted and tilted southward during their deposition. Finally the deposits of the Pleistocene continental glacier transgress indiscriminately over all the other rocks in the region.

CHAPTER 6

The Canadian Appalachians and Maine

Appalachian trends continue to the northeast from central New England across the southeastern part of the province of Quebec, the state of Maine, and the Maritime Provinces (New Brunswick, Nova Scotia, and Prince Edward Island) to the Gulf of St. Lawrence. The geology of this large region has been rather spottily known, but work is progressing very fast and new insights are appearing every year. Most of the major tectonic belts recognizable in New England can be followed northeastward into and most of the way across the region, although the more southeastern belts are not linearly continuous and some of them are partly interrupted by the Carboniferous basins around the Gulf of St. Lawrence. The grade of metamorphism falls off in the same direction, and mesozonal rocks hardly reach central Maine; moreover, fossils are considerably commoner, particularly in Silurian and later strata, though there are still many poorly dated terrains. On the other hand, plutonic rocks are about as abundant as to the southwest in New England, except in the Carboniferous basins and on the peninsula of Gaspé.

Sutton, Notre Dame, and Shickshock Anticlinoria and Belts to the Northwest.

The valley and estuary of the St. Lawrence River mark the northwest margin of the Canadian Appa-

lachians; on the far side rise the Laurentian Mountains, comparable to but much more extensive than the Adirondack Mountains in New York and forming the rim of the Canadian shield. In the valley and under the estuary, between the crystalline Precambrian rocks of the shield and the deformed Paleozoic rocks of the Appalachian belt, nearly flat-lying lower Paleozoic strata underlie an area shaped something like a very slim hourglass tilted diagonally. The southwest bulb of the hourglass is the St. Lawrence Lowland between Quebec City and the Adirondacks (Houde and Clark, 1962). Here 700 meters (2000 feet) of Lower and Middle Ordovician carbonate rocks (generally with Lower Ordovician or Upper Cambrian sandstone at the base) are overlain by 2000 meters (about 6000 feet) of Middle and Upper Ordovician shale and sandstone, evidently debris eroded from the Appalachians during the uplift accompanying the Taconic orogeny. No younger sedimentary rocks are known, save for some Devonian fragments preserved in a vent breccia at Montreal. Much of the area is covered with a deep blanket of Pleistocene marine clay. Except near the southeast margin, the Paleozoic strata are merely warped into an elongate basin, the trough of which extends 150 kilometers (90 miles) northeastward from a point 30 kilometers (20 miles) east of Montreal; the southwest end of the basin near Montreal shows a few very gentle folds with northeast trends. The strata are also broken by normal faults, some of them large, especially near the edge of the basin, and they are cut by a family of alkalic igneous plugs in the vicinity of Montreal (the Monteregian intrusives), dated radiometrically as Cretaceous; these stand out in the lowland as bold mountains, like Mount Royal or Mont Réal itself.

The other bulb of the hourglass is mostly submerged beneath the St. Lawrence estuary; all we see is 700 meters (2000 feet) of conformable (Middle? and) Upper Ordovician and Silurian limestone with some shale and a very little sandstone exposed on the large island of Anticosti, plus 100 meters or so (several hundred feet) of Early and Middle Ordovician carbonate rock exposed on the north shore of the estuary opposite Anticosti and in the Mingan Islands along that shore. Wells prove that the total thickness is at least 2300 meters (7500 feet; Roliff, 1968), and that there is no thick clastic wedge to record the Taconic orogeny, which seems to be reflected by less than a hundred meters (less than 300 feet) of black shale spanning perhaps half the Middle Ordovician and the base of the Upper (Riva, 1969, p. 533–540). In the stem of the hourglass, Middle Ordovician rocks are preserved in patches along the north shore of the estuary for 130 kilometers (80 miles) northeast from Quebec City; they are flat-lying except where involved in the La Malbaie or Charlevoix cryptoexplosion structure (Robertson, 1968; Rondot, 1968). In these patches, and also along the north side of the St. Lawrence Lowland for about the same distance west of Quebec City, Middle Ordovician stata rest directly on the Precambrian. Otherwise the estuary washes Precambrian gneiss on one side and deformed Cambrian and Ordovician slate and sandstone on the other side or on the small islands within it.

The northwest boundary of the Appalachian deformed belt is largely hidden—to the southwest of Quebec City under wide expanses of glacial drift and Pleistocene marine clay, to the northeast under the estuary. In the vicinity of Quebec City, however (Raymond, 1913; Osborne, 1956, p. 170–173), it is clearly visible; a frontal thrust fault brings Cambrian and Ordovician Appalachian rocks out over the lowland strata, which here are Middle Ordovician shale that is badly deformed for a couple of kilometers (about a mile) in front of the fault. This thrust fault was first recognized as such by Sir William Logan over a century ago (Logan, 1861), and it has been called Logan's line ever since; it is probably continuous for at least a couple of hundred kilometers (well over a hundred miles) in both directions from Quebec City. The belt of deformed shale in front of the fault has been mapped from Quebec nearly to Lake Champlain

(St. Germain complex of Houde and Clark, 1962). In many places the shale contains "Wildflysch-type" breccias (see Bailey, Collet, and Field, 1928, p. 607–608) made of older rocks from the southeast side of the fault (Citadel formation of Osborne, 1956, p. 189–191; "argiles-à-blocs" of St-Julien, 1968; also Hathaway formation of Hawley, 1957, at the north end of Lake Champlain); they are quite comparable to the breccias that accompany the Taconic klippe in New York (Chapter 4, p. 84–86). St-Julien reports that some of the blocks in the "Wildflysch" are themselves made of slightly older "Wildflysch".

Except near the international boundary, where the rocks of the Highgate Springs and Philipsburg slices and of the St. Albans synclinorium are present (see Chapter 4, p. 73), the rocks next southeast of Logan's line are badly deformed slate and sandstone, locally conglomeratic (Quebec group or complex), closely resembling the rocks of the Taconic sequence in easternmost New York and adjacent New England, in places even to stratigraphic details. Such rocks extend northeastward along the south shore of the St. Lawrence estuary to the end of the Gaspé Peninsula; near the end of the peninsula, indeed, one can still recognize typically Taconic Lower and Middle Ordovician strata in a typically Taconic stratigraphic sequence. Slaty cleavage is commonly present, but otherwise metamorphism is minimal. As in the Taconic region, the none too common fossils are either graptolites from the earlier half of the Ordovician or trilobites and associated forms of Cambrian age; Cambrian fossils have been found especially in the vicinity of Quebec City. Limestone-conglomerate and limestone-breccia beds are locally abundant and spectacular and are found almost entirely on the northwest side of the belt; the pebbles and boulders are chiefly carbonate rock, but locally include granite and gneiss, presumably from the Canadian shield. Some of the carbonate boulders are fossiliferous, across the river from Quebec City, indeed, certain Middle and Upper Cambrian faunas, unknown elsewhere in the region, come from enormous exotic blocks in such breccias (see Osborne, 1956, p. 187–188).

The belt of Taconic-type rocks southeast of the St. Lawrence valley and estuary ranges from 15 to 40 kilometers (10 to 25 miles) in width. Southwest of a point opposite the north tip of Maine (160 kilometers—100 miles—east-northeast of Quebec City), it is succeeded southeastward by a belt of slightly higher-grade metamorphic rocks—sericite and chlorite phyllite and schist, quartzite, and metagraywacke—that form the core of an anticlinorium underlying the Notre Dame Mountains (Béland, 1957). The anticlinorium is doubly plunging, its north end about opposite the northern point of Maine, its south end about 90 kilometers (55 miles) north of the Vermont border, where it is relayed en echelon to the west by the north-plunging Sutton or Sutton Mountains anticlinorium, which is the north end of the Green Mountains anticlinorium of Vermont. The rocks in the Sutton anticlinorium certainly, and those in the Notre Dame anticlinorium probably, are the northern continuation of those in the Green Mountains anticlinorium, the basal clastic sequence and overlying strata, probably mainly Cambrian.

The relation of the rocks in these anticlinoria to the Taconic-type rocks nearer the St. Lawrence is obscured by thick glacial drift on the northwest flank of the mountains. Where detailed mapping has been done among the latter rocks, they clearly form a series of thrust slices, thrust toward the northwest (Osborne, 1956; Hubert, 1967). At either end of the belt, moreover, the higher slices, generally composed of Lower Ordovician and older strata, seem to be separated from the lowest, composed of Middle Ordovician strata, by more of the "Wildflysch-type" breccia, suggesting that the higher slices represent allochthonous slide masses like those postulated in the Taconic region (St-Julien, 1968; Riva, 1968; Stevens, ms. 1969).

The strata on the east flank of the St. Albans synclinorium at the international border can be followed northeastward along the west flank of the Sutton anticlinorium, but what carbonate they contain gradually fades out into slate until they merge into the largely slaty or phyllitic terrain where the Sutton anticlinorium plunges down. The south end of the Taconic-type rocks (Sillery or Granby formation in the Granby slice) lies *west* of this area in poorly exposed country not more than 25 kilometers (16 miles) north of the border, more or less on strike with the axis of the St. Albans synclinorium or its western flank and surrounded on three sides by the shale in the core of that synclinorium, locally containing the "Wildflysch-type" breccia. Farther northeast, however, there are exposures of Ordovician carbonate rock of a facies appropriate to the synclinorium, apparently underlying the surrounding Taconic-type rocks (limestone of Acton Vale; Gorman cited by Osberg, 1969, p. 698).

The anticlinoria in this part of Quebec continue the line of anticlinoria represented in the United States by the Blue Ridge and South Mountain, the Hudson and Berkshire Highlands, and the Green Mountains, and like them they lie approximately along the northwest edge of significant metamorphism in the Paleozoic rocks of the Appalachian belt. The basement is nowhere exposed in the Quebec Appalachians, however, and there is no

Valley and Ridge province to the northwest; instead, beyond the belt of Taconic-type rocks, one comes at once to the foreland where Ordovician, even Middle Ordovician, strata rest undisturbed on the Precambrian rocks of the Canadian shield. Yet, as was pointed out years ago by Raymond (1913, p. 30; see also Bailey, Collet, and Field, 1928, p. 601 ff.), the boulders in the conglomerates and breccias in the Taconic-type rocks near Quebec City and northeastward were evidently derived from a carbonate sequence that included a fossiliferous Cambrian succession, now nowhere exposed at the present land surface.

Clearly, therefore, a Cambro-Ordovician carbonate sequence, perhaps with Valley and Ridge structure, once existed between the Notre Dame anticlinorium and the Canadian shield, but it has been eliminated from the present surface by large-scale faulting (or sliding) along Logan's line. If so, it could have been disposed of in two different ways. On one hypothesis, it could have been lifted up along Logan's line and thrust forward over the margin of the Canadian shield along a decollement somewhat above the present land surface and then entirely eroded away; that such a hypothesis is reasonable is shown by the relations at the margin of the Caledonide orogenic belt in southern Norway where a "Valley and Ridge" belt apparently about 100 kilometers (60 miles) wide has been entirely eliminated by erosion except where later downfaulting has preserved a narrow transverse slice of it in the Oslo graben. On a second hypothesis (Raymond's), the carbonate belt, originally perhaps no wider than the present Valley and Ridge belt in the Champlain Valley, could have been completely overlapped by the belt of Taconic-type rocks west of the anticlinorium, being still hidden at depth beneath them. On this second hypothesis, the south end of the Taconic-type rocks (Granby slice), lying on strike with and as if nested within the north-plunging St. Albans synclinorium, would be allochthonous and symmetrical with the north end of the Taconic slate mass nested in the south-plunging Middlebury synclinorium. The Taconic-type rocks of Quebec may not constitute a klippe, however, even if their south end is floating in the St. Albans synclinorium, for nothing similar to the eastern carbonate belt ("marble belt") of the Taconic region separates them from the Notre Dame anticlinorium; rather they may still be roughly attached to their original "roots" on the crest or northwest flank of that anticlinorium, having simply slumped northwestward and down over the adjacent carbonate belt when the anticlinorium rose (Kay, 1937, Pl. 5; Henderson, 1958) and having been cut up into thrust slices then or later.

Furthermore, the northward plunge of the St. Albans synclinorium and the consequent disappearance of the carbonate rocks of the Champlain Valley under breccia-bearing slate in southernmost Quebec speak in favor of this second hypothesis. Despite the failure of basement to crop out in the Quebec anticlinoria, the difference in relief between the anticlinorium on the southeast and the synclinorium on the northwest (the latter formed of Taconic-type rocks superposed on carbonate rocks) could thus be as great here as in the Taconic region, but both would stand considerably lower, as though the Quebec salient corresponded to a depression rather than a culmination in the chain. The speculation that the Taconic-type rocks here are allochthonous is not acceptable to many workers in the region, however; for example, Cady, although agreeing that the Taconic klippe is nested rootlessly above the rocks of the Middlebury synclinorium (Cady, 1945, p. 567–570), denies that the comparable rocks in Quebec are similarly nested in the St. Albans synclinorium (Cady, 1960, p. 558), believing rather that the facies of the rocks within the synclinorium changes from carbonate to slate along the strike, the Taconic-type rocks being uplifted from the bottom of the synclinorium more or less at their present position instead of slumping in from the southeast.

In a general way, the strata on the east flank of the Green Mountains anticlinorium in Vermont continue northward along the east flank of the Sutton and Notre Dame anticlinoria in Quebec; indeed the Middle Ordovician fossil locality at Magog (Berry, 1962a), the best tie point for the pre-Silurian stratigraphy of this belt in New England, is in Quebec about 30 kilometers (20 miles) north of the border, near the base of a unit characterized by graphitic slate and including some mainly felsic volcanics (Magog or Beauceville formation.) An unconformity (St-Julien, 1967, p. 47) separates this unit from underlying unfossiliferous strata in the anticlinoria (Caldwell, Brompton, and Mansonville formations), perhaps the same unconformity as that recognized within the Ordovician in northern Vermont (beneath the Umbrella Hill conglomerate; Chapter 5, p. 97) but regionally more extensive. It is probably not the same as the disconformity or unconformity beneath the Middle Ordovician in the carbonate sequence of the Lake Champlain-Taconic region (Chapter 4, p. 72, 78) but might perhaps be the same as the unconformity within the Taconic sequence in the northern part of the Taconic slate mass (Chapter 4, p. 79), to judge by the graptolites found immediately above it.

The strata beneath this unconformity include green and red slate, phyllite, or schist, dirty quartzite, polymictic breccia, perhaps of "Wildflysch" type, and mafic metavolcanics, and they also contain large bodies of ultramafic rock and serpentine (cut by small bodies of granite dated radiometrically as Ordovician; Poole, Kelley, and Neale, 1964, p. 76), probably older than the unconformity; in serpentine bodies near the south-plunging end of the Notre Dame anticlinorium are the famous asbestos deposits of Thetford Mines and vicinity. Phyllite and metavolcanic rocks, without serpentine but apparently cut by pre-Middle Ordovician albite granite or porphyry (pebbles are reported in the Middle Ordovician unit), reappear in the Stoke Mountain anticline to the east, at least in the Magog-Sherbrooke region. In the syncline between (St. Victor synclinorium of St-Julien, 1967), over which the Stoke Mountain anticline has been thrust northwestward, the Middle Ordovician passes upward into Upper Ordovician graywacke, tuff, and slate (containing the only Upper Ordovician fossils in the northwestern part of the northern Appalachians between the St. Lawrence Lowland or the foreland west of Albany and the vicinity of the Aroostook-Matapédia anticlinorium in northeastern Maine; see p. 125, 129 ft.), and these in turn are overlain unconformably by Silurian strata, containing an especially large proportion of limestone. On the east side of the Stoke Mountain anticline, on the other hand, the pre-Middle Ordovician rocks are overlain directly by Silurian and Devonian strata, largely phyllite, forming the northern continuation of the Connecticut Valley synclinorium (see below, p. 122). This region thus provides excellent evidence of two phases of orogeny during the Ordovician, a later "classical" Taconic phase and an earlier "precocious" phase, which may be contemporaneous with the Penobscot orogenic phase of northern Maine (see below, p. 125), although the oldest fossils found above the unconformity there are considerably older, at least in a few places (the rocks beneath are unfossiliferous in both areas).

Several recent studies (e.g., Osberg, 1965; St-Julien, 1967; see also summary in Béland, 1967) have shown that the history of deformation in the northern Green Mountains, Sutton, and Notre Dame anticlinoria is complex, although they do not agree entirely on the details of the successive deformational stages. In general, early isoclinal and commonly more or less recumbent folds (some with axes trending northwest, some northeast—the northwest folds appear to be older), accompanied by a strong axial-surface schistosity, have been refolded by later northeast-trending folds with relatively steep axial surfaces, generally paralleled by slip or fracture cleavage, but in places by a second schistosity; the large, obvious folds making up the anticlinoria belong to the later group. The age of these features has also been in debate; at least the later folds and the accompanying cleavage seem much the same as those found in the Silurian and Devonian rocks to the east (Dennis, 1960, and Osberg, 1969, p. 697–698, would include the earlier schistosity as well), but radiometric evidence (Rickard, 1965) from southernmost Quebec suggests that even the later cleavage in the anticlinoria is Ordovician. Such an age would be consistent with the view (Chapter 5, p. 96) that the Green Mountains anticlinorium was formed and its rocks metamorphosed mainly in the Taconic rather than the Acadian orogeny. So far, no evidence has been adduced to associate the two periods of folding with one or other of the Taconic phases.

Northeast of the plunging north end of the Notre Dame anticlinorium, Siluro-Devonian strata lap unconformably northwestward across the belt of Cambro-Ordovician rocks under discussion, covering completely the northeastern extension of the anticlinorial axis and its east flank and reaching within 10 kilometers (7 miles) of the St. Lawrence estuary at Rimouski. Farther east along the north side of the Gaspé Peninsula (McGerrigle, 1953; McGerrigle and Skidmore, 1967; Béland, 1969), the Cambro-Ordovician or Taconic-type belt averages about 30 kilometers (20 miles) wide, but it narrows again at the east end. Along the coast the strongly deformed rocks show very typical Taconic Ordovician facies and faunas, whereas inland Cambrian fossils have been found in a few places near the two ends of this part of the belt (Hutchinson, 1956, p. 303; Ollerenshaw, 1967, p. 16). As noted above (p. 118), toward the east end of the belt the higher slices may be allochthonous relative to the lowest, which is here composed of Middle Ordovician flyschlike strata (Cloridorme formation of Enos, 1969) with some "Wildflysch-type" breccia (Stevens, ms. 1969).

In the west part of the peninsula along the south side of the belt lies a mass 90 kilometers (55 miles) long and up to 11 kilometers (7 miles) wide of greenstone volcanics and associated metasediments (Shickshock group), dipping generally south and apparently separated from the Silurian rocks to the south by a high-angle fault, at least in part. This mass, in which metamorphism increases rapidly southward, forms the backbone of the rugged Shickshock Mountains, the highest range in the Canadian Appalachians, though the highest summit, Mt. Jacques Cartier (1268 meters—4160 feet) is underlain by granite that intrudes the Taconic-type rocks just east of the east end of the volcanic mass. Moreover, several bodies of serpentine are present in the eastern part of the volcanic mass, notably the large Mt. Albert body, which is dated as pre-Middle Ordovician, both because chromite and serpentine fragments are found in overlying sediments, including the Middle Ordovician flysch along the north shore (Enos, 1969, p. 46 ff.), and by radiometry of its contact aureole (Poole, Kelley, and Neale, 1964, p. 76).

The place of the volcanic rocks within the belt of Taconic-type rocks has been in debate. On one hypothesis, the volcanic rocks are older than the others, overturned or thrust northward upon them, and are comparable to the volcanic rocks in the core of the Green Mountains or Sutton anticlinorium close to the international border (Tibbit Hill volcanics). On the other hypothesis, they rest conformably upon and interfinger with the Taconic-type metasediments, so that they are comparable rather to the pre-Middle Ordovician volcanic rocks along the east flank of the Sutton and Notre Dame anticlinoria. The most recent work (Mattinson, 1964; Ollerenshaw, 1967) confirms the second hypothesis, which is reinforced by the presence of the serpentine bodies. Moreover, a lens of black shale with Middle Ordovician fossils (Mattinson, 1964, p. 69–70) lies (unconformably or in a fault slice?) on the south margin of the volcanics but north of the Silurian and may be the same as the Middle Ordovician graphitic slate unit on the east flank of the anticlinoria in southern Quebec. Probably therefore an anticlinorial axis (Shickshock anticlinorium) reappears on the Gaspé Peninsula within the southern part of the outcrop belt of Taconic-type rocks, passing near the few Cambrian fossil localities. Precisely the same arguments, notably the presence of carbonate fragments in numerous lime-breccia beds and of much fine-grained carbonate debris in other layers (Enos, 1969, p. 50–51), can be used here in favor of the hypothesis that a carbonate or Valley and Ridge belt formerly existed between the deformed rocks on the north shore of the peninsula and the flat-lying rocks of Anticosti, 75 kilometers (45 miles) offshore, but no additional evidence can be adduced.

The trends of the anticlinoria across the province of Quebec outline the great Quebec salient or northern arc of the Appalachians. From due north in central Vermont, they swing to N25°–30°E at the international border and along the Sutton anticlinorium. The central part of the Notre Dame anticlinorium trends about N45°E but at both ends it swings to about N35°E; its northern part is thus gently concave to the northwest and forms a minor dimple on the major salient, centered about opposite Quebec City and spanning approximately the stretch where Middle Ordovician strata are known to lie directly upon the Precambrian rocks of the Canadian shield, as though it were molded about a blunt former high on the edge of the shield. Farther northeast, the general strike swings eastward again; it enters the Gaspé Peninsula with a trend of about N60°E and sketches a broad arc convex to the north, passing through due east to about S55°E at the east end of the peninsula. As already noted, none of the anticlinoria in Quebec expose Precambrian basement, and one can interpret this as implying a major depression corresponding to the salient, the lowest point apparently being behind Rimouski, where Siluro-Devonian rocks encroach farthest northwest. The main deformation and metamorphism in the anticlinoria are pre-Silurian—Taconic—certainly in the Shickshock anticlinorium, probably in the others. Much of it indeed may date from an early Taconic, pre-Middle Ordovician phase, to judge by the pre-Middle Ordovician unconformity on the southeast flanks of the anticlinoria, although no such unconformity appears to be present on their northwest flanks.

Gaspé folded belt and Gaspé-Connecticut Valley synclinorium

On the Gaspé Peninsula, south of the belt of highly deformed and locally metamorphosed Taconic-type rocks and associated volcanics just discussed, lies a reasonably well known, fossiliferous, and much less deformed sequence of Silurian and Devonian strata (McGerrigle, 1950), 3 to 6 kilometers (2 to 4 miles) thick, certainly a "geosynclinal" thickness. The two sequences of rocks are certainly separated by a major angular unconformity, but the contact is a high-angle fault along much of its present trace. Above the unconformity are sandy strata, locally with a basal conglomerate (in which pebbles of serpentine are reported); higher in the Silurian, shaly sandstone and sandy and argillaceous limestone and dolostone predominate. The Silurian sequence (Lajoie, Lespérance, and Béland, 1968) is fairly thick and complete at the west end of the peninsula and beyond; disconformities are reported within it and especially at or close to its top in several places—the latter record the Salinic disturbance of Boucot (1962, p. 156). The Silurian thins eastward, however, disappearing entirely near the east end of the peninsula, at least along the contact with the older rocks to the north. Above the Silurian come resistant Lower Devonian limestone units, in which are cut the picturesque cliffs of the tip of the peninsula, such as Cape Gaspé and the famous Percé Rock. The upper half or more of the sequence consists,

however, of a great pile of sandy shale and arkosic sandstone, gray or green and marine below, red and continental above; the marine fossils present are upper Lower Devonian, and according to the poor plant remains even the overlying continental beds may not reach into the Middle Devonian (McGregor and Owens, 1966; Boucot, Cumming, and Jaeger, 1967). Volcanic rocks are present in the central part of the peninsula, mainly in the lower part of the Devonian clastics. The whole sequence seems to have been deposited in relatively shallow marine water or, later, on a delta; the clastic deposits below appear to contain the last debris coming from the Taconic orogeny, and those above record the beginning of the Acadian orogeny in more internal parts of the chain.

This sequence of strata has many features, both lithologic and faunal, in common with the sequence of roughly the same age in the Helderberg and Catskill Mountains of New York State, southwest of Albany, which similarly reflects these two orogenies, although the upper clastic deposits do not appear there until well within the Middle Devonian (roughly basal Givetian). The rocks in New York State lie almost entirely outside the zone of Appalachian deformation, whereas those in Gaspé are folded in Valley-and-Ridge style (Béland, 1969), with wave lengths and amplitudes measured in kilometers (miles) and with thrust faults on the north flanks of a few of the anticlines. This belt of open folds ranges in width from 30 to 40 kilometers (20 to 25 miles), being narrowest at the two ends of the peninsula, and it describes a broad arc convex northward within the similar arc in the belt of Taconic-type rocks to the north; the individual folds tend to lie en echelon to the whole belt of folding, their axes turned a bit counterclockwise. On the peninsula, the older Taconic-type rocks do not appear in any of the anticlines in the folded belt, except that serpentine, associated with volcanic rocks, breaks through at one place along the thrust fault on the northernmost anticline, 5 kilometers (3 miles) south of the unconformity. In the southernmost anticline (St. Jean River anticline), on the other hand, a considerable thickness of supposedly Upper Ordovician argillaceous limestone appears, apparently quite conformable beneath mainly similar Silurian rocks (Skidmore, 1967, p. 28–30).

South of this anticline lies the deep, complex, but rather narrow Gaspé synclinorium, perhaps 10 kilometers (6 miles) wide in eastern Gaspé. At the east end of the peninsula, it contains the sequence described above, including the youngest Devonian rocks in the belt—red sandstone and conglomerate (Malbaie formation)—which are overlain unconformably by more red sandstone and conglomerate of Carboniferous, probably Pennsylvanian age (Bonaventure sandstone). Westward, however, a part, perhaps a large part, of this Devonian sequence grades laterally into a thick and monotonous mass of dark partly limy shale and shaly limestone, commonly with silty and sandy laminae and beds. These strata (Fortin formation), tightly folded and crumpled and showing some slaty cleavage, occupy almost the whole synclinorium; they have few fossils and are of unknown but probably great thickness. They appear to represent deep-water deposition, in strong contrast to the contemporary beds in the folded belt just to the north. The Gaspé synclinorium widens somewhat toward the west end of the peninsula; on the Matapédia River the belt of monotonous shale is about 28 kilometers (18 miles) wide, and the contrast with the varied sequence of sandstone, shale, and limestone to the north is even sharper, the two facies apparently being brought into contact by a steep fault of uncertain character. Indeed both margins of the synclinorium may be faults here and for many kilometers (miles) in either direction.

Farther west and southwest, the belts of the two sequences suffer different fates. The folded belt of shallow-water strata on the north widens again to 40 kilometers (25 miles) southeast of Rimouski; the folds, however, are more open and are cut by high-angle strike faults (not necessarily all thrust faults), and to the southwest their axes rise, so that the Devonian and Silurian rocks in the synclines are eroded more and more, whereas in the anticlines Middle Ordovician and lower strata appear, plunging off the northeast end of the Notre Dame anticlinorium. The synclinorium of deep-water shale, on the other hand, continues largely unchanged, widening and perhaps deepening, the shale becoming rather less calcareous, especially along the southeast side. On the shore of Lake Témiscouata, 90 kilometers (55 miles) south of Rimouski and a little more than 30 kilometers (20 miles) north of the Maine border, the two sequences are in contact with each other, apparently along a steep thrust fault (Lespérance and Greiner, 1969, see especially note, p. viii), and the contrast between them is striking, in both facies and tectonics. Southeast of the fault lie tightly crumpled deep-water partly limy shale and associated siltstone and sandstone (Témiscouata formation, Lower Devonian); northwest of it more broadly folded shallow-water redbeds, gray limy siltstone, and carbonate rocks (Upper Silurian and Lower or lower Middle Devonian), although in the belt immediately adjacent to the fault the latter are underlain (disconformably?) by about 3 kilometers (9000 feet) of probably deep-water clastics with

conglomerate at the base (Cabano formation, Lower Silurian), associated with intermediate volcanics. In this area, the northern sequence is preserved only in that belt and in one additional syncline (Squatec-Cabano syncline), and it disappears entirely less than 20 kilometers (12 miles) to the southwest, whereas the Gaspé synclinorium on the south is 65 kilometers (40 miles) wide, extending southeastward into New Brunswick and Maine.

Still farther southwest, on the southeast flanks of the Notre Dame anticlinorium, are preserved a few tight synclines of Silurian and Devonian rocks (as young as Eifelian; Boucot, 1968, p. 92), but in a somewhat more intermediate facies, so that the contrast is considerably softened; in southern Quebec, several larger remnants are preserved in the St. Victor syncline west of the Stoke Mountain anticline, the last one lying along Lake Memphramagog just north of the Quebec-Vermont border (Boucot and Drapeau, 1968). The Middle or upper Lower Devonian in these remnants appears to rest unconformably on the Silurian and in places even on the Ordovician. The especially large proportion of limestone they contain has been mentioned above (p. 119).

The synclinorium, on the other hand, continues southwestward across northwesternmost Maine and southeasternmost Quebec into northernmost New Hampshire and northern Vermont, where it is exactly the Connecticut Valley synclinorium discussed in Chapter 5 (p. 96 ff.), and its Silurian and Devonian strata become the upper third of the Paleozoic sequence on the east flank of the Green Mountains anticlinorium, the degree of metamorphism rising gradually along strike from insignificant at Lake Témiscouata to mesozonal in southern Quebec and northern Vermont, especially around the many bodies of post-Lower Devonian granite that intrude the belt for approximately 100 kilometers (60 miles) on either side of the border.

A prominent body of argillaceous sandstone (Frontenac formation; Marleau, 1968), nested in a large syncline on the southeast flank of the synclinorium, underlies much of the Boundary Mountains between Quebec and Maine and extends into northernmost New Hampshire; associated with the sandstone are mafic and lesser felsic metavolcanics, especially in New Hampshire, and also several small serpentine bodies. As all the other serpentine bodies in the Appalachians appear to be Ordovician (and indeed small bodies intrude the Ordovician rocks on the Boundary Mountains anticlinorium just to the east), one might ask if these bodies are not actually remobilized Ordovician masses, reintruded into the

Devonian rocks (Green, 1968, p. 1623; Green and Guidotti, 1968, p. 261), although their association with mafic metavolcanics would then have to be considered a mere coincidence.

The Gaspé-Connecticut Valley synclinorium thus extends from eastern Gaspé to southern New England, a distance of more than 1000 kilometers (about 700 miles). Although it was first recognized as a continuous structure and named by Logan over a century ago, its nature was lost sight of because the relatively unfossiliferous strata it contains were assigned in different regions to various ages (most commonly Ordovician), and their uniformity in facies and age has only recently been reestablished. Its trend follows faithfully the trend of the belts to the north and west. On the Gaspé Peninsula, it forms a broad arc convex to the north, the strike changing from about S75°E at the east end to about N65°E on the Matapédia River. Farther southwest, the strike swings as far as N35°E in northernmost Maine, then back to about N50°E in southeastern Quebec, and finally to about N40°E at the Vermont border and N15°E in southern Vermont.

The contrast in facies and tectonics between the rocks in the Gaspé-Connecticut Valley synclinorium just discussed and those in the Gaspé folded belt to the north is strikingly like the contrast between the Cambro-Ordovician sequences on the two sides of the Green Mountains anticlinorium in Vermont (Cady, 1960), discussed in the last two chapters, although the two Siluro-Devonian belts are not separated by a broad basement anticlinorium marking the outer limit of metamorphism. One might almost say that in Quebec the elusive Valley and Ridge province of the northern Appalachians led a double life, its Cambro-Ordovician incarnation being hidden beneath the northwest margin of the Notre Dame anticlinorium, whereas in the Silurian and Devonian it crossed the anticlinorium on the bias and took up a position behind it in Gaspé, perhaps because the anticlinorium had become a thoroughly consolidated part of the continent. One cannot yet tell with certainty whether the tectonics of the Gaspé folded belt is simple cover tectonics not affecting the underlying, already deformed Cambro-Ordovician rocks; in favor of this view is the absence of older rocks (except for one serpentine body) in the cores of anticlines on the peninsula and the general style of the folding, against it the relations to the west beyond the peninsula where the folds in the Silurian strata rise and are eroded away, the older rocks appearing between and beyond. The detailed tectonics of the Gaspé-Connecticut Valley synclinorium are hardly known in Canada or Maine; nothing like the domes of central and southern Vermont has been recognized, perhaps because data are lacking, but more probably because the degree of metamorphism was too low to permit flowage, favoring instead intense crumpling of the shaly rocks.

Nowhere in the Northern Appalachians is evidence for two Paleozoic pre-Carboniferous orogenies—Taconic and Acadian—clearer than in the Gaspé folded belt. Folded Silurian and Devonian strata lie beside or unconformably upon much more strongly deformed and locally metamorphosed Cambrian and Ordovician rocks and are overlain by merely tilted Carboniferous redbeds, and the facies of the strata record the influxes of sediment from the highlands raised by the two orogenies. The deformation and, to the southwest, metamorphism and granite intrusion in the Gaspé-Connecticut Valley synclinorium are presumably all Acadian. As Eifelian rocks are involved at several places, the deformation in this belt must have been as late as mid-Middle Devonian, but the appearance of clastics in the Gaspé folded belt in the upper Lower Devonian (Emsian) suggests that orogeny may have begun earlier in more interior belts.

Volcanic Belt of Northern Maine

As mentioned in Chapter 5 (p. 104), the northernmost of the typical Oliverian gneiss domes along the Bronson Hill anticlinorium plunges down just west of the New Hampshire-Maine border; about 15 kilometers (9 miles) farther northeast on the same trend, however, Milton (1960) has found folded folds involving some of the same units (Albee formation, Ammonoosuc volcanics with lighter "Oliverian" gneiss, Partridge formation), the later folding being a doming like that in New Hampshire. To the northeast and northwest, relatively more orthodox folds form a continuation of the same uplift—the Coos or Boundary Mountains anticlinorium—and the whole belt continues northeastward into northwestern Maine (Albee, 1961; Green and Guidotti, 1968), where it underlies most of the Rangeley Lakes and forms the central part of the Blue Mountains, though the highest peaks are a little farther southeast. Middle Ordovician fossils have been found north of the Lakes (in the Partridge equivalent; Harwood and Berry, 1967). The unconformity beneath the Silurian and Devonian is particularly clear on the northwest flank of the anticlinorium (Silurian rocks are only locally present here), where it bevels across tight folds in the underlying units. The rocks below were deformed twice, and minor fold axes are generally steep; those above were apparently deformed only once, and the axes plunge gently. Both pre-Silurian (Highlandcroft series) and post-Silurian (New Hampshire series) granitic rocks intrude the rocks of the anticlinorium.

About 60 kilometers (40 miles) northeast of the state line, the anticlinorium is split by the northeast-plunging southwest tip of the Moose River synclinorium of Silurian and Lower Devonian strata (Boucot, 1969), and the two arms of older rock on either side have rather different terminations. Along the southeast arm, a narrow strip of Ordovician (and perhaps older) rocks mostly about 8 kilometers (5 miles) wide persists for 100 kilometers (60 miles) before plunging down 45 kilometers (28 miles) west of Mount Katahdin; the rocks are slate, phyllite, graywacke, quartz sandstone, and volcanics, at most mildly metamorphosed and structurally roughly concordant with the Silurian and Devonian strata on either side, although an angular unconformity is present near the tip of the arm, and low-angle truncation of units elsewhere suggests unconformity or faulting or both. The northwest arm, in contrast, is a blunt nose, 40 kilometers long by 30 wide (25 by 20 miles), along whose southeast, northeast, and northwest sides little or not at all metamorphosed Silurian or Devonian beds rest with profound unconformity on mesozonal gneiss, granodiorite and other plutonic rocks, metasediments, and amphibolite (metavolcanics?) within the nose. The sharp contrast in metamorphism across the southwest end of the Moose River synclinorium led Boucot to consider the rocks in the nose Precambrian, but a fairly large thrust fault intervenes, and continuity with the rocks farther southwest in the anticlinorium makes an Ordovician age seem more probable. According to radiometry, the granodiorite represents the Highlandcroft plutonic series of New Hampshire.

The fossiliferous Silurian and Devonian strata of the Moose River synclinorium, known for a century, have been admirably summarized by Boucot (1961). The Silurian strata are mainly shaly limestone and limy shale, but coarser clastics are present, especially at the base. In places their thickness reaches 1000 meters (3000 feet), but they are bevelled above by an unconformity beneath the overlying Lower Devonian (possibly including highest Silurian) rocks and, especially around the blunt nose, are commonly missing. No certainly Silurian volcanic rocks are known here, but some patches of little metamorphosed volcanics along the unconformity above the mesozonal rocks of the nose are probably Silurian. The Lower Devonian sequence begins variously, with patchy units of arkosic conglom-

erate, of limestone (partly sandy and conglomeratic), and of felsite, but the main bulk of it, forming the core of the synclinorium, consists of nearly 5000 meters (nearly 3 miles) of dark quartz sandstone or tuffaceous sandstone, with minor amounts of siltstone and slate (Moose River group). Near the middle is a unit, or series of lenses, of felsite (Kineo rhyolite), ranging up to more than a kilometer (up to 4000 feet) thick and forming conspicuous mountains like Mount Kineo in Moosehead Lake (Rankin, 1968, p. 363–365). Marginally to the synclinorium, however, this body of sandstone, or at least its lower part, grades laterally into an even greater thickness of noncalcareous slate (Seboomook formation) with graded beds of sandstone and siltstone, which to the northwest merges with the slate of the Gaspé-Connecticut Valley synclinorium along the international border.

The northeast end of the sandstone mass in the core of the Moose River synclinorium lies just west of the northeast tip of the long narrow southeast arm of the Boundary Mountains anticlinorium; over a considerable area farther north one finds only the monotonous Lower Devonian slate sequence (Seboomook formation), forming an eastward protuberance from the Gaspé-Connecticut Valley synclinorium. Out of it rise several additional anticlines or anticlinoria of Ordovician and older rocks, between which arms of the protuberance extend. One such anticline (Chesuncook anticline), near the southern part of Chesuncook Lake, 30 kilometers (20 miles) west of Mount Katahdin, trends northwest across the general strike, its plunging northwest tip only 13 kilometers (8 miles) north-northeast of the northeast tip of the Boundary Mountains anticlinorium; its aberrant trend persists for only about 20 kilometers (13 miles) southeastward. Along its flanks are several well known exposures of fossiliferous Silurian limestone (see Boucot, 1954), lying unconformably on the older rocks. The southwest-plunging tip of another anticline lies only 16 kilometers (9 miles) farther north at the other end of Chesuncook Lake; this is the southwest end of a major anticlinorium, called the Munsungun anticlinorium for Lake Munsungun, 50 kilometers (30 miles) north of Mount Katahdin.

Between the two anticlines just mentioned opens out a large synclinorium of Silurian and especially Lower Devonian strata (Rankin, 1968, p. 359–362) called the Traveler Mountain synclinorium for Traveler Mountain, about 20 kilometers (12 miles) north of Mount Katahdin. It is more or less symmetrical with the Moose River synclinorium across the protuberance mentioned above, and it too contains more than a kilometer (over 4000 feet) of Lower Devonian dark sandstone (Matagamon sandstone) and above that a very thick pile (3400 meters—11,000 feet) of felsitic volcanics, which upholds Traveler Mountain. The volcanics are largely welded ash-flow tuffs and may represent the filling of a caldera. Upon these volcanics, possibly unconformably, lies a sequence of completely unmetamorphosed, little deformed, and indeed barely consolidated nonmarine conglomerate, sandstone, and shale (Trout Valley formation), with a few poor coal seams containing Lower or Middle Devonian plants (see Schopf, 1964, p. D48–D49). These rocks look post-tectonic, but possibly they owe their lack of deformation to protection by the thick felsite mass that underlies them.

The south side of the Traveler Mountain synclinorium is cut off by the Katahdin granite, a mass of late, coarse, unfoliated granite measuring 35 by 60 kilometers (20 by 30 miles) (Boucot, 1954). Mount Katahdin, the highest point in Maine and indeed in the whole northern Appalachians northeast of the high range of the White Mountains in New Hampshire, is upheld by this granite, but most of the other high mountains in northern Maine are underlain either by felsitic volcanics or by hornfels rims around granite masses that themselves have weathered into basins commonly containing lakes.

West of the aberrant Chesuncook anticline, a narrower arm of Devonian slate extends southward and it connects, behind the southeast arm of the Boundary Mountains anticlinorium, with the Devonian rocks in the Merrimack synclinorium next southeast. It contains two more masses of Lower Devonian sandstone and one of volcanics, the latter underlying Big Spencer Mountain east of Moosehead Lake.

The Munsungun anticlinorium, in the area due north of Mount Katahdin and Traveler Mountain (Hall, ms. 1964), exposes a thick sequence of Ordovician rocks consisting of black shale, chert, graywacke, tuffaceous sandstone, and greenstone volcanics and containing several Middle (but not lower Middle) Ordovician faunas, graptolitic and shelly. Around much of the anticlinorium, the Ordovician rocks are overlain unconformably by Silurian clastics, reefy limestone, and volcanics, and these by similar Lower Devonian rocks (they rest unconformably on the Silurian on the southeast flank); above these comes the ubiquitous slate (Seboomook formation), and indeed in places the slate rests directly on the Ordovician. Unconformably *beneath* the Middle Ordovician rocks in the core of the anticlinorium appears an older sequence—quartzite, graywacke, and slate—showing considerably greater deformation but still

only mild metamorphism (Hall, 1969, p. 471). The age of this older sequence is quite uncertain; it might be Precambrian, but Cambrian seems equally probable. Similar rocks occur in the core of the Chesuncook anticline west of Mt. Katahdin, unconformably beneath fossiliferous Lower Silurian strata and locally beneath probably Ordovician volcanics (themselves cut by gabbro dated radiometrically as probably Ordovician; Faul and others, 1963, p. 3), and they may also be present near Moosehead Lake in the southeast arm of the Boundary Mountains anticlinorium.

East of the Traveler Mountain synclinorium, a somewhat similar older sequence has been found by Neuman (1967, p. I5–I7) in the core of the Weeksboro-Lunksoos Lake anticlinorium, which extends for about 70 kilometers (45 miles) northeastward from the Mount Katahdin batholith. Predominantly volcanic Middle Ordovician rocks are underlain unconformably by more severely deformed gray quartzite and red and greenish slate (Grand Pitch formation); these lower rocks, obviously similar in structural position to the older sequence in the Munsungun anticlinorium, contain the track *Oldhamia*, which suggests but does not prove a Cambrian age. Around the core, the next oldest dated rocks are middle Middle Ordovician, as in the Munsungun anticlinorium, but in tight synclines entirely within it, surrounded by the Cambrian (?) rocks, low Middle Ordovician (possibly uppermost Lower Ordovician) rocks are preserved; their relation to the middle Middle Ordovician rocks is not clear, but an unconformity is suspected on account of the spotty distribution of the older Ordovician. Both Cambrian (?) and Ordovician rocks are cut by a somewhat altered quartz diorite, pebbles of which are reported from nearby Silurian conglomerate; presumably therefore it belongs to the Highlandcroft series, of which it may be the northeasternmost representative. In places, the basal Silurian unconformity has cut out all the Middle Ordovician rocks and reached the underlying Cambrian (?) unit; in one area at the west end of the anticlinorium, indeed, the basal conglomerate above that unconformity contains Upper Ordovician fossils.

The pre-Silurian or pre-Upper Ordovician unconformity in this area evidently records the "classical" Taconic orogeny, but the pre-Middle Ordovician unconformity records an older period of deformation, here actually more severe, which Neuman (Neuman and Rankin, 1966, p. 9; Neuman, 1967, p. I–32) has named the Penobscot disturbance, from Penobscot County, which includes the west half of the anticlinorium. It seems logical to hold this "disturbance" or orogeny responsible also for the main deformation of the older sequence in the other nearby anticlinoria, and perhaps also for the pre-middle Middle Ordovician unconformity on the southeast flank of the Sutton and Notre Dame anticlinoria in Quebec (p. 119; Hall, 1969). Nevertheless, as older Middle Ordovician rocks are known above the unconformity only on the Weeksboro-Lunksoos Lake anticlinorium (except that they may also occur on the southeast arm of the Boundary Mountains anticlinorium near Moosehead Lake; Neuman, 1968, p. 37) and as another unconformity may overlie them there, the main disturbance may have been somewhat earlier there than in the other areas. It is not necessary of course that orogenic events be exactly contemporaneous over such large regions, especially across the orogenic strike. Indeed one might consider the deformation recorded by the various pre-Middle Ordovician unconformities simply as early or "precocious" phases of the Taconic orogeny, at least if one assumes that the rocks below belong in the age range Cambrian to Lower Ordovician.

The northeastern extension of these anticlinoria is not well known (but see Pavlides and others, 1964). A band of fossiliferous Silurian and Lower Devonian rocks (both sediments and volcanics) can be followed northeastward along the northwest flank of the Munsungun anticlinorium or a northeastern equivalent, between probably Middle Ordovician volcanics on the east and Devonian slate in the Gaspé-Connecticut Valley synclinorium on the west. The volcanics fade out, however, in both the Ordovician and the younger rocks, tens of kilometers (tens of miles) before the international boundary is reached, the Ordovician section becomes largely argillaceous, and the post-Ordovician unconformity seems to disappear. (The fossiliferous band can be followed, however, across the Saint John River into New Brunswick.) From this point northeastward, no volcanic axis can be recognized, and the Aroostook-Matapédia anticlinorium, which there seems to take the place of the Bronson Hill, Boundary Mountains, and Munsungun anticlinoria on the southeast side of the Gaspé-Connecticut Valley synclinorium, is of a totally different character from them (see p. 129–130). Apparently the volcanic belt never extended beyond northern Maine. Ordovician volcanic rocks also occur in the Castle Hill anticline east of the Munsungun anticlinorium and in other small anticlines between; above the volcanics are beds of siltstone (locally pebbly) containing Upper Ordovician fossils, and above these are Lower Silurian sandstone and graywacke. At Castle Hill the sequence is broken, if at all, only by disconformities, but on one of the anticlines to the west an angular unconformity is reported

above the Upper Ordovician rocks. Middle Ordovician and possibly Ordovician volcanics also occur at the northeast end of the Weeksboro-Lunksoos Lake anticlinorium, where they are overlain, perhaps unconformably, by Lower Silurian conglomerate and graywacke. Evidently in these areas one is approaching the eastern edge of the belt of repeated uplifts, for farther east no unconformities (and no Ordovician volcanics) are known as far as the Miramichi anticlinorium in central New Brunswick.

Taken as a whole, the northern Maine volcanic belt consists of a string of anticlines and anticlinoria, in which are exposed Ordovician volcanics and granodiorite bodies as well as Ordovician and older metasediments, and between which lie synclinoria filled with Devonian clastics, generally coarser than in the major synclinoria on either side and associated with felsic volcanics. The general trend of the folds is about N45°E, but individual segments trend from N60°E (southwest end of the Moose River synclinorium) to nearly north-south (parts of the Munsungun anticlinorium), not to mention the northwest-trending Chesuncook anticline. The protuberance of Devonian slate, which with its arms connects the Gaspé-Connecticut Valley and Merrimack synclinoria, may represent a major depression, lying in a vague irregular recess opposite the minor recess or dimple in the trends of the belts farther northwest.

Like the Bronson Hill anticlinorium in southern and central New England, this belt is characterized by the irregular shape of its constituent folds, by abundant volcanics, and by repeated unconformities, many angular, and the latter features are clearer in northern Maine because the rocks there are for the most part barely or not at all metamorphosed. Nappes and gneiss domes, on the other hand, are absent, also no doubt because of the lack of metamorphism. Thus the northern Maine volcanic belt records the northeastern continuation, and probably the end, of the volcanic arc postulated in Chapter 5 (p. 106); indeed Rankin (1968) called the line of volcanic centers from the Moose River synclinorium to Traveler Mountain the Piscataquis volcanic belt, an island arc of Early Devonian age, and the Ordovician rocks (and to a lesser degree the Silurian) are also strikingly more volcanic than to either side. Furthermore, again as along the Bronson Hill anticlinorium, bodies of Ordovician granodiorite are common, suggesting again that this belt was the core belt of the Taconic orogeny (taken in a broad sense); not only are Silurian strata generally unconformable on Middle Ordovician here ("classical" Taconic), but in several places Devonian on

Silurian (Salinic disturbance) and Middle Ordovician on still older rocks (Penobscot disturbance). Finally, the whole belt was affected by the Acadian orogeny, which accentuated the already existing uplifts and was accompanied by large granite intrusions, such as the Katahdin batholith; possibly that orogeny was earlier here than in the Gaspé-Connecticut Valley synclinorium, if the undeformed rocks in the Traveler Mountain area are both Lower Devonian and post-tectonic. In any case, the belt was one of maximum orogenic restlessness from the Early Ordovician to the Middle Devonian.

Nonvolcanic Belt: Merrimack Synclinorium, Central Maine Slate Belt, and Aroostook-Matapédia Anticlinorium

Southeast of the volcanic axis just described or, where it is absent, of the Gaspé-Connecticut Valley synclinorium, is a belt containing vast thicknesses of metasedimentary rocks, with relatively few volcanics and also few fossils. Except in western Maine, exposures are mostly poor and there are large areas of low relief covered with glacial drift and, in the northeast part of the belt, spruce forest—a sort of glaciated Piedmont Plateau. In much of this belt the age and sequence of the rocks have been poorly known until recently, but work is now going on in many areas, and a picture is emerging. The next decade of work will undoubtedly lead to many surprises, however, and the present picture may turn out to be grossly inadequate.

The rocks of western Maine, in a triangular area extending over 100 kilometers (over 60 miles) eastward from the New Hampshire border, are the continuation of the high-grade rocks in the Merrimack synclinorium of central New Hampshire— mica schist and gneiss with some quartzite and calc-silicate rock, cut by large granitic masses and by numerous pegmatite bodies, some of which are famous for rare and gem minerals. The belt of lower grade, partly calcareous slate, siltstone, and impure quartzite on the southeast flank of the synclinorium in southeastern New Hampshire can be followed northeastward parallel to the coast of southwestern Maine as far as Casco Bay just east of Portland, but there it is swallowed up in an area of higher grade metamorphism. These low-grade rocks used to be called Carboniferous, but almost certainly they are Silurian and perhaps in part Lower Devonian (Hussey, 1968). Younger rocks lie to the northwest, in the direction of increasing metamorphism, and Hussey gives a thickness of over 6 kilometers (over 20,000 feet) for the entire

section, low- and high-grade together. As in New Hampshire, the higher grade rocks in the core of the synclinorium may be entirely Devonian but more probably they include Silurian rocks as well.

Farther northeastward, the grade of metamorphism in the synclinorium drops off fairly rapidly to low grade (biotite or chlorite zone), except that higher grade rocks persist in a strip 60 kilometers (35 miles) wide along the coast almost to Penobscot Bay. A few Silurian graptolites were found some decades ago in the low-grade rocks near Waterville, and stratigraphic sections have been worked out there and also in areas to the west and northwest in the transitional zone from high to low grade; they have been correlated by Osberg, Moench, and Warner (1968). They are thick and monotonous and consist of the metamorphic equivalents of shale, siltstone, and impure sandstone tending toward graywacke, alternating on all scales from thin graded beds to formations hundreds of meters (1000 feet or more) thick: the total thickness is not less than $1\frac{1}{2}$ kilometers (1 mile) near Waterville where the section is certainly incomplete (the Silurian fossils occur near its base) and increases to 6 kilometers or so (over 3 miles) just southeast of the Boundary Mountains anticlinorium.

In this northwestern area, the lower part of the section is coarser than elsewhere and includes large thicknesses of mainly polymictic conglomerate and pebbly mudstone (Rangeley conglomerate), and it rests, apparently quite conformably, on Ordovician shale, graywacke, and metavolcanics. Clearly these coarser clastic rocks represent the debris eroded from the anticlinorium to the northwest after its uplift during the Taconic orogeny (in the broad sense), and a large amount of the finer clastic material farther southeast may also come from there; the ratio of sand to mud varies greatly both across and along stike. The uppermost part of the section on the northwest is more shaly and corresponds exactly to the thick Lower Devonian shale unit (Seboomook formation) preserved in the synclines crossing the anticlinorium and in the Gaspé-Connecticut Valley synclinorium beyond; only the interposition of large intrusive bodies prevents tracing it through. The middle part of the section here includes a lenticular unit of black graphitic pyrrhotitic shale or schist (Smalls Falls formation) and similar shale is present in thinner zones southeastward as far as Waterville.

A considerable part of the sandstone or graywacke in all these sections is slightly calcareous, and in the lower (presumably Silurian) parts of all but the northwestern section there are one or more relatively thin units of thin-bedded argillaceous (and locally sandy) "ribbon" limestone—similar limestone occurs in the corresponding position in the low-grade belt of southeastern New Hampshire and southwestern Maine (Eliot formation). These units may represent the feather edges of a much thicker body of "ribbon" limestone up the strike in northeastern Maine; they are not necessarily all the same age.

All these rocks are thrown into nearly upright, nearly or quite isoclinal folds of all scales; this is most evident in low-grade areas like that around Waterville (Osberg, 1968) where bedding is still obvious. The long, parallel, tight anticlines in that area, only slightly disturbed by later folds, seem indeed to mark out an anticlinorium (Waterville anticlinorium) in the midst of the Merrimack synclinorium. In the higher grade areas to the west, however, bedding is obscured and the continuity of units broken by the many granitic plutons; fold axes appear to be shorter and they trend in aberrant directions, including northwest, as if tracing out a sigmoid between the plutons. Perhaps folded folds or nappes are present here, still unrecognized. The intrusives belong mainly to the New Hampshire plutonic series, but the White Mountain series is represented in southwesternmost Maine, and post-tectonic sheets of mafic rock, some showing gravity differentiation, occur along the northwest border of the synclinorium (Espenshade and Boudette, 1967), encroaching in places onto the southeast arm of the Boundary Mountains anticlinorium.

The rocks around Casco Bay appear to form a subordinate synclinorium on the southeast flank of the main one, separated from it by the southwest end of the Waterville anticlinorium, but they are not readily correlated with its rocks (see Hussey, 1968, p. 300–301, for a discussion of some of the possibilities; I prefer a combination of his alternatives 1 and 2, but he prefers alternative 3). Metavolcanic rocks, both felsic and mafic, appear in the lower part of the sequence here (they are absent in the main synclinorium), suggesting a correlation with the probably Ordovician metavolcanics in the Rockingham anticlinorium and other belts to the southwest and perhaps with similar pre-Silurian metavolcanics in the Penobscot Bay region. The conformably overlying metasediments are more like those in the main synclinorium but appear much thinner; the highest strata preserved include much black graphitic pyrrhotitic schist, as though stagnant conditions had been more common or more persistent along the two margins of the Merrimack synclinorium than in its center. Moreover, near the top of the sequence is a unit of "ribbon" limestone much like those in the Silurian part of the main sequence at Waterville and in southwestern Maine. On the other hand, the sequence in the Casco Bay synclinorium is reported to lie entirely above the Silurian strata in those two areas, suggesting that it is all younger; to avoid this conclusion it would be necessary to postulate complicated refolding or a fault, presumably a major thrust fault, on the northwest flank of the synclinorium. A fault does exist here (Bodine, 1965, p. 71 and Fig. 1), but it is apparently a postmetamorphic normal fault downthrown to the southeast—the wrong direction—and it may indeed be a continuation of the (Triassic?) Flint Hill fault of southeastern New Hampshire.

Northeastward the Casco Bay synclinorium appears to turn inland, traversing the high-grade coastal strip to the Penobscot River just above the head of Penobscot Bay. The repetition of rock units across an axis in that area had already been recognized by Trefethen (ms. about 1950), but because it coincided with a metamorphic high, it was interpreted as evidence of an anticlinorium ("Knox anticlinorium"). The more recent stratigraphic work has inverted the section and thus turned it into a synclinorium; the map pattern between the head of the bay and Bangor (Trefethen, ms.; see 1967 geologic map of Maine) suggests, however, the presence of large-scale folded folds, perhaps even nappes, and the last word may not have been spoken.

Between the axis mentioned and the western shore of Penobscot Bay is a terrain of relatively fine-grained schist and phyllite (Penobscot formation) with a few bands of quartzite and of limestone or marble. If the metavolcanics in the Casco Bay area are Ordovician, this terrain could represent the prevolcanic Cambro-Ordovician (?) rocks of eastern Massachusetts (including the Westboro quartzite), and if the metavolcanics in Penobscot Bay (North Haven greenstone) are also correlative with those in Casco Bay, it could form an anticlinorium. On the island of North Haven, the metavolcanics mentioned are overlain with sharp angular unconformity by unmetamorphosed, fossiliferous Upper Silurian sediments at the base of a thick volcanic pile; we are here, however, entirely beyond the Merrimack synclinorium (see p. 137).

East-northeast of Waterville and north of the coastal strip, the monotonous clastic sequence of the main synclinorium underlies a wide belt through central Maine, becoming generally finer grained and less differentiable; central Maine is in effect a vast slate belt, in which few subdivisions have been mapped or fossils found. Granite bodies are present here and there in the slate belt, surrounded by hornfels rims that uphold groups of mountains; otherwise the area is relatively flat and widely covered with glacial drift and marine clay.

The strike in the slate belt, which averages N65°E from east of the Kennebec River to east of the Penobscot, turns in eastern Maine to N30°E or even more nearly north-south, although it swings to east-west and then back in passing through a pronounced local cross-structure near Houlton. In this region, moreover, Ordovician strata appear from beneath the presumably Silurian slate and siltstone, and north of Houlton they come to form the greater part of the belt. The bulk of these strata are quite different from the contemporaneous Ordovician strata in the anticlinoria of the northern Maine volcanic belt (and also different from those in anticlines farther south and east); instead of black slate, chert, and graywacke with abundant mafic metavolcanics, they are mainly a monotonous sequence of argillaceous and silty limestone, which shows characteristic "ribbons" on weathered surfaces, produced by alternating more and less shaly bands (Carys Mills formation of Meduxnekeag group; Pavlides, 1968). Abundant sedimentary features in these rocks indicate that they were deposited in relatively deep water; they form a sort of calcareous flysch. The impure limestone or "ribbon-rock" weathers to a calcareous rendzina soil, whose agricultural richness contrasts strongly with the poorness of the acid and strongly leached podsols over the other rocks of the region, even the pure limestone units, and which has made northeastern Maine (Aroostook County) and adjacent New Brunswick famous for potatoes. The thickness of the sequence is estimated at more than 3 kilometers (12,000 feet), and fossils show that fine-grained calcareous sediment was laid down uninterruptedly from late Middle Ordovician through Late Ordovician into Early Silurian (Llandovery) time, precisely the time of the "classical" Taconic orogeny in the anticlinoria to the west.

The calcareous sequence grades upward conformably into mostly noncalcareous slate, siltstone, and quartzite, much like and probably continuous with the rocks of the central Maine slate belt from here to Waterville, and here too conglomerate occurs in the lower beds close to the anticlinoria. These strata range on through the Silurian into the Lower Devonian. In several areas they contain manganiferous layers that have been of some commercial interest (the manganese is largely in the form of carbonate, associated in some layers with manganese silicates and iron oxides). Around the margins of its outcrop belt, the calcareous sequence also grades laterally into contemporaneous noncalcareous sediment; for example, in an area just northeast of the end of the Weeksboro-Lunksoos Lake anticlinorium, it thins down greatly between thick tongues of slate, siltstone, and graywacke, and there are lenses of those rocks (with some beds of conglomerate) within (or beneath) the calcareous strata somewhat farther east and northeast. Moreover, the upper limit of calcareous sediments is not the same age everywhere; near Houlton they reach only into the lower Lower Silurian (lower Llandovery), whereas around Presque Isle they span most or all of the Lower Silurian (though chiefly in a nodular rather than a "ribbon" facies—Spragueville formation) and may reach into the Upper Silurian (Wenlock) to judge by fossils (lower Ludlow) near the base of the overlying noncalcareous shale in some places. Yet here also they must grade westward into the contemporaneous noncalcareous strata of the Castle Hill anticline— volcanics in the Middle Ordovician, siltstone in the Upper Ordovician, sandstone and graywacke in the Lower Silurian (see p. 126); also Boucot and others, 1964; Pavlides and others, 1964). In the Chapman syncline next to the east, moreover, the Silurian strata are overlain, probably disconformably, by a great thickness (over 2 kilometers— 8000 feet) of lower Lower Devonian volcanics, felsic and mafic (Dockendorff group of Boucot and others, 1964), which pass laterally into equally thick dark volcanic sandstone, siltstone, and shale, the last being the local representative of the widespread Lower Devonian slate (Seboomook formation) to the west. The presence of this thick pile of volcanics is unexpected in this otherwise entirely nonvolcanic belt; the implications are discussed below (p. 135).

In the nose of this syncline, resting with distinct unconformity across the older rocks, is a unit of red sandstone and conglomerate (Mapleton sandstone), simply folded and not very strongly indurated; clearly it is post-tectonic. It was long considered Mississippian, or perhaps Upper Devonian, by analogy with post-tectonic red sandstone units in New Brunswick, but plant fossils within it suggest a Middle Devonian age (Schopf, 1964). If so, the main pulse of the Acadian orogeny in this region was over by the middle of the Devonian period.

Except in a few folds like the Chapman syncline, which probably owes its relative simplicity to the massive volcanics it contains, all the rocks in this belt have been deformed incompetently into nearly isoclinal folds of all scales. The presence of the Ordovician calcareous sequence in its center shows that the belt is broadly an anticlinorium, called the Aroostook-Matapédia anticlinorium;

from northeastern Maine (Aroostook County) it can be followed across northwestern New Brunswick (where it reaches a width of 50 kilometers—30 miles) and the Matapédia River into the southern part of the Gaspé Peninsula, its trend swinging in a broad arc from northerly to easterly. What with the monotony of the sequence, the complexity of the folding, and the rarity of fossils, individual anticlinal axes are difficult to follow through the central part of the belt, but to judge by the relations at the margins, they run largely en echelon. Thus the anticlinorium they form shifts progressively to the left as the anticlinoria of the northern Maine volcanic belt fade out, until from the international boundary northeastward it adjoins directly the Gaspé-Connecticut Valley synclinorium, its fine-grained calcareous Ordovician rocks being separated from the Devonian slate of the synclinorium either by a band of Silurian strata (more or less the continuation of the fossiliferous band on the northwest flank of the Munsungun anticlinorium; see p. 126) or by a fault (thrust fault?) or by both.

The belt of "ribbon" limestone and associated limy strata (Matapédia group) can be followed the full length of the Gaspé Peninsula (Skidmore, 1967, p. 28–30); it narrows down to 5 kilometers (3 miles) or less in the western part but widens again to 22 kilometers (14 miles) near the east end, where it largely disappears beneath an unconformable cover of Carboniferous red sandstone (Bonaventure sandstone) but reaches the coast just south of Percé. Fossils show that the age range is the same here as in Maine—upper Middle Ordovician to Lower Silurian. Along the south side of much of the eastern part of the belt, less calcareous strata appear (Honorat group), grading (downward?) from fine-grained mudstone with some calcareous layers into strata ranging from slate to conglomerate. These rocks may be older than the calcareous ones, laterally equivalent to their Ordovician part, or partly both; the two are mostly separated by a longitudinal fault. The thicknesses of both groups are undetermined but large, and the structure is complex, particularly that of the noncalcareous group, which probably conceals the anticlinorial axis.

Along parts of the northern side of the anticlinorium, notably around and west-southwest of Mont Alexandre, the deformed "ribbon" limestone gives way upward to more regularly northwest-dipping silty limestone and generally limy shale (still a deep-water facies?) ranging well into the Upper Silurian and including a band of largely mafic volcanics. In the Mont Alexandre area, the thickness of these strata is as much as 3 kilometers (2 miles), of the volcanics a kilometer

or more (about a mile). Only beyond them does one come to the thick Lower Devonian shale and sandstone unit (Fortin group, here in good part calcareous) that fills the Gaspé synclinorium. The mutual limb of anticlinorium and synclinorium is broken in many places, perhaps throughout, by large longitudinal faults, probably mainly thrust faults, but there seems no reason to postulate a disconformity anywhere between the Middle Ordovician and the Lower Devonian, any more than on the St. Jean River anticline farther north (p. 121), although there the section is considerably thinner (one is entering the Gaspé folded belt) and the volcanics are represented only by pebbles and cobbles in conglomerate in the lower part of the Upper Silurian.

The south margin of the Matapédia anticlinorium is quite different, at least in the eastern half of the peninsula, for the less calcareous strata there (Honorat group) are overlain (where the contact is not a fault) by the quite different, less calcareous Silurian sequence (Chaleur Bay group) of the Chaleur Bay synclinorium, full of fossils and clearly deposited mainly in shallow water. In places, Lower Devonian continental strata lie directly above the pre-Silurian rocks and the contact is an angular unconformity; elsewhere also it is probably unconformable, at least in the eastern half of the peninsula (Skidmore, 1967, p. 30). The rocks south of this contact do not belong to this belt, however, and they are discussed in the next section.

One curious anomaly remains to be mentioned. Near the east end of the peninsula, about 10 kilometers (6 miles) west of Percé and close to the steep and probably thrust-faulted northern edge of the anticlinorium, appear a few isolated exposures of limestone, some shaly and some pure, containing Upper Cambrian (Murphy Creek limestone) and lower Middle Cambrian (Corner-of-the-Beach limestone) faunas (Kindle, 1942, 1948), whose nearest affinities appear to be with the Valley and Ridge province or the North American platform rather than with rocks of the same age known in the southeastern belts of the Northern Appalachians. The overlying upper Middle or Upper Ordovician calcareous unit (Matapédia group) may begin with a basal quartz-pebble conglomerate. It is difficult to avoid the conclusion that the Ordovician strata overlapped an already deformed and eroded terrain, and one is at once reminded of the Penobscot disturbance of northern Maine (p. 125), despite the entire difference in the rock types both above and below the unconformity.

It may seem improper to group the areas discussed in the present section as if they formed a single structural belt, for the supposed belt begins as the Merrimack synclinorium, perhaps the deepest synclinorium in central New England, lying between two reasonably well marked anticlinoria, and ends on the Gaspé Peninsula as the Aroostook-Matapédia anticlinorium, lying between two synclinoria. The reasons for so doing will be clearer after the description in the next section of the volcanic belt in northern and western New Brunswick, but the unifying features of the belt presently in question are (1) the immense thickness of the deposits and their unbroken continuity from the Ordovician into the Devonian, (2) the monotonous repetition of mud, silt, and sand (including lime-mud and lime-silt) in beds with all the marks of deep-water (flysch) sedimentation, and (3) the absence of volcanic rocks, except in a few places on the margins. Conglomerate seems to be restricted to the northwest margin, though common enough there along the length of the northern Maine volcanic belt; from near the end of that belt northeastward, limy rocks predominate, containing only very fine noncalcareous debris—in Maine only in the older rocks in the center of the belt, but in Canada throughout the belt, except along part of the southeastern margin. Farther southwest, a vast pile of siliceous clastic material accumulated, perhaps derived from the volcanic anticlinoria on both sides. In southern New England, however, limy sediments apparently reappear in force, although now largely metamorphosed to diopside-quartz granulite and other calc-silicate rocks (Paxton and Hebron formations), and again they may span the Ordovician-Silurian boundary (p. 107, 108).

The belt thus defined forms two broad arcs convex to the northwest, one in New England (N20°E to N65°E), the other in Canada (N35°E to S80°E), articulated by a more irregular vaguely sigmoidal zone in easternmost Maine, in the same general area as the transition from dominantly noncalcareous to dominantly calcareous deposition and from synclinorium to anticlinorium (although the Waterville anticlinorium in southwestern Maine and the "ribbon-limestone" units there blunt the contrast). In the sigmoidal zone, as noted above (p. 130), the individual fold axes appear to run en echelon to the belt as a whole, which is here crossing the regional strike as if to compensate for the disappearance of the northern Maine volcanic belt. Another, sharper, sigmoid appears to be present in the high-grade rocks of western Maine, but largely or entirely included within the Merrimack synclinorium. In the southern arc the belt widens from about 40 kilometers (25 miles) at the two ends to at least 120

kilometers (75 miles) in the middle, but in the northern arc it seems to be narrowest in the middle.

Tight to isoclinal, nearly upright folding on all scales is also a characteristic feature of the belt, at least from western Maine northeastward. In the low-grade rocks where bedding is still obvious and stretching along it must have been minimal, such folding must represent a very great shortening of the original basin across the strike, and the shortening could hardly have been less in the high-grade areas. Probably the present width of the belt is only a relatively small fraction of its original width—this would make it easier to understand the generally fine grain of the sediments in the central part of the belt, especially in the Aroostook-Matapédia anticlinorium, despite the presence of actively rising anticlinoria topped with volcanoes, which are now so nearby on either side. No sign of the floor on which these sediments were laid down is visible anywhere in the belt, and if it was shortened with them it must have been disposed of in some other way, presumably downward, rather militating, it seems to me, against the idea that it was sialic or continental.

Volcanic Belt of Chaleur Bay (Baie des Chaleurs) and Western New Brunswick

In Gaspé (p. 130), the rocks of the eastern end of the Aroostook-Matapédia anticlinorium are overlain on the south, probably unconformably although parts of the contact are faulted, by a Silurian sequence quite different from that next north of the anticlinorium (or from that within the anticlinorium itself in northeastern Maine and adjacent New Brunswick). This sequence (Chaleur Bay group) has long been known and studied in the outcrop belt along Chaleur Bay near and west of Port Daniel, where parts of it are richly fossiliferous; it consists of more than 2 kilometers ($1\frac{1}{2}$ miles) of varied sedimentary rocks, largely greenish quartz-rich sandstone and siltstone, with conglomerate at the base, green and red shale at various levels, and two units of partly nodular, partly reefy limestone. At the west end of this outcrop area, 1 kilometer (over $\frac{1}{2}$ mile) of basaltic lava is intercalated in the upper part of the sequence. The fossils and sedimentary features in these strata show that they were deposited in fairly shallow water, in strong contrast to the Silurian and other sediments in the Aroostook-Matapédia anticlinorium and the main part of the Gaspé synclinorium to the north, but more like the Silurian rocks of the Gaspé folded belt beyond.

The sequence spans virtually the whole of the Silurian.

These strata are thrown into fairly regular northeast-trending folds with a wave length of a few kilometers (2 or 3 miles), some of the anticlines being broken by thrust faults; the asymmetry of folding and thrust faulting appears to reverse across a broad syncline in the middle of the belt, being to the southeast near Port Daniel, to the northwest farther west. The lowest formation in the sequence is brought to the surface along most of the anticlines and faults, yet its base is exposed only close to Port Daniel; perhaps there is a decollement near the base of the sequence in most of the area, so that the folding is confined to the Silurian strata. (A curious faulted dome mapped by Badgley, 1956, could result from erosion through a folded bedding-plane fault at that level, forming a window.)

In the vicinity of Port Daniel, two groups of older rocks appear unconformably beneath the Silurian (Ayrton, 1967), and they too are in strong contrast to the sediments in the belts next to the north. The younger group (Mictaw group), lying northwest of Port Daniel, consists of volcanic graywacke, siltstone, and shale; graptolites show that it is middle and upper Middle Ordovician, exactly contemporaneous with the oldest dated strata in the calcareous unit in the Aroostook-Matapédia anticlinorium, which is exposed not 10 kilometers (5 miles) to the north and from which it differs greatly (it is somewhat more like the noncalcareous unit in the same belt), and also contemporaneous with the youngest strata among the Taconic-type rocks along the north shore of the Gaspé Peninsula, from which it differs less. The rocks of the group are complexly folded, probably on intersecting axes; it is not certain that they were already folded before the deposition of the overlying Silurian, but it is very probable.

North of Port Daniel, these strata come into contact with the older of the two pre-Silurian groups (Maquereau group) along a well marked fault line; as they approach the fault they become coarser and coarser, and along it they merge into a spectacular conglomerate or breccia hundreds of meters (perhaps a thousand feet) thick, consisting of fragments up to $\frac{1}{2}$ meter ($1\frac{1}{2}$ feet) across of the older group, along with pebbles of granitic gneiss of unknown origin. This rock has been interpreted as a basal conglomerate, but according to Ayrton (1967, p. 23–25) it is more probably a sedimentary breccia that accumulated along an active fault scarp; in any case it proves a profound unconformity between the two groups, for the fragments had already been severely deformed

and foliated before falling into the breccia. Mafic volcanic and intrusive rocks (including some serpentine) appear in a small area along the fault, and some of the intrusive rocks cut the surrounding graywacke; presumably they come up along the fault. (A mass of serpentine accompanied by blocks of granite and of rocks apparently belonging to both the pre-Silurian groups cuts across the Silurian rocks not far to the northwest, probably as a cold protrusion along another fault; Ayrton, 1967, p. 46–51.).

The older group (Maquereau group) lying east of the fault and also unconformable beneath the Silurian consists of still more highly deformed and mildly metamorphosed rocks, including green and purple graywacke, impure quartzite, siltstone, and slate, plus chlorite schist and greenstone volcanics. Ayrton has divided the group into formations and has mapped isoclinal if not recumbent folds; he suggests further an angular unconformity *within* the group, the rocks below showing two foliations in places, and he assigns all this deformation to a pre-Taconic, Gaspesian orogeny. The age of the rocks is quite unknown, except that they are older than Middle Ordovician; both Cambrian and Precambrian ages have been suggested. By their character, position, and stronger deformation, they recall forcibly the possible Cambrian rocks in the anticlinoria of the northern Maine volcanic belt (Grand Pitch formation), although volcanic rocks are rare or absent there; they are also not unlike the older part of the Taconic-type sequence in the northern part of the Gaspé Peninsula and the rocks in the core of the Notre Dame and Sutton anticlinoria, which do contain volcanics and which are also overlain unconformably by Middle Ordovician strata. These comparisons suggest equating the Gaspesian orogeny to the Penobscot "disturbance," and here as in northern Maine this early orogenic episode was if anything stronger than the "classical" Taconic orogeny. On the other hand, the polydeformation and metamorphism have led to the suggestion that the rocks may be Precambrian, in which case part of all of their deformation might be late Precambrian, contemporaneous with the late Precambrian (Avalonian) orogeny along the southeast side of the northern Appalachians (see p. 114, 139, 144, 146, 161).

Although the rocks of this older group can thus be compared with pre-Middle Ordovician rocks in several surrounding areas, especially with those of the Taconic-like sequence of Quebec, they stand in complete contrast to the nearest such rocks, the Cambrian limestone units near Percé (p. 130), which unconformably underlie the calcareous Ordovician strata of the Aroostook-Matapédia anticlinorium barely 30 kilometers (20 miles) away, and which resemble rather the carbonate sequence of Valley-and-Ridge type in the Champlain Valley or northwestern Newfoundland; moreover, the faunas reinforce this comparison. A speculative and quite unsupported hypothesis would be that these two groups of pre-Middle Ordovician rocks in southeastern Gaspé are the local representatives of the Taconic and carbonate sequences of the Taconic-Lake Champlain-Saint Lawrence belt and that they are still more or less in their original position, in which case the belt of Taconic-type rocks in northern Gaspé would have to be entirely allochthonous, brought 40 to 60 kilometers (25 to 35 miles) north from a source area south of the Cambrian carbonate exposures in question during some phase of the Taconic orogeny; later overlap by Middle and Upper Ordovician, Silurian, and Lower Devonian strata now conceals almost all evidence of the structure produced here in that orogenic phase. Such a hypothesis would help explain incidentally the extraordinary contrast between the deformed and clastic Taconic rocks of northern Gaspé and the quite undisturbed mainly carbonate rocks of Anticosti Island, 75 kilometers (45 miles) away, in which there is nothing to suggest proximity to any Taconic orogenic uplift. Whether this hypothesis is valid or not, the two areas in question, now not very far apart, record very different geologic histories: Cambrian limestone unconformably overlapped by Middle and Upper Ordovician argillaceous limestone apparently followed without break by deep-water Silurian and Lower Devonian strata characteristic of the Gaspé synclinorium vs. rocks of Taconic aspect but unknown age unconformably overlapped by Middle Ordovician conglomerate, graywacke, and graptolitic slate, in turn overlapped by the shallow-water Silurian strata of the Chaleur Bay sequence.

The Silurian rocks around Port Daniel are overlain only by post-tectonic red Carboniferous sandstone and conglomerate (Bonaventure sandstone), but farther west Devonian rocks appear, and Silurian and Devonian rocks together (Alcock, 1935) form the Chaleur Bay synclinorium, which underlies much of Chaleur Bay and its shores and extends southwestward into New Brunswick. The Silurian sedimentary rocks are much like those around Port Daniel, although apparently only the lower part of the sequence is present in New Brunswick, but above come large thicknesses of volcanics, both felsic and mafic. Red volcanic-boulder conglomerate and finer sediments are intercalated with or overlie the volcanics, and

there is also a unit (Dalhousie formation) of fossiliferous Lower Devonian silty and shaly limestone and limy shale. Unconformities are reported in this section, especially between Silurian and Devonian, but some of them may be simply overlaps of coarse sediment on half-eroded volcanic islands; the upper part of the Silurian may be absent by erosion or nondeposition or its place may be taken by the volcanics.

These mixed sedimentary and volcanic rocks form the large, relatively simple Restigouche syncline around the head of Chaleur Bay and a much more tightly folded and faulted synclinorial belt to the south. In the core of the Restigouche syncline, they are overlain, unconformably at least in places, by a kilometer or more (thousands of feet) of probably fluviatile sandstone and conglomerate, gray and buff below but becoming red and coarser upward (Dineley and Williams, 1968b); these beds are coarser than but otherwise resemble the sandy shale and sandstone strata at the top of the Devonian section in the Gaspé folded belt and like them contain Lower to lower Middle Devonian plants and even a thin coal seam. The pebbles in the upper conglomerate beds are dominantly of Ordovician and Silurian rocks like those nearby, showing that deformation, uplift, and erosion was already under way in this region by the beginning of the Middle Devonian. On the north shore of the bay, these beds in turn are overlain unconformably by over 100 meters (450 feet) of Upper Devonian strata, conglomerate at the base but mostly calcareous gray lacustrine shale and thin-bedded sandstone (Escuminac formation), containing the well known Escuminac fish fauna (Dineley and Williams, 1968a). Patches of flat-lying Carboniferous red sandstone (Bonaventure sandstone) sit unconformably on all the other rocks all around the shore of Chaleur Bay.

The Restigouche syncline ends to the southwest between two anticlines of the Aroostook-Matapédia anticlinorium in which the characteristic Ordovician calcareous rocks crop out, but the main synclinorial belt to the south extends southwestward from the shore of Chaleur Bay far into the highlands of northwestern New Brunswick—Mount Carleton, the highest point in the province, is upheld by felsic volcanics within this belt. The character of the rocks changes somewhat in this direction, however; calcareous rocks become less abundant, and more and more shale and graywacke enter the section, until the rocks merge with the noncalcareous Silurian strata on the east flank of the Aroostook-Matapédia anticlinorium. The volcanics persist some 150 kilometers (100 miles) from Chaleur Bay, but then they too seem to fade out. At the

Saint John River, the synclinorium is represented only by a discontinuous belt of relatively non-calcareous slate and graywacke between the calcareous Ordovician and Lower Silurian rocks of the Aroostook-Matapédia anticlinorium to the west and entirely noncalcareous probably Ordovician rocks in the Miramichi anticlinorium to the east (see below). Conglomerate occurs in many places along the eastern side of the belt near the anticlinorium on that side; in a few places in the same part of the belt, probably Lower Devonian plants have been found associated with conglomerate, sandstone, and slate. Still farther southwest, the synclinorium is lost in the southeastern part of the central Maine slate belt.

Two moderately large outliers of Carboniferous strata occur near the Saint John River, bounded on the west by longitudinal faults. The rocks are mainly red sandstone and conglomerate, but the northern outlier includes beds of limestone and gypsum, which probably represent the Lower Carboniferous marine zone (Windsor formation) of southeastern New Brunswick (see below, p. 138). The highest beds in the southern outlier are gray conglomerate and sandstone and may be Upper Carboniferous. The strata dip rather gently, except near the border faults. The northern outlier lies within the Chaleur Bay synclinorium, the southern on the margin of the Miramichi anticlinorium but apparently superposed on a saddle in which Silurian and Devonian beds encroach upon the anticlinorium. The western boundary fault of this outlier seems to be continuous with the western boundary fault of the anticlinorium, but if so the fault must have reversed its throw during or after the deposition of the Carboniferous beds.

Beginning at the corner of Chaleur Bay near Bathurst, New Brunswick, the Chaleur Bay synclinorium is bounded on the south and southeast by an area of older, more deformed and metamorphosed rocks, forming the core of the rather vaguely defined Miramichi anticlinorium and also of the highland belt of western New Brunswick. There seems no doubt that these rocks were deformed before the Silurian, but west of Bathurst the presumed unconformity is cut out by a zone of east-west faults; partly the older rocks may be thrust northward over the younger, but some of the faults are steep and late. Indeed a small patch of Carboniferous rock is down-dropped on the south side of one of them, and again it may record a reversal of the original throw or perhaps strike-slip. Along an eastern branch fault within the Silurian rocks (Rocky Brook-Millstream fault), small bodies of serpentine are found, associated with veins of base-metal sulfides; it is not clear

whether the serpentine cuts the Silurian or was brought up as slivers along the fault. Within the synclinorium to the north, probably pre-Silurian rocks also form the core of the Elmtree dome.

The northeast end of the Miramichi anticlinorium (see Fig. 1 in Davies and others, 1969) is formed of a great body of interbedded metavolcanic and metasedimentary rocks (Tetagouche group), mainly in the greenschist facies, although higher grade near granitic intrusions. The metavolcanics are both felsic and mafic, and the metasediments are those that normally accompany metavolcanics—graywacke, slate, and chert; middle Middle Ordovician graptolites have been found. The rocks are intensely deformed, partly thrown into recumbent folds and partly into great domelike folds with steep foliation and axes; perhaps indeed recumbent folds have been folded into the domes. A number of major copper mines have been opened in this region since 1952, the ore occurring in metasediments associated with felsic metavolcanics.

Farther southwest, somewhat quartzitic metasediments appear (stratigraphically beneath the volcanics?), and the metavolcanics seem to become less abundant, especially the felsic varieties, but much of the axial part of the anticlinorium is occupied by large granite plutons. As smaller bodies of the same granite cut the Silurian and Lower Devonian rocks in the Chaleur Bay synclinorium to the north, the granite masses are probably Devonian, but radiometry shows that there is also older, probably Ordovician, granitoid gneiss in the anticlinorium (Poole, Kelley, and Neale, 1964, p. 76), part of which may indeed be metamorphosed felsic metavolcanics. Rocks of these types form the body of the anticlinorium as far as the Saint John River (beyond which volcanics reappear locally in greater force). The degree of metamorphism drops off also in that direction, so that the contrast with the surrounding rocks is less, although there are contact aureoles around the younger granite masses in both pre-Silurian and Silurian rocks. Fossils are rare, but the few found indicate the presence of lower Middle and middle Middle Ordovician, and perhaps of Lower Ordovician as well.

On the east flank of the anticlinorium, Poole (Anderson and Poole, 1959; Poole, 1963; see also Poole, 1967, p. 18, 24; Neuman, 1968, p. 37) has worked out a stratigraphy that suggests a comparison with that of the Weeksboro-Lunksoos Lake anticlinorium in northern Maine. The oldest unit is largely gray quartzite, siltstone, and slate in the cores of several anticlines; fossils of the same age as the older Middle Ordovician fauna in northern Maine are known in calcareous siltstone at the top of this unit on the easternmost anticline. Next above is black graphitic slate and chert with middle Middle Ordovician graptolites, but the bulk of the rocks above is gray and green slate, siltstone, and graywacke with layers of mafic volcanics, chert, and manganiferous iron-formation. Similar gray and green slate, siltstone, and graywacke (even including manganiferous beds) have yielded Silurian fossils on both flanks of the anticlinorium, however, and so far no unconformities have been recognized anywhere in the section, so that evidence of orogenic episodes like those in northern Maine is lacking and no sharp boundary for the anticlinorium can be found, except where faults are present. Possible Silurian fossils are even reported from near the crest of the anticlinorium in a few places northeast of the Saint John River, perhaps in the southeastern continuation of the saddle mentioned above.

Like the Silurian on the northwest flank of the anticlinorium, that on the southeast contains conglomerate close to the anticlinorium; farther away the rocks are mostly finer grained and maroon slate appears. Clearly the relation of the Silurian conglomerate to the Miramichi anticlinorium is like that of the conglomerate along the southeast flank of the anticlinoria that make up the northern Maine volcanic belt, and furthermore the pebbles are of rock types that could readily come from the Ordovician rocks of the anticlinorium, suggesting its uplift in later Ordovician time, despite the absence of evidence of unconformity.

Approaching the international boundary, the Miramichi anticlinorium appears to become still less well defined and to plunge out of sight. Across the border in Maine (Larrabee, Spencer, and Swift, 1965), somewhat en echelon across a granite batholith around the Chiputneticook Lakes, is one last anticline containing Ordovician rocks—black slate and chert with middle Middle Ordovician graptolites, associated with gray slate and siltstone and felsic tuff. On the west side of the anticline, the Silurian begins with a conglomerate containing limestone pebbles (with Silurian

fossils), but most of it on both sides is the monotonous, slightly calcareous gray slate, siltstone, and and sandstone typical of the central Maine slate belt. One might say indeed that here the anticlinorium simply peters out in the southeast part of the slate belt, an arm of which extends around it and up its southeast side to disappear finally under flat-lying Carboniferous rocks.*

Although the Miramichi anticlinorium dies out as it enters Maine, the belt of granitic plutons that marks its axial region north of the Saint John River continues in full force to the southwest, sliding off the southeast side of the anticlinorium and extending across southeastern Maine to the east side of Penobscot Bay. It forms a distinct zone of hills and mountains that prolongs the highlands of western New Brunswick through to the coast and stands in strong contrast to the flat, drift-covered country over the main slate belt along the Penobscot River. At the coast, however, the plutons intersect a belt of quite different geology, discussed in the next section.

The belt described in the present section (omitting the Carboniferous basin of central and eastern New Brunswick) is distinguished from its surroundings by the presence of volcanic rocks and by considerable differences in the sedimentary rocks, although both distinctions fade out to the southwest and disappear entirely in Maine (plutonic activity on the other hand is strongest in Maine and west-central New Brunswick and becomes less and less important northeastward). One is tempted therefore to think again of a chain of volcanic islands—in the Ordovician along the present Miramichi anticlinorium, which may have been uplifted near the end of that period, in the Silurian and Early Devonian mainly within the Chaleur Bay synclinorium. The Ordovician volcanoes seem to have been a quite separate line from those of the northern Maine volcanic belt, for the trends are different and between them lie the fine-grained calcareous deposits of the Aroostook-Matapedia anticlinorium, quite lacking in the coarse clastics and pyroclastics one might expect to find near such volcanoes and anticlinorial uplifts. On the other hand, the Silurian and Lower Devonian volcanoes may

*These Carboniferous rocks form a vast triangular basin or half-basin east of the Miramichi anticlinorium and underlie about a third of the province of New Brunswick. In a narrow belt along the northwest side, thin units of probably Lower Carboniferous (Mississippian) rocks appear, mainly red sandstone and conglomerate but including several bands of volcanic rock; they are overlapped by a thick sequence of Upper Carboniferous (Pennsylvanian) brown and gray sandstone with beds of conglomerate, siltstone, shale, and coal, lying almost flat, except locally near normal faults, and inclining gently east-southeastward toward the Gulf of Saint Lawrence, under which they pass. Geophysical evidence shows that the total thickness of Carboniferous strata is more than 1 kilometer (4000 feet) near the coast. On the south side of the basin, however, the Carboniferous rocks are folded and faulted, as discussed in the next section. The southwest corner of the basin reaches within 16 kilometers (11 miles) of the Maine border, and isolated patches of Carboniferous rocks are found in both New Brunswick and Maine along a fault or zone of faults that cuts diagonally across the southwestward continuation of the Miramichi anticlinorium trend.

have been more nearly aligned, the Lower Devonian volcanic center in the Chapman syncline in northeastern Maine being a connecting link and the volcanics around Mt. Alexandre a further outpost (for the Lower Devonian alignment, see Boucot and others, 1964, p. 75 ff. and Fig. 2), although here too one finds a belt of entirely nonvolcanic Silurian sediments between the two volcanic areas. Moreover, as argued above (p. 131), the tight isoclinal folding in the nonvolcanic belt strongly suggests that that belt was originally much wider than it is today, at least up to the time of the Acadian orogeny in the Middle Devonian.

The trend of the Miramichi anticlinorium and of the plutonic belt that prolongs it to the southwest averages about N30°E, whereas trends in the Chaleur Bay synclinorium range from N35°E southwest of Mt. Carleton to N60°E or even more easterly on the shores of Chaleur Bay where they approach the Gaspé arc. The somewhat diagonal position of the anticlinorium (and perhaps of the northwest margin of the Carboniferous basin to the east) relative to the expectable trends in this part of the Quebec salient seems related to the sigmoid curve of the nonvolcanic belt, itself perhaps related to the northeastward disappearance of the northern Maine volcanic belt. In any case, one has here an excellent example of the fallacy of assuming that original sedimentary, volcanic, or even tectonic trends were always parallel and continuous along the general strike of a developing geosynclinal belt. Moreover, just as one might say that the Valley and Ridge province in Quebec shifted its position southward from its Cambro-Ordovician location next the Canadian shield to its Siluro-Devonian position in the Gaspé folded belt, so one might say that the Siluro-Devonian volcanic belt found itself forced to abandon its normal strike continuation off the end of the northern Maine Ordovician anticlinoria and to shift across to the northern end of the previously quite separate Miramichi volcanic belt.

The principal orogenic deformation in this belt, accompanied by much granite intrusion, was the Acadian, as for several belts to the northwest, and the unconformities underlying the various sandstone and conglomerate units in the Restigouche syncline suggest several episodes, one in the Early Devonian, another in the Middle Devonian, and a third after the Upper Devonian. Indeed orogeny may have been fairly continuous in this region through the Devonian period and into the Carboniferous, supplying sandstone and conglomerate to various local basins, only a few of which are still preserved, thus giving the impression of discrete episodes. There was older orogeny as well, however; a post-Middle Ordovician phase of the Taconic orogeny evidently affected at least the northern part of the Miramichi anticlinorium and the Port Daniel region, and uplift and intrusion of granitoids may have occurred along much of the anticlinorium. An earlier phase (possibly more than one) is evident near Port Daniel and may have affected part of the Miramichi anticlinorium; as the oldest rocks are undated in either area, the age of the phase (or phases) is not certain, although a correlation with the Penobscot disturbance seems reasonable.

Kennebecasis Anticlinorium in Southern New Brunswick and Adjoining Belts

Along the coast of southern New Brunswick and southeastern Maine, the geology is considerably better known than inland, thanks to moderately good exposures and especially to fossiliferous strata belonging to each of the Paleozoic systems except the Permian. The most nearly complete sequence is in the region around Saint John, New Brunswick (Hayes and Howell, 1937; Alcock, 1938).

The oldest rocks in this region form the Caledonia Mountains along the shore of the Bay of Fundy northeast of Saint John and follow the shore southwestward to Grand Manan Island at the mouth of the bay, opposite the eastern point of Maine. Two groups are distinguished. The older one (Green Head group) consists of moderately metamorphosed sedimentary rocks including much limestone and dolostone, quartzite, slate, and schist; within the group a unit dominated by quartzite overlies a unit dominated by limestone, perhaps unconformably (Leavitt, in Hamilton, 1965). The younger one (Coldbrook group) includes some zones of sandstone and conglomerate but consists mainly of felsic volcanic rocks, massive in some places but badly sheared in others, especially along several prominent steep longitudinal faults that break the region into long striplike fault blocks (see Webb, 1969, p. 760–764 and Fig. 2). The older group crops out in a central northeast-trending block (Kennebecasis block) that passes just northwest of Saint John, and the younger group appears in the blocks on either side (Kingston block on the northwest, Caledonian block on the southeast); for the most part they are separated by the longitudinal faults, but an angular unconformity is reported between the two groups on Grand Manan. On the Caledonian block, the younger group underlies Lower Cambrian strata, so that both groups are considered Precambrian in age; a disconformity is reported under the Cambrian but evidence for it seems dubious. The older group is intimately penetrated by intrusives ranging from gabbro to granite, near which it is altered to marble, schist, and gneiss, and granite pebbles occur in conglomerate beds in the volcanic group, but granite is also known intruding the latter group, so that two ages of granite are present. Taken together these rocks form the core of a compound horst or faulted anticlinorium (Kennebecasis anticlinorium, named for Kennebecasis Bay just north of Saint John).

The succeeding certainly Lower Paleozoic sequence (Saint John group) is preserved in a number of isolated patches within 50 kilometers (30 miles) northeast and north of Saint John; the largest areas are on the Caledonian block on the downthrown side of minor faults, but others are known on the Kennebecasis block and beyond (but not on) the Kingston block. This sequence consists of up to 600 meters (2000 feet) of purplish, white, and gray sandstone or quartzite, locally pebbly at the base, followed by dark shale or slate 200 to 300 meters (nearly 1000 feet) thick. Fossils occur at several levels in the shale and range from from Lower Cambrian to Lower Ordovician (Arenig); they are European rather than North American in their affinities, like those found in eastern Massachusetts (p. 112).

The main area of Precambrian rocks is bounded on the northwest by another steep, through-going longitudinal fault (Belleisle fault in New Brunswick, Lubec fault in Maine), perhaps the most extensive in the region. Beyond it, especially in the region around Passamaquoddy Bay (Cumming, 1967), one finds a thick sequence of Middle Paleozoic volcanic and sedimentary rocks (Mascarene group), considerably deformed but little or not at all metamorphosed except in contact zones around intrusive bodies. All gradations are present from lava flows (mafic and felsic) through tuffs to sandstone, slate, and limestone; volcanic rocks predominate in many areas, but sedimentary are dominant in some, especially to the northwest. Fossils are fairly common and indicate an age range from late Early Silurian to Early Devonian. These rocks, especially the volcanics, can be followed southwestward into and along the coast of Maine, and they are well displayed in a great sigmoidal fold near Eastport (Bastin and Williams, 1914), where a thickness of 14 kilometers (45,000 feet) is reported. They form a virtually continuous belt for 50 kilometers (30 miles) on either side of the international boundary and occur in patches, separated by intrusive mas-

ses, from the Saint John River 30 kilometers (20 miles) due north of Saint John to the outer islands of Penobscot Bay, a distance of 280 kilometers (175 miles). Throughout this distance they are accompanied by and perhaps genetically associated with a great layered complex of gabbro and granophyre, the Bays-of-Maine igneous complex of Chapman (1962), which in turn is cut discordantly by other intrusive rocks, mainly granitic but some mildly alkalic. In a relatively small area astride the international border, all these rocks are overlain unconformably by nearly 1000 meters (2800 feet) of post-tectonic redbeds (Perry formation) carrying an Upper Devonian flora, entirely unmetamorphosed and barely deformed except close to the longitudinal faults. In few places is the Acadian orogeny more dramatically recorded.

The belt of Silurian rocks is nearly 40 kilometers (25 miles) wide at the international border but tapers in both directions; its northwest margin is preserved only in places betweeen the intrusive masses of gabbro, granophyre, and granite. At Oak Bay, New Brunswick, just east of the border, a coarse basal conglomerate containing pebbles with Lower Silurian fossils rests unconformably on dark slate containing Lower Ordovician (Arenig) graptolites (Cumming, 1967, p. 5) and intruded not far away by probably Ordovician ultramafics (Poole, Kelley, and Neale, 1964, p. 76, fn.). This slate is part of a thick, monotonous, and so far otherwise unfossiliferous sequence of mostly dark slate with thin graded beds of siltstone and fine sandstone and rare volcanics ("dark argillite division" of Charlotte group). To the northwest across strike, on both sides of the international border, the dark slate sequence is in contact with lighter colored siltier and sandier strata ("pale argillite division" of Charlotte group), which merges with the probably Silurian sediments of the eastern arm of the central Maine slate belt, south of the end of the Miramichi anticlinorium. The contact between dark and light strata has been considered gradational by most observers (according, to Amos, 1963, p. 175, graded bedding indicates that the dark division overlies the pale, but according to Larrabee, Spencer, and Swift, 1965, p. E13, it indicates the opposite), but Ruitenburg (1968) has mapped it as a southeast-dipping thrust fault in New Brunswick. In any case no unconformity has been recognized here, although the contact lies only 10 kilometers (6 miles) across strike from the exposed unconformity between the two systems (Lower Silurian on Lower Ordovician); to be sure, the slaty rocks here as elsewhere are tightly folded by upright, nearly isoclinal folds, so that the present width may be far less than the original width.

East and west both contacts of the dark slate sequence are cut off by large granite masses within 30 kilometers (20 miles) of the border. Nevertheless, the sequence can be followed interruptedly along strike for at least 100 kilometers (many tens of miles) in either direction. In Maine, as far as can be observed in isolated areas between granite plutons, it appears to grade into somewhat more volcanic and more metamorphosed phyllite and chlorite-actinolite schist (Ellsworth schist, North Haven greenstone); these rocks in turn are overlain unconformably in several places by the Silurian volcanic-sedimentary sequence along the Maine coast, notably on North Haven in Penobscot Bay (as mentioned above, p. 128). In New Brunswick also, near the Saint John River, metavolcanics are associated with the dark slate sequence, which there may be converging with the much thinner and distinctly more fossiliferous but otherwise not dissimilar Cambrian and Lower Ordovician dark slate sequence (and with the underlying volcanic group?) around Saint John. No obvious unconformity with the Silurian has been located in that area.

Northeastward all the belts of rocks so far discussed—the dark slate sequence, the Silurian volcanic group, and the Precambrian groups with patches of Cambro-Ordovician strata—are bevelled by the south margin of the Carboniferous basin of central and eastern New Brunswick or plunge between fault-bounded arms extending southwest from it. The stratigraphic sequence in this part of the Carboniferous basin is complex. The lower strata (mainly Mississippian but including the whole Namurian and also some Upper Devonian) range up to 4500 meters (over 14,000 feet) thick and are characterized by fluviatile redbeds, with coarse conglomerate at the base and sporadically throughout. In the lower part is a thick but fairly local unit of dark gray, probably lacustrine, shale, siltstone, and sandstone (Albert formation) with oil shale near the base and evaporites close to the top; in the upper part is a thinner but more persistent zone containing several distinct beds of marine limestone and also considerable gypsum as well as redbeds (Windsor formation) and carrying Viséan faunas of distinctly European affinities.

These strata are thickest in a narrow trough, evidently a fault-bounded rift (Belt, 1968b) superposed on the Kennebecasis and Kingston blocks of the Kennebecasis anticlinorium, the bounding faults being continuations of longitudinal faults in the pre-Carboniferous rocks to the southwest. Indeed strata older than the marine zone (two-thirds of the thickness) are virtually confined to the rift, and they grade into coarse fanglomerate close to the bounding faults, which were evidently ac-

tive during deposition. Only about the time of the marine invasion did sedimentation encroach much beyond the rift; northward it then spread as a thin, perhaps discontinous sheet over much of central New Brunswick and as far as the outliers beyond the Miramichi anticlinorium, but southward the Caledonian block apparently remained high, continuing to provide coarse sediment. Northeastward the rift seems to be split by another uplifted but now almost entirely buried block (Westmorland block, south and east of Moncton), one arm of the rift continuing northeast under northwestern Prince Edward Island, the other turning due east, cutting off the end of the Caledonian block and merging beyond it with another large basin or rift in the region of the isthmus connecting New Brunswick with Nova Scotia and the south shore of Northumberland Strait. Disconformities and even angular unconformities appear here and there in the sequence, especially around the east end of the Caledonian block, and almost any unit may locally overlap directly onto the pre-Carboniferous rocks, generally with a basal conglomerate. The strata within the rift are folded on axes ranging from N45° to 60°E. The throw of the various longitudinal faults, particularly the rift-bounding faults, is commonly inconsistent from one stratigraphic level to another, especially from pre-Carboniferous to Carboniferous, suggesting repeated dip-slip movement in different senses, strike-slip movement, or both; there was certainly considerable strike-slip movement in Carboniferous time (Webb, 1963; 1969).

The entirely nonmarine Upper Carboniferous strata above (Pennsylvanian, mainly Westphalian) reach a thickness of about 1 kilometer (3000 to 4000 feet) and consist dominantly of gray or brown sandstone and shale with commercial coal seams, but some redbeds are present, especially at the base. North of the Caledonian block, these strata are nearly flat-lying or gently folded, and they rest with strong unconformity on the folded Lower Carboniferous, uncut by the rift-border faults and locally overlapping onto pre-Carboniferous rocks, but around the east end of that block, the main body of them is also folded (diapirically?) and faulted and an upper part lies unconformably on the rest. Most of the folds in all these strata plunge northeastward, disappearing under higher, unconformable, at most only gently folded beds, but some have been traced for many kilometers (miles) in the subsurface beneath the unconformable cover, which thickens in that direction. On Prince Edward Island are exposed the highest strata preserved in the basin; these are redbeds again (chiefly sandstone and conglomerate) of latest Carboniferous and Early Permian age (Frankel,

1966; Barss and Hacquebard, 1967, p. 274–278). Geophysical evidence indicates that the northeast fold trends in the older Carboniferous rocks continue beneath the island, and even the Lower Permian rocks at the surface are gently folded. (Frankel recognizes a disconformity or gently angular unconformity beneath the highest beds preserved on the island.) Still farther northeast on the Magdalen Islands in the middle of the Gulf of Saint Lawrence (Sanschagrin, 1964), similar but moderately folded probably Upper Carboniferous redbeds unconformably overlie basaltic volcanics, marine limestone and gypsum, and gray sandstone, siltstone, and shale, sharply (probably diapirically) folded on almost easterly trends; fossils in the marine beds show that they correlate with the Viséan (upper Mississippian) marine zone (Windsor formation) of the mainland.

Patches of Carboniferous rocks are also preserved in places along the Bay of Fundy shore for 40 or 50 kilometers (25 or 30 miles) on either side of Saint John, again partly bounded by steep longitudinal faults. The upper strata here are gray and brown sandstone (Lancaster formation) as in the main basin, but they overlie unconformably purplish sandstone and conglomerate and associated volcanics (Mispec formation, of which the age is uncertain) that are commonly very badly sheared, mildly metamorphosed, and locally cut by small rhyolitic or granitic intrusions. Chiefly felsic volcanics are also known in the Lower Carboniferous strata along much of the south margin of the main basin along and west of the Saint John River, especially in the Mt. Pleasant area, where tin ore is associated with them (van de Poll, 1967).

Finally, red conglomerate and sandstone of Late Triassic age are preserved in several places along the shore of the Bay of Fundy, faulted against or unconformably overlapping Carboniferous or Precambrian rocks; evidently they are marginal outliers of the Triassic basin under the bay and in Nova Scotia. Flows of Triassic basalt underlie the western half or more of Grand Manan, faulted against rocks of the two Precambrian groups.

The Precambrian area of southern New Brunswick has thus played the role of a persistent tectonic high or geanticline. Repeatedly it was covered by sediments and volcanics—upper Precambrian and Cambrian, Silurian, Lower Carboniferous (locally Upper Devonian), Upper Carboniferous (twice?), Upper Triassic—and then partly exposed again by erosion before the next unit was deposited. During the first half of the Paleozoic the sediments were marine, during the second half (beginning in the Upper Devonian and extending

into the Triassic) they were mainly redbeds (associated in several areas with basaltic volcanics). Angular unconformities, coarse clastics, volcanics abound, and plutonic rocks of several ages seem to be present, although metamorphism has been surprisingly mild on the whole. A more thorough contrast with the nearby central Maine slate belt could hardly be imagined, but there are several parallels with the volcanic belts beyond. The first movements (perhaps accompanied by low-grade metamorphism and granite intrusion and followed by large-scale volcanism) appear to have been Precambrian, presumably late Precambrian, and represent the early-Appalachian (Avalonian) orogenic phase, known in several other places along the Atlantic seaboard of the northern Appalachians (see p. 114). Taconic movements are recorded along the northwest margin of the Silurian volcanic belt, as at Oak Bay, but on the anticlinorium itself the relations are not known; the only intrusives fairly definitely belonging to this period are the ultramafics in the Ordovician slate close to the international border. The Acadian orogeny was certainly the major one in the region and was accompanied by massive intrusions. In the Silurian belt it was certainly mostly over by Late Devonian time, but along the anticlinorium major movements continued through the Early Carboniferous and into the Late Carboniferous; these later movements (Maritime disturbance of Poole, 1967, p. 40–41) included both folding and faulting. Some of the faulting was probably thrusting associated with the folding, but a good part of the movement on the larger longitudinal faults was probably strike slip (Webb, 1963, 1969); such faults are most obvious in southeastern New Brunswick but can be found from there southwestward into Maine and may well be part of a major Carboniferous strike-slip fault zone (including the faults grouped as the Cabot fault by Wilson, 1962). One may ask if the sigmoidal fold near Eastport is not also the result of left-lateral strike-slip at this time. Which of these later movements should be considered late Acadian and which early Alleghany or Maritime is not clear, and perhaps the question is not meaningful, but the wide spread of the relatively thin Viséan (Windsor) marine zone across the Maritime Provinces suggests a lull in orogenic activity that may be taken as a convenient dividing line, the more so as it corresponds fairly closely in time with the maximum extension of limestone into the southern and central Appalachians between the Acadian and Alleghany clastic wedges. But whatever names are attached to the various movements, the belt was uplifted by them all; thus it was a persistent geanticline lying between marine troughs in which deposition was apparently nearly continuous at least into Early Devonian time.

Except in the sigmoidal fold near Eastport, Maine, where northwest strikes persist for 20 kilometers (12 miles) across the regional trend before bending through north to northeast, the trends in the belt here discussed are mostly northeast; although they are not very regular, their average ranges from N45–50°E in southeastern Maine and southwestern New Brunswick to N55–60°E (and locally almost east-west) in southeastern New Brunswick, and there are no obvious diagonal trends like that of the Miramichi anticlinorium. The Precambrian belt from the Caledonian Mountains to Grand Manan is evidently a major culmination; it plunges northeastward under the Carboniferous basin around the Gulf of Saint Lawrence, but its southwestern extension is hidden beneath the Gulf of Maine. It is very tempting to consider the presumed anticlinorium in eastern Massachusetts as its direct continuation, and the lower and middle Paleozoic sequences in the two areas are remarkably alike, though those in Massachusetts are far more fragmentary. Southeastern Massachusetts and Rhode Island also have a Carboniferous basin or two, but the sequence there is rather different from that in New Brunswick and the deformation and metamorphism much more severe.

Nova Scotia

The pre-Carboniferous rocks of Nova Scotia belong to two very different assemblages, separated by an east-west rift-zone (central Nova Scotia rift) of especially badly deformed Lower Carboniferous rocks extending from Guysborough at the head of Chedabucto Bay south of Cape Breton Island to Truro at the head of Cobequid Bay, the east end of the Bay of Fundy (one can argue indeed that the zone reappears in the badly deformed Carboniferous rocks on the New Brunswick coast around Saint John; p. 139). The assemblage in northern Nova Scotia, north of this zone, is varied and has much in common with the rocks of the Kennebecasis anticlinorium of southern New Brunswick or its immediate flanks; it is exposed in several isolated highland areas around and between which belts of Carboniferous rocks anastomose, generally forming lower ground except that the lower part of the Lower Carboniferous underlies wooded hills. The assemblage in southern Nova Scotia is more monotonous and forms a single block, only locally overlapped by Carboniferous rocks; the surface of this block, though irregular in detail, is very even in the large and slopes

gradually south-southeast toward the ocean.

The widest variety of rock types and ages and also the rock sequence most obviously like that of southern New Brunswick are found in southeastern Cape Breton Island (Hutchinson, 1952; Weeks, 1954). Two belts may be distinguished. In a northwestern belt of northeast-trending faultblock highlands (Boisdale Hills, North Mountain) between arms of the Bras d'Or, the large salt-water lake within Cape Breton Island, the oldest rocks are much like the oldest Precambrian group in New Brunswick—moderately metamorphosed limestone and dolostone, quartzite and graywacke, mica, chlorite and talc schist (George River group), intruded by granite and other plutonic rocks; according to one interpretation, the stratigraphic order is the same as in New Brunswick (Green Head group). In a southeastern belt or belts southeast of the lake, on the other hand, the oldest rocks are a thick group of felsic pyroclastics with some sedimentary layers and some lava flows (Fourchu group) in which metamorphism is minor, except close to intrusive masses, but deformation is considerable, especially along longitudinal faults; the resemblance to the volcanic rocks beneath the Cambrian strata of New Brunswick (Coldbrook group) is obvious, and radiometry enforces the correlation (Fairbairn and others, 1966). These volcanic rocks pass upward into red sandstone and conglomerate as much as 600 meters (2000 feet) thick (Morrison River formation) with shale and white quartzite at the top, succeeded in turn by 1000 meters or so (about 3500 feet) of dark shaly strata with fossils ranging through the Cambrian; to the southwest along strike, however, mafic volcanics, graywacke, and conglomerate (with a few beds of oölitic hematite) appear, and part at least of these are Middle Cambrian. No disconformity appears to be present beneath the fossiliferous strata, but there is a hiatus between Middle Cambrian and Upper Cambrian fossil zones. On the other hand, the metamorphosed rocks (George River group) in the northwestern belt are directly and unconformably overlain by mafic volcanic rocks and associated shale and quartzite of Middle Cambrian age (the volcanics were formerly assigned to the Precambrian), above which is black shale ranging up into the Lower Ordovician (the hiatus between Middle and Upper Cambrian seems to be larger here). Thus the two belts had rather different histories in the Cambrian and earlier, the northwestern belt lacking Lower Cambrian and conformably underlying strata. Except for the mafic volcanics, the rock types and the faunas in the Lower Paleozoic rocks closely resemble those in the Saint John region of New Brunswick.

Locally patches of gray and red feldspathic sandstone, quartzite, and conglomerate, perhaps of more than one age, rest unconformably upon Cambrian and older rocks; in one such patch in the northwestern belt (McAdam Lake formation), probably Lower Devonian plant remains have been found. Pre-Carboniferous intrusive rocks— granite to gabbro—cut all these rocks, including at least one of the sandstone patches just mentioned (but not the fossiliferous one); probably, however, there are intrusives of more than one age, not only Acadian but also Taconic (as suggested by radiometric ages; Poole, Kelley, and Neale, 1964, p. 73) or late Precambrian (older than the Precambrian volcanics but younger than the metamorphics; ibid., p. 75) or both.

The northern part of Cape Breton Island consists chiefly of a high tableland of pre-Carboniferous rocks (up to 500 meters—1700 feet—above sea level), with patches of Carboniferous around the edges; the western part consists of several small pre-Carboniferous highlands surrounded by larger Carboniferous areas. The pre-Carboniferous rocks are a complex of plutonic rocks (mainly granite to granodiorite, but including altered anorthosite; Jenness, 1966) with larger and smaller patches of metamorphosed sedimentary (including carbonate) and volcanic rocks; there are no fossils, and comparison with the southeastern part of the island suggests that the metamorphics at least are Precambrian (George River group). The ages of the intrusives are also uncertain; the possibilities are the same as on southern Cape Breton Island. Here and there patches of unmetamorphosed volcanics and red clastics rest unconformably upon the plutonic and metamorphic rocks; in the past these have been compared to the probably Lower Devonian rocks in the southern part of the island (McAdam Lake formation), but at least the bulk of them are basal Carboniferous (Fisset Brook formation; Kelley and Mackasey, 1965).

On the mainland of Nova Scotia west of Antigonish, some 50 kilometers (30 miles) west of Cape Breton Island, rises another pre-Carboniferous highland (Antigonish or Browns Mountain Highland). In a fault block along the north shore north of Browns Mountain is exposed an exceptionally fine section spanning the whole of the Silurian and extending into the Lower Devonian—the Arisaig section (Williams, 1914)—mainly gray marine sandstone, siltstone, and shale, over 1000 meters (nearly 4000 feet) thick and richly fossiliferous. At the base of the section are felsic volcanics; at the top 300 meters (1000 feet) of continental red and gray sandstone carrying Lower Devonian fish. These Silurian and Lower Devonian strata are also recognized around the western end of the highland; they are folded and faulted but not metamorphosed. The rocks beneath the known Silurian strata are less well known; mainly they are badly deformed and mildly metamorphosed slate, graywacke, and quartzite, with a few beds of oölitic hematite (Browns Mountain group), plus greenstone volcanics (also some felsic types), all cut by granodiorite. In places coarse red conglomerate and sandstone intervene between these rocks and the Silurian. The ages are indefinite, though poor fossils in the slate indicate an Early Paleozoic (Early Ordovician?) age (probably Middle Ordovician brachiopods have been found in hematitic quartzite pebbles, not necessarily from this group, in a fault breccia and a Carboniferous conglomerate north of Antigonish). None of the rocks (except the oölitic hematite) resemble very closely those on Cape Breton Island, but the pre-Silurian rocks recall the slate sequence northwest of the Kennebecasis anticlinorium (Charlotte group).

The Cobequid Mountains are a long, narrow, north-tilted fault block, extending 160 kilometers (100 miles) eastward from Cape Chignecto, the cape that separates the two main arms of the Bay of Fundy. They consist of granitic intrusives cutting sedimentary and volcanic rocks; the sedimentary rocks are chiefly parts of the Arisaig sequence, variably metamorphosed near the intrusives. Near the south boundary fault of the block, all the rocks are badly sheared. At the northeast corner and locally elsewhere, strata that probably correspond to the top of the Arisaig section or lie even higher include basalt and red and gray conglomerate as well as sandstone (River John group) and are dated as Lower or Middle Devonian.

As already mentioned, southern Nova Scotia is far more uniform, both geographically and geologically. A large part of it is underlain by a thick, monotonous, isoclinally folded sequence of impure quartzite or graywacke and slate (Meguma group), reported to be 10 kilometers (30,000 feet) thick; in general a lower, more quartzitic part and an upper, more slaty part can be separately mapped. Slaty cleavage or schistosity is ubiquitous, and the argillaceous rocks range from slate to sillimanite schist (Taylor and Schiller, 1966). Originally thought to be Paleozoic, the sequence was then classed as Precambrian because of similarities with probably Precambrian strata in southeastern Newfoundland, but Lower Ordovician graptolites have been found in the upper part, and an Early Paleozoic age seems probable for the whole. Indeed, it resembles the thick slate sequence northwest of the Kennebecasis anticlinorium (Charlotte group), now also classed as Lower

Paleozoic after a period of doubt, more than it does the rocks in Newfoundland.

In a few synclines along the north and west side of the region, younger strata are preserved. They begin with a unit containing relatively pure quartzite, siltstone, slate, and volcanic rocks (White Rock formation) and pass upward into dark slate and siltstone (with a local unit of volcanic breccia) and then into lighter, locally reddish, silty shale and shaly siltstone (Torbrook formation) with beds of quartzite and of quartzitic iron-formation, once an iron ore. Upper Silurian graptolites are found in the slate, and Lower Devonian shelly fossils are found in the quartzite and especially the iron-formation. The whole is 2500 meters (8000 feet) or more thick and has generally been considered conformable with the Ordovician below, although the fossil hiatus (Lower Ordovician to Upper Silurian) is large. In view of the similarity of the quartzite-containing unit to basal Silurian units in central New England (Clough quartzite and Shaw Mountain formation; see above, p. 97, 103), I believe that a disconformity is present beneath it throughout the region and an unconformity at least in the westernmost syncline northwest of Yarmouth; Taylor (1965, p. 17–22) gives the evidence for the unconformity but concludes, with most other observers, that it is local and that in most of the region sedimentation was continuous, despite the large hiatus in the known fossils. In any case, the great thickness and uniformity of the whole sequence is in the strongest contrast to the variable sequences in northern Nova Scotia and southern New Brunswick and reminds one instead of the central Maine slate belt.

Cutting sharply across all these strata are bodies of granite, including one of batholithic proportions extending more than 150 kilometers (100 miles) west from Halifax, far enough to break up the continuity of the Silurian synclines. Contact metamorphism is marked in the rocks close to the granite bodies, which range from andalusite-staurolite schist to migmatitic gneiss, and quartz veins carrying gold are present in many districts out from their borders; a well known name for the older slate sequence (Meguma group) is Gold-bearing series.

The Carboniferous stratigraphy of Nova Scotia has much in common with that of New Brunswick; thicknesses are comparable—in the Upper Carboniferous even greater. Fluviatile redbeds predominate in the Lower Carboniferous, but bodies of lacustrine gray beds are also present, both below and above the persistent Viséan marine zone (Windsor formation) (Belt, 1965, 1968a). Beds older than the marine zone (Horton group) are thickest in and largely confined to a series of fault-bounded basins or rifts. There are two main east-west rifts, one on either side of the Cobequid and Browns Mountain highlands; the one on the south is the central Nova Scotia rift already mentioned (p. 140), and the one on the north is the eastward continuation of the southern arm of the rift zone of southeastern New Brunswick (p. 138). They are apparently connected by a transverse depression in the George Bay area east of the Browns Mountain highland, where the total thickness of the Lower Carboniferous may reach 5 kilometers (15,000 feet). Farther east, the southern rift probably continues out to sea under Chedabucto Bay and beyond, and it appears to send an arm northeastward onto Cape Breton Island south of the Bras d'Or. From the George Bay area, other arms extend into western Cape Breton, one as far as the north shore of the Bras d'Or, and what is probably the main rift trends northeastward along the northwest coast to the north tip of the island, although small blocks of older rocks appear here and there within it. Only locally, however, do relatively thin representatives of the upper part of these lower strata appear on the platformlike areas south and east of the rift, most notably in the area southwest of Truro.

The marine zone and the overlying beds also reach their maximum thicknesses in various parts of the rift zones (except that on southern Cape Breton Island the locus of maximum deposition shifted to the north and west), but they are less strictly confined to it. The marine zone overlaps especially widely; for example, it spreads over part of central southern Nova Scotia as far as the south coast west of Halifax. On the other hand, the Cobequid block continued to stand high and to shed sediment into the rifts on either side well into Late Carboniferous time; the other blocks succumbed earlier.

Volcanic rocks occur in the basal layers of the Carboniferous in several places (those on northern Cape Breton Island are mentioned above, p. 141), and they are also present very locally as high as the marine zone; small intrusions of basalt or gabbro and of rhyolite or microgranite occur in the lower beds near Guysborough near the east end of the central Nova Scotia rift. Conglomerate, in many places fanglomerate, is common in whatever unit approaches an active rift-border fault or overlaps onto pre-Carboniferous rocks; even the marine zone grades locally into red conglomerate. Not only gypsum but also large quantities of rock salt are associated with the marine limestone, notably in the rift zone north of the Cobequids, and they are mined in places. Redbeds persist in some areas into the Upper

Carboniferous, but more commonly that consists of yellow, brown, or gray sandstone (locally conglomeratic), gray siltstone and shale, and coal; such strata may be the lateral facies equivalents of redbed units or may overlap them unconformably. The most pronounced disconformity or unconformity generally lies within the Upper Carboniferous, probably equivalent to the main unconformity in southeasternmost New Brunswick southeast of the Caledonian Mountains but not to the one farther northwest around Moncton. The beds above it are thickest in basins that only partially coincide with the rift, which had largely ceased to function as such. Coal is mined in several such basins along the north coast of Nova Scotia and also around Sydney in eastern Cape Breton Island.

Deformation is greater in the Carboniferous of Nova Scotia than in that of New Brunswick or Prince Edward Island. Already along the north coast, there is considerable sharp folding, even of the coal-bearing beds, and diapirs of salt from the marine zone appear along anticlinal axes in the rift north of the Cobequids and locally on western Cape Breton Island. (Deformation beneath the marine zone was probably different, mainly block movement.) Farther south, especially in the central Nova Scotia rift, the folding in the Carboniferous rocks is still more intense and slaty cleavage appears locally, although the thinner sections outside the rift on either side are much less deformed. Weeks (1954, p. 77–78, 92–96) has suggested that a mass of Lower Carboniferous rocks in the arm of that rift on southern Cape Breton Island—in an area 12 kilometers (8 miles) wide and perhaps 50 kilometers (30 miles) long—is allochthonous, having moved into place from some kilometers (miles) to the south. His argument depends in good part on the presence there of thick lower Lower Carboniferous strata, whereas on either side higher Lower Carboniferous beds rest directly on the pre-Carboniferous rocks, but the same relation exists all along the rift to Truro, a distance of 200 kilometers (120 miles), and appears to be normal in all the rifts. An alternative explanation is that during deformation the thick rift filling reacted differently from the thinner sequences resting on older more competent rocks on either side and was locally thrust up and out over the rift margins; indeed, such an explanation fits the entire rift system. Most or all of this intense deformation probably took place during the Late Carboniferous at the time of the most pronounced unconformity; there was later folding, to be sure, as late as the Early Permian, but it was much less severe.

Many of the faults in the region, especially the rift-border faults, were evidently active for considerable periods of time during the Carboniferous, strongly affecting sedimentation; moreover, the relative importance of dip-slip and strike-slip components in their displacement probably varied from fault to fault and with time along any one fault. In particular, the fault on the south side of the Cobequid block was active until late in the Carboniferous, with a strong dextral strike-slip component (Eisbacher, 1969).

Along the northwest coast of Nova Scotia and east as far as Truro, all these rocks from the Lower Paleozoic (Meguma group) to the Carboniferous are overlain unconformably by Upper Triassic continental deposits, chiefly redbeds, which dip gently northwest toward a synclinal axis under the Bay of Fundy (it passes through the Cape Blomidon Peninsula, close to the cape). Beyond the axis, on the north shore of Cobequid Bay, the Triassic strata are limited by one of several longitudinal faults in the northern part of the central Nova Scotia rift, near which they show variable dips and along one of which blocks of older rocks are brought up. The Triassic section also includes a sequence of lava flows (North Mountain basalt) that, dipping northwest like the enclosing sediments, forms North Mountain along the south shore of the main part of the Bay of Fundy for 200 kilometers (120 miles); at the east it is bent back across the syncline to form the hook of the Cape Blomidon Peninsula. As Poole (1967, p. 41–42) points out, the Triassic trough is roughly superposed on the west end of the central Nova Scotia rift; moreover, at Guysborough at the east end of the rift, Triassic sediments reappear in a couple of small patches, and both Triassic and Carboniferous may extend well to the east under Chedabucto Bay and the continental shelf. In the opposite direction, Triassic rocks are known to extend under the Gulf of Maine as far as a point about 140 kilometers (90 miles) due west of Yarmouth, where they apparently dip west into a fault or fault zone (Uchupi, 1966, westernmost Triassic on profiles 42 and 40). The synclinal structure under the Bay of Fundy apparently persists for much of this distance (Uchupi, 1966, profiles 48 and 45; much of what Uchupi interprets as basement in these profiles could well be the sequence of lava flows within the Triassic, folded into this syncline, and indeed the basement masses he shows north of the southernmost Triassic on profile 48 and west of the easternmost Triassic on profile 42 are almost directly on strike with North Mountain on Nova Scotia, long parallel ridges on the sea floor filling much of the gap).

In two small areas in south-central Nova Scotia northeast of Halifax, stratified layers of clay, sand, and lignite overlie Carboniferous rocks (Stevenson, 1959, p. 34–35). Spores and pollen from the lignite indicate a Cretaceous, probably Early Cretaceous, age, and these sediments are presumably outliers of the Coastal Plain sediments known to be present under the continental shelf.

The main trends of Carboniferous folding and faulting in northern Nova Scotia outline a broad recess around the south side of the great basin under Prince Edward Island and the Gulf of St. Lawrence; they range from practically due east in and on either side of the Cobequid Mountains and also on the isthmus that connects Nova Scotia to New Brunswick, through N70°–50°E in and around the Browns Mountain highland, to N30°E in western and northern Cape Breton Island (in the southeastern part of the island they remain about N50°E, but they tend to splay out in the Sydney area). The older rocks have generally similar but considerably more irregular trends, reaching roughly north-south in parts of northern Cape Breton Island. In southern Nova Scotia, on the other hand, the average strike of the older rocks defines a salient, ranging from N30°E near Yarmouth (even north-south not far to the southeast) through N60°E north of Halifax (trends in the overlying Carboniferous are the same) to about N85°E, but somewhat irregular, southeast of Guysborough. Thus the rift between northern and southern Nova Scotia is about parallel to trends on the north but cuts those to the south near Truro, vice versa near Guysborough. Northern and southeastern Cape Breton Island may mark a culmination on anticlinorial axes bringing the older rocks to the surface, east of which the Carboniferous rocks, especially the coal-bearing beds, drop off past Sydney into Cabot Strait, and the Browns Mountain and Cobequid highlands may be lesser culminations, but in general the distribution of neither Carboniferous nor pre-Carboniferous rocks suggests any regular ups and downs.

The Cobequid and Browns Mountain highlands and the various large and small pre-Carboniferous highlands of Cape Breton Island give the impression of being fragments of a terrain like southern New Brunswick and adjacent Maine; the fragmentary impression is strengthened by variations in stratigraphy from one to the next. It would be possible to imagine indeed that they really are fragments torn off the southwestern continuation of that terrain in the area of the present Gulf of Maine and transported by sinistral strike slip some hundreds of kilometers (hundreds of miles) to their present positions; the highlands of Cape Breton Island might be torn from the southwest end of the Kennebecasis anticlinorium itself, and those on the mainland from one of its flanks, though the relative paucity of volcanics in the Silurian of Nova Scotia distinguishes it from the Silurian northwest of that anticlinorium. A possible parallel would be southern California in the late Cenozoic (Webb, 1963); indeed, Wilson (1962) expressly compares his Cabot fault, in which he includes certain of the longitudinal faults in northern Nova Scotia and southern New Brunswick, with the San Andreas fault. As he points out, if any such large movement took place, it must have been virtually complete by mid-Carboniferous time. The large block of southern Nova Scotia fits less well into such a speculative scheme; its affinities would seem to be with the central Maine slate belt and its continuations, no part of which is covered by the sea or otherwise missing short of Connecticut. A somewhat less hardy reconstruction, requiring instead large-scale dextral strike slip (see Webb, 1969, Figs. 4 and 5), would bring the Cape Breton Island highlands and those of mainland Nova Scotia from a northeastern continuation of the Kennebecasis anticlinorium or from its south flank, and southern Nova Scotia from an area south of that continuation. Belt (1968b, p. 104–105, and personal communication) agrees with Webb that most of the rift-border faults had dextral and not sinistral movement, which was responsible for the fragmentation and the formation of the rifts; at first such movement was active along two parallel northeast-trending rift zones, one from Guysborough and George Bay to western Newfoundland and a second from southern New Brunswick near Saint John to northwestern Prince Edward Island, connected to the first by the east-west rift in mainland Nova Scotia, and then the second broke through directly from Prince Edward Island just south of the Magdalen Islands to Newfoundland to form a single major zone, leaving the area of Northumberland Strait and its shores particularly broken up and depressed. A conservative hypothesis would be that the northern Nova Scotia highlands are simply en echelon eastward continuations of the Kennebecasis anticlinorium, which need not have been rectilinear or uniform along its trend; the fragmentation would then have been essentially local, extending through Carboniferous time. In any case, unless one accepts an extreme form of the first hypothesis, southern Nova Scotia is our only glimpse of a deep marine trough that lay south of the anticlinorium.

In any case, Nova Scotia records as varied an orogenic history as any part of the Northern

Appalachians. As in southern New Brunswick, there was apparently a late Precambrian (Avalonian) period of low-grade metamorphism and granite intrusion, followed by intense volcanism. Taconic movements are recorded by angular unconformities and metamorphic discontinuities in southeastern Cape Breton Island and the Browns Mountain highland; in several areas, Taconic granodiorite appears to be present. The Acadian orogeny was everywhere important, and the major granitic intrusives of southern Nova Scotia certainly and those of northern Nova Scotia probably were emplaced then. The Alleghany orogeny (Maritime disturbance of Poole, 1967, p. 40–41) was also significant, deforming the Carboniferous rocks throughout the province, most intensely to the southeast; deformation apparently occurred at intervals through the Carboniferous, and igneous rocks appear to cut at least Lower Carboniferous strata. Finally, Nova Scotia includes the bulk of the northeasternmost of the Appalachian Triassic basins, aside from that part hidden beneath the sea.

Summary

Nowhere else is so wide a belt of the Appalachians exposed as across the Gaspé Peninsula and the Maritime Provinces; from the north shore of Gaspé to the south tip of Nova Scotia measures 650 kilometers (400 miles). As in New England, the geology, at least the pre-Carboniferous geology, can be summarized in terms of alternating anticlinorial and synclinorial belts, some of which are continuations of those in central and southern New England, though none are exactly the same. The northwestern anticlinorium, the one in the Notre Dame Mountains, differs from the Green Mountains anticlinorium in nowhere exposing Precambrian rocks; moreover, its axis is not obvious on the Gaspé Peninsula. The central anticlinorial belt, the northern Maine volcanic belt, consists not of a string of gneiss domes like the Bronson Hill anticlinorium but of a series of irregular anticlinoria with deep synclinoria between, yet the difference may result partly from the lower metamorphic grade, too low for bodies of light rock to rise plastically to the level that is now the land surface, and there are several similarities, notably the abundance of volcanics and the presence of pre-Silurian intrusives. Rocks unconformably underlying Middle Ordovician strata appear in several places, but whether they are Precambrian or Early Paleozoic in age is not certain; the latter is perhaps more probable, in which case they may be little if at all older than the oldest beds exposed in the Stony Creek dome at the south end of the Bronson Hill anticlinorium. In any case, restlessness has characterized the entire recorded history of the belt, from this unconformity to the Lower Devonian sediments and volcanics preserved in some of its synclinoria.

The Miramichi anticlinorium seems like a diagonally placed offset of this belt, isolated from the other anticlinoria by arms of the central Maine slate belt; its poorly known Ordovician history may be somewhat like that of the northern Maine volcanic belt, whereas in the Silurian and Early Devonian the locus of maximum volcanism and restlessness seems to have been farther north, in the Chaleur Bay synclinorium. The southeastern anticlinorium, only hinted at in eastern Massachusetts, is well exposed in southern New Brunswick and reappears on Cape Breton Island, if not elsewhere in northern Nova Scotia; even more than the central one it seems to have been persistently restless, with frequent volcanic episodes and periods of uplift and erosion that repeatedly reexposed the Precambrian rocks in its core. Moreover, all along and beside it the rocks are cut by steep longitudinal faults, probably in good part strike-slip faults, which have fragmented it to a degree not matched anywhere else in the Appalachians. Wilson (1962) suggests that these faults add up to a major sinistral strike-slip fault zone hundreds of kilometers (miles) long, which he has named the Cabot fault and compares with the San Andreas fault of California and the Great Glen fault of Scotland, but the data indicate an even more complicated picture of intersecting rifts (Belt, 1968b; Webb, 1969) and suggest dominant dextral slip.

The major synclinorial belts stand in contrast; sedimentation in them was thick and continuous, or interrupted only by disconformities. To be sure, the western carbonate-bearing synclinorial belt of New England is not visible in Canada, but pieces of its carbonate rocks in lime breccia beds indicate that it was once there; possibly the belt of clastic strata northwest of the Notre Dame anticlinorium conceals it. In the others, mud and silt greatly predominated, and even, commonly graded, bedding and other sedimentary features suggest deep-water troughs. The Connecticut Valley synclinorium can be traced to Gaspé, and the Merrimack synclinorium apparently to east-central Maine where it bifurcated, one arm extending northeastward into southern Gaspé, at least during the later Ordovician and earlier Silurian, the other eastward to include the slate sequence (Charlotte group) north of the Kennebecasis anticlinorium and to disappear under the Carboniferous basin of central New Brunswick. Finally, southern Nova

Scotia reveals a fragment of still another such trough, not visible in New England. In all but the northwesternmost synclinorium marine sedimentation persisted from some time in the Ordovician, if not earlier, through the Lower Devonian, when it was brought to an end by orogeny accompanied by considerable plutonism (Devonian plutonism also affected the anticlinoria, again excepting the northwesternmost).

Later Devonian and Carboniferous sedimentation was very different and mostly continental. It began with well oxidized coarse clastic deposits (associated with volcanics in western New Brunswick and eastern Nova Scotia, especially Cape Breton Island), deposited by rivers in the low spots of a very uneven topography, probably in an area of active longitudinal block faulting—a rift valley system—but as the Carboniferous wore on, sedimentation also spread outside the rifts. Large but ephemeral lakes were present here and there, and during the Viséan (late Mississippian) the sea several times invaded the region, briefly but widely. The present area of central and eastern New Brunswick, northern Nova Scotia, Prince Edward Island, and the Gulf of St. Lawrence then became a broad basin some hundreds of kilometers (miles) across, although some blocks within and around it remained restless. This basin silted up under largely reducing conditions, and in broad lowland swamps between the rivers sheets of coal were deposited. Oxidizing conditions persisted on the margins of the basin, however, and returned to the center before the end of sedimentation.

The sector here considered constitutes the greater part of the Northern Appalachian arc or Quebec salient. The recess between this arc and the Newfoundland sector of the chain is hidden beneath the Gulf of St. Lawrence, unless the curvature of strikes in northern Nova Scotia from the Cobequid Mountains to Cape Breton Island is considered to represent it; intersecting trends like those in the major recesses farther southwest are not lacking here, but they seem to result less from the intersection of two arcs than from interferences and irregularity produced by superposed deformation, especially longitudinal faulting superposed on folding.

The orogenic history of the region is as complicated as that of any part of the Appalachians, but fortunately the orogenic events are comparatively well dated. Apparently there was a period (Avalonian) of metamorphism and granitic plutonism during the latest Precambrian along the Kennebecasis anticlinorium and its extensions, although the evidence leaves something to be desired; whether Precambrian sialic rocks exist or ever existed between that anticlinorium and

the Green Mountains is quite uncertain. The Taconic orogeny is recorded by deformation, mild metamorphism, and granodioritic intrusion on at least part of each of the major anticlinoria, and there are serpentine intrusions on the northwestern one. Not only was there a pulse (or pulses) after Middle Ordovician but before Early Silurian and perhaps part of Late Ordovician time, but at least one earlier pulse (Penobscot) is recorded in the central anticlinorial belt (earliest Middle Ordovician or earlier) and in the northwestern one (pre-middle Middle Ordovician). In the major synclinoria, the orogeny is recorded mainly by quartz sand and pebbles and volcanic material intercalated in the prevailing mud and silt, and even they are lacking over large areas. In general, Taconic trends now appear to parallel the regional strike (probably imposed mainly by the Acadian orogeny though perhaps inherited from older arcs and troughs), espousing the major salient, but local deviations have been reported; no consistent pattern of such deviations has been deciphered, however.

The Acadian orogeny was the most far-reaching in its results; it is named of course for Acadia, the French colony that once occupied parts of Nova Scotia and New Brunswick. Not only did this orogeny close the marine troughs for good, initiating the period of continental deposition, but it produced most of the observable structural features in the pre-Carboniferous rocks, especially in the synclinoria, and most of the granitic and other intrusive bodies of the region were then emplaced. Radiometry suggests that these bodies were emplaced over a considerable period of time or perhaps in two pulses (Faul and others, 1963, p. 4 ff., Fig. 1; Poole, Kelley, and Neale, 1964, p. 76–77). The orogeny dies out northward, however, in the Gaspé folded belt, north of which it seems to have had little effect, except that the granite mass at Mt. Jacques Cartier, at the east end of the Shickshock Mountains on the south edge of the Cambro-Ordovician belt of northern Gaspé, appears to be a Devonian intrusive. Farther southwest its outer limit is uncertain, unless it reappears in the Hudson Valley just south of Albany, New York.

In several places in the region, the major activity of the Acadian orogeny is fairly closely dated; it affects Lower Devonian strata generally and lower Middle Devonian strata in the Gaspé-Connecticut Valley synclinorium, and Upper Devonian beds certainly postdate its intrusive phase. The change from marine to continental sedimentation in the higher Lower Devonian beds of the Gaspé folded belt, the Chaleur Bay synclinorium, Arisaig, and elsewhere, testify to its initial stages. Deformation—both sharp folding and faulting, especially longitudinal strike-slip faulting—continued much later, however, through the Late Devonian and well into the Carboniferous. In general this later folding and faulting parallels earlier trends, but in places it bevels them at low angles, as on Cape Breton Island where, however, the earlier trends may be older than Acadian. As already mentioned, it is perhaps meaningless to ask which angular unconformities in the Carboniferous rocks of southern New Brunswick and northern Nova Scotia record late Acadian and which early Alleghany movements, but the Viséan marine zone (Windsor formation) makes a convenient boundary.

The Alleghany orogeny, and indeed the significant late Acadian pulses (taken together, these are the Maritime disturbance of Poole, 1967), are approximately confined to the southeastern part of the great Carboniferous basin and its margins, though extending in the subsurface under Prince Edward Island and appearing on the Magdalen Islands. This is roughly the area of the Kennebecasis anticlinorium and its extensions, and also the zone of pronounced longitudinal strike-slip faulting; the trends of the later folding are about those of the earlier. Deformation was particularly severe in the rifts, where Lower Carboniferous strata were caught between fault blocks of older rocks, and slaty cleavage was produced in such strata in both New Brunswick and Nova Scotia. Deformation decreases, however, not only northward into the main basin but also upward in any one area into younger strata; these relations and various angular unconformities show that in this region the Alleghany orogeny was not a single pulse but a series of pulses, no one of which can be called principal. The youngest rocks affected are earliest Permian in age, nearly contemporaneous with the latest strata affected in the Allegheny region of Pennsylvania and vicinity; structural evidence of several pulses is not reported in that region, but the stratigraphic evidence certainly suggests that movement had begun there as in Acadia by the end of the Early Carboniferous. In the Maritime Provinces, as elsewhere in the Appalachians, only the unaffected Upper Triassic beds provide an upper limit for the Alleghany orogeny.

CHAPTER 7

Newfoundland

The island of Newfoundland is all we can see of what appears to be a fourth northeasternmost Appalachian arc; it exposes rocks that were deformed in Paleozoic time for about 600 kilometers (360 miles) both across and along strike. Geographically the land slopes eastward from a high western backbone called the Long Range (or the Long Range Mountains) only 50 to 75 kilometers (30 to 50 miles) from the west coast. A number of summits on the range and also in more isolated mountain masses on either side, especially to the west, pass 600 meters (2000 feet) in height, and the flanks of the range and of those masses are quite rugged, but the crest of the range is mostly a rather flat plateau, up to 50 kilometers (30 miles) wide. East of a line about 120 kilometers (80 miles) from the west coast, a lower plateau surface slopes gradually toward the sea, near which it is somewhat dissected; like much of southern Nova Scotia and central New Brunswick, this eastern half of Newfoundland is a sort of glaciated, spruce-covered, lake-filled Piedmont Plateau.

Geologically Newfoundland can be divided into three main belts (see Williams, 1964, 1969): a western belt including the Great Northern Peninsula and a strip along the rest of the west coast; a highly irregular southeastern area including the peninsulas from Bonavista Bay around to Fortune and Hermitage Bays, with the adjacent mainland; and a relatively compact central block. The Long Range is geologically composite, and the parts are not on strike with each other. The part northeast

of Bonne Bay, here called the northern Long Range, is a great uplifted block of Precambrian gneiss and granite belonging to western Newfoundland; the part south and southwest of Grand Lake—the southern Long Range—is a similar block but probably consists mainly of high-grade Paleozoic metamorphic rocks and belongs to central Newfoundland; in between are certain intermediate blocks, separated from each other by Grand Lake and the Humber River, and probably more allied to the western than to the central belt. The three belts in Newfoundland show some obvious parallels with belts in Gaspé and the Maritime Provinces on the opposite shore of the Gulf of St. Lawrence, but they are mostly offset to the right several hundred kilometers (a couple of hundred miles), and there are also obvious differences.

Western Newfoundland

The boundary between western and central Newfoundland may be drawn along the faulted eastern margin of the two main Carboniferous basins on the island, one lying southeast of St. George's Bay and the other extending from White Bay to Grand Lake. In the intervening 90 kilometers (55 miles), the boundary is not clear; some maps show continuous faults connecting the two basins, but others show rock units crossing the supposed faults (which would separate the intermediate blocks mentioned in the preceding paragraph from the southern Long Range). In addition to the Carboniferous basins, western Newfoundland contains thick sequences of Lower Paleozoic strata, similar in many respects to those along the south shore of the St. Lawrence estuary and in the Champlain-Taconic region, and blocks of Precambrian rocks, the largest of which, the northern Long Range, is 200 kilometers (120 miles) long and averages 50 kilometers (30 miles) wide. The basis of our knowledge of the lower Paleozoic stratigraphy was laid by Schuchert and Dunbar (1934); for a recent summary, see Whittington and Kindle (1969).

The rocks of the northern Long Range (Clifford and Baird, 1962) are complexly folded high-grade gneiss, schist, and granite of various types, with a body or two of gabbro and anorthosite near the south end and a large swarm of dolerite dikes in the northeastern part. They closely resemble the Precambrian rocks of the Laurentian or Grenville belt of the Canadian shield, which crop out in Labrador and Quebec across the Strait of Belle Isle, not 75 kilometers (50 miles) from the north end of the Long Range. Like the similar Green Mountains, Hudson and New Jersey Highlands, and Blue Ridge in the United States, therefore, the northern Long Range block is a fragment of the pre-Paleozoic (pre-Appalachian) basement, brought up by Paleozoic deformation and affected to varying degrees by Paleozoic metamorphism. Thus retrogressive alteration, especially epidotization, is common in the western part of the block (one finds unakite as colorful as that in the Unaka Mountains portion of the Blue Ridge), and Paleozoic granite is reported just to the southeast of and perhaps within the block (Neale and Nash, 1963, p. 24–25). The northwest and southeast margins of the block are mainly longitudinal faults, the northwestern one almost certainly a fairly steep thrust fault with a somewhat sinuous trace, the southeastern perhaps nearly vertical and either normal or strike-slip. At the ends of the block, however, and along part of the northwest side, the Precambrian rocks are overlain with profound unconformity by the base of the main Lower Paleozoic sequence.

Precambrian rocks also appear 100 kilometers (60 miles) farther southwest in the much smaller Indian Head Range, extending 25 kilometers (15 miles) north from the head of St. George's Bay, and probably also in parts of the intermediate Long Range blocks farther east. In the Indian Head Range, the rocks are much like those of the northern Long Range, but the proportion of mafic rocks, especially hypersthene rocks, is greater;

retrogressive metamorphism is conspicuous. The southwesternmost of the intermediate blocks, southeast of the head of the bay, is a large mass of anorthosite and anorthositic gabbro (approximately 12 by 40 kilometers—8 by 25 miles), but the rest are schist and gneiss, clearly metamorphosed in Paleozoic time and probably in large part composed of Paleozoic metasedimentary and metaplutonic material.

Recent work (Williams and Stevens, 1969) has shown that Belle Isle, 30 kilometers (18 miles) north of the northeast tip of the Great Northern Peninsula and 130 kilometers (80 miles) northeast of the north end of the Precambrian inlier of the northern Long Range, is another Precambrian block, around whose margins are small patches of Lower Cambrian rocks, some resting unconformably on the Precambrian, some downfaulted against it (the faults are mainly high-angle and apparently include both normal and reverse). As the Paleozoic rocks are themselves deformed and cleaved and as abundant mafic dikes traversing the Precambrian gneiss are retrograded, Belle Isle definitely belongs not to the Canadian shield but to the Appalachian Mountains, of which it is the northeasternmost extremity; it is like a half-drowned Indian Head Range, lying about as far northeast of the Long Range Precambrian as the Indian Head Range lies to the southwest.

Again as in the Green Mountains and Blue Ridge, the basal portion of the Lower Paleozoic in western Newfoundland is a sequence of clastic rocks (Labrador group), ranging from white and pink quartzite and reddish arkosic sandstone to dark shale, slate, or phyllite; beds of limestone and dolostone occur nearly everywhere in small amount. The group is thickest and shaliest to the southeast but so deformed and metamorphosed there that no thickness figures can be given; on the intermediate blocks indeed it appears to merge into the adjacent schists and gneisses. It thins northwestward, being nearly 500 meters (1500 feet) thick on the northwest flank of the Indian Head Range, where shales still dominate, and about 300 meters (1000 feet) thick west of the north end of the Long Range, where it is largely sandstone and quartzite, shale and limestone being mainly confined to the middle third; less than 150 meters (500 feet) is preserved on the northwest shore of the Strait of Belle Isle, lying with gentle southeast dip on the Precambrian rocks of the Canadian shield. Lower Cambrian fossils are known in all the unmetamorphosed areas. Basaltic volcanic rocks appear at the base of the Cambrian in northeastern areas, as at the northeast corner of the Precambrian inlier of the northern Long Range and on Belle Isle and the coast of Labrador opposite (in these areas, except on Belle Isle, the volcanics and the accompanying sediments dip rather gently). The mafic dikes that cut the Precambrian rocks of the Long Range and of Belle Isle appear to be feeders for these volcanics.

The basal clastic sequence grades upward (more gradually than in Vermont or farther south) through perhaps 200 meters (600 feet) of siltstone, shale, and silty and shaly limestone and dolostone into a thick unit (600 to 1200 meters—2000 to 4000 feet) of relatively massive carbonate rock, mainly dolostone with some limestone in the upper part (St. George group). Middle and lower Upper Cambrian fossils are known in the transition beds and Lower Ordovician in the massive carbonate unit, but it may include Upper Cambrian beds as well. In most parts of the region this unit is terminated by a disconformity (Cumming, 1968), above which follows lower Middle Ordovician limestone, commonly argillaceous and becoming shaly upwards, grading into graptolitic black shale (Table Head group). The similarity of this whole sequence, from the Lower Cambrian to the Middle Ordovician, with the carbonate sequence of the Taconic-Champlain region is remarkable (the faunas are also very similar), and probably the two were once connected by the carbonate belt postulated in Chapter 6 (p. 118) along the St. Lawrence, since removed or else covered by the thrusting along Logan's line. Black shale appears somewhat lower in the Middle Ordovician in Newfoundland, however; it contains graptolites about four zones below those at the base of the black shale in the western part of the Taconic-Champlain region (Whittington, 1968, p. 53).

North and west of the north half of the northern Long Range, the carbonate sequence just described lies nearly flat, deformed only along the northwest marginal fault of the range and along others roughly parallel to it; similarly, west of the Indian Head Range, the deformation lessens westward into the southern Port au Port Peninsula, where the formations in the sequence are particularly well displayed, dipping rather gently northward and cut only by a few N45°E faults. Along the southern part of the northwest margin of the northern Long Range, however, the sequence is visible only in a series of slices along the marginal thrust fault. It reappears at the south end of the range and from there can be followed, along a rather sinuous outcrop belt but with only minor interruptions, along the west side of the intermediate blocks of the Long Range to the east side of the Indian Head Range; throughout this stretch it is severely folded, and metamorphism appears in the lower beds and especially in two eastward-projecting sinuosities or recesses of the belt. In the wider part of this outcrop belt between the two recesses, as at the Humber River and to the north, the folding is of Valley and Ridge type; some of the northwest flanks of the anticlines are overturned and cut by thrust faults, and anticlines and faults bring up the shaly transition beds beneath the massive carbonate unit but not the basal clastic group, which appears only next to the intermediate blocks. Even at its widest, however, the belt is only about 20 kilometers (12 miles) or 4 or 5 folds wide at the present surface.

The resemblances with the Taconic region do not end with the carbonate sequence. Between the outcrop belt just described and the Gulf of St. Lawrence lies the large Bay of Islands synclinorium, in which two deep pockets, one on either side of the Bay of Islands, correspond to the two recesses in the carbonate outcrop belt; from the ends of the main synclinorium fingerlike projections reach southwest onto the northern Port au Port Peninsula and northeast along the coast for 75 kilometers (nearly 50 miles) beyond Bonne Bay. The total length of the synclinorium is 200 kilometers (120 miles); the greatest width, near the Humber Arm of the Bay of Islands in the southern pocket, is 45 kilometers (27 miles).

The Bay of Islands synclinorium is filled with a great thickness of clastic deposits (Humber Arm terrain), mainly dark shale and slate, but including red and green shale and much sandstone of both graywacke and quartzite types in the main synclinorial area, and many beds of lime-sandstone and lime-breccia, both there and especially in the northeastern finger. In each of the pockets is a pair of large masses of layered gabbro and serpentinized peridotite and dunite, associated with mafic volcanic rocks in which they have produced contact metamorphism; these masses form high mountains on either side of the Bay of Islands, including the highest mountains in Newfoundland. Opinion has differed on whether they are separate bodies or broken fragments of one or more large laccoliths, lopoliths, or wedge-shaped stocks (see Smith, 1958, p. 69–71); certainly they are cut apart by a number of large faults that do not seem to extend far into the surrounding sedimentary rocks.

The sedimentary rocks in this terrain are mostly intensely crumpled, except in the upper part close to the mafic intrusives where the structure is simpler; the total thickness must be large, certainly several thousands of meters (probably between 5000 and 10,000 feet) in the main synclinorial area, though probably much less in the fingers. Fossils have been found here and there in fragments in the lime-breccia beds, but diagnostic fossils indigenous to the strata themselves have been found so far chiefly in the two fingers away from the main area.

In view of the position of these clastics above known lower Middle Ordovician shale at the top of the carbonate sequence, they used to be considered Middle or even in part Upper Ordovician; in a few places, however, Lower Ordovician or Cambrian fossils have been found, and in such places the beds containing them were given separate formation names and excluded from the terrain, faults being postulated between. In two areas, however, detailed stratigraphic work has now been done, and in neither does this procedure seem justified, for in each area the rocks present seem to make a consistent stratigraphic sequence.

As already mentioned, lime-sandstone and lime-breccia beds are particularly prominent in the northeast finger, where locally, as at Cow Head, 40 kilometers (25 miles) north of Bonne Bay, single blocks are the size of automobiles or boxcars. All the coarser breccias were at first assigned to a single unit (Cow Head breccia), considered to lie in the black slate not far above the top of the limestone and hence close to the bottom of the synclinorial clastic terrain; coarse breccias certainly appear at that level in several places, notably on Port au Port Peninsula (Cormorant Head) in the southwestern finger, where the accompanying shales carry lower Middle Ordovician graptolites. But around Cow Head, Kindle and Whittington (1958; 1959) have shown that breccia beds occur almost throughout a sequence about 300 meters (1000 feet) thick, that in most of the breccia beds fossils in the limestone blocks are almost all of about one age, that this "block-age" progresses regularly from Middle Cambrian near the bottom to Middle Ordovician near the top of the sequence, and that fossils in the interbedded shale and shaly limestone show the same progression, generally being about the same age as the fossils in the blocks in the next overlying breccia bed. Some of the fossiliferous blocks appear to have come from units in the carbonate sequence, though some seem to have no match there. One is forced to the conclusion that very coarse breccia composed of fragments of the carbonate sequence was deposited at intervals through much of the Cambrian and Ordovician in one small part of a basin where mud and lime-mud was accumulating, close to but not within the area where the carbonate sequence itself was being deposited, perhaps at the base of a scarp (a fault-scarp or simply the edge of a bank) bounding the carbonate area.

This breccia-bearing sequence crops out in several belts in the coastal lowland behind Cow Head, between the Gulf and the fault along the northwest margin of the northern Long Range; according to Oxley (1953, p. 36 ff.), these belts are repeated by tight folds or imbricate thrust faults. Kindle and Whittington's data show that both the thickness of the breccia beds and the coarseness of the largest blocks decrease fairly regularly belt by belt southeastward, implying that the source area for the blocks lay to the northwest, probably very close to the northwesternmost belts with their enormous boulders. Many of the finer-grained breccia beds and associated lime-sandstone beds show excellent graded bedding, suggesting that the materials were moved from the carbonate area by turbidity currents. In addition to limestone blocks, clean quartz sand appears in the breccia beds in the Upper Cambrian part of the sequence, and above the highest breccia beds there seems to be a considerable thickness of slate and graywacke, but these rocks crop out much less well than the lime-breccia.

Around the Bay of Islands, especially along its Humber Arm, Lilly (1963, p. 60–75; 1967; Brückner, 1966, p. 145–147), following Walthier (1949, p. 23 ff.) and others, has put together another consistent stratigraphic sequence, beginning at the top of the carbonate sequence and going up westward toward the mafic intrusive masses— this despite severe crumpling of all but the highest strata and the absence of fossils except locally in the limestone blocks in breccia beds (which are not as coarse as around Cow Head). Black shale or slate is present almost throughout (it is phyllitic at the bottom). The lower part contains beds of relatively clean but ill sorted quartzite, with a few pebble beds (some of the pebbles contain Lower Cambrian fossils); in one laterally persistent zone, green and reddish-purple slate replaces the black. Farther up lime-sandstone and lime-breccia beds are particularly common, forming a mappable limestone zone; Middle Cambrian to lowest Ordovician fossils occur in this zone. Near the top are thick beds of graywacke, some quite coarse, partly derived from volcanic rocks. Many of the rock types in this sequence are like those in the Taconic sequence of the Taconic region or the Taconic-type rocks along the south shore of the St. Lawrence, and even the sequence of rock types is similar, though not identical. Apparently the sequence on the Humber Arm, following upon clearly lower Middle Ordovician black slate on top of the carbonate rocks, begins in the Cambrian, probably the Lower Cambrian, and continues regularly back up into the lower Middle Ordovician. Thus this sequence, like the one at Cow Head, is contemporaneous with the carbonate sequence and must have been deposited in a basin to one side of it, where, at least part of the time, carbonate blocks could slide in.

In view of the many striking resemblances with the Taconic region, Rodgers and Neale (1963) were led to argue for the hypothesis, first adumbrated by Kay in the 1930's (see Kay, 1945, p. 442 and Fig. 7), that the clastic terrain (Humber Arm terrain) of western Newfoundland forms a large klippe, roughly the same size as the supposed klippe in the Taconic region. They postulated (see also Rodgers, 1968) that the carbonate sequence was deposited in shallow water on a bank along the margin of the central platform of the continent, like its correlatives from Vermont to Alabama, that this bank extended east at least as far as White Bay (rock probably belonging to the carbonate sequence is exposed west of the bay close to the southeastern margin of the northern Long Range), that the breccia-bearing sequence around Cow Head was deposited in relatively deep water at the east foot of this bank, being fed mainly from it, that the sequence on the Humber Arm was deposited still farther east in the same basin (in what is now the western part of central Newfoundland), where turbidity currents carrying limestone blocks were less frequent and were replaced at times by currents carrying quartz sand and, later, volcanic debris, and that finally during Middle Ordovician time the former carbonate bank subsided and the former basin rose until the deposits in the basin (now containing also volcanic rocks and mafic and ultramafic intrusives) were high enough to slide westward, passing over the future site of the Long Range and arriving on top of the carbonate sequence while black mud was still being deposited there. Indeed Lilly and Brückner discovered coarse chaotic breccias of slate, quartzite, and lime-breccia fragments in a slate matrix at the top of the presumably autochthonous black slate immediately beneath the first presumably allochthonous sediments, comparable in character and position to breccias found by Zen, Rodgers, Elam, and Bird in the Taconic region (see Chapter 4, p. 84–86); such breccias have since been found in several parts of the area (Brückner, 1966, p. 147). In later deformation—for example, when the Long Range was uplifted and the Bay of Islands synclinorium depressed—the two superposed sequences were deformed together as a single tectonic unity, except insofar as differences in competence of the rocks led to differences in tectonic behavior.

Another large area of very similar clastic rocks stretches for 120 kilometers (75 miles) along the east coast of the north end of the Great Northern Peninsula on either side of Hare Bay. It is separated from the north end of the Long Range and from the flat-lying carbonate rocks farther north by a narrow belt of deformed carbonate rocks (which also appear beneath it close to the tip of the peninsula); moreover, coarse lime-breccia, volcanics, and mafic and ultramafic intrusives are all associated with the clastic rocks. Rodgers and Neale (1963, p. 723–724) therefore suggested that a klippe was emplaced here as well, and work by Tuke (Tuke and Baird, 1967; Tuke, 1968) has virtually proved the klippe hypothesis. The clastic terrain here would not have had to slide so far, and in later deformation it found itself in a saddle northeast of the Long Range instead of beyond it. Quartzite that presumably belongs to the autochthonous sequence is exposed in the White Islands just east of the north end of the peninsula; its presence here emphasizes the allochthony of the clastic rocks to the west, although probably a major later fault intervenes (a continuation or branch of the longitudinal fault that bounds the Long Range Precambrian on the east; this fault may continue to the east coast of Belle Isle).

Along the northwest coast of Port au Port Peninsula, a quite different sequence of strata crops out for a strike distance of about 30 kilometers (20 miles) (Rodgers, 1965). It consists of 800 meters (2500 feet) of Middle Ordovician limestone, sandstone, and shale (Long Point formation) followed, probably disconformably but without any angular break, by 450 meters (1500 feet) of redbeds and paler clastic rocks in the midst of which is a zone of impure limestone containing fossils of earliest Devonian (possibly latest Silurian) age (Clam Bank formation). The beds dip gently to the northwest at the northeast end of the outcrop belt (the tip of Long Point of the peninsula) but become steeper and steeper southwestward and are overturned for the last 10 kilometers (6 or 7 miles). The base of the sequence is exposed locally, resting unconformably on highly disturbed rocks of the clastic terrain (Humber Arm terrain) in the southwest finger of the Bay of Islands synclinorium. Thus not only the emplacement of the clastic terrain in its present position above the carbonate sequence but also much of its deformation was over by later Middle Ordovician time; furthermore, the parallelism of the strata within the overlying sequence argues against any later Ordovician or Silurian deformation in the area. The redbed unit apparently reflects continental deposition in the Late Silurian (Salinic disturbance?) and Early Devonian (an early phase of the Acadian orogeny?), separated by a fleeting marine invasion. Submarine exploration by Lilly (1966, p. 573) and geophysical work by Ruffman and Woodside 1970 further indicate that this later sequence of strata can be followed north-northeastward for 130 kilometers (80 miles) from the tip of Long Point, averaging perhaps 10 kilometers (6 miles) offshore; throughout its extent, it would rest upon and mark the western boundary (at the present land surface) of the western Newfoundland (Humber Arm) klippe.

A sequence of somewhat metamorphosed sedimentary and volcanic rocks intervenes between the west shore of the head of White Bay and the southeast marginal fault of the northern Long Range. The lower part of this sequence consists of quartzite, phyllite, and especially marble, and, as mentioned above, represents the Cambro-Ordovician carbonate sequence of western Newfoundland, here preserved on the east side of the Long Range. The thicker upper part (about 3 kilometers—10,000 feet—Lock, 1969) consists of green and gray clastic rocks, ranging from conglomerate and feldspathic sandstone to shale and including a few beds of limestone, and of volcanic rocks of several kinds. The conglomerate consists largely of fragments of felsic volcanic rocks, but includes some of metamorphic rocks and of granite or granodiorite. Marine Silurian fossils have been found in the upper beds in several places, and the lower beds are also presumed to be Silurian, for like the fossiliferous beds they are less deformed and less metamorphosed than the adjacent rocks assigned to the Cambro-Ordovician (the contact is everywhere a fault). The probably Silurian beds, and perhaps the certainly Silurian ones, are cut by pink, coarse-grained granite, which in turn is overlapped unconformably by Carboniferous strata of the main northern basin and appears to be a northwestern representative of the widespread Devonian granite of central Newfoundland.

As already mentioned, Carboniferous rocks occupy two large basins in western Newfoundland; in addition there are smaller patches on the Port au Port Peninsula and between it and the Indian Head Range, and also far to the north along the east coast of the Great Northern Peninsula 80 to 90 kilometers (50 to 55 miles) from its tip (Baird, 1966). The stratigraphy resembles that of the Maritime Provinces—a lower Lower Carboniferous unit (Anguille group) of mainly gray sandstone and conglomerate with some lacustrine siltstone and shale is overlain, unconformably in the northern basin, by redbed units (Codroy and Deer Lake groups) with gypsum and marine limestone (Viséan) below and lacustrine beds above in some areas, and these by Upper Carboniferous gray and brown coal measures (Barachois group). The lower unit is resistant and underlies hilly or even mountainous country, such as the Cape Anguille Mountains along the coast south of St.

George's Bay, but the other units mostly form lowlands. Several thousand meters (5000 to 10,000 feet) are present; some at least of the coarser clastics were deposited beside moving fault blocks. As in Nova Scotia, the lower unit is virtually confined to the larger basins, having been deposited in a single nearly straight rift zone (Belt, 1968b) that extended from Cape Anguille northeast to the head of White Bay, and probably as far as the outliers south of the tip of the Great Northern Peninsula, whereas the higher beds overlap onto the surrounding areas and form most of the outliers. The coal measures are preserved in synclines in the main basins and also in the outlier west of the Indian Head Range.

In the main basins—the rift zone—the Carboniferous rocks are mostly severely folded, especially where the lower unit is present or where younger units are close to the border fault that bounds the basins on the southeast. Most of the folds in the main rift zone trend northeast, but a few trend west or northwest. In the northwest part of the northern basin, however, the lower unit is absent and the higher units dip gently southeast into a broad shallow basin through which flows the upper Humber River. Similarly, in the outliers to the west of the southern basin, the beds have only gentle dips except close to small normal faults or where gypsum has been dissolved.

The northern Long Range is obviously a major culmination on the general anticlinorial axis that follows the northwest side of the Appalachian folded belt next southeast of the Valley and Ridge province or its equivalents. The Bay of Islands synclinorium is as obviously a major depression nearly on the same line, between it and the minor culmination in the Indian Head Range, and the area of similar clastic rocks on the northeast coast of the Great Northern Peninsula marks another depression, between the Long Range and Belle Isle.

Around the northern Long Range, longitudinal faults and folds in the Paleozoic rocks trend N25°–30°E; locally, as on the western coastal plain near Cow Head, they swing to N35°–40°E. The trends in the Precambrian rocks of the range are quite different, however, mainly north and northwest but apparently affected by superposed folding, and they are truncated by the marginal faults. Southwest of the northern Long Range, the trends in the Lower Paleozoic rocks are more variable, ranging from N45°E to N–S as they outline the two pockets of the Bay of Islands synclinorium, but they still average N25°E as far as St. George's Bay. On Port au Port Peninsula, trends swing around to about N70°E, but as these trends also involve Siluro-Devonian strata, they may be younger than those on the nearby mainland.

Near White Bay, the trends of both folding and faulting in the Carboniferous rocks parallel those in the older rocks, but farther south they swing to N40°E near Grand Lake and to N50°E in the southern basin; thus they bevel the trends in the older rocks. N45°E faults also appear to cross the N70°E trends on the Port au Port Peninsula.

The roles played by the various orogenic episodes that affected western Newfoundland and the ages of the different structural features and trends are not easy to determine. The clastic terrain (Humber Arm terrain) in the Bay of Islands synclinorium, assuming it to be allochthonous, arrived after the beginning of Middle Ordovician time, but it was apparently in place and considerably deformed before the deposition of the Middle Ordovician limestone (Long Point formation) on Port au Port Peninsula. Perhaps the general N25°E trend it shows dates from this Middle Ordovician or Taconic deformation. On the other hand, it and the underlying rocks were deformed again by the orogeny that produced the N70°E trends on the peninsula and upturned the Siluro-Devonian strata there (the Carboniferous outliers seem not to be affected); that trend is unlike any other in the region, but northeastward it appears to swing to about N40°E (one might imagine it has undergone a right-handed twist into its present position), and it may then continue along the coast and possibly even into the thrust fault on the northwest margin of the northern Long Range, or the tight folding and faulting on the coastal plain in front. Along the east side of the Bay of Islands synclinorium, the carbonate sequence shows folding of Valley and Ridge type that must postdate at least the emplacement of the clastic terrain in the synclinorium and may be later than much of its deformation; moreover, the metamorphism that appears here increases steadily southeastward through the intermediate blocks into the southern Long Range and its northeastern continuation, where it appears to be post-Early Devonian. These very tenuous lines of evidence suggest a large role for the Acadian orogeny.

Finally the Carboniferous rocks were obviously affected by folding in their turn and especially by the longitudinal faults that bound the rift zone; these would express the Alleghany orogeny (Maritime disturbance of Poole, 1967, p. 40—41), yet some of the faults were evidently active during Carboniferous, especially early Carboniferous deposition. The fault on the southeast margin of the northern Long Range and some of the others in and around the range are roughly parallel to these Carboniferous faults and may well have been active at this time; the southeast margin fault appears to cut off the Carboniferous outliers along the northeast coast, but it is perhaps overlapped by the strata of about the age of the Viséan marine zone along the northwest side of the main northern basin. Faults trending N45°E parallel to known Carboniferous faults are also present on the Port au Port Peninsula but are not known to cut the Carboniferous rocks there.

The pre-Carboniferous geology of western Newfoundland shows many parallels with that of the northwesternmost belt of the northern Appalachians, which comes to the opposite shore of the Gulf of St. Lawrence in northeastern Gaspé, yet the two areas are now 400 kilometers (250 miles) apart and their strikes are almost at right angles, except that the N70°E trend on the Port au Port Peninsula blunts the angle. In common are the Taconic-type clastic sequence, the volcanics, and even the serpentine masses, also the post-Taconic overlap (in Newfoundland the overlap is actually by Middle Ordovician strata). On Newfoundland also the carbonate sequence reappears in force, for the first time since the Champlain Valley, 800 kilometers (500 miles) down the strike from eastern Gaspé, although, as noted in Chapter 6, it must have been present once throughout the interval. Finally, the northern Long Range is the last continuation of the Blue Ridge-Highlands-Green Mountains anticlinorium. Nevertheless, a connection between these two related belts would demand a dextral offset of several hundred kilometers (a couple of hundred miles).

The Carboniferous geology of western Newfoundland, on the other hand, compares best with that of Cape Breton Island and of northern Nova Scotia generally; they have in common rift zones of deformed lower Lower Carboniferous rocks overlapped by the Viséan marine zone, and especially the longitudinal faults active during Carboniferous deposition. As Wilson (1962) points out, these faults trend directly across Cabot Strait with no offset; he therefore includes the Newfoundland faults in his sinistral Cabot fault system. On the other hand, Betz (1943) assembled considerable evidence for thrust movement on these faults, and Belt (1969, p. 743, 745) and Webb (1969, p. 777), from the distribution of anorthosite bodies, have adduced very large dextral slip. If the postulated strike-slip displacements are real, then the first set of movements must have been completed by the end of the Devonian and most of the second by the late Carboniferous, long before the usual dates assigned to continental drift in the North Atlantic.

Central Newfoundland

Geologically, central Newfoundland embraces a broad swath across the middle of the island, 200 kilometers (120 miles) or so wide, bounded on the west by the longitudinal faults along the eastern side of the main Carboniferous basins of western Newfoundland, as described above, and on the east by a somewhat curved line connecting the northwest shore of Bonavista Bay with the southeast shore of Hermitage Bay. The northeast part of the latter boundary, probably also a longitudinal fault or faults, separates middle-grade, mainly metasedimentary rocks of presumed Ordovician (possibly Cambrian) age in central Newfoundland from low-grade, mainly metavolcanic rocks of presumed Precambrian age in southeastern Newfoundland, but in the southern interior both groups of rocks are engulfed in later granite and the boundary is untraceable; farther southwest, metavolcanics appear again southeast of the boundary (south of Hermitage Bay), but here they are classed as Ordovician or even Silurian. In central Newfoundland between these two boundaries, a wide variety of Paleozoic sedimentary and volcanic rocks are intruded by plutonic rocks of more than one age; the complex local geologic history is fairly well known in several parts of the belt, but the correlations from area to area are not yet secure, and large parts of the interior remain little explored.

Perhaps the largest amount of work has been done around western Notre Dame Bay and on its innumerable arms, headlands, and islands. The oldest rocks here belong to a widespread terrain of basaltic and andesitic volcanics, now largely altered to greenstone, interbedded with varying amounts of slate, graywacke, graywacke conglomerate, chert, and tuff (Exploits group and many other local names); the sedimentary component increases toward the southeast. Lower and Middle Ordovician fossils have been found locally in these rocks; clearly thousands of meters (of feet) of both volcanic and sedimentary rocks are present. Copper mines have been opened at several places in the metavolcanic rocks in the western part of the district.

A large area around and southwest of Springdale near the southwest angle of Notre Dame Bay is underlain by a sequence 3000 meters (10,000 feet) thick (Springdale group) of quite unaltered, dominantly but not exclusively rhyolitic volcanic rocks, with red sandstone and conglomerate forming thin units at the base of and within the volcanics and a thicker body above. These rocks are folded into a rather simple syncline, in strong contrast to the strongly deformed Ordovician metavolcanics nearby, on which they presumably

rest unconformably. North of the regional Lobster Cove fault (which may be one of several eastern splits from the main zone of longitudinal faults along the Carboniferous rift to the west) are similar but somewhat more deformed and altered volcanics, reported to contain Silurian fossils in one area. Across another fault, a belt of such volcanics (Micmac group and part of Baie Verte group), probably in a tight syncline, can be followed north-northeast up the middle of the Burlington Peninsula (between Notre Dame and White Bays); on the east they lie with a spectacular basal unconformity on granodiorite (Burlington granodiorite) reported to cut Lower Ordovician metavolcanics. In the northeast corner of the peninsula, still another largely felsic volcanic terrain (Cape St. John group) rests unconformably on ultramafic rocks cutting similar, dated, Lower Ordovician metavolcanics but is itself much deformed and even metamorphosed, especially to the north and near late, presumably Devonian, granite bodies— indeed it is there as altered as nearby Ordovician or older rocks, and the boundary between is insecure. On the basis of the fossils in the one area, however, and of lithologic correlations with better dated rocks to the east, all these more felsic volcanics are now generally classed as Silurian, although the age of some bodies of metavolcanics is still in debate, particularly in the north and northeast parts of the peninsula (Williams, 1967, p. 120–121; Neale and Kennedy, 1967, p. 146– 147; Phillips, Kennedy, and Dunlop, 1969, p. 205; Church, 1969, p. 220). The unconformable superposition of more felsic Silurian volcanics on more mafic Ordovician volcanics cut by Taconic granodiorite reminds one forcibly of the Bronson Hill and related anticlinoria in New England (Chapter 5, p. 106; Chapter 6, p. 126) and indicates that we are here in the core of the Taconic orogenic belt.

West of the middle of the Burlington Peninsula and also along its north shore and in the islands to the north are seemingly older, higher grade metamorphic rocks (Fleur de Lys group), mainly mica schist and gneiss but including marble (partly from lime-breccia?), quartzite, conglomerate (tillite?—Church, 1969, p. 218; Harland, 1969), and amphibolite (locally including pods of eclogite, the only eclogite reported to date in the entire Appalachians; Church, 1969, p. 224). These rocks seem to form an anticlinorium, or the east flank of an anticlinorium, along the west side of the peninsula, but their age is unknown; they may be early Paleozoic or late Precambrian or both, but their present metamorphism is probably Paleozoic. They are intruded locally by the Taconic granodiorite and widely by Devonian granite. Mafic volcanics and tuffs appear in the stratigraphically higher part of the group, especially in the northern part of the peninsula (Birchy schist and probably part of rocks formerly mapped as Baie Verte group). The supposedly Silurian volcanics in the tight syncline in the middle of the peninsula (and also those in its northeast corner) should rest unconformably on these rocks, but most of the contact is a major longitudinal fault—Baie Verte Road fault, probably still another branch of the Carboniferous fault system—near and along which linear bodies of serpentinized peridotite and related rocks intrude the older rocks and perhaps (secondarily?) the younger volcanics.

Southwestward from the Notre Dame Bay region, the same general rock groups can be recognized most of the way across the island, although invaded by vast batholiths of Devonian or Acadian granite. The felsic Silurian volcanics may continue as far as the north shore of Red Indian Lake, where the major Buchans copper-lead-zinc deposit appears to lie within them. Taconic plutonic rocks have not been separately mapped but are probably present—for example, some large bodies of gabbro like that in the Annieopsquotch Mountains southwest of Red Indian Lake. Post-Ordovician rocks, both volcanic (mainly felsic) and sedimentary (graywacke, slate, and conglomerate), reappear near the south coast (Cooper, 1954), where at least some contain Lower Devonian plants; along with possible older metavolcanic rocks, they become considerably metamorphosed northwestward and grade into schist and gneiss cut by the Acadian granite. Indeed, a major part of the southern Long Range consists of gneiss and various other high-grade rocks, which appear to grade northwestward into the lower (possibly latest Precambrian) part of the Cambro-Ordovician sequence of western Newfoundland, northeastward into the various metavolcanic sequences of north-central Newfoundland, and southward into Silurian or Devonian rocks along the south coast; representatives of the gneiss on the Burlington Peninsula or of the Precambrian gneiss and anorthosite of the northern Long Range may also be present, but if so the physical connection has been cut off by later granite or covered up by overlapping Carboniferous beds. Once these gneisses were all considered Precambrian, the eroded stumps of an old geanticline that from the first split the Paleozoic geosyncline in the northern Appalachians into two separate troughs, but according to present knowledge Precambrian rocks, if present at all, are minor in amount and in any case rose to their present relative position during the Paleozoic, for whatever the age of the original materials, the presently observable meta-

morphism of the gneisses was probably mainly Acadian, like the widespread granitic intrusions within them.

The only known patch of Carboniferous rocks southeast of the basins of western Newfoundland lies unconformably on metavolcanics and Acadian granite along Red Indian Lake south of Buchans. Some longitudinal faults are present in and southeast of the southern Long Range, but they are less prominent here than to the west or north.

In the eastern part of Notre Dame Bay, the major Luke's Arm fault (probably a continuation of the Lobster Cove fault) separates two different terrains. That to the northwest is the eastern extension of the Lower and Middle Ordovician volcanic terrain in western Notre Dame Bay, cut on northern New World Island and adjacent islands by a batholith of probably Ordovician granodiorite (Williams, 1963, p. 22—24). Southeast of the Luke's Arm fault, especially on southern and eastern New World Island, a succession of Ordovician and Silurian strata several thousand meters (many thousand feet) thick is tipped up vertically or overturned to the northwest and repeated in three parallel slices by large strike faults (from the northwest, the Toogood, Cobbs Arm, and Dildo slices, each named for the fault bounding it on the southeast; Kay, 1969, p. 420, and personal communication, now recognizes a fourth southeastermost slice in which the beds face in the opposite direction). The nature of these faults is in debate; successive suggestions have been: low-angle thrusting to the north followed by tilting and overturning to the north so as to scramble the order of the blocks (Kay and Williams, 1963; Williams, 1963, p. 25—26), high-angle normal faulting (Williams, 1964, p. 1149), strike-slip faulting (Kay, 1967, p. 590—592), and reactivation of synsedimentary high-angle faults to form "tectonic slides" cutting out the south limbs of northward-overturned anticlines (Horne, ms. 1968). I would suggest a variant of the first possibility: low-angle thrusting to the *south* followed by tilting and overturning to the north, for the facies relationships between the blocks show that they are still in their original relative positions (moreover, this explanation meets the criticism by Kay, 1967, p. 590, based on the orientation of the slaty cleavage).

On each of the slices (Horne and Helwig, 1969, p. 391—395; Kay, 1969, p. 416—420), the stratigraphic succession begins with Lower or Middle Ordovician mafic volcanics associated with black slate, chert, and volcanic graywacke; lenses of locally fossiliferous limestone occur within the volcanics. In the Toogood slice, these rocks or a relatively thin overlying graywacke unit are unconformably overlain by coarse conglomerate (with boulders up to 75 centimeters—over 2 feet—across; Helwig and Sarpi, 1969) interbedded with and overlain by green and red graywacke and siltstone (Goldson conglomerate or group) and containing marine Silurian fossils. Among the generally well rounded pebbles and cobbles, sedimentary rocks, metavolcanic rocks, and plutonic rocks predominate in turn upward from the base. In the other slices, on the other hand, the Middle Ordovician rocks grade up into a thick unit of graywacke and siltstone and this is overlain, mainly conformably, by the Silurian conglomerate and graywacke, in general finer than in the Toogood slice; Silurian fossils also appear locally at the top of the graywacke-siltstone unit here, but the bulk of that is probably Upper Ordovician. Furthermore, in each of the slices (Horne, 1969), the Ordovician strata contain beds of chaotic breccia not unlike that accompanying the Ordovician slide masses or klippen in western and northern Newfoundland and in the Taconic region; locally the breccia contains blocks of plutonic rock (granodiorite like that northwest of the Luke's Arm fault), and at one place, in limestone within what is perhaps a large block of volcanics, Middle Cambrian trilobites have been found (Kay and Eldredge, 1968). Clearly this belt (the New World Island belt of Williams, 1967, p. 107–112) lay just southeast of the core belt of Taconic orogeny, intrusion, and uplift—here just across the Luke's Arm fault—from which were derived not only the conglomerates, breccias, and other clastic sediments just mentioned but also the Ordovician clastic sediments and slide masses of western Newfoundland. The parallel of the Silurian conglomerates here with those in the Silurian strata just southeast of the northern Maine volcanic belt (Chapter 6, p. 127, 129) is striking.

In a belt south and southeast of New World Island and separated from it by still another strike fault (Dildo fault), the basal Silurian conglomerate underlies a thick sequence of largely felsic volcanics, and both grade southeastward and upward into micaceous sandstone (Botwood sandstone), much of it red and cross-bedded and probably in good part continental, although marine fossils occur near the base in several areas. These rocks form a major synclinorium (Botwood synclinorium) that can be followed from Fogo Island far into the center of Newfoundland. The rock types are not unlike those in the Springdale synclinorium, but they are considerably more deformed, sedimentary rocks predominate over volcanics,

and they apparently rest conformably on the Ordovician rocks on either side, in which sedimentary rocks also predominate. The Ordovician rocks to the east form a sort of slate belt centered around Gander Lake; again one is strongly reminded of the transition in central Maine from the Ordovician volcanic belt on the Munsungun and other "Bronson Hill" anticlinoria into the central Maine slate belt. Within the Gander Lake belt, slate predominates to the northwest and above, graywacke to the southeast and below (here the strata could well be pre-Ordovician); in between, a narrow zone of mafic and ultramafic intrusions associated with a belt of mafic metavolcanics can be followed from the northeast corner of the island for 150 kilometers (95 miles) southwestward along strike, and other such intrusions lie to the west, close to the center of the island.

Southward and southwestward the grade of metamorphism rises and more and more granite appears, engulfing the sedimentary rocks; indeed the south-central part of Newfoundland is probably the least known part of the island—granitic, metavolcanic, and metasedimentary rocks are still largely unseparated, and their ages are unknown. The occurrence of apparently synclinal bodies of conglomerate, graywacke, and, to the west, relatively felsic metavolcanics suggests the presence of Silurian or even Devonian as well as Ordovician. The Ordovician slates of the Gander Lake belt do reach to the south shore at Bay d'Espoir (pronounced despair), where they display a structural gradient north to south from nearly upright folds with steep slaty cleavage in slate through recumbent folds with flat-flying but folded cleavage in phyllite* to strongly metamorphic schist and gneiss near granite intrusions (Anderson, 1967). To the south, moreover, the rocks are cut by a number of strike faults, probably belonging to the family of major longitudinal faults that dominate the structure of southeastern Newfoundland.

Structural trends in central Newfoundland average about N45°E but show considerable fluctuations, particularly in and around areas of high-grade metamorphism and granitic intrusion, which are more important toward the south coast. Silurian rocks seem to be most widespread near the north coast, but this may be in good part a reflection of the greater amount of work that has been done there. Longitudinal faults bound the region on either side and are rather prominent around Notre Dame Bay and on the Burlington Peninsula, where they appear to be major

*I would interpret the "gently dipping strata" in Zone 3 of Anderson (1967, p. 196) as folded cleavage rather than folded bedding, in view of the increasing metamorphism southward; it seems unlikely that the structure would become markedly simpler where slate merges into phyllite.

branches of the western boundary fault and may have considerable displacement (perhaps strike-slip).

The foundation of central Newfoundland is formed by a vast thickness of Lower and Middle Ordovician graywacke, slate, and greenstone, interbedded in varying proportions. The meta-volcanics predominate to the northwest and decrease markedly southeastward; the meta-sedimentary rocks become generally finer grained and somewhat better sorted (more quartzitic) to the southeast. Pre-Ordovician rocks are suspected only at the northwest margin of the belt, in the gneiss of the western Burlington Peninsula (Fleur de Lys group) and in the southern Long Range, but they reappear beyond the southeast margin. Pre-Silurian intrusives, both granitoid and ultra-mafic, occur on the Burlington Peninsula and may well be present elsewhere—for example, in the eastern ultramafic belt; at least some low-grade metamorphism dates from the same time, and so, possibly, does the higher grade meta-morphism of the older gneiss on the Burlington Peninsula. Silurian (locally also Lower Devonian) strata rest unconformably on these older rocks in the northwestern part of the belt but conformably in the southeastern; again volcanic rocks pre-dominate to the northwest but become less impor-tant southeastward. Redbeds are prominent among the Silurian sediments in most areas, but marine beds occur; the different areas may have had somewhat different histories.

The main period of granitic intrusion in central Newfoundland and at least the higher grade metamorphism in the southwestern and southern parts was certainly Acadian, for Lower Devonian rocks are affected, whereas Upper Devonian or Carboniferous rocks rest unconformably upon the intrusive granite near or beyond the two margins. Conversely, central Newfoundland nearly coincides with the belt of major Acadian metamorphism and granitic intrusion, though both encroached a little on the adjacent belts.

Thus there are obvious parallels between central Newfoundland and the central belts of the north-ern Appalachian arc, especially in Maine. Nothing like the typical Gaspé-Connecticut Valley syn-clinorium appears in Newfoundland, but that belt is already losing its character in easternmost Gaspé; on the other hand, one might interpret the gneiss belt of the Burlington Peninsula and southern Long Range as representing the Green Mountains-Notre Dame anticlinorium or better its southeastern flank. The possible equivalents of the Bronson Hill and related anticlinoria and of the central Maine slate belt have been mentioned. As in western Newfoundland, the parallels do not apply to the Carboniferous geology; there is nothing like the great Carboniferous basin of central New Brunswick, and longitudinal faults are most prominent along the northwest side of central Newfoundland but the southeast side of the Maritime Provinces. In essence, however, one can characterize central Newfoundland as the core belt of the Acadian orogeny, which here, as in the northern Appalachian arc, was the most impor-tant orogeny. If this core belt was originally reason-ably straight, then central Newfoundland has been offset by dextral movement amounting to a couple of hundred kilometers (over a hundred miles).

Southeastern Newfoundland

The ragged peninsulas of southeastern New-foundland—Bonavista, Avalon, and Burin—differ markedly from the rest of the island both geographically and geologically. Thus they are cut to pieces by deeply indented bays, large and small, until no point in them is more than 30 kilo-meters (20 miles) from the ocean, near which their flat to rolling upland surfaces are roughly dis-sected. Offering many fine harbors and lying close to the Grand Banks, they were early settled, and to this day half of Newfoundland's population lives here, 40 percent on the Avalon Peninsula alone. In contrast with the rest of the island, only modest amounts of Paleozoic rocks are present, and none of the sedimentary rocks are known to be younger than Early Ordovician, save in the wedge between Hermitage and Fortune Bays where Silurian (?) and Devonian strata are also represented; the Paleozoic rocks rest, however, on vast thicknesses of older strata, presumably Precambrian but generally little if at all metamorphosed (McCartney, 1967, 1969).

These older strata are well displayed around St. John's, the capital city, where a succession of clastic rocks 6000 meters (nearly 4 miles) thick strikes parallel to the east coast of the Avalon Peninsula, considerably folded (axial planes and occasional thrust faults dip west) but generally younger toward the sea (Rose, 1952; Brückner, 1969). The upper portion of this succession (Cabot group) is generally arkosic, red, green, and gray, though some dark slate is present, especially as a basal unit; the lower portion (Conception group) consists of green and gray slate, argillite, gray-wacke, and graywacke conglomerate, much of the coarser material at least being derived from a volcanic source. The upper portion is commonly cross-bedded and was probably deposited in shal-low water if not by rivers on a delta or flood plain; the lower portion is well laminated or exhibits graded bedding and was probably deposited in deeper water, except for its basal layers (tillite-like breccias are also reported in these layers). What appear to be similar rocks have been found for 200 kilometers (130 miles) out to sea southeast of St. John's, at the Virgin Rocks and elsewhere on the Grand Banks (Lilly, 1966, p. 571).

To the west, on the east and south shores of Conception Bay and southward, a thick mass of volcanic rocks (felsic and mafic) with some red and greenish clastic sedimentary layers (Harbour Main group, perhaps 2000 meters—6000 feet—thick) appears from beneath the succession just described in a faulted anticlinorium or horst, the Holyrood horst (Holyrood is at the head of the bay). The volcanic rocks are intruded and contact-metamorphosed by granite (Holyrood plutonic series) with minor diorite and gabbro; these plutonic rocks were earlier thought to intrude also the basal part of the overlying clastic succession, but an angular unconformity and a basal conglomerate with pebbles of volcanic and plutonic rocks (generally in different localities) have since been discovered (McCartney, 1967, p. 29, 31–32, 95–99). Yet even these volcanic and plutonic rocks are themselves very late Precambrian, to judge by the available radiometric dates (575 to 600 million years, depending on the decay constant used; McCartney and others, 1966).

In several places around the head of Conception Bay, Lower Cambrian strata lie with spectacular unconformity on the granite, the volcanics, or the lower graywacke portion of the clastic succession; evidently the horst had already been upfaulted and truncated before their deposition. They have a thin basal conglomerate or sandstone but consist mainly of red and green shale, some of it limy. Above come Middle and Upper Cambrian strata, mainly dark shale (manganiferous at the base) but with some limestone and, toward the top, siltstone and sandstone beds. Dips in the Cambrian beds here rarely exceed 15 degrees, but the different areas are separated by faults (mainly longitudinal); in general these faults displace the Cambrian far less than the Precambrian or even in the opposite direction. In the largest area of Cambrian strata, on the southeast shore of Conception Bay, they dip toward the bay, in which stand several islands of similarly dipping Lower Ordovician, dominantly sandstone below and shale with Arenig graptolites above. At Wabana on Bell Island, several beds of hematitic iron ore at about the transition from sandstone to shale have been mined on a large scale for many years. The total thickness of the Paleozoic strata here is at least 2000 meters (6500 feet), of which all but about the lowest 300 meters (1000 feet) is Lower Ordovician.

West of the Holyrood horst lies the broad complex Trinity Bay synclinorium, the deepest part of which extends from the head of that bay into the peninsula west of St. Mary's Bay. In this synclinorium, the entire clastic succession reappears, somewhat finer-grained and with less red than near St. John's, probably thicker, and apparently conformable throughout. It is overlain by a unit up to 150 meters (500 feet) thick containing clean white quartzite beds (Random quartzite), which in turn passes upward into the Cambrian succession, much thicker than but mostly like that around Conception Bay except for the addition of pink muddy limestone in the Lower and of volcanic rocks in the Middle Cambrian. All these strata are folded together into steep-sided, nearly upright folds, fairly broad and open in the competent Precambrian strata but tight and even isoclinal in the overlying Cambrian. Some of the fold axes are displaced by conjugate tear faults with displacements up to 4 kilometers $(2-\frac{1}{2}$ miles). Disconformities are reported locally below and above the quartzite unit here, but the absence of an obvious angular unconformity beneath the Cambrian is striking, for one is well displayed barely 30 kilometers (20 miles) to the east on the Holyrood horst.

On the west flank of the Trinity Bay synclinorium the arkosic upper portion of the clastic succession becomes coarser and redder again (Musgravetown group); it is still thicker and contains a thick lens of volcanic rocks (Bull Arm formation) in its lower part. Just to the west, the lower graywacke portion (Connecting Point group) outlines the core of another faulted anticlinorium or horst, the Isthmus horst, reaching from the northeast corner of Placentia Bay to the south and west shores of Bonavista Bay. Volcanic rocks are reported in this group also, especially near the top. In a few places on the flanks of the horst an angular unconformity separates the graywacke from the arkosic portions of the succession; moreover, Cambrian (and in one area Lower Ordovician) shaly strata appear again in several synclines, generally rimmed by the quartzite unit, probably resting unconformably on the graywacke in the horst but conformably or at most disconformably on the arkosic beds on either side.

Except for such Cambrian synclines, the belt west of the Isthmus horst, extending from the west shore of Bonavista Bay (Jenness, 1963) to the west shore of Placentia Bay and the islands in its upper part (Anderson, 1965), seems to consist of two strips of the deformed but unmetamorphosed, largely arkosic clastic rocks (Musgravetown group) alternating with two horsts formed of mildly metamorphosed (greenschist facies), mixed sedimentary and volcanic rocks (Love Cove group—type locality on eastern horst). These strips and horsts are separated by longitudinal faults (thrust or strike-slip faults?) and invaded by granitic (also dioritic) intrusions similar to those just to the west in central Newfoundland but unknown on or east of the Isthmus horst (except for a small gabbro-to-granite intrusive complex in eastern Placentia Bay). The correlation of the mixed sedimentary and volcanic rocks in the horsts is uncertain; they may represent the lower portion of the Precambrian clastic succession as exposed in the Isthmus horst (Connecting Point group) but containing still more volcanics and somewhat metamorphosed, or they may be equivalent to the rocks that appear beneath that succession on the Holyrood horst (Harbour Main group); their greater degree of deformation and metamorphism suggests the latter, but the character of the metasedimentary rocks suggests the former. The dominantly volcanic rocks in the southern part of the eastern horst also extend the length of the Burin Peninsula, outlining an anticlinorium and flanked near the end of the peninsula by belts of lower Paleozoic rocks, thinner again than in the Trinity Bay synclinorium. On the southeast side of the peninsula, Cambrian strata locally rest unconformably upon the older volcanics and are followed by other volcanic and sedimentary rocks, doubtfully Ordovician; a large fluorite deposit is mined at St. Lawrence in granite intruding these rocks. At the west end of the peninsula, the arkosic rocks appear once more, faulted against the older volcanics and including narrow synclines of apparently conformable Cambrian beds.

West of the end of the Burin Peninsula lie the French islands of St. Pierre and Miquelon (Aubert de la Rüe, 1951), the latter consisting of three high islands—from south to north, Langlade or Petite Miquelon, Grande Miquelon, and Le Cap or Cap Miquelon—now tied together by large sand bars. St. Pierre and Grande Miquelon consist of volcanic rocks, probably the same as those on the Burin Peninsula; Langlade between them exposes Cambrian strata and the underlying quartzite unit; and Le Cap consists of schist intruded by granite and may indeed belong geologically to the wedge of rocks between Fortune Bay and Hermitage Bay.

The rocks in this fault-bounded wedge differ considerably from those on either side. Fossiliferous Cambrian (but not Lower Cambrian) strata are present but in a somewhat different facies than farther south and east; they are underlain as there by a white quartzite unit and then by green and red clastic sediments (Hutchinson, 1962, p. 29—40). They are accompanied (overlain unconformably?) by thick mafic volcanics associated with con-

siderable graywacke, which have been assigned to the Ordovician but are totally different from the entirely sedimentary Ordovician strata on either side (except for the doubtfully Ordovician volcanics on the southeast side of the Burin Peninsula). One wonders if these rocks could be Cambrian, since Middle Cambrian volcanics are known in the Trinity Bay synclinorium and also on Cape Breton Island (Chapter 6, p. 140), or Precambrian (Williams, 1970), for they lie directly on strike with the westernmost horst west of Bonavista Bay; the rocks there (assigned to the Love Cove group) are similar in character although more metamorphosed, but they have been considered to be the oldest Precambrian exposed in that region. Where closest, the two groups of rocks are only 15 kilometers (10 miles) apart, but they are separated by a Devonian granite batholith (Ackley granite) that cuts and metamorphoses both and by a major cross-fault (the longitudinal faults bounding the horst and the wedge have not been traced through the batholith and may indeed be older).

Along the north shore of Fortune Bay and at its head (Bradley, 1962), two sequences of arkosic, probably continental redbeds rest unconformably above all these rocks. One (Rencontre formation) contains mainly felsic volcanics and is considerably folded and cleaved; the other (Great Bay de l'Eau and Terrenceville formations) contains fragments of all older units and is little deformed, except where it is caught along faults. The younger group contains Upper Devonian plants; the older is unfossiliferous but is generally assigned to the Silurian, although it is down strike (separated by the Ackley granite batholith) from the western strip of supposed late Precambrian sediments between the horsts west of Bonavista Bay — hence Williams (1970) assigns it a Precambrian age. Both are locally invaded by a granodiorite body (Belleoram granodiorite), which must therefore be post-Devonian, and both are cut by the longitudinal faults, notably the steep Terrenceville thrust fault on the northwest side of the Burin Peninsula at the head of Fortune Bay, which must therefore have moved as late as Carboniferous time, although its principal displacement may well be early Paleozoic or even late Precambrian. These are the only evidences of post-Acadian orogeny east of the Carboniferous basins of western Newfoundland and their bounding faults.

The history of the Fortune Bay wedge is thus rather unlike that of the belts on either side, or at least rather different events are recorded; it is perhaps most like the history of the northwest flank of the Kennebecasis anticlinorium in southern New Brunswick, where one finds again a thick sedimentary-volcanic sequence of rather indefinite age overlain unconformably by Silurian volcanics and Upper Devonian redbeds (Chapter 6, p. 137). The similarity of the history of the Avalon Peninsula to that of the central part of the Kennebecasis anticlinorium has been recognized for a long time.

Through most of southeastern Newfoundland, the strike of folds and faults averages about N20°E, though ranging up to 20 degrees in either direction. On the Burin Peninsula, however, it swings to N30°E, on St. Pierre and Miquelon it averages perhaps N45°E, and in the wedge north of Fortune Bay it reaches N55°E; possibly one might speak of a recess near the base of the peninsula. The near restriction of Cambrian outliers on the Avalon Peninsula to the shore of the larger bays suggests that the axis of that peninsula may mark a gentle culmination (opposite the supposed recess).

The age of the main deformation in southeastern Newfoundland is uncertain; one can guess, however, from the presence of relatively underformed Upper Devonian red sandstone on Fortune Bay, along the border with central Newfoundland, that the Acadian orogeny was important. The unconformity beneath the older redbed unit in Fortune Bay may record the main Taconic orogeny, if that unit is Silurian, and the older volcanic-sedimentary group there may be evidence of earlier phases, if indeed the group is Ordovician. On the other hand, two older Precambrian deformations are well recorded—one by the unconformable overlap of the Lower Cambrian and locally of the underlying arkosic portion of the clastic succession onto the graywacke portion or even older rocks in the Isthmus and Holyrood horsts, the other by the unconformity at the base of the clastic succession upon the volcanic and plutonic rocks in the core of the present Holyrood horst. The later of these deformations seems to have taken the form of block-faulting rather than folding, producing the horsts which then probably supplied much of the material for the arkosic portion; the earlier, though only certainly visible in the one area, involved plutonism and metamorphism and was perhaps more general in extent.

These two deformations may be considered two phases of an Avalonian orogeny (Lilly, 1966, p. 572), the oldest to affect the Appalachian belt as such. Several writers (e.g., Williams, 1964, p. 1140, 1154; 1969; Poole, 1967, p. 14, 19) have suggested that this early orogeny consolidated an Avalon platform, on which the lower Paleozoic strata accumulated as thin platform deposits, like those at the edge of the Canadian shield on the northwest margin of the Appalachian geosyncline. The lower Paleozoic strata are largely dark shale, siltstone, and sandstone, however, of types suggesting rather deep water, and they are in fact moderately thick—the Cambrian totals at least ½ kilometer (over 1500 feet) near the head of Trinity Bay and the base of the Bonavista Peninsula, and the Lower Ordovician nearly 2 kilometers (6000 feet) in Conception Bay. Moreover, except on the horsts, these strata are folded as much as the underlying late Precambrian, so that the main deformation of the latter must also be Paleozoic, at least younger than Early Ordovician. The Avalonian orogeny certainly produced horsts or anticlinoria or lines of islands and quite possibly some new sialic crust but hardly a platform of continental type within the overall Appalachian geosyncline.

The Cambrian and Lower Ordovician rocks of southeastern Newfoundland (Hutchinson, 1962) are remarkably similar in both rock type and fauna to those of southeastern Cape Breton Island, southern New Brunswick, and southeastern Massachusetts. On Cape Breton Island (and also in the Browns Mountain uplift of Nova Scotia), hematite beds like those on Bell Island appear, though they are not mineable, and beneath the Lower Cambrian fossiliferous strata comes first quartzite and then arkose. There can be no doubt that during the Early Paleozoic all these regions had the same geologic history; if in addition they were parts of a single continuous belt, then southeastern Newfoundland has been torn from Cape Breton Island by dextral movement of a couple of hundred kilometers (over a hundred miles). If one accepts such an offset, then one might explain the prominent longitudinal faults of southeastern Newfoundland, movement on which probably began in the Precambrian, as the original pre-Devonian extensions of those in the southern Maritime Provinces; those of western Newfoundland as their extensions after the offset, in Carboniferous time.

As already noted in discussing each of the other regions mentioned in the last paragraph (Chapter 5, p. 112; Chapter 6, p. 137, 140), the Lower Paleozoic faunas of southeastern Newfoundland are much more like those of contemporary beds in Europe than those of Cambrian and Lower Ordovician strata on the northwest side of the Appalachian chain, and one may even say the same of the rock types (Henningsmoen, 1969); thus black shale (locally manganiferous) characterizes the Middle Cambrian in both Wales and Scandinavia but not in the Valley and Ridge province, and beds of hematitic iron ore, intercalated between sandstone below and shale with Arenig graptolites above, have been mined in Brittany and Normandy.

The Precambrian rocks of southeastern Newfoundland are less easily matched elsewhere in the Appalachians. The thick volcanic units beneath the Lower Cambrian on Cape Breton Island and in southern New Brunswick may be compared with those within the clastic succession on the west flank of the Trinity Bay synclinorium (Weeks, 1957), less probably with those of the Holyrood horst (see also Fairbairn and others, 1966). Nothing like the great thickness of Precambrian clastic rocks in southeastern Newfoundland occurs in the Maritime Provinces, however; these clastic rocks resemble more the basal clastic sequence below the Cambrian carbonate rocks on the flanks of the northern Long Range, Green Mountains, and Blue Ridge anticlinoria, though the parallel is not very close. Indeed one might find a better parallel in the "Eocambrian" sparagmites of Norway, the Longmyndian of the Welsh Border, or the "Infracambrian" Brioverian rocks of Normandy.

The older Precambrian metamorphic rocks of Cape Breton Island and southern New Brunswick suggest a significant Precambrian orogeny there, which might be correlated with the Avalonian orogeny of southeastern Newfoundland, but the rocks involved are not particularly alike, and the correlation remains speculative. Nevertheless, these three areas and they alone give us glimpses into the Precambrian history of the Appalachian orogenic belt, at least southeast of the cores of the Long Range, the Green Mountains, and the Blue Ridge, whose *Precambrian* history was not specifically Appalachian but Laurentian or Grenville.

Summary, and Comparison with the Northern Appalachian Arc

A geologic cross section through Newfoundland would be at least as much like one through the western Maritime Provinces and adjacent Maine as the latter would be like one through central New England. On the northwest, indeed, the Newfoundland section would actually be more like the New England one, the belt of Cambrian and Ordovician carbonate rocks being comparable to the Champlain Valley and the marble belt of western Vermont and Massachusetts, the clastic (Humber Arm) terrain to the Taconic slate mass, and the northern Long Range to the Green Mountains anticlinorium. On the other hand, as already noted, there is nothing comparable to the Gaspé-Connecticut Valley synclinorium. The central portions of all three cross sections would display a major, probably synclinorial belt of metamorphosed argillaceous rocks—in Newfoundland

the Botwood synclinorium and the Gander Lake slate belt—flanked by two more or less anticlinorial belts characterized by unconformities and volcanic rocks—on one side the Burlington Peninsula and vicinity, on the other the Fortune Bay wedge, the Burin Peninsula, and the horsts west of Bonavista Bay. In each cross section, moreover, this central portion, apparently composed entirely of Paleozoic rocks, is the zone of maximum Acadian intrusion and metamorphism, highest in grade in central and southern New England though also including considerable areas of mesozonal rocks in southern, especially southwestern, Newfoundland. The fragmentary southeastern ends of the cross sections would show greater differences; in southeastern Massachusetts one hardly gets past the southeastern anticlinorium flanking the central belt, but in southern Nova Scotia one finds another synclinorium filled with argillaceous Paleozoic rocks and Acadian intrusives, whereas in southeastern Newfoundland one enters a unique terrain largely composed of a thick succession of Precambrian clastic strata, in which even the deepest synclines contain nothing higher than Early Ordovician. Perhaps the distribution and structure of the Carboniferous rocks would present the greatest contrasts from section to section; they are confined to the southeastern corner of New England, are spread widely over the Maritime Provinces and even invade the Gaspé Peninsula, but are almost restricted to the western side of Newfoundland.

Newfoundland's orogenic history is also basically the same as that of the Northern Appalachian arc. As in that arc, what may be called its prehistory was the major orogenic cycle that, acting all along the southeast side of the Canadian shield, finally consolidated as sialic crust the broad Laurentian or Grenville belt, characterized by especially intense katazonal metamorphism and plutonism, by charnockite and anorthosite. This belt then became a foreland for the newly forming Appalachian geosyncline and for the strictly Appalachian orogenies that later took place there, some of which redeformed its southeast margin into a series of anticlinoria and crumpled the thicker adjacent parts of its Paleozoic cover to produce the tectonic belts of northwestern Newfoundland and their analogues along the northwest side of the Appalachian chain. No evidence of sialic crust of Laurentian or Grenville age has yet been found southeast of the anticlinoria in question, save perhaps in certain gneiss domes in western New England (and certainly around Baltimore, Maryland; see Chapter 9, p. 190). I prefer to think, therefore, that the first Paleozoic strata in the central belt of the Appalachians were laid down on a simatic ocean floor (see also Helwig and Sarpi, 1969) and that granitic rocks only evolved there later, during the various Appalachian orogenies.

To be sure, there is also clear evidence for Precambrian orogenic episodes on the opposite side of the island, as on the Avalon Peninsula whence Lilly proposed the name Avalonian for them, and probably they were also responsible for mild metamorphism and plutonism on Cape Breton Island and in southern New Brunswick, if not elsewhere along the southeast side of the chain. According to radiometry, however, these episodes were considerably later than the Laurentian or Grenville orogeny (or orogenies); probably they were unconnected with and unrelated to those in the Laurentian belt, representing rather the beginning of truly Appalachian orogenic development, the first steps in the evolution of a new sialic belt.

In any case, the next step in the evolution, the Taconic orogeny, affected more particularly the northwest side of the Appalachian belt. Evidence for this orogeny is particularly clear in the northwest part of central Newfoundland: pre-Silurian plutonic rocks in the Burlington Peninsula and vicinity, and low-grade metamorphism over a considerable area to the southeast and probably also to the southwest. As along the Bronson Hill anticlinorium in New England and its continuations to the northeast, the zone so affected had been a major locus of volcanism during the Ordovician before the orogeny and continued to be in the Silurian afterward. To the northwest, only the emplacement and accompanying deformation of the Taconic-type klippen (Humber Arm terrain), if indeed they are klippen, are clearly Taconic in age, though at least some of the deformation of the underlying carbonate sequence may also be. Evidence of more than one phase of orogeny is lacking, except perhaps for the various bursts of volcanism during the first half of the Ordovician; the age of the principal phase is also uncertain but was very probably Middle Ordovician.

As repeatedly mentioned above, the culminating orogeny was the Acadian, whose effects appear in all three geologic belts of Newfoundland, although they are especially strong across the broad central belt. Again the timing is not very precise, although the major pulse was certainly after some part of the Early Devonian and probably before some part of the late Devonian, and again there is no evidence for more than one phase, unless some of the deformation of the Lower Carboniferous rocks of western Newfoundland should be considered late Acadian. On the other hand, indisputable evidence for Alleghany (or Maritime) deformation is virtually limited to the main Carboniferous basins of western Newfoundland, but probably many of the high-angle longitudinal faults in north-central Newfoundland and perhaps some of those along the west coast from Port au Port Peninsula northward were also produced in Alleghany orogenic episodes, which, in contrast to those in the Northern Appalachian arc, here affected primarily the northwest side of the chain. On the other hand, certainly the Terrenceville fault and possibly some of the other longitudinal faults in southeastern Newfoundland moved during the Carboniferous, but certainly also their first and probably their major movements were late Precambrian (Avalonian). Triassic faulting, if present, is unrecognizable, and evidence for the later Mesozoic and Cenozoic history is hidden beneath the Grand Banks, except for the ubiquitous deposits of the Pleistocene glacier.

Nothing in Newfoundland suggests that we are there approaching the end of the Appalachian orogenic belt. The individual belts with their distinctive geology continue in full force to the last exposures and strike out to sea, and the separate orogenic episodes seem as significant there as anywhere to the southwest. The northeast and east coast of Newfoundland is a typical Atlantic or rias coast; it does not bound the continental geology but chops it off. Yet nothing we know of the deeper ocean bottom beyond suggests that it conceals any continuation of the Appalachian chain; its trends appear to be about at right angles and its nature is strictly oceanic (Heezen, Tharp, and Ewing, 1959; Godby, Baker, Bower, and Hood, 1966; Mayhew, Drake, and Nafe, 1968).

CHAPTER 8

Blue Ridge Province and Anticlinorium (and Southwestern Extension to Alabama)

The Blue Ridge physiographic province extends from southern Pennsylvania to northern Georgia, a distance of 900 kilometers (550 miles). Throughout its extent, it rises abruptly from lower country on either side—the Great Appalachian Valley on the northwest, the Piedmont Plateau on the southeast (outlying mountain ridges and spurs are commoner on the Piedmont side). In the Central Appalachian arc northeast of Roanoke, Virginia, it consists of a single mountain ridge 10 to 20 kilometers (5 to 10 miles) across; the highest points on this ridge rise a little over 1200 meters (4000 feet) but are not as high as mountains to the west in the western part of the Valley and Ridge province or the eastern part of the Appalachian Plateau. Southwestward into the Southern Appalachian arc, however, the province broadens steadily to 100 kilometers (60 miles) and contains the highest mountains in the entire Appalachian chain, including all the peaks south of New Hampshire (or the Adirondack Mountains of New York) that rise over 1500 meters (5000 feet) above sea level. As a result of its relative elevation and of its dissection by the many streams that drop down into the adjacent lowlands, the rocks within it are fairly well exposed, despite dense forests and a residual mantle of weathered material and in strong contrast to the Piedmont province

on the southeast; hence its geology, though complex, is considerably better known than that of the Piedmont.

Across most of Virginia, the Blue Ridge province corresponds roughly to the large Blue Ridge or South Mountain anticlinorium, in which a core of basement rocks is widely exposed, and whose northwest flank is the Blue Ridge structural front. Northward, the basement plunges out of sight in Maryland, about 15 kilometers (10 miles) north of the Potomac River, but the anticlinorium can be traced along the Blue Ridge (here called South Mountain) into Pennsylvania, almost to the Susquehanna River. Southwestward, the basement can be followed, except for a probable interruption in southwest Virginia, into westernmost North Carolina and along the border of North Carolina and Tennessee at least halfway to Georgia, along the northwest side of the Blue Ridge physiographic province. The basement exposures thus extend for 650 kilometers (400 miles) along the anticlinorium, some 150 kilometers (nearly 100 miles) more than along the Green Mountains and Highlands anticlinoria combined, even including their western extension into eastern Pennsylvania. Curiously, the midpoints of these two basement strips, and perhaps the highest and widest parts of the anticlinoria that expose them, lie close to the angular reentrants in the chain near New York and Roanoke, and indeed the anticlinorial trends show the same angular inflections as the trends in the Valley and Ridge province—the one near New York corresponds to the angular gap in the Highlands mentioned in Chapter 5 (p. 93). Furthermore, at Roanoke the Blue Ridge anticlinorium undergoes a change in style comparable to that in the Valley and Ridge province between the Central and Southern Appalachian arcs (see Chapter 3, p. 39–43; from Roanoke southwest its northwest border is everywhere thrust out over the structural front and the Valley and Ridge province, commonly for many kilometers (miles), whereas northeast of the James River such thrusting is only local, and the rocks on the northwest flank of the Blue Ridge anticlinorium seem simply to rise from under those of the Valley and Ridge, though commonly overturned upon them.

Blue Ridge in Virginia, Maryland, and Pennsylvania

The geology of the Blue Ridge province north of the James River has been carefully summarized by Espenshade (1970). In northern Virginia, the basement rocks in the core of the anticlinorium form a band as much as 30 kilometers (20 miles) wide and consist chiefly of gneiss, ranging in composition from granite to granodiorite (the latter commonly containing hypersthene, recalling the quartz-hypersthene or charnockitic rocks of the Adirondacks and the Grenville province generally). Roughly 30 kilometers (roughly 20 miles) northeast of the James River is a mass of rather sodic anorthosite, associated with which are commercial titanium deposits in a rutile-bearing ilmenite-apatite rock called nelsonite. Most of the basement rocks show some retrogressive metamorphism; characteristic is the striking rock called unakite, consisting of blue quartz, reddened potassium feldspar, and greenish epidotized plagioclase, with small amounts of chloritized mafic minerals (similar rock is known in the Green Mountains and in the northern Long Range of Newfoundland, in precisely similar settings).

On the west flank of the anticlinorium in northern Virginia and around its plunging end in Maryland, the basement core is unconformably overlain by a sequence of volcanic rocks more than 600 meters (2000 feet) thick (Catoctin formation; Reed, 1955); these rocks also form the crest of the anticlinorium northward across Maryland and for 50 kilometers (30 miles) into Pennsylvania. Mafic lavas (andesitic and basaltic, now greenstone) predominate in Virginia and Maryland, but some rhyolitic layers (partly tuff, now slate) are also present, and these increase northward, becoming dominant in Pennsylvania. A thin zone (maximum 130 meters—400 feet) of more or less conglomeratic, locally tuffaceous arkose (Swift Run formation) generally separates the volcanic rocks from the basement gneiss, and others occur locally within the sequence.

Above the volcanic sequence on this flank comes a basal clastic sequence (Chilhowee group) up to 1000 meters (3000 feet) thick, entirely comparable to the basal Cambrian clastic sequence on the west flank of the Green Mountains anticlinorium in Vermont (see p. 74, 92), and like it comprising clean white quartzite in the upper part, darker and less well sorted rocks from silty shale to arkosic conglomerate below. Lower Cambrian fossils are known locally close to the top, and *Scolithus* appears in the purer quartzite beds. The volcanic sequence thins out and disappears toward the southwest (and locally toward the northwest) between these rocks and the basement, beneath a disconformity according to some (e.g., King, 1950, p. 13–14), by change of facies into the basal layers of the clastic sequence according to others (e.g., Bloomer and Werner, 1955); radiometry (Rankin and others, 1969) favors the former view. Stratigraphically above the basal clastic sequence comes the normal Paleozoic sequence of the Valley and Ridge province, but the beds are generally overturned along the Blue Ridge structural front, and locally thrust faults cut out part of the section. The basal clastic sequence and the underlying greenstone volcanics form the topographic crest of the Blue Ridge in northern Virginia (as in the Shenandoah National Park) and of South Mountain in Maryland and Pennsylvania; thus the topographic crest is situated west of the crest of the anticlinorium.

On the east flank of the anticlinorium, the stratigraphy is less obvious, partly because the grade of metamorphism rises rapidly in that direction and partly because much of the east flank is cut out by the large normal fault (Catoctin border fault) that bounds on the northwest the largest of the Triassic basins (Whitaker, 1955); northward the fault bevels into the core of the anticlinorium near the north boundary of Maryland, and the anticlinorium finally plunges down and disappears (beneath a thrust sheet that brings forward the Lebanon Valley synclinorium—Root, 1970) about 25 kilometers (15 miles) southwest of the Susquehanna. Southward along this flank, on the other hand, the volcanic rocks (Catoctin group) can be followed for a long distance, changing from greenstone through epidote amphibolite to hornblende schist; near them, mainly just to the west (below?), are elongate bodies of serpentine, including deposits of talc and asbestos. Here also the zone of clastic metasediments at the base of the volcanics thickens enormously into a vast sequence of mica gneiss and schist (Lynchburg gneiss), kilometers (miles) thick, which rests unconformably on the basement (locally with a prominent basal conglomerate—Rockfish conglomerate) and into which the volcanic sequence interfingers as it thins out near Lynchburg. Beyond the south end of the main Triassic basin, clastic rocks, mainly phyllitic but with thin layers of quartzite (Candler phyllite), appear east of and presumably above the volcanics; they may represent the basal Cambrian clastic sequence (Brown, 1970, p. 344).

Along the Potomac River where it is best known (Cloos, 1947; Nickelsen, 1956), the Blue Ridge anticlinorium is double, divided by a narrow, tight syncline; a similar syncline divides it in the vicinity of Charlottesville, Virginia (Gooch, 1958). On the east flank, the metamorphosed cover rocks show abundant but mostly small isoclinal folds, and the units appear to succeed each other fairly regularly except where cut out by the Triassic normal fault. The west flank, on the other hand, shows a variety of large-scale structure (Cloos, 1951, p. 139–143; King, 1950; Bloomer and Werner, 1955). In some places one finds simply the Blue Ridge (or South Mountain) structural front with all the beds from the basement to the Middle Ordovician present, generally vertical or overturned; in others there are a few large folds, with a wave length of more than a kilometer (about a mile) in the clastic rocks, larger still in the volcanic sequence; in still others thrust faults cut these folds or even replace them entirely—in one such place in northern Virginia the basement gneiss is thrust over Lower Ordovician limestone. To the south, on the James River and beyond, such faults become continuous, and from there they can be traced into Tennessee.

The deformation in the anticlinorium has been intensively studied by Cloos (1947, 1950) and his students, especially in Maryland and along the Potomac River. On the west flank, the basal Cambrian clastic sequence is little metamorphosed, though cleavage is present and the rocks show severe distortion and incipient recrystallization. Eastward the grade of metamorphism rises rapidly, and on the east flank biotite and garnet are common. The cleavage of the west

flank becomes the schistosity here, and one finds the same cleavage and schistosity also in the volcanic rocks and the basement gneiss, though generally as bands of intense cleavage alternating with almost massive zones. In the basement, the older schistosity or gneissic banding is commonly preserved in these unsheared zones. The strike of the main cleavage is parallel to the regional tectonic strike, the structural front, and the anticlinorial axis: N15°–25°E in Virginia and Maryland but swinging around as far as N50°E in Pennsylvania before being cut off by the Triassic border fault. Its dip ranges from 20 to 60 degrees southeast, fanning markedly across the anticlinorium; everywhere it displays a prominent down-dip lineation, whose direction of plunge, S60°E±10°, is very regular. This lineation is expressed especially by stretched elements—pebbles, oöids, amygdales—and by mineral elongation and streaming. Another lineation, almost perpendicular to the first and hence roughly parallel to strike, is recorded by the axes of small folds and by cleavage-bedding intersections, much more rarely by stretched or elongated elements.

Cloos has discussed at length the mechanics of this anticlinorium, his South Mountain fold. He considers that it was produced not by ordinary folding but by slip along the cleavage parallel to the down-dip lineation, accompanied by thinning and by stretching, in the same direction, of the plates between the cleavage planes. The fold would therefore be a great shear or slip fold, the fold form being accentuated by solid flow of the rock; the solid flow is demonstrated clearly by strained oöids in the Cambrian oölitic limestone (Conococheague limestone) on the west flank within the structural front, and Cloos has been able to obtain measurements of the amount of strain in various parts of the fold. He concludes that slip, distributed along innumerable closely spaced cleavage planes and hence quasi-continuous, is primarily responsible for carrying the basement core of the Blue Ridge anticlinorium some 5 kilometers (3 miles) upward and perhaps an equal distance to the west relative to the originally adjacent basement still concealed beneath the Valley and Ridge province. (Gwinn, 1970, p. 143–144, suggests indeed that the whole anticlinorium may be rootless, thrust tens of kilometers (tens of miles) westward over the Valley and Ridge province, but the presence of a steep gravity gradient along the Blue Ridge, from negative in the Valley and Ridge to positive in the Piedmont, rather militates against this idea.)

One might ask, however, if the primary process involved was not rather the solid or plastic flow, straining the rock as observed and producing the cleavage in the process, but perhaps the difference in interpretation implied is largely semantic. Like the Green Mountains anticlinorium, the Blue Ridge anticlinorium apparently records the western limit of such plastic flow in the basement; thus the cause of the greater plasticity eastward—hydrostatic pressure and differential stress, but above all rising temperature and hot solutions—would also be the cause of all the observed phenomena—oöid strain, cleavage, lineation, metamorphism, and the fold itself. As Cloos (1964b, p. 831—832) points out, radiometry suggests that the age of this deformation is not late Paleozoic but Ordovician.

Southwest of the latitude of Roanoke, much less is known about the core of the Blue Ridge anticlinorium. Even the course of the postbasement unconformity on the east flank is uncertain; already equivocal at the James River (Brown, 1958, p. 21—22), it becomes harder and harder to recognize southwestward, and Dietrich (1959, p. 111—114) denies that it exists across Floyd County, 100 kilometers (60 miles) farther on (at the latitude of Pulaski). To the southeast, the quartzite-bearing phyllite on the east flank of the anticlinorium (Candler phyllite) makes a strike ridge that can be followed intermittently nearly 100 kilometers (60 miles) southwestward from the James but then dies out, if indeed it does not double back to the east, as though around the end of a syncline or synclinorium east of the Blue Ridge anticlinorium (no detailed report or map is available for this area).

The northwest flank of the anticlinorium from the James southwest is better known, though coverage is incomplete and conflicting (see Bloomer and Werner, 1955; Woodward, 1932; Dietrich, 1954; Currier, 1935; Stose and Stose, 1957; also older smaller-scale maps by Stose and others, 1919; Butts, 1933). As noted above (p. 165), although the Blue Ridge structural front can be followed readily around the Central Appalachian arc, beginning at the James River it becomes covered up or replaced by low-angle thrust faults of large throw; in general, one can recognize a lower thrust fault or group of thrust faults and a higher one. Already around Fullhardt Knob and Roanoke, the sinuous trace of the lower fault implies a throw of 8 to 12 kilometers (5 to 8 miles). The thrust sheets above the lower fault or faults (Blue Ridge fault, Pilot Mountain fault, Poplar Camp fault and its branches) contain the basal Cambrian clastic sequence (Chilhowee group) and also locally the base of the overlying carbonates, thrown into folds and cut by minor thrust faults, cleaved but otherwise little metamorphosed; in a few places the underlying basement rocks also

appear. Evidently these lower thrust sheets are pieces of the northwest flank of the anticlinorium—of the structural front—thrust northwestward beyond the front over the folds and thrust faults of the Valley and Ridge province which here in places involve the base of the Cambrian carbonates (Shady dolostone) and the upper part of the basal clastic sequence, but never the basement (see p. 46—47).

Above these rocks comes an upper thrust sheet, consisting of metamorphic rocks ranging from phyllite to granitic gneiss; the fault between, called the Fries fault to the southwest, is marked in places by a wide band of mylonite. In several areas—for example, at Roanoke and on the southeast side of the Goose Greek half-window just to the northeast—this sheet overlaps the lower sheets to rest directly on Valley and Ridge rocks. Whether the rocks in this sheet represent the basement core of the Blue Ridge anticlinorium or the metasedimentary rocks on its southeast flank is not clear; probably both are involved, basement lying next the fault from the James River to a point in western Floyd County about 20 kilometers (13 miles) southeast of Pulaski, but being cut out beyond. It must be admitted that, where basement in this upper sheet adjoins basement in the lower, the fault is not easy to trace (if indeed a fault exists)—for example, northeast of the Goose Creek half-window. In any case, the basement core of the anticlinorium, and even in places its southeast flank, seems to be thrust out over the structural front that originally formed its northwest flank.

In the last 50 kilometers (30 miles) in Virginia, the true basement core of the anticlinorium certainly reappears as a strip either along the northwest side of the main upper thrust sheet or, more probably, on an intermediate sheet below, separated from the main sheet by the Fries fault. In the area around Mt. Rogers (the highest mountain in Virginia and indeed in the Appalachians between North Carolina and New Hampshire), a thick pile (up to 3 kilometers—2 miles) of predominantly rhyolitic volcanics appears above this basement (Mt. Rogers volcanic group or formation; Rankin, 1967, p. 10—13; 1970, p. 231—232), containing also much poorly sorted sedimentary material (greenish below, maroon above) with beds of coarse conglomerate that may have formed as volcanic mud flows or else as glacial till and of rhythmically laminated but pebbly mudstone. These rocks also appear on fault slices below the upper or intermediate sheet and along the southeast margin of the main lower thrust sheet, and on these sheets and slices they extend a few kilometers (a few miles) into the adjacent corners of

North Carolina and Tennessee and are overlain by the "basal" clastic sequence, the top of which is Lower Cambrian. As with the comparable volcanics in northern Virginia, their upper contact has been called an unconformity; Rankin found no evidence for this view, but radiometry (Rankin and others, 1969) strongly suggests a hiatus. Whereas the postbasement rocks on the southeast side of the basement core in this region are metamorphosed to the amphibolite facies, those in the Mt. Rogers area are in the low greenschist facies and those on the lower slices are little altered, though considerably deformed. Evidently the sheets and slices of the Mt. Rogers area represent fragments of the northwest flank of the Blue Ridge anticlinorium.

Blue Ridge in Northeastern Tennessee and Northwestern North Carolina

The boundary between North Carolina and Tennessee follows generally the crest of the Unaka Mountains,* which form the high northwestern margin of the Blue Ridge province but are cut into a series of separate ranges by the profound gorges of seven rivers that drain the interior of the province. The highest and most massive of these ranges, the Great Smoky Mountains southeast of Knoxville, Tennessee, includes the second highest peak in the Appalachians. Where detailed work has been done, the rocks in these ranges have been found to form a pile of superposed thrust sheets (nappes of the second kind, in the terminology of Pierre Termier). Furthermore, these sheets have themselves been folded and faulted, and erosion has cut through them to form several large windows; indeed such windows are present for at least 125 kilometers (80 miles) of the 300 kilometers (200 miles) that the Unaka Mountains extend between Virginia and Georgia.

Such a pile of thrust sheets has been worked out in detail in the northeastern corner of Tennessee (King and others, 1944, p. 10–13; King and Ferguson, 1960); the superposed sheets here have been folded into the broad, almost simple Stony Creek syncline on the northwest and a complementary anticline on the southeast, erosion of which has produced the great compound Mountain City window, about 90 kilometers (55 miles) long and up to 15 kilometers (10 miles) broad. The bottom of the pile seems to be exposed in an inner window forming most of the wide northeast half

of the main window; within the inner window, the basal Cambrian clastic sequence (Chilhowee group, of which some 500 meters—1800 feet—are exposed) and the overlying Lower Cambrian carbonate rocks (Shady and Rome formations) form a tightly folded and faulted anticlinorium (Doe Mountain anticlinorium). This anticlinorium closely resembles in size and structure the Lick Mountain and Glade Mountain anticlinoria on the Pulaski thrust sheet in southwest Virginia (Chapter 3, p. 46), and moreover it is not far from on strike with them, for the Poplar Camp fault at the front of the Blue Ridge province south of those anticlinoria bevels at a low angle across their strike as it comes west-southwest into Tennessee, where it is called the Holston Mountain fault. If the "correlation" of these anticlinoria is correct, then Valley and Ridge rocks are exposed once more in the floor of the inner window, and the Blue Ridge structural front may appear along its southeast side, where the entire section down to the basement is locally exposed, turned up on end and badly sliced by small thrust faults beneath the main fault bounding this part of the window (Stone Mountain fault)—the basement rocks appear only in these slices, however, and are not continuous with the rocks in the inner window. If this is indeed the front, it lies at least 25 kilometers (16 miles) southeast of the present northwest margin of the Blue Ridge province at the Holston Mountain fault.

The narrower southwest half of the Mountain City window has a different structure; it exposes up to four superposed slices, each with a stratigraphic sequence that extends from basement (except in the highest) through the basal clastics (here about 1200 meters—4000 feet—thick) into the overlying carbonates (Shady dolostone, also Rome formation in the lowest and highest slices). Each of these sequences faces northwest, the dips being steep northwest or overturned, as are presumably the dips of the faults between the slices. The structurally lowest slice, the Limestone Cove inner window, covers an area about 20 by 4 kilometers (12 by 3 miles) at the southeast border of the main window. Southwestward, the higher slices wrap around its southwest end and wedge out or disappear under the fault bounding the whole window on the southeast; northeastward they merge as the faults between them die out. This part of the main window is separated from the inner window in the northeast half by the Little Pond Mountain fault, which dips southwest and

*The accent in the name Unaka (from a Cherokee word meaning "white") is generally placed on the second syllable, but etymologically it is more correctly placed on the first.

appears to combine thrust and dextral wrench slip; apparently it is overridden at each end by the faults bounding the window, but other dextral faults in the vicinity displace the window faults.

The Iron Mountain fault, which forms the northwest boundary of the Mountain City window, also dips northwest, as shown especially in surface and underground exposures made in 1942 during construction of the Watauga Dam of the Tennessee Valley Authority, about 8 kilometers (5 miles) east of Elizabethton, Tennessee (the accent is on the syllable "beth"). That the upper block or hanging wall of this fault moved relatively down to the northwest is shown by features in that block, described below. This fault can be traced the full length of the window, and it wraps around both ends and disappears beneath the higher faults that form the window's southeast side. About 12 kilometers (8 miles) northwest of its trace on the northwest side of the window, it reappears as the southeast-dipping Holston Mountain fault, directly overriding the rocks of the Pulaski thrust sheet in the Valley and Ridge province. Between the two surface traces of the fault, it and the overlying Shady Valley thrust sheet are folded into the Stony Creek syncline.

Considering its position in the middle of the thrusted pile, the structure of the Shady Valley thrust sheet is remarkably simple. Northeast of a point a few kilometers (miles) east of Elizabethton, the syncline is open and nearly symmetrical; the basal clastic sequence (Chilhowee group) is exposed on both flanks (forming Holston and Iron Mountains), and the overlying Lower Cambrian strata (Shady dolostone and locally part of the Rome formation) fill the core (Stony Creek and Shady Valleys). In places along the Iron Mountain fault, slices of basement rock appear above the fault but unconformably beneath the clastic sequence, which here ranges up to 2300 meters (7500 feet) thick and contains a few basalt flows in the lower part. About halfway from Elizabethton to the Virginia line, the whole synclinal arrangement, including the folded fault beneath, is displaced to the right perhaps 3 kilometers (2 miles) by the east-west Cross Mountain wrench fault, which lies in line with east-west wrench faults on the Pulaski thrust sheet and with east-west deflections of the Pulaski (Seven Springs or Greeneville) and Saltville faults, described in Chapter 3 (p. 49–50). The cross-fault is associated with a culmination of the synclinal axis.

Opposite the northeast end of the Mountain City window, the syncline becomes shallower again, and here the Shady Valley thrust sheet merges with the lower thrust sheet (or sheets) in

the Blue Ridge of southern Virginia (see preceding section). The volcanic rocks (Mt. Rogers volcanic group) in that region reach the northeast end of the window and can be followed about 10 kilometers (6 miles) southwestward down either side, but there either they pinch out beneath or into the base of the clastic sequence or they are cut out by the faults bounding the window.

A little east of Elizabethton, both flanks of the syncline are cut by sinistral wrench faults, southwest of which the structure is somewhat different. The wrench fault on the northwest flank, which starts as one of a pair of imbrications on the back of the Holston Mountain fault, completely cuts off the basal clastic sequence; to the southwest, the Holston Mountain fault brings to the surface nothing lower than Middle Cambrian (Honaker dolostone, especially the shaly zone at its base) and though it can be followed for more than 40 kilometers (more than 25 miles) farther, it here resembles the nearby faults of the Pulaski system more than those of the Blue Ridge province and like the Pulaski faults finally disappears under the next higher fault (here the Buffalo Mountain fault). On the southeast flank of the syncline, the changes are less drastic, but for several kilometers (miles) southwest of the wrench fault the rocks display recumbent folds, with wave lengths and amplitudes measured in hundreds of meters (thousands of feet), with axial planes (and axial-plane cleavage) dipping northwest more gently than the bedding, and with a few "thrust" faults on the overturned limbs, also dipping gently northwest—all consonant with the interpretation that, on the northwest-dipping Iron Mountain fault beneath, the Shady Valley thrust sheet moved northwestward relative to the rocks of the window. Farther southwest, the Iron Mountain fault and the adjacent flank of the syncline become steeper and even locally overturned (especially beyond a dextral cross-fault nearly south of Elizabethton); from here on "drag" folds stand on their heads, with older rocks in the centers of synforms and the reverse. Moreover, the fault cuts upward in the section; for about $6\frac{1}{2}$ kilometers ($4\frac{1}{2}$ miles) the basal clastic sequence above is entirely missing, but it reappears beyond and the fault cuts back down to near its base.

The steepening of its southeast flank converts the Stony Creek syncline into a strongly asymmetrical, overturned fold; furthermore, it plunges southwestward from just east of Elizabethton, deepening until the entire carbonate sequence up to the top of the Lower Ordovician (top of the Knox group) and locally even the base of the Middle Ordovician shale is preserved in it. Southwestward from a point only 13 kilometers (8 miles) southwest of Elizabethton, a still higher thrust sheet, the Buffalo Mountain thrust sheet, rests on these rocks, nested in the trough of the syncline, the underlying Buffalo Mountain fault being warped into the synclinal form. This thrust sheet is broken by thrust faults into three main slices (Ordway, 1959; Rodgers, 1948): smaller, more or less monoclinal northwestern and intermediate slices, consisting of the middle and upper parts of the basal Cambrian clastic sequence (Chilhowee group, even thicker than in the lower sheets) and a small thickness of the overlying carbonate rock (Shady dolostone in Horse and Bumpus Coves), and a larger, rather simply synclinal southeastern slice, consisting of the lower part of the clastic sequence and beneath that a considerable thickness of poorly sorted clastics (part of Ocoee group), probably lower stratigraphically than any beds present above the basement farther northeast in Tennessee or Virginia. Beyond the southwest end of the Mountain City window, the underlying basement appears on the southeast flank of the syncline in this highest slice. Whether the Buffalo Mountain fault turns around the end of the window to become the Unaka Mountain fault on the southeast side or whether the latter cuts it off is uncertain; the second seems more probable, but if so the Unaka Mountain fault should continue southwestward through a wide area of still unmapped basement southwest of the end of the window (Devil Fork fault of Rodgers, 1953a, p. 142).

All along the southeast side of the Mountain City window, basement is thrust over the window rocks, whether these are the basal Cambrian clastic sequence, the overlying carbonates, or part of the basement itself. In at least some areas, the basement rocks within the window are readily distinguishable from those above the bounding thrust faults (Hamilton, *in* King and Ferguson, 1960, p. 13–27); whereas the mainly granitoid rocks within the window (and also those in the slivers on the Shady Valley thrust sheet) have been locally retrograded but not conspicuously sheared, those above the thrusts have been sheared to mylonite, phyllonite, and augen, flaser, and mortar gneiss over a belt several kilometers (miles) wide. Apparently a single major fault, the Unaka Mountain fault, forms the southeast side of the southwest half of the window, but an anastomosing system of faults bounds much of the northeast half, the most prominent being the Stone Mountain fault; the Unaka Mountain fault seems to overlap the others where they meet (King and Ferguson, 1960, p. 78 and Fig. 18; Bryant, 1962, p. D 23), becoming the highest in the system. At the north-

east end of the window, the main Stone Mountain fault becomes the fault beneath the intermediate sheet in the Mt. Rogers area; the Unaka Mountain fault may well continue northeastward to become the Fries fault above that sheet (p. 167), as suggested by Rankin (1969).

The piled-up thrust sheets in and around the Mountain City window, like the lower thrust sheets in the Blue Ridge of southern Virginia, are presumably slices from an original Blue Ridge anticlinorium. All but perhaps the lowest carry basement (though mostly not a great "thickness" of it, and it is absent from some of the constituent slices), and all but the highest carry several thousand meters (many thousand feet) of overlying sedimentary rocks; except on the Shady Valley thrust sheet, however, the section goes no higher than the top of the Lower Cambrian, the *lowest* level ordinarily reached in the thrust sheets of the Valley and Ridge province. Despite the presence of basement in these sheets, the mechanics of the thrusting seems to have been not unlike that in the Valley and Ridge. King and Ferguson (1960, p. 79 ff.) show that the Shady Valley thrust sheet can be interpreted as a plate that slid forward on three movement horizons or decollement zones (successively lower southeastward), one near the base of the Middle Cambrian (shale at the base of the Honaker dolostone), one near the base of the clastic sequence (top of the shaly lower part of the Unicoi formation of the Chilhowee group), and one within the basement; data are not sufficient to establish such a mechanism for the other sheets, but they do not forbid it.

The relations of the sheets to the anticline and syncline that fold them and to each other—the highest cuts off the rear of each of the others until it rests against the very lowest at the back of the two inner windows—indicate that their mechanics is that deduced by Gilluly (1960) for the fault slices around the Goat Ridge window in the Roberts Mountains thrust sheet of Nevada and applied by him also to the Mountain City and other Appalachian windows and half-windows; after a first sheet had formed and moved forward, it began to be folded until the fault, unable to slip in the folded position, broke across the back slope of the growing anticline, producing a new sheet that covered the old and was then folded in its turn. In every case the new breakthrough took place in that part of the fault that was still within the basement. Including the minor slices in the southwest end of the Mountain City window, this process was repeated six or seven times. Considering only the two largest sheets (the Shady Valley and Buffalo Mountain sheets), the process demands not less than 50 kilometers (30 miles) of shortening in the sedimentary rocks and hence presumably in the underlying basement, which is clearly involved, and the total shortening must be considerably more. This distance is at least as great as the present width of the Blue Ridge anticlinorium in northern Virginia and Maryland and of the Green Mountains anticlinorium in Vermont, but of course in both those areas the present width is less than the original width by an unknown but large amount, to judge from the observed folding, body deformation, and metamorphism.

But this is not all. Only a few kilometers (miles) south of the widest part of the Mountain City window, erosion has broken through the thrust sheet of metamorphic rocks behind the Stone Mountain and Unaka Mountain faults (Blue Ridge thrust sheet of Bryant and Reed, 1970) to eat out another great window—the Grandfather Mountain window, 65 kilometers (40 miles) long and up to 30 kilometers (20 miles) wide (Bryant and Reed, 1962). Within the main part of this window, sheared and locally phyllonitized basement rocks are overlain on the northwest (and locally on the southeast) by several kilometers (miles) of tightly folded and mildly metamorphosed clastic rocks— arkose, graywacke, siltstone, and shale (now phyllite)—with some interbedded volcanic rocks and related intrusives (Grandfather Mountain formation). These strata do not resemble the typical rocks of the basal Cambrian clastic sequence (Chilhowee group) as exposed in the nearby thrust sheets in and around the Mountain City window but rather the thicker sequence of poorly sorted clastic rocks (Ocoee group) that appears beneath on the Buffalo Mountain sheet around the southwest end of that window and farther southwest into the Great Smoky Mountains (the volcanics suggest the Mt. Rogers volcanic group and radiometry confirms the correlation). Along the west side and in the southwest end of the Grandfather Mountain window, on the other hand, is an intermediate slice (Table Rock thrust sheet) 30 kilometers (20 miles) long, consisting of over 1000 meters (about 4000 feet) of strata that do resemble the typical basal Cambrian clastic sequence, though metamorphosed, and even include a little carbonate at the top (above this slice is a further slice of basement rocks, still within the window).

The Grandfather Mountain window is bounded on the north and west by the fairly low-angle north- and west-dipping Linville Falls fault, and it is framed by granitic and migmatitic rocks, presumably basement, continuous with those southeast of the Mountain City window and like those

retrograded and sheared to phyllonite and blastomylonite for a considerable distance above the fault, including the entire area of the saddle between the two windows. The fault on the southeast side of the window, on the other hand, is straight and steep, and it is succeeded to the southeast by intensely sheared and retrograded rocks in the Brevard zone, a belt of such rocks that can be traced for hundreds of kilometers (miles) to the southwest and is evidently quite independent of the window (see below, p. 182—184).

The structural saddle between the Mountain City and Grandfather Mountain windows is narrow, only 11 kilometers (7 miles) between the windows proper and less than 5 kilometers (3 miles) between the highest branch faults on either side. The saddle shape is well expressed by the attitude of the dominant foliation in the phyllonitized rocks, which follows the window borders. Two prominent lineations trend fairly regularly northwest-southeast and northeast-southwest through the rocks both inside and outside the Grandfather Mountain window; the northwest lineation is produced by stretched and aligned mineral grains, followed by a few tight folds, the northeast by fold and crinkle axes.

From the saddle, foliation synclinoria plunge both northeast and southwest, and the sheared and retrograded granitic and migmatitic rocks of the saddle yield upward, as the retrogressive metamorphism fades out, to vast thicknesses of mica schist and mica gneiss, commonly with garnet, staurolite, and kyanite, and including also great bodies of amphibolite and hornblende schist and gneiss, especially on the northwest flanks of the two synclinoria (Carolina gneiss and Roan gneiss of older reports; Ashe formation of Rankin, 1970, p. 232—233). The one to the northeast, the Snake Mountain synclinorium, has been little known until the work of Rankin (1967, p. 16—17, 44—45; 1970); its rocks extend northeastward and apparently become the metamorphic rocks of the southern Virginia Blue Ridge. The one to the southwest, the Spruce Pine synclinorium, has been studied in more detail because much mica and feldspar have been mined from the large number of pegmatites it contains. In its midst, about 50 kilometers (35 miles) southwest of the saddle, rise the Black Mountains, containing the highest point in the Appalachians, Mount Mitchell.

Those who have worked in the Spruce Pine district (e.g., Kulp and Poldervaart, 1956; Brobst, 1962) have considered that all the rocks in the two synclinoria are basement because they are continuous with the basement rocks around the windows.* The great thickness of mica schist and mica gneiss, presumably originally shale and graywacke, with bodies of hornblende schist and gneiss that may have been volcanic rocks, has however long suggested to me and others a post-basement sequence, perhaps equivalent to the thick sedimentary sequence of the Great Smoky Mountains (Ocoee group) with an equivalent of the volcanics of the Virginia Blue Ridge (Catoctin and Mt. Rogers groups) on the northwest side; this point of view is now confirmed by Rankin (1967, 1970) on the basis of work in the north-western corner of North Carolina and is expressed on the map (Pl. 1) accompanying this book. Such a view also agrees better with the concept that much of the southern Virginia Blue Ridge is postbasement but, as stated above, the relative importance of basement and postbasement rocks is debatable there as well. The pegmatite and alaskite dikes cutting the synclinorial sequence are well dated by radiometry as Paleozoic, and the metamorphism that produced the present mineralogy of the schists and gneisses seems to be Paleozoic also, probably Ordovician and in any case older than the retrogression that accompanied the faults surrounding the windows. Amphibolite dikes and stocks that cut the granitoid rocks below can be followed up into the basal layers of the overlying sequence where they became indistinguishable from the hornblende gneiss (Wilcox and Poldervaart, 1958; Rankin, 1970, p. 233); they may represent feeders to the volcanic sequence. Rankin recognizes mildly alkalic felsic intrusives as well and groups all these intrusives and extrusives in his Mt. Rogers magma series. Finally numerous, mostly small ultramafic bodies cut most of the rocks, though they are especially associated with the hornblende schist and gneiss; they are themselves cut and altered by pegmatite.

The presence of the Grandfather Mountain window adds not less than another 40 kilometers (25 miles) to the apparent basement shortening in this region. (Rankin's more conservative estimate—1970, p. 243—relates only to the intermediate sheet in the Mt. Rogers area, i.e., the sheet over the Stone Mountain fault, and he admits a large additional displacement along the Fries fault, which may be equivalent to the Unaka Mountain fault; see p. 170.) Moreover, the relation of the window rocks to the thrust sheets around the Mountain City window is difficult to determine. The usual assumption has

been that the rocks within the Grandfather Mountain window represent the Shady Valley thrust sheet, because the volcanics in the sedimentary sequence are equated with those on that sheet at the northeast end of the Mountain City window (Mt. Rogers volcanic group), but volcanics occur also on higher sheets there, especially that above the Stone Mountain fault, and the sedimentary rocks are not like those on the Shady Valley sheet. Stratigraphically, a better case might perhaps be made for the Buffalo Mountain thrust sheet, which has more similar sedimentary rocks next above the basement, though they are by no means as thick and volcanics are absent in that part of the section. Likewise, the Table Rock thrust sheet might be a fragment from any of the thrust sheets in northeast Tennessee, and indeed smaller slices of such rock occur along minor faults branching from both the Stone Mountain fault family and the Linville Falls fault.

Structurally, on the other hand, as Bryant and Reed (1970, p. 222) point out, it is difficult to assign the Grandfather Mountain window to any of the pile of thrust sheets in and around the Mountain City window, especially if Gilluly's Goat-Ridge-window mechanism is invoked for the latter, for the faults between those sheets must all enter the basement close to the south-east side of that window, particularly if they are branches from a master fault within the basement. Thus any hypothesis that equates one of those faults with the Linville Falls fault requires that the fault cut up into the postbasement sediments in the vicinity of the Grandfather Mountain window but then reenter the basement before it reaches the Mountain City window, an unlikely arrangement. More probably, the rocks in the Grandfather Mountain window originally lay southeast even of those now in the Buffalo Mountain thrust sheet, were overridden by the Linville Falls fault at an early stage in the thrusting, and then were brought forward, along with the overlying thrust sheet, on the master fault in the basement below, whose branching produced the faults in and around the Mountain City window. That is, the Grandfather Mountain window would be the top of a sort of gigantic slice above the master fault (perhaps where it rose from one level in the basement to another); possibly the plunging down of the window anticline in both directions along strike reflects the ends of the slice. It must be admitted that even this hypothesis does not explain the Table Rock thrust sheet, which is bounded by basement above and below for half its length; perhaps it can be explained as a slice dragged forward from a deep, otherwise unknown synclinorium still farther southeast (along the Brevard zone?), or perhaps it can be explained only by movements in directions other than the conventional northwest-over, southeast-under appealed to in the hypothesis. The anticline whose erosion produced the Grandfather Mountain window might also be explained by Goat-Ridge-type folding accompanying thrusting along the Brevard zone, but this explanation does not seem necessary.

If the master fault behind the Mountain City window only finds its real roots at the back of the Grandfather Mountain window, then the entire Blue Ridge province here, basement and all, is floating over some unknown footwall. The same conclusion follows indeed from the course of the steep gravity gradient (positive to the southeast, negative to the northwest), whose toe follows the Blue Ridge anticlinorium across Virginia but retreats in North Carolina to the vicinity of the Brevard zone, the Blue Ridge province there being marked by the largest Bouguer gravity low in the eastern United States (Woollard and others, 1964). This low may represent either a large body of postbasement sediments, concealed beneath the far-traveled granitic basement of the Blue Ridge, or only a double thickness of that basement; in the latter case the Blue Ridge structural front would presumably appear at the inner side of the Mountain City window, as suggested above (p. 168), but in the former it would have to lie near the Brevard zone. In any case, the Blue Ridge anticlinorium, which is simply a great overturned fold in Maryland and northern Virginia, has become in Tennessee and North Carolina a pile of gigantic slices pushed out not a few kilometers (miles) but a few tens of kilometers (tens of miles) over the Valley and Ridge province. Nevertheless, as pointed out by Cloos (1957), the same deformational features—for example, the two lineations—can be found from Maryland to North Carolina. Apparently, therefore, the Blue Ridge anticlinorium in North Carolina originally formed in much the same way as in Maryland but was broken up into the present thrust sheets at a later stage of the deformation.

Blue Ridge in Southeastern Tennessee, Southwestern North Carolina, and Northern Georgia

Southwest of the Mountain City window is a less well known stretch of the Unaka Mountains, but farther on, in the mountains on either side of the French Broad River east of Knoxville and beyond in the Great Smoky Mountains, piled-up thrust sheets have again been demonstrated. In these areas, the sequence of poorly sorted rocks (Ocoee group) that appears already in the Buffalo Mountain thrust sheet and perhaps in the Grandfather Mountain window, beneath the "basal" Cambrian clastic sequence (Chilhowee group) but unconformably above the basement, thickens enormously; in the Great Smoky Mountains three quite different sections, each kilometers (miles) thick, can be measured on different thrust sheets, and their interrelations are not certainly known.

On the French Broad River (Oriel, 1960; Ferguson and Jewell, 1961), at the state line but mostly in North Carolina, erosion has cut into the pile of sheets to produce the Hot Springs window, 15 by 8 kilometers (10 by 5 miles). In In it are exposed some 3 kilometers (2 miles) of strata from the Middle and Lower Cambrian carbonate rocks (Honaker, Rome, and Shady formations) down through the Cambrian clastic sequence (Chilhowee group) into the underlying poorly sorted clastics (Ocoee group), of which only about 1 kilometer (somewhat less than 1 mile) appear. Basement rocks are also present in the southeast corner of the window, but their contact with the overlying strata is sheared and mylonitized and cuts across those strata, suggesting that it is a fault rather than a simple unconformity. The strata in the window mostly stand nearly vertical and face north; one might suppose therefore that they represent an exposure of the Blue Ridge structural front beneath the pile of thrust sheets, perhaps like that on the southeast side of the inner Mountain City window, but their stratigraphy resembles more that in the Shady Valley thrust sheet of northeast Tennessee, implying that they too have been moved far from their original position and that erosion has not yet reached the bottom of the pile.

The Hot Spring window is framed by at least four separate faults and thrust sheets. The Mine Ridge fault on its northwest side dips northwest under a structural saddle in the overlying Del Rio thrust sheet; the strata here include the Cambrian clastic sequence (Chilhowee group), some 2500 meters (8500 feet) thick, and the base of the overlying carbonates (Shady and Rome formations). Northwest of the saddle, the strata in this thrust sheet dip generally south-southeast; they are repeated as two slices by the Houston Valley fault and are thrust over the Valley and Ridge province on the Meadow Creek Mountain fault. Of these, the Meadow Creek Mountain fault more probably represents the reappearance at the surface of the Mine Ridge fault, for the strata in the two slices are much alike. The Meadow Creek Mountain fault lies 10 kilometers (6 miles) northwest of the Mine Ridge fault and 22 kilometers (13 miles) northwest of the southeast side of the window, its probable root zone.

The Houston Valley fault between the two slices appears to die out southwestward, but to the west three lower slices appear next above the fault along the Valley and Ridge border; the first and third of these have a somewhat different stratigraphy from the rest of the Del Rio sheet and may represent a lower sheet, perhaps the one exposed in the Hot Springs window. If so, the thrust faults above these slices are both parts of the Meadow Creek Mountain-Mine Ridge fault, repeated by a steep thrust fault so as to scramble the order of the slices. None of these faults has yet been traced in detail southwestward; the Del Rio sheet appears to project into a large area of the older clastic rocks (Ocoee group, Snowbird or Walden Creek group), which are here already several kilometers (miles) thick.

The east side of the Hot Springs window is formed by the Hot Springs fault, which swings northwestward into the saddle northwest of the window and then curves away northeastward, cutting across the slices in the Del Rio thrust sheet until it overlaps onto the Valley and Ridge province. Thence it appears to trace northeastward into the southwestern continuation of the Buffalo Mountain fault. The sheet above it comprises several apparently monoclinal slices next to the Valley and Ridge province and above them a large synclinal slice; these slices appear to be comparable to the slices in the Buffalo Mountain thrust sheet northwest of the end of the Mountain City window. Northeast of the Hot Springs window, this sheet, especially its highest slice, is composed mainly of the thick, poorly sorted clastic sequence (Ocoee group); the overlying Cambrian clastic sequence (Chilhowee group) appears on the lower slices, but basement is present only in a zone of imbrication at the southeast edge of the sheet, beneath the higher Rector Branch fault. A comparable thrust sheet appears above the Brushy Mountain fault on the southwest side of the Hot Springs window, but it includes large areas of basement, which are cut through by mylonite zones, probably following other faults. Finally, the south corner of the window is cut off by the Rector Branch fault, which brings strongly mylonitized basement against the other thrust sheets and the window rocks. It clearly plays the same role here as the Unaka Mountain fault at the southwest end of the Mountain City window and may indeed be con-

tinuous with it (via the Devil Fork fault of Rodgers, 1953a, p. 142).

As around the Mountain City window, so along the Rector Branch fault one thrust sheet after another seems to have been folded and then cut off from behind as thrusting proceeded, but in addition there has been considerable imbricate slicing within the thrust sheets and some that apparently involved more than one of them. Basement appears on the higher thrust sheets, and again in the window (though there with equivocal relations); except in the window, the highest strata preserved are Lower Cambrian (Rome formation) about correlative with the lowest strata involved in the Valley and Ridge province to the north. Thus the mechanics seems to have been comparable to that around the Mountain City window, and the number of superposed major thrust sheets is also roughly comparable, although equivalencies are not certain. There is no reason to doubt that the total displacement on these faults is of the same order of magnitude as in northeastern Tennessee, say 50 kilometers (30 miles).

A short, unmapped gap separates the work in the French Broad area from that in the Great Smoky Mountains (Hadley and Goldsmith, 1963; Hamilton, 1961; King, 1964; Neuman and Nelson, 1965; stratigraphic summaries in King and others, 1958; Hadley, 1970). Here the clastic rocks reach their maximum known thickness; 8 kilometers (5 miles) of strata can be measured in a single section on the highest thrust sheet with neither top nor bottom exposed. In a rough way, the different thrust sheets succeed each other southward from the edge of the Valley and Ridge province, but complications abound— windows, klippen, wrench faults, and especially high-angle thrust faults that cut across and repeat parts of the low-angle thrust sheets. The whole pile of sheets is brought forward over the Valley and Ridge rocks along the Great Smoky fault, whose roughly horizontal attitude and large throw are attested by half a dozen windows eroded through it to expose the Valley and Ridge rocks again, up to 15 kilometers (nearly 10 miles) southeast of its principal trace at the front of the mountains.

Strata corresponding to the "basal" Cambrian clastic sequence of northeast Tennessee and Virginia (Chilhowee group) are preserved here only on the lowest and northernmost of the thrust sheets (Chilhowee Mountain sheet or slice), along with patches of the overlying carbonate rocks (Shady and Rome formations). Furthermore, this sheet is exposed only in two great slices (plus a few small fragments) along the Great Smoky fault; the slices are 50 and 18 kilometers (30 and 11 miles) long and up to 5 kilometers (3 miles) wide, and they form the prominent Chilhowee and English Mountains at the edge of the mountain belt south and east of Knoxville. The structure of each is roughly synclinal, but the southeast flanks of the synclines are cut off on the southeast by the fault beneath the next higher sheet (e.g., Miller Cove fault south of Chilhowee Mountain).

Behind these slices and the mountains they form is a belt of lower foothills, underlain by relatively fine-grained clastic strata—siltstone and shale—with discontinuous lenses of quartz-conglomerate, quartzite, and carbonate rocks (Walden Creek group, part of Ocoee group). The rocks are tightly folded, cut into irregular slices by lesser thrust faults, and mildly metamorphosed (lower part of chlorite grade); furthermore, they are not too well exposed, but they appear to form a sequence at least $2\frac{1}{2}$ kilometers ($1\frac{1}{2}$ miles) thick. The highest strata here are considered equivalent to the lowest on the slices to the north; certainly there is no other stratigraphical overlap between the two sequences. This northern foothills thrust sheet is continuous east to west and ranges from $2\frac{1}{2}$ to 8 kilometers ($1\frac{1}{2}$ to 5 miles) wide.

In the eastern part of the Great Smoky Mountains, this sheet is bounded on the south by the Dunn Creek fault; farther west, by the two largest windows in the Great Smoky fault, by the Line Springs fault between them and by the Rabbit Creek fault beyond them. The thrust sheet above the Dunn Creek and Line Springs faults (probably also above the Rabbit Creek fault, but its equivalence to the others is not certain) underlies most of a belt, 6 to 12 kilometers (4 to 8 miles) wide, of higher foothills including some fairly substantial mountains; it contains a rather different sequence, at least 5 kilometers (3 miles) thick, of generally coarser, mostly feldspathic, well bedded clastic rocks (Snowbird group, part of Ocoee group), ranging from conglomerate, especially below, to siltstone, especially above and toward the southwest—true shale is rare, and arkose greatly predominates over graywacke. Cross-bedding is common but graded bedding rare. Basement appears beneath the sequence, but only east of the Great Smoky Mountains. At the top are units of feldspathic sandstone (Rich Butt sandstone and related units) that differ from those below in showing graded bedding; indeed they resemble rather the sandstone in the lower part of the next overlying thrust sheet, above the Greenbrier fault. None of the rocks in this sequence have much resemblance to those in the northern foothills sheet below the Dunn Creek and related faults, except perhaps for some of the siltstone; if there is a correlation, the top of this sequence should be equivalent to the base of that, though as just noted it resembles rather the lower part of the sequence in the next thrust sheet southeast.

The structure in this southern foothills thrust sheet, a fairly simple southwestward-plunging syncline at the east end of the Great Smoky Mountains, becomes increasingly complex westward; the rocks are broken by both low-angle and high-angle thrust faults, the latter commonly cutting and displacing the former and also the faults bounding the sheet, the Dunn Creek and Greenbrier faults. The largest of these high-angle faults—the Gatlinburg fault or fault system, for it is nearly everywhere compound, forming a zone 1 or 2 kilometers (about 1 mile) wide—has been traced for at least 50 kilometers (30 miles) from east-northeast to west-southwest at a low angle to the more nearly east-west trend of the thrust sheet; apparently it combines thrust and dextral wrench movement—south side up and to the west. To the east, beyond the Great Smoky Mountains, it may intersect the Dunn Creek fault; to the west it does intersect and displace the Greenbrier fault, and a large, down-dropped patch of the overlying thrust sheet is preserved north of it (Cove Mountain outlier), intricately sliced with the rocks of the southern foothills sheet. Because of the resemblance of adjacent rocks in these two thrust sheets, the assignment of some large bodies of sandstone still farther southwest above the Rabbit Creek fault (Cades sandstone) is equivocal and the structure correspondingly uncertain; at the west end of the mountains the southern foothills sheet is apparently represented only by such sandstone, if it is not cut out completely.

The rocks in the southern foothills thrust sheet are more metamorphosed than those to the north, being mostly in the chlorite grade north of the Gatlinburg fault but rising into the biotite grade southward (the Gatlinburg fault may displace the isograds). On the other hand, the Lower and Middle Ordovician strata (mainly limestone with a little shale at the top) that appear beneath these rocks, in the windows through the Great Smoky fault, are virtually unmetamorphosed, even where the surrounding rocks contain biotite. The windows are cut either directly through the southern foothills sheet (one lies just north of the Gatlinburg fault) or into the southernmost part of the northern foothills sheet, just north of the Dunn Creek-Line Springs-Rabbit Creek fault, and they show that neither the northern foothills sheet nor the Chilhowee Mountain sheet persists to the south beneath the southern foothills sheet. Apparently, therefore, the Dunn Creek and Miller Cove faults separating these three sheets rise as great imbrications directly from the Great Smoky fault, which retains its more or less horizontal attitude southward at least to the vicinity of the high-angle Gatlinburg fault, itself perhaps a late imbrication above the "root" of the Great Smoky fault.

The various sheets above the Great Smoky fault may represent different segments of an immensely thick column of clastic rock (extending from the basement on the southern foothills thrust sheet to the known Lower Cambrian on the Chilhowee Mountain sheet; the total thickness would be about 10 kilometers—6 miles), sheared from each other along weak zones in the column, piled one upon the other in reverse order, and then driven northward not less than 15 kilometers (10 miles) over the Valley and Ridge province (Neuman and Nelson, 1965, Fig. 18, p. D65). King (1964, p. 120–121, Fig. 23), however, interprets the Chilhowee Mountain sheet as a large block torn from the footwall of the Great Smoky fault rather than the top of the column in the original hanging wall. As the Valley and Ridge rocks in the windows are unmetamorphosed, the Great Smoky fault and most of the associated faults are post-metamorphic, but the Dunn Creek fault is an exception, for it is cut by later high-angle faults and unlike them does not apear to deform older cleavage or displace metamorphic isograds. If it is truly older than the rest of the faults associated with the Great Smoky fault, then the piling of the southern on the northern foothills sheet antedates, perhaps by a long period, their thrusting over the Valley and Ridge province.

The relations of these faults and thrust sheets to those near the French Broad River are not known and, if some of the faults are much older than others, may not be simple. The Great Smoky fault appears to trace eastward (around a major reentrant in the mountain front at the Pigeon River in which a remnant of a low thrust sheet appears—perhaps equivalent to the English Mountain and Chilhowee Mountain slices farther west but more likely lower) into the Meadow Creek Mountain fault beneath the Del Rio thrust sheet or into some of its branches. The Chilhowee and English Mountain slices may be equivalent to the lower slice or slices of the Del Rio sheet, especially to those at its west end that have a somewhat different stratigraphy from the rest; as noted above, these slices in turn may be more related to the Hot Springs window than to the rest of the Del Rio sheet. The northern foothills sheet can apparently be traced as a thin sliver around the same reentrant (not cut off against it, as shown by Rodgers, 1953a, Pl. 10),

into a part of the Del Rio sheet. Whether the southern foothills sheet also continues into the upper part of the Del Rio sheet is uncertain, and depends on whether the Dunn Creek fault is considerably displaced by the Gatlinburg fault in an unmapped area east of the Great Smoky Mountains; if so, this sheet may instead represent the one above the Brushy Mountain fault (and hence the Buffalo Mountain sheet?). Thus the three sheets in question may all represent parts of the Del Rio thrust sheet or they may also include equivalents of the sheets above and below.

Above the southern foothills sheet and the Greenbrier fault comes the highest thrust sheet in the Great Smoky Mountains; it underlies the main range and extends south and southwest for many kilometers (miles). It contains a vast thickness (perhaps as much as 8 kilometers—5 miles—in the central and western parts of the range) of moderately feldspathic sandstone or graywacke and fine conglomerate (Great Smoky group, part of Ocoee group), generally in thick, conspicuously graded beds, coarsest and most thick-bedded in the middle, finer and with more silty and shaly layers below and especially above, where considerable bodies of black pyritic shale or slate are intercalated.

At the east end of the range, the Greenbrier fault, with the rocks above and below, is folded into a broad syncline and a tighter anticlinorium (Cataloochee anticlinorium) plunging southwest; it swings around them to form a great Z. The core of the anticlinorium exposes rocks of the southern foothills thrust sheet (Snowbird group with a sliver of basement) and is cut by high-angle thrust faults, at least one of which displaces the Greenbrier fault above. In the sheet above the fault, on the far side of the anticlinorium, the base of the clastic sequence appears; a thin group of feldspathic sandstone and conglomerate, comparable to the lower part of the thick sequence of such rocks on the southern foothills sheet (Snowbird group), overlies basement, which appears here immediately above the Greenbrier fault and can be followed northeastward into the region south and southwest of the Hot Springs window. Although the Greenbrier fault has not been traced through this region, where it would throw basement on basement, it is tempting to equate it with the Rector Branch fault south of the window or with one of the mylonite zones in the basement a little to the northwest; if so, the thrust sheet above the Greenbrier fault would correspond to the highest thrust sheets both on the French Broad and around the Mountain City and Grandfather Mountain windows. On the other hand, its immensely thick postbasement sequence is absent on them, unless as I believe it is represented by the mica shist and mica gneiss in the Spruce Pine and Snake Mountain synclinoria. Furthermore, the Greenbrier fault is premetamorphic (see below), whereas the Rector Branch and related faults appear to be late (they lie, however, north of the limit of any but the mildest metamorphism), so that they are related rather to the late thrusts that cut the Greenbrier fault in the Cataloochee anticlinorium.

The postbasement sequence above the Greenbrier fault has little in common with any of those on the lower sheets in the Great Smoky Mountains, yet, if they are fragments of a stratigraphic column extending from the basement up to the Cambrian, it ought to be equivalent to some part of them. As already noted, it rests on basal layers that do resemble the sequence in the highest of those sheets (probably the lowest sequence stratigraphically), and the sandstone at the top of that sequence resembles its rocks. Probably it represents a lateral facies equivalent of the upper part of that sequence (Snowbird group) and of much of the sequence in the next sheet below (Walden Creek group). In any case, its difference from them compels the conclusion that it has been brought in from a considerable distance along the Greenbrier fault, probably even more than the 20 kilometers (12 miles) demonstrated by the Z-shaped offset of the fault around the Cataloochee anticlinorium.

The rocks within the synclinal bend of the Greenbrier fault and westward along the crest of the east half of the range are folded synclinally; the northwest flank, in massive sandstone layers, is fairly simple, but the trough, in the overlying rocks containing more shale, is complicated by tight folds and minor thrust faults. A large, late, dextral wrench fault (Oconaluftee fault) cuts westnorthwest across the highest part of the range and appears to merge westward into the Gatlinburg fault system. Metamorphism increases steadily southward; biotite is present throughout, garnet appears near the crest of the range, and staurolite and then kyanite appear some kilometers (miles) to the south. The isograds continue eastward across the fault into the Cataloochee anticlinorium almost undeflected, showing that the Greenbrier fault, in contrast to the Great Smoky fault, is premetamorphic. A little south of the crest of the range, moreover, a second generation of folds appears, crumpling the axial-plane cleavage and schistosity of the first generation and accompanied by its own axial-plane slip cleavage. Indeed, a later slip cleavage cutting an older slaty cleavage can be found at a number of places well north of the Greenbrier fault, especially near late faults like those of the Gatlinburg system. Where the two generations of folding and cleavage intersect, the older one trends north of east, the younger northeast.

The Cataloochee anticlinorium, which folds the Greenbrier fault, appears to be, in part at least, a large complex fold of this second generation. Even more spectacular is the Ravenswood anticlinorium a few kilometers (miles) to the west, in which basement and overlying metasedimentary rocks from below the Greenbrier fault have punched up through the overlying thrust sheet to form a sort of window (actually not quite closed at the southwest end) 25 kilometers (15 miles) long and up to 5 kilometers (3 miles) wide. Some faulting is involved, but the faults are themselves folded, and the anticlinorium is really an elongate gneiss dome; the metasedimentary rocks here contain staurolite and, to the south, kyanite. West of the south end of the Ravenswood anticlinorium are two more orthodox gneiss domes (Ela and Bryson City domes), roughly 8 by 3 kilometers (5 by 2 miles); in view of the high-grade metamorphism it is not possible to be certain whether the core gneiss is basement from beneath the Greenbrier fault. Around the western dome, indeed, small bodies of pegmatite and other granitic rocks cut the metasediments, probably remobilized at the time of doming.

Southeast of the Ravenswood and Cataloochee anticlinoria, the obviously metasedimentary rocks (mainly feldspathic quartzite and mica schist) of the Greenbrier thrust sheet give way to alternating strips of such rocks and of various gneisses, ranging from granitoid gneiss through migmatite to mica gneiss and amphibolite and considered by Hadley and Goldsmith (1963) to be basement. As even the metasedimentary rocks here are high in the almandine amphibolite facies, these gneisses do not show the retrogression that characterizes the rocks in all the basement belts farther north and northeast. Beyond the limit of the area mapped around the Great Smoky Mountains, they in turn are followed by a vast area of mica schist and mica gneiss, apparently continuous northeastward into the rocks of the Spruce Pine synclinorium and extending southeastward to the Brevard zone, southwest of the Grandfather Mountain window (sillimanite appears in a belt near the Brevard zone). Ultramafic bodies are scattered throughout these rocks, mostly rather small but including one remarkable elliptical ring-dike of dunite, 9 by 5 kilometers (6 by 3 miles). If the schist and gneiss in the Spruce Pine synclinorium are all part of the basement, then so are these rocks (or most of them; if any are not, the contact remains untraced), and basement covers a belt 40 kilometers (25 miles) or more wide in the southeast part of the Blue Ridge province all across North Carolina and extending southwestward into Georgia. If, however, the Spruce Pine rocks are postbasement, the metamorphosed equivalents of the sedimentary rocks of the Great Smoky Mountains, then a boundary between them and the true basement farther northwest in the Unaka Mountains is as yet unmapped in detail, but basement may not continue at the surface southwestward beyond the southeastern part of the Great Smoky Mountains, appearing last perhaps in the Bryson City gneiss dome (this is the interpretation expressed on the tectonic map accompanying this book). Basement may also appear (as the Whiteside "granite") across strike in the cores of several domes in southern North Carolina just northwest of the Brevard zone. In any case, the rocks in question ought to represent the crest (if they are basement) or the southeast flank (if they are not) of the Blue Ridge anticlinorium, thrust tens of kilometers (miles) northwestward over the thrust sheets derived from its northwest flank and over the Valley and Ridge province.

The mechanics of the thrust sheets in the Great Smoky Mountains evidently differs profoundly from that of the sheets around the Mountain City window. Whereas there the lowest thrust sheets were apparently formed first, then folded and cut off at their roots by higher ones, in the Great Smokies the highest thrust fault, the Greenbrier fault, is evidently one of the earliest in the region, and the lower faults appear to be merely imbrications on the back of the lowest fault of all, the late Great Smoky fault. Such a difference renders rather suspect any attempt to equate thrust faults in the Smokies with those on the French Broad or farther northeast. The difference may be related to the materials involved; basement is present in most of the thrust sheets from west of the Hot Springs window northeastward to Virginia, but does not appear in the Great Smoky Mountains except on their southeast side, deep in the zone of almandine amphibolite metamorphism; instead the thrust sheets appear to be fragments of an immensely thick column of overlying sediments. In addition, however, a period of metamorphism intervened between older and younger periods of folding and faulting. King (1964, p. 129–130) indeed gives reasons for suggesting that the older folding and faulting (Greenbrier fault and perhaps Dunn Creek fault), along with the formation of schistosity and the metamorphism, are Ordovician, whereas the younger folding and faulting (Great Smoky, Gatlinburg, and related faults) are late Carboniferous or Permian. Farther northeast, the metamorphism of the rocks in the Spruce Pine synclinorium would belong to the first period, but all the major faults and the accompanying retrogression would belong to the second.

Southwest of the Great Smoky Mountains, much less is known of the geology regionally, although several separated areas have been studied in detail. The Cambrian clastic sequence (Chilhowee group) in the Chilhowee Mountain slice disappears at the west end of the Great Smokies, and the Miller Cove fault behind appears to end against the Great Smoky fault. The clastic sequence reappears, however, 40 kilometers (25 miles) farther southwest, beyond the Tellico Plains reentrant of the Great Valley (in which the same rocks appear as tight anticlines surrounded by the younger carbonate rocks; see Chapter 3, p. 55); here it forms a relatively simple syncline, 30 kilometers (20 miles) long and 3 to 4 kilometers (2 to 3 miles) wide (Starr and Bean Mountains, separated by the gorge of the Hiwassee River). Apparently no fault like the Miller Cove fault separates this syncline from a belt about equally wide of older clastic rocks immediately to the southeast, which forms an outer foothills belt to the Unaka Range. These rocks appear to belong to the northern foothills sheet of the Great Smoky Mountain area, although the connection is probably broken at the Tellico Plains reentrant; at least the characteristic rocks of that sheet (Walden Creek group) are known at several localities, notably along the Hiwassee and Ocoee Rivers near the southern border of Tennessee and just across the border in Georgia (Salisbury, 1961). On the other hand, the characteristic rocks of the southern foothills sheet (Snowbird group) are not known southwest of the Great Smoky Mountains. Their place in the inner foothills appears to be taken by relatively fine-grained rocks that fall within the range of variation known in the northern foothills sheet but that are nevertheless distinctly different from those of the outer foothills belt (Hurst and Schlee, 1962; Salisbury, 1961), from which they are separated by the Sylco Creek or Alaculsy Valley fault. This fault intersects the Great Smoky fault at the front of the mountains only 5 kilometers (3 miles) south of the Tennessee-Georgia state line, cutting off the outer foothills belt.

Southeastward, the rocks of the inner foothills are succeeded by coarse graded sandstone and conglomerate, forming the crest of the Unaka Range along the Tennessee-North Carolina border and evidently continuous with the rocks above the Greenbrier fault in the main range of the Great Smoky Mountains (Great Smoky group). Here, however, no fault separates mountains and inner foothills rocks, which appear to be in stratigraphic sequence; most observers (e.g., Salisbury, 1961, p. 40–41) have placed the mountain rocks above, but Hurst and Schlee (1962) have shown that on the Ocoee River the foothills rocks lie above, presumably being equivalent to the slaty rocks at the top of the sequence above the Greenbrier fault in the Smokies. In any case, all these rocks appear to belong to the Greenbrier thrust sheet. Inner foothills and mountains continue southwest into Georgia until they too are cut off by the north south trending Great Smoky fault; thus the Unaka Mountains end abruptly at Cohutta Mountain, about 25 kilometers (16 miles) south of the state line.

As in the Great Smoky Mountains, so here metamorphism increases southeastward, biotite appearing near the crest of the Unaka Mountains, and garnet and staurolite farther southeast, as around Ducktown in the southeast corner of Tennessee, where copper and iron sulfides have been mined from lenticular ore bodies in quartzite and mica schist. The isograds, like the structural belts, trend northeast-southwest and appear to abut against the Great Smoky fault in Georgia, which here as in Tennessee is postmetamorphic. The metamorphic rocks underlie a belt 12 to 20 kilometers (8 to 12 miles) wide southeast of the crest of the Unaka Range, continuous with the belt of metamorphic rocks on the south side of the Great Smokies. According to Hurst (1955, p. 71; Hurst and Schlee, 1962, p. 5), they form a major anticlinorium (Ducktown anticlinorium), whose axis crosses the extreme southeast corner of Tennessee and in which, although the rocks are isoclinally folded in places, the stratigraphic succession is fairly straightforward, reaching a thickness of not less than 5 kilometers (3 miles).

Near the center of the south flank of the Great Smoky Mountains, just northwest of the Bryson City gneiss dome, a major syncline or synclinorium (Murphy synclinorium) appears, plunging southwest; because of its trend parallel to the Cataloochee and Ravensford anticlinoria, it probably belongs to the second generation of folds in that area. Southwestward it deepens rapidly, and about 20 kilometers (12 miles) south of the crest of the Smokies, a distinctive sequence of metasedimentary rocks appears in its core, above the thick clastic sequence (Great Smoky group) of the Greenbrier thrust sheet. This new sequence includes dark graphitic slate and fine-grained schist (chloritoid is common in North Carolina, but not in Georgia), quartzite, and marble (Murphy marble) and is over 1 kilometer (about 1 mile) thick (Hurst, 1955). The belt underlain by these rocks, commonly called the Murphy marble belt, can be followed for 120 kilometers (75 miles) through North Carolina into northern Georgia, southeast of the belt of metamorphic rocks mentioned in the last paragraph. In Georgia the strike swings from southwest to south and then outlines a broad S-shaped curve that carries the belt 25 kilometers (15 miles) southeast before it resumes the normal southwest

strike. Here, moreover, it leaves the Blue Ridge province, for the southeast-trending segment of the belt, lying at the southwest foot of Mt. Oglethorpe, forms part of the northwest-southeast line that truncates that province; thus the Blue Ridge proper, the mountain range that forms the southeast margin of the province, ends as abruptly at Mt. Oglethorpe as the Unaka Range ends at Cohutta Mountain, 42 kilometers (26 miles) to the northwest. Southwest of this line, the Piedmont Plateau and not the Blue Ridge forms the southeast border of the Valley and Ridge province, which is marked, approximately along the line of the Great Smoky or Cartersville fault, not by a great mountain front as across Virginia and Tennessee, but by a line of hills, rising a couple of hundred meters (some hundreds of feet) above the Valley.

The structure of the Murphy belt has been variously interpreted as a synclinorium, an anticline, a homocline, and a window, but the first interpretation is now firmly established by the work of Hurst (1955). Where Hurst studied it in northernmost Georgia, the synclinorium is fairly simple, though nearly isoclinal, overturned to the northwest, and cut by discontinuous thrust faults; evidence of a deformation later than the formation of the main fold is mainly cataclasis, minor crumpling, and alteration of minerals. In North Carolina, however (Forrest, 1969), the synclinorium widens and the axial plane itself may be folded —here the total width underlain by the distinctive sequence reaches 22 kilometers (14 miles). The S-shaped curve of the belt in Georgia may also be the result of later folding of the main fold (Fairley, 1965, p. 60–62), but its position nearly in the same east-west line as the extraordinary transverse stretch of the Gadsden fault in the Valley and Ridge province suggests instead the hypothesis that it reflects an older period of mild east-west folding (see Chapter 3, p. 61). A continuous thrust fault (Whitestone fault) has been mapped along the southeast side of the synclinorium in Georgia, but the recent work there suggests that faulting is present only in part of the belt; one might instead interpret the eastern flank of the synclinorium as a structural front. A fault is present in North Carolina, however (Mary King Mountain fault of Forrest, 1969).

The stratigraphic relation of the rocks has been equally debated, but it is now clear that they lie above the coarse clastics of the Great Smoky Mountains (Great Smoky group), whether unconformably or not is uncertain. They have commonly been compared with the Cambrian rocks of the Great Valley, principally because of the presence of nearly pure carbonate rock (partly pure calcite marble, partly dolomitic); nothing forbids this assignment, and relations around Cartersville, some kilometers (miles) to the southwest, though equivocal, tend to support it. If so, these may be the only such Cambrian rocks to occur in the strongly metamorphosed part of the Blue Ridge province (except in the Table Rock sheet in the Grandfather Mountain window). On the other hand, nothing forbids their correlation with the somewhat older rocks of the northern foothills sheet of the Great Smoky Mountains (Walden Creek group, p. 175) or with those in the foothills farther southwest (p. 178–179; Hurst, 1970, p. 388).

Southeast of the Murphy synclinorium, the remainder of the Blue Ridge province in southern North Carolina and northern Georgia consists of high-grade gneiss and schist, cut by pegmatite and granite, especially in North Carolina, and by ultramafic bodies. As noted above (p. 171–172), most workers in North Carolina consider these rocks basement, older than any of the clastic rocks (Ocoee group) to the northwest (but Hadley, 1970, p. 253–254, has recently changed his position on this point), but recent workers in Georgia tend (like the author) to consider most or all of them postbasement (Crickmay, 1952, p. 50; Furcron, 1953, p. 33; Hurst, 1970, p. 388–389); Furcron in particular considers that they form a broad synclinorium under the Blue Ridge proper. (Furcron and Teague, 1945, p. 31–34 and Pl. 3, postulate that basement reappears from beneath these rocks near Mt. Oglethorpe, but Fairley, 1965, p. 63, denies it.) In northeast Georgia and extending about 1 kilometer (about 1 mile) into the western tip of South Carolina, a domical uplift exposes quartzite (Tallulah Falls quartzite) associated with kyanite schist; gneiss in the core of this dome may be underlying metasediment or possibly an exposure of basement, but it has not yet been possible to relate the rocks in the dome to those elsewhere. The position of this dome just northwest of the Brevard zone (which passes from the Blue Ridge province into the Piedmont as it enters Georgia) invites comparison with the domes (containing Whiteside "granite") in southern North Carolina and with the Grandfather Mountain window. In northern Georgia the southeast front of the Blue Ridge cuts diagonally across the strike, so that the rocks of the southeast part of the province strike out into the Piedmont, where exposures are fewer and poorer and little coherent mapping has been done.

Northwest Margin of Piedmont Province in Georgia and Alabama

Beyond its S-shaped curve at the southwest end of the Blue Ridge province, the Murphy belt continues southwestward and the Great Smoky or Cartersville fault southward until they meet at the pit of the Cartersville recess (Chapter 3, p. 58) about 50 kilometers (35 miles) southwest of Mt. Oglethorpe. The metamorphosed clastic rocks west of the Murphy belt can be followed into the triangle of hills between the S-curve and Cartersville; a small dome (Salem Chuch dome) lies in the east part of the triangle within the lower curve of the S, and to the northwest a syncline separates the dome from the south end of the Ducktown anticlinorium. Feldspathic rocks, called granite or basement gneiss by earlier workers, appear in this dome, but they may be only feldspathic metasediments (Fairley, 1965, p. 64). In the southwest part of the triangle, a larger body of gneiss, mainly augen gneiss, appears in the metasediments, perhaps replacing them (Kesler, 1950, p. 38–45).

Where the rocks of the Murphy belt approach those of the Valley and Ridge province in the Cartersville recess, they have some similarities, especially the carbonate rocks, and are associated with ore deposits of the same sort, namely barite, manganese, and brown iron (all mined from clay residual from the carbonate rocks). Because of these similarities, indeed, Kesler denies the existence of the Cartersville fault (see discussion in Chapter 3, p. 58). In any case, the belt of older clastic rocks (Ocoee group) disappears here, perhaps plunging down between younger rocks on both sides, having been continuous along strike for 300 kilometers (180 miles) from northeast Tennessee. This can hardly be considered the end of the Blue Ridge anticlinorium, however, for the belt in question is simply part of its northwest flank.

Southeast of the triangle, the rocks of the Murphy belt are adjoined by a belt of mica schist, some of it very graphitic, called the Canton or Dahlonega belt. Where, going northward, the Murphy belt enters the southern bend of its S-curve, this other belt continues directly northeastward, at first in the Piedmont southeast of the Blue Ridge front, then in northeastern Georgia climbing diagonally up into the Blue Ridge. Here it lies between the possible synclinorium in the Blue Ridge proper and the dome at Tallulah Falls on the South Carolina border, but apparently it disappears in southernmost North Carolina, fading out in the gneiss of the Blue Ridge province. The structure of this belt is unknown, though a syncline or synclinorium is plausible; on the other hand, intense shearing and retrogressive metamorphism are reported along it, and according to Sever (1964, p. 17) and Hurst (1970, p. 388) it is followed by a major shear zone or zone of faulting, perhaps like the Brevard zone.

Southwest of the Cartersville recess, the Cartersville fault and the southwestward extension of the Canton-Dahlonega belt diverge again; between them, from here to the Coastal Plain in Alabama, lies a belt of low-grade metamorphic rocks, chiefly slate or phyllite and quartzite (Talladega group), rather different from the higher grade schist and gneiss that dominate much of the Piedmont province. This belt, called the Talladega belt for Talladega (County, Creek, and Mountain), Alabama, ranges from 8 to 30 kilometers (5 to 20 miles) wide and fronts the Valley and Ridge province as a continuous line of hills or low mountains; behind Talladega, however, a linear ridge, upheld by a major quartzite unit (Cheaha quartzite), rises amidst the hills to form the highest mountain in Alabama (Cheaha Mountain, the northeast end of Talladega Mountain—accent on the *e* in both names). Lower Devonian fossils have been found at one place near the southwest end of the belt, and Paleozoic fossils have been reported at a couple of other places; these are much the youngest fossils known in the metamorphic rocks of the Appalachians south of New England. Some have considered the fossil-bearing rocks to be exposed only in windows cut into Valley and Ridge rocks through the rocks of the Talladega belt, and Crickmay (1936) equated the Talladega rocks with the older clastic rocks of the Unaka Mountains (now considered a metamorphosed part of the Ocoee group), calling them Precambrian, but the resemblance is not close, and later work has shown that the fossil-bearing beds are an integral part of the sequence in the belt.

Southeast of Talladega and southwestward to the Coastal Plain, the rocks in the belt dip almost homoclinally southeast and south and form a sequence that can be divided into two parts, each perhaps 1 or 2 kilometers (about 1 mile) thick (Prouty, 1923, p. 34–37; Shaw and Rodgers, 1963). The lower part consists mainly of greenish silty shale and shaly sandstone, both phyllitic and both locally limy; the upper part consists of dark to black fissile slate or phyllite with the major quarzite unit (Cheaha or Butting Ram quartzite) in its lower portion. The Devonian fossils occur in chert not far above the quartzite unit; the upper part of the sequence is therefore certainly middle Paleozoic, and no evident unconformity separates it from the lower part. Where the lower part rests on thick Cambrian and Lower Ordovician carbonate rocks (Knox group and older formations), as east of Talladega and Columbiana, the contact has been mapped as a major thrust fault, but an unconformity is equally probable; conglomerate is known at the contact in places, locally containing large cobbles of granite, gneiss, dolostone,

and other rocks. Rodgers and Shaw (1963) have therefore suggested a Middle Ordovician age for this lower part, comparing the rocks with the thick Middle Ordovician clastic sequence on the southeast side of the Valley and Ridge province in East Tennessee (p. 55).

The carbonate rocks beneath the Talladega sequence rest in turn on quartzite and slate (Weisner formation), which clearly represent the basal clastic sequence known from Tennessee to Vermont and which are thrust over the Valley and Ridge province proper on the major Columbiana thrust fault (see Chapter 3, p. 60). Southwestward toward the Coastal Plain, the carbonate rocks (Jumbo dolomite) thin nearly to disappearance (perhaps beneath the unconformity), and the basal clastic sequence thickens enormously. Where, as near Columbiana, the basal clastic sequence is very thick and the carbonate rocks above them thin, the strip they underlie immediately southeast of the Columbiana fault is naturally referred to the Piedmont province and hence to the Talladega belt (thus Butts—1926, p. 49–53; 1940 p. 2–4, 12—included the basal clastic sequence here in the Talladega group). Where, on the other hand, the carbonate rocks are thick and the clastic rocks of ordinary thickness, the strip has been included in the Valley and Ridge province, and the major fault has been sought southeast instead of northwest of it. Actually the Columbiana fault appears to follow the northwest margin of the strip everywhere, thrusting it over rocks as young as Carboniferous (Mississippian), and to trace northeastward into the group of probable thrust sheets along the southeast side of the Valley and Ridge in easternmost Alabama (Chocolocco Mountain and Indian Mountain faults; Chapter 3, p. 58–59). These thrust sheets resemble the thrust sheets at the edge of the Blue Ridge province in southwestern Virginia and northeastern Tennessee, and the Columbiana fault can be compared to the Great Smoky or Cartersville fault (though it is locally quite strongly folded). Thus the Talladega belt as a whole (including the group of thrust sheets on its northwestern margin) may play the same role as the various lower thrust sheets in Tennessee and Virginia described in preceding sections of this chapter, that of the northwest flank of a "Blue Ridge" anticlinorium, but very much younger beds are preserved in it than anywhere to the northeast along strike, suggesting that the anticlinorium, if present, never rose very high.

The sequence in the Talladega belt has been traced northeastward into westernmost Georgia (Charles W. Cressler, personal communication) where both parts are still present, though the upper part is cut off immediately above the quartzite unit. To the northwest, the belt is thrust over rocks as high as Carboniferous (Mississippian) along the Cartersville fault. The relations of these rocks to those around and on the other side of the Cartersville recess are not clear; perhaps the belt here represents the continuation of the Murphy synclinorium, but mostly expressed in strata younger than any preserved northeast of Cartersville.

The southeast contact of the Talladega belt, like the northwest, has generally been considered a major thrust fault; a fairly sharp change in metamorphic character (sericite phyllite to mica schist) supports this view. The fault may indeed be continuous with the fault inferred to follow the Canton-Dahlonega zone farther northeast (or possibly with the Whitestone fault postulated along the east side of the Murphy synclinorium). Through most of its course in Alabama, the contact is followed by a sheetlike, highly chloritized mafic intrusive (Hillabee chlorite schist; Griffin, 1951), thought to have been intruded along the fault during movement. This contact shows a sharp S-curve about on the latitude of similar curves in the Valley and Ridge province to the west (Chapter 3, p. 60, 61), and less pronounced curves affect the rock units within the Talladega belt. Like the S-curve in the Murphy belt (see above, p. 179), these may reflect mild east-west folding older than the main deformation and metamorphism in the belt.

In northeast Georgia, where they leave the Blue Ridge province, the Brevard and Dahlonega zones are about 25 kilometers (15 miles) apart; southwestward they gradually diverge, being 40 kilometers (25 miles) apart at the Alabama line and 55 kilometers (35 miles) near the Coastal Plain. The rocks between are schist and gneiss of various kinds, apparently continuous with those in the southeast part of the Blue Ridge province in North Carolina; if a basement-cored Blue Ridge anticlinorium extends across Georgia, it must be in this interval. The Tallulah Falls dome, with its quartzite and muscovite-kyanite schist, lies athwart the connection, however. Farther southwest in Georgia, belts of mica schist associated with quartzite can be traced for varying distances, outlining synclinal folds (Hurst, 1956; 1970, p. 378−389; Higgins, 1968); migmatitic gneiss is common, and northwest of Atlanta an area of amphibolitic metavolcanics may form an anticlinal core. From westernmost Georgia across Alabama, on the other hand, mainly graphitic mica schist (Ashland and Wedowee schists) dominates the interval, though masses of granitic gneiss, perhaps intrusive, appear here and there.

Graphite has indeed been produced commercially from such schist in Alabama, and small gold mines follow the Dahlonega-Canton belt across both Georgia and Alabama and are scattered southeastward to the Brevard zone in Alabama. The age of these schists (like that of the gneisses farther northeast) is quite uncertain; in their graphitic character they resemble some of the strata in the upper part of the Talladega group next to the northwest (though at a higher grade), implying a Paleozoic, perhaps even middle Paleozoic age; on the other hand, carbonaceous or graphitic schists are known not only in the Dahlonega belt but in the Murphy marble belt, just beneath the possibly Lower Cambrian carbonate rocks, and also in the Brevard zone. In any case, one suspects the rocks become younger to the southwest, reflecting perhaps a gradual southwestward lowering of the whole Blue Ridge belt.

The Brevard Zone and Its Implications

The southeastern border of the Blue Ridge anticlinorium and its extensions from northern North Carolina southwest into Alabama is formed by the Brevard zone, already mentioned several times in the preceding sections. Although this zone lies mainly in the Piedmont province, it seems to be intimately related to the Blue Ridge anticlinorium and is therefore treated here. It has been most thoroughly studied near the Grandfather Mountain window (Reed and Bryant, 1964, and references there given); southeast of the window intense shearing under low-grade metamorphic conditions has produced graphitic blastomylonite and phyllonite in an inner zone about 1 kilometer (generally less than 1 mile) wide, set in the northwest part of a larger zone, perhaps 8 kilometers (5 miles) wide, in which all the rocks show conspicuous polymetamorphism, the result of shearing and recrystallization at low to middle grade (rising southeastward). The zone (and associated foliation) here strikes about N55°E and dips steeply, mainly to the southeast; a prominent lineation lies nearly horizontal or plunges gently northeast. The intense shearing in the inner zone is apparently younger than the shearing that produced blastomylonite and phyllonite in the rocks around and within the Grandfather Mountain window, and the strong southeast-trending transverse lineation that pervades the window rocks swings to south or even southwest as it approaches the Brevard zone.

Through much of its extent, the Brevard zone makes a very prominent topographic lineament; by this and by its characteristic sheared rocks it has been traced for 650 kilometers (400 miles), from near the border between North Carolina and Virginia to the Coastal Plain in Alabama. For the most part it lies on the Piedmont Plateau, but for about 150 kilometers (90 miles) in southwestern North Carolina and northwesternmost South Carolina it lies northwest of the topographic Blue Ridge front. Here its strike averages N40°E; across Georgia it swings gradually back to N50°E, but in Alabama near the Coastal Plain it appears to widen markedly, its two margins diverging at N50°E and N25°E, and at the same time mylonites disappear and augen gneiss fills much of the belt (Bentley and Neathery, 1970; Neathery and Bentley, 1970). These swings in strike reflect in very subdued form the East Tennessee salient, Rome-Cartersville recess, and Alabama "salient" in the Valley and Ridge province; the Brevard zone does not, as sometimes stated, cut indiscriminately across Appalachian structures but is an integral part of them. In North Carolina at least, the trend of the zone is slightly to the right of the trends in the enclosing rocks, so that it very gently bevels them.

The rocks on either side of the zone are dominantly medium-grade metamorphic or plutonic rocks, commonly somewhat different on the two sides, to be sure, so that correlation across the zone is not possible. The rocks in the zone itself, where it has been studied with care, seem of lower grade and generally show evidence of intense shearing and retrogression; they are mainly phyllite or phyllonite, commonly graphitic, associated with sheared graywacke and siltstone, but lenses of mildly metamorphosed dolostone and limestone are known here and there from central North Carolina to central Georgia.

In northwesternmost South Carolina and adjacent North Carolina, the zone may possess a stratigraphy (Hatcher, 1969, 1970 a,b; John L. Livingston, personal communication, 1965). Next to a sharp contact with somewhat sheared mica schist in the Blue Ridge province are the most intensely sheared rocks, notably graphitic phyllite, with lenses of quartzite and of calcareous phyllite or marble. To the southeast are less graphitic phyllite and sheared siltstone and graywacke, and these in turn grade into feldspathic rocks, either sheared feldspathic graywacke or sheared granite. If the graphitic phyllite is the youngest unit (Griffin, 1969b, p. 25), the sequence might originally have been rather like that in the Murphy belt, but according to Hatcher, the graphitic phyllite is the oldest and the sequence forms a synclinorium overturned to the northwest, between the sharp contact with the Blue Ridge rocks (which would be a high-angle thrust) and nappelike bodies of

migmatite in the Inner Piedmont that have apparently overridden the southeast flank of the synclinorium.

Northeast of the Grandfather Mountain window the Brevard zone broadens, swings to a strike of about N70°E, and splits into several strands, which can be traced into northernmost North Carolina; topography suggests that one or more continue to the Virginia line. The Stony Ridge fault discovered by Dunn, Butler, and Centini (1966) may be the southernmost of these strands, or it may be a Triassic fault; the presence along it of silicification rather than mylonitization rather suggests the latter. In the south half of the belt between the strands southeast of Mount Airy, North Carolina, a prominent group of mountains—Pilot Knob, Sauratown Mountain, Hanging Rock Mountain, called collectively the Sauratown Mountains—rises 500 meters (1500 feet) above the general Piedmont surface some 30 kilometers (20 miles) from the Blue Ridge front, exposing quartzite and quartzitic conglomerate, some very massive, unknown in the surrounding Piedmont (Butler and Dunn, 1968). These rocks appear to outline half of an elongate dome (Sauratown Mountains anticlinorium), cut across on the south by the Stony Ridge fault; although folded, they dip generally northward under the schist and gneiss that otherwise fill the 13 kilometers (8 miles) between the strands of the Brevard zone (Espenshade and Rankin, 1970). The rocks and structure here remind one of the Tallulah Falls dome in northeast Georgia, between the Brevard and Dahlonega zones, and in some respects of the Grandfather Mountain window itself; indeed a window has been postulated here more than once (Bryant and Reed, 1961), but clear evidence is still lacking. On the other hand, the quartzite and associated rocks show evidence of recumbent folds older than and folded into the half-dome (Butler and Dunn, 1968, p. 39 and Fig. 9). It is not yet known how much farther east the strands of the Brevard zone can be traced, whether they die out or whether they intersect the nearby Dan River Triassic basin, irregularities in the margins of which may reflect them.

The nature of the Brevard zone has long been in dispute (see summary in Reed, Bryant, and Myers, 1970, p. 262); the principal theories have been that it is a tight downfold of Paleozoic rocks into Precambrian basement, a zone of retrogression along a major through-going thrust fault or root zone, and a major strike-slip or wrench fault. Reed and Bryant (1964) have championed the last theory, on the grounds of the relative straightness of the zone, the intense late shearing, and the consistent, rather abrupt swing of the main transverse lineation in the Grandfather Mountain window area clockwise into the strike of the zone; from the last they deduced dextral movement. Because no rocks can be matched from one side to the other in the part of North Carolina they studied, they inferred a slip of at least 200 kilometers (135 miles). If the fault followed a pre-existing structural feature, however, such as a root zone or zone of *Verschluckung* (Burchfiel and Livingston, 1967), the rocks on opposite sides could not be expected to match; the splitting up and possible dying out of the zone near the North Carolina-Virginia border also argues against such a large strike slip. Furthermore, the stratigraphy mentioned above suggests an original syncline (though not necessarily infolded into basement). The various theories are not entirely incompatible; an original downfold might have developed into a zone of *Verschluckung* that finally became the locus of late wrench movement. Reed, Bryant, and Myers (1970) suggest, on the other hand, that thrusting and formation of a root zone were contemporaneous with (sinistral) wrench movement and that all were caused by the smashing together of large crustal blocks.

As mentioned above (p. 173), the shift of the steep gravity gradient from near the crest of the Blue Ridge in Virginia to near the Brevard zone in the Carolinas may indicate a similar shift of the position of the Blue Ridge structural front, at least as expressed deep in the basement, departing from the present northwest flank of the Blue Ridge anticlinorium exactly where that flank changes (going southwest) from the relatively simple structural front of the Central Appalachian arc to the zone of continuous thrust faults of large throw that characterize it in the Southern Appalachian arc. Thus the Brevard downfold and root zone may represent, like the structural front farther north, the northwestern limit of plasticity in the deep basement but, whereas the Blue Ridge anticlinorium in the Central Appalachians rose like a great welt just inside that limit and is still probably not far from in place, being simply uplifted and overturned upon the adjacent part of the Valley and Ridge province, the whole of the South-

ern Appalachian Blue Ridge, although originally similar, may have been thrust forward from the vicinity of the Brevard zone or farther southeast out over the Valley and Ridge rocks, for distances measured in tens of kilometers (tens of miles)—nearly 50 kilometers (nearly 30 miles) in southwestern Virginia and at the Cartersville recess, about 70 kilometers (45 miles) in northeastern Tennessee and in Alabama, and as much as 120 kilometers (75 miles) at the apex of the East Tennessee salient.

The Blue Ridge deformation is not certainly dated, and in the Southern Appalachians at least may well have taken place in two quite separate episodes, as suggested by King for the Great Smoky Mountain region. Cloos (1964b, p. 831–832) indeed gives reasons for thinking that the earlier of these episodes—in the Ordovician, perhaps Middle Ordovician—produced most or all of the deformation in the central Appalachian Blue Ridge; at this time the shear fold of the Blue Ridge or South Mountain would have been formed and pushed out over the Valley and Ridge province and the two strong perpendicular lineations been impressed on the rocks. The medium-grade metamorphism in the southern Appalachians would beong to this period. The gigantesque slicing and accompanying Goat-Ridge-type folding that produced the great thrust sheets of the southern Appalachians presumably took place in the later episode, during the Alleghany orogeny in the later Carboniferous or Permian or both; at this time or even later the Brevard zone acquired its present structure. The close relation of the lineations in the Grandfather Mountain window area to the thrust faulting there makes one wonder, however, if at least part of the rise of the anticlinorium and of the retrogression of the metamorphic rocks in its core might not also belong to the later episode. In any case, the deformation and mild metamorphism of the Talladega belt must all have been post-Taconic, though the conglomerate at the base of the Talladega group suggests that here also an early phase of the Taconic orogeny was taking place not too far away to the southeast.

CHAPTER 9

The Piedmont Province

Typically, as in the Carolinas, the Piedmont province is simply a broad plateau sloping gently down from the foot of the precipitous east front of the Blue Ridge to the edge of the Coastal Plain, nearly 200 kilometers (over 100 miles) away. Close to the Blue Ridge some fairly large mountain groups rise above the general level, and a few monadnocks are present farther out; moreover, the whole plateau is intricately though not deeply dissected. Along the Coastal Plain border, the plateau surface is intersected at a low angle by the somewhat more steeply sloping Fall Zone surface, which continues underground as the base of the Coastal Plain sediments. Many of the large streams have cut gorges with waterfalls or rapids as they flow over this steeper gradient into the weaker rocks of the Coastal Plain, where they are at grade or drowned, and here, at the head of navigation on the rivers, have grown up the cities of the Fall Line.

Most of the Piedmont province is underlain by metamorphic or plutonic rocks, but basins of Triassic sedimentary rocks are present here and there as far south as the boundary between the Carolinas. The present chapter is concerned only with the older rocks; the Triassic rocks are discussed in Chapter 10 along with those in the Northern Appalachians. The entire Piedmont province is covered with a residual mantle of thoroughly weathered material, called saprolite, very uneven in thickness though generally increasing south-

ward; in many places indeed such material extends well below the level of the streams, as shown in mines and in borings for dam foundations. Exposures of bedrock are correspondingly scarce, becoming scarcer southward and especially southeastward into the lower part of the plateau near the Coastal Plain, although they appear again in the gorges of the Fall Zone. They occur mostly along the streams, except where especially resistant rocks form monadnocks. Where the resistant rock bodies are linear, so are the monadnocks, and linear topography, locally almost with a Valley and Ridge aspect, occurs in several separated parts of the Piedmont, but otherwise the valleys are randomly dendritic and the hills rise to a remarkably even common level so that the higher the viewpoint, the flatter the landscape appears.

The geologic age of almost none of the Piedmont rocks is known for certain—fossils have been found in only a very few places—and even the relative ages are often not at all clear. Radiometric dates are beginning to be common but, as often in complicated metamorphic terrains, they are not always mutually consistent and their evidence is commonly equivocal (see summaries by Hadley, 1964, and by Tilton, Doe, and Hopson, 1970).

The combination of poor exposures, difficult metamorphic geology, and few interested geologists has greatly retarded study of the Piedmont; only in recent years has the region begun to attract the attention it deserves. Much of the greatest effort in the past has been in the northeastern extremity, northeast of the Potomac, but now work is going forward rapidly in many sectors, and one may anticipate a renaissance of Piedmont geology comparable to the one in New England geology that began with the work of Marland P. Billings. For this reason, the attempt to synthesize Piedmont geology in the present chapter is necessarily incomplete; in a decade or two a far richer and probably quite different picture should have emerged.

Piedmont Province in Pennsylvania and Maryland

The largest of the Triassic basins extends from the west bank of the Hudson River opposite New York City to beyond the Potomac River in northern Virginia; in New Jersey and Pennsylvania it cuts diagonally across the older structural trends and thus separates the metamorphic rocks of New England and the Highlands of New Jersey from those in the northeastern extremity of the Piedmont province. The latter appear first near Trenton, New Jersey, 7 kilometers (4 miles) northeast of the Delaware River and not 55 kilometers (35 miles) from the southwest tip of the New England province on Staten Island in New York City; between these two points southeast-dipping Cretaceous strata of the Coastal Plain lap over northwest-dipping Triassic strata, but the metamorphic rocks are only 100 meters or so (a few hundred feet) below the surface. Southwestward the Cretaceous and Triassic outcrop belts diverge rapidly until the belt between is 75 kilometers (40 miles) wide along the Susquehanna River in southeastern Pennsylvania and northeasternmost Maryland; they then converge again until they are only 15 kilometers (10 miles) apart in northern Virginia, some 50 kilometers (30 miles) southwest of Washington, D.C., and about 300 kilometers (180 miles) southwest of Trenton. Thus the metamorphic rocks of Maryland and Pennsylvania form a sort of lenslike appendix, the head of Fisher's wild duck (Fisher and others, eds., 1970, p. 295), nearly cut off from the main body of the Piedmont rocks; the northwest margin of the lens is arcuate and roughly parallels the Central Appalachian salient of the Valley and Ridge province, but the southeast margin, the Coastal Plain border, is more nearly straight. This appendix is much the best known part of the Piedmont, being almost completely covered by geologic maps on the scale of 1/62,500, yet even here many fundamental points in the geology

are unclear and have been the subject of controversies, some of them prolonged and bitter.

Where widest, the lens can be divided into a number of northeast-southwest zones. The zone farthest to the northwest, which may be called the Lititz zone for the town of Lititz 13 kilometers (8 miles) north of Lancaster, Pennsylvania, appears from beneath the Triassic rocks only for about 60 kilometers (38 miles) eastward from the Susquehanna River. Its geology resembles rather closely that in the nearest part of the Great Valley on the other side of the Triassic basin, here only a few kilometers (a few miles) wide; the rocks are Cambro-Ordovician carbonate rocks (Kittatinny group) and Middle Ordovician shale (Martinsburg or Cocalico formation, including some rocks of Taconic aspect), and they are thrown into east-west isoclinal, nearly recumbent folds on all scales, though generally the older rocks appear to the south. One is tempted to assign them to the same recumbent synclinorium as the rocks next north of the Triassic basin (see Chapter 4, p. 69), perhaps to its axial region (those north of the Triassic belong rather to its upper overturned limb). The major normal fault bounding the Triassic basin on the north is, however, downthrown to the south, probably by a large amount (perhaps several kilometers or miles), so that more likely they belong to a higher synclinorium, over rather than under the recumbent anticlinorium that brought forward the Precambrian rocks in the western extension of the New Jersey Highlands. Although deformation is intense, metamorphism is mild; cleavage is common, some pure limestone beds are altered to marble, and clay minerals have begun to recrystallize, especially near the southern margin of the zone. The zone is somewhat broken up by later faults, presumably Triassic.

South of the Lititz zone, older rocks come to the surface in the more or less anticlinorial Honeybrook-Hanover zone. To the east is a large uplift (Honeybrook uplift) of Precambrian basement, 25 by 15 kilometers (15 by 10 miles), overlapped on the northeast by Triassic strata. These basement rocks are not unlike those in the New Jersey Highlands, and the presence of anorthosite and hypersthene granodiorite tends to link them with the Adirondacks and other parts of the Grenville province of the Canadian shield, marginal parts of which were incorporated into the Appalachians in the Green Mountains, Highlands, and Blue Ridge anticlinoria. Unconformably over these rocks comes the basal Cambrian clastic sequence, here about 600 meters (2000 feet) thick; it is unlike the thin basal quartzite in the New Jersey Highlands but resembles the basal clastic sequence in the Blue Ridge of Pennsylvania and Maryland (Chilhowee group), though a little thinner.

Westward the Honeybrook uplift splits into two major anticlines or anticlinoria, the Welsh Mountain and Mine Ridge anticlines, which are overturned in opposite directions away from the intervening complex Lancaster synclinorium; all these folds plunge west-southwestward. The synclinorium is filled with a Cambro-Ordovician carbonate sequence, which also swings around the southwest end of the Mine Ridge uplift and extends east as a narrow belt (Chester Valley) along the south side of the Honeybrook uplift until it disappears just north of Philadelphia. Its lower part also reaches northward across a saddle in the Welsh Mountain anticline into the Lititz zone. This carbonate sequence differs considerably from that in the Lititz zone or the Great Valley; it is considerably thinner, and its upper part, toward the south indeed the whole of it, is much more shaly (Conestoga limestone; in part at least Lower Ordovician but in part probably older). The base of this shaly upper part has generally been considered an unconformity, bevelling down across the more massive lower part to rest in places on the basal Cambrian clastic sequence, but by analogy with northwestern Vermont (Chapter 4, p. 73), it may represent a facies change from platform to basin carbonates (Rodgers, 1968, p. 144–145, Fig. 2; Wise, 1970, esp. Figs. 3 and 7). The shaly limestone does not now extend north of the south flank of the Welsh Mountain anticlinorium, correlative rocks in the Lititz zone being more massive carbonate. On the other hand, the underlying massive carbonate in the Lancaster synclinorium pinches out southward along an east-west line that crosses the southwestern part of the Mine Ridge anticline.

Just east of the Susquehanna, the west-southwest plunge of the Lancaster synclinorium and the Mine Ridge anticline carry these carbonate rocks under the schists of the next zone. To the north close to Lancaster, however, the plunge of the Welsh Mountain anticlinorium reverses, and at the Susquehanna River two faulted anticlines along its trend bring up the basal clastic sequence again. In the northern of these anticlines (Chickies anticline), at two places not far west of the river, the base of that sequence rests not on basement rocks like those in the Honeybrook uplift but on metavolcanic rocks like those in the Blue Ridge to the west (Catoctin group). In the York syncline between the two anticlines, both parts of the carbonate sequence are preserved almost throughout. All these folds or their en echelon continuations, together representing the western con-

tinuation of the Welsh Mountain anticlinorium, disappear under the Triassic west and southwest of Hanover, Pennsylvania, close to the Maryland line and 50 kilometers (30 miles) southwest of the Susquehanna.

The grade of metamorphism rises fairly regularly across this zone, biotite and garnet appearing in the basal clastic sequence on the southwest end of the Mine Ridge anticline, though commonly retrograded to chlorite. Deformation of the Paleozoic rocks is complex and polyphase (Freedman, Wise, and Bentley, 1964; Wise, 1970). The oldest deformation evident in the small-scale structures involves isoclinal recumbent folding like that in the Lititz zone and the nearby Great Valley; possibly more than one generation is involved, for in the southwest part of the Lancaster synclinorium the carbonate sequence and the upper part of the clastic sequence are repeated in a series of up to five imbricate slices, which have themselves been tightly folded in places and are probably premetamorphic. The more nearly upright Mine Ridge, Lancaster, and Welsh Mountain-Chickies folds are later; they deformed the axial planes of the recumbent folds (and also the imbricate slices) and came after the climax of metamorphism.

As noted above, Triassic rocks cover the northern anticlinorium of this zone close to the Pennsylvania-Maryland border, but about 25 kilometers (15 miles) farther southwest, around Frederick, Maryland, they have been eroded again to expose an area 40 kilometers (25 miles) long and up to 9 kilometers (6 miles) wide of fossiliferous Upper Cambrian and Lower Ordovician limestone (Frederick and Grove limestones), bordered on the east by a strip of the basal clastic sequence; the contact may be a fault or simply a west-facing structural front. These rocks would appear to represent the upper shaly part of the carbonate sequence in the York syncline and Lancaster synclinorium, although they include some massive dolomitic limestone, some of it lime-breccia. They cover a wider belt, however, and are less metamorphosed, although tightly folded and cleaved; indeed they show considerably less metamorphism than the rocks in the Blue Ridge anticlinorium just to the west and less body deformation even than comparable limestone units on its west flank, on the east margin of the Valley and Ridge province at least 25 kilometers (15 miles) farther west, presumably because they have been downdropped several kilometers (miles) along the Triassic normal fault that separates them from the Blue Ridge. Southward these rocks disappear at the Potomac River, covered again by the Triassic strata.

The southern boundary of the carbonate rocks in the Lancaster synclinorium and south of the Mine Ridge and Honeybrook uplifts is the Martic line, which has been the center of furious debate. The rocks south of the line are albite-chlorite schist (Wissahickon or Octoraro schist), locally showing retrogression from higher grade; east of the Susquehanna River this schist overlies the shaly upper part of the carbonate sequence, but west of the river it is in contact mainly with the basal clastic sequence in the continuation of the Welsh Mountain anticlinorium. In the classic phase of the controversy, two hypotheses were put forward:

(1) The schist south of the Martic line is Upper Precambrian, younger than the basement exposed on Mine Ridge but older than the overlying "basal" Cambrian clastic sequence. It is part of a great thrust sheet brought forward over the Paleozoic rocks to the north along a major thrust fault, the Martic overthrust, before the metamorphism of the rocks or the formation of the Mine Ridge anticline, which folds the overthrust (Knopf and Jonas, 1929).

(2) The schist south of the Martic line is Ordovician, resting in stratigraphic sequence on the carbonate rocks (with or without unconformity); there is no overthrust (Miller, 1935).

Hoping to settle the controversy, Ernst Cloos remapped the critical area of the Martic Hills, between the Susquehanna River and the southwest end of the Mine Ridge uplift (Cloos and Hietanen, 1941). Cloos, skeptical of the many faults previously mapped in the area, showed no faults whatever on his map and concluded that the Martic overthrust does not exist.* But he both mapped and described (p. 14–16, 34–35) the fivefold imbrication of the clastic and carbonate sequences just north of the Martic line in the southern part of the Lancaster synclinorium; in other words, he proved the presence here of not one but at least four thrust faults, all older than the metamorphism and the more obvious folding. (Only two of these could be shown, considerably generalized, on the tectonic map accompanying this book; for details, see Cloos and Hietanen, 1941, Pl. 10, and Wise, 1970.) Furthermore, he showed that the clastic rocks within the imbricate slices are very similar to the schist south of the line (as had indeed been pointed out by Knopf and Jonas, 1929, p. 50) and that from the highest of the slices they can almost be followed into

that schist. These facts lead to a third hypothesis:

(3) The schist south of the Martic line is a much thickened equivalent of the basal clastic sequence on Mine Ridge. The "line" follows one or another of a series of premetamorphic thrust faults that can be followed through the region from northwest of Philadelphia to the Susquehanna River; west of the river such faults may or may not continue southwestward into Maryland.

Representatives of the two parties to the controversy have adopted this interpretation, at least its stratigraphic part (Cloos and Hietanen, 1941, p. 193; Stose and Stose, 1946, p. 82–83).

The schist south of the Martic line is part of a vast terrain of metasedimentary rocks (Glenarm group), which underlies most of the rest of the Piedmont of Pennsylvania and Maryland. The northwest part of this terrain, which may be called the Westminster zone for Westminster, Maryland, 45 kilometers (25 miles) northwest of Baltimore, is largely monotonous albite-chlorite schist; the zone is 25 to 30 kilometers (15 to 20 miles) wide in Maryland and northeast to the Susquehanna, but much narrower farther northeast, where the Lancaster synclinorium and the Mine Ridge anticline rise up from beneath it, so to speak, and it pinches out entirely northwest of Philadelphia. Southwest of the Susquehanna, a belt 5 to 8 kilometers (3 to 5 miles) wide along its northwest margin contains numerous quartzite beds (Marburg schist, Urbana phyllite, Sugarloaf Mountain quartzite) and resembles more than ever the basal Cambrian clastic sequence, from which it is separated here, if at all, only by minor thrust faults (cf. Scotford, 1951, p. 63) or a structural front. This arrangement is evidently compatible with hypothesis 3 above, less so with either 1 or 2, which were proposed mainly to explain the relations east of the river, where the schist is in contact with the Paleozoic carbonates. In a lenticular belt next to the southeast, up to 15 kilometers (10 miles) wide in northern Maryland (where there is complex folding on steeply plunging axes) but tapering in both directions, metavolcanic rocks (greenstone and metarhyolite) abound, associated with some limestone or marble. Their position next the quartzite-bearing schist suggests a correlation with the volcanic rocks on the Blue Ridge (Catoctin group), beneath the quartzite-bearing clastic sequence there (Chilhowee group). Finally, recent work (Hopson, 1964, p. 72ff.; Fisher, 1970, p. 304) has shown that near the

---

*It is instructive to compare the two detailed geologic maps of the region (Pl. 1 of Knopf and Jonas, 1929; Pl. 10 of Cloos and Hietanen, 1941), made on the same topographic base at the same scale; one can readily infer from the differences how few and how poor the outcrops are. Unfortunately, neither map indicates their location.

Potomac the tops of the beds face generally west across the whole Westminster zone and far to the southeast, nearly to Washington. Accordingly the main body of the schist can be compared to the vast sequence of schist and gneiss (Lynchburg gneiss) that appears beneath the volcanic rocks on the east flank of the Blue Ridge anticlinorium in Virginia. Thus the rocks in the Westminster zone may all belong to an enormously thickened clastic sequence, like that on the east flank of the Blue Ridge but facing in the opposite direction, extending from far below the volcanics up to the Cambrian carbonate rocks in the York syncline and around Frederick.

The rocks of the Westminster zone belong mainly to the greenschist facies and are characterized by albite and chlorite. Along the southeast margin biotite appears and also locally garnet and other higher grade minerals, but they commonly show retrogression. Deformation was polyphase, closely resembling that in the Lancaster synclinorium; the thrusting (if any) along the Martic line appears to predate most of the deformation and the metamorphism, at least east of the Susquehanna. The older isoclinal folds are nearly recumbent and have been arched across a later anticline, the Tucquan anticline, which is in a rough way the southwestern continuation of the Mine Ridge anticline (the distinction is explained by Wise, 1970, p. 323) and can be followed far into Maryland (garnet is common in the rocks along its crest). In most of the zone, the most prominent lineations are the axes of these two sets of folds and lie roughly horizontal or plunge gently southwest (zone of tangential axes of Cloos, 1953), but toward the west and northwest downdip lineations appear, and in some respects the detailed structure there resembles that in the Blue Ridge anticlinorium (p. 166).

The remainder of the Piedmont of Maryland and Pennsylvania is the Baltimore zone (zone of gneiss domes and radial lineation of Cloos, 1953); a width of 35 kilometers (23 miles) is exposed northwest of the Coastal Plain around and northeast of Baltimore. The dominant structural features are two groups of gneiss domes, one in Maryland near Baltimore but extending 30 kilometers (20 miles) to the north and southwest (Broedel, 1937, but note that according to Tilton, Doe, and Hopson, 1970, p. 429–430, the so-called Baltimore belt, including the type locality of the Baltimore gneiss, is *not* one of these domes but a band of metavolcanic rocks in the overlying strata), the other in Pennsylvania best developed in the Doe Run-Avondale area, 50 kilometers (30 miles) west of Philadelphia, and northeastward. The stratigraphic sequence is the same in both; the cores of the domes are gneiss (Baltimore gneiss, but excluding the type locality), the mantle mainly schist but including a quartzite-bearing unit at the base (Setters formation) and a marble unit next above (Cockeysville marble). Presumed intrusive rocks abound; some granitic rocks appear to be remobilized from the gneiss in the domes, but others seem to have no connection with the domes. Large bodies of gabbro and related rocks are present almost throughout the zone; around Baltimore such a body forms a huge sheet, with masses of ultramafic rocks along its lower contact and also as separate bodies in the rocks to the northwest and southwest (Cohen, 1937; Hopson, 1964, p. 132–135). The sheet is folded over the domes and pinched into the synclines between.

In the schist not far above this sheet, on the west flank of the southwesternmost dome (and also on its southeast flank, half-hidden under the Coastal Plain) is intercalated a remarkable body of "boulder" gneiss (Sykesville formation; Laurel formation on southeast flank). This gneiss contains inclusions of all sizes up to $4\frac{1}{2}$ meters (15 feet), made of quartz (generally well rounded), mica schist, micaceous quartzite, and other metamorphic rocks. Their resemblance to xenoliths in a magmatic rock made most observers class the gneiss as intrusive granite (Sykesville "granite"), but it contains 30 to 65 percent quartz and no potassium feldspar and has a relict clastic texture and completely gradational contacts with the surrounding, obviously metasedimentary schist. Cloos and Hopson (Hopson, 1964, p. 101–112) have shown that instead it is a poorly sorted or unsorted clastic sedimentary breccia, probably produced by one or several great submarine landslides, intercalated into the stratigraphic sequence between the schist around the domes and the schist in the Westminster zone and now metamorphosed to a gneiss. Northward roughly along strike its place is taken by a unit of quartzose schist (Peters Creek quartzite; type in Pennsylvania east of the Susquehanna), displaying graded bedding and locally chaotic zones and other evidence of submarine slumping. Farther east, near the mouth of the Susquehanna, other bodies of concordant quartz-rich inclusion-filled "granodiorite" gneiss represent similar slide masses intercalated in the schist.

Roughly in the middle of the depression between the two groups of domes, the especially deep Peach Bottom syncline (Agron, 1950) preserves a few hundreds of meters (perhaps 1000 feet) of dark slate (Peach Bottom slate) underlain by a few tens of meters (less than 100 feet) of conglomeratic quartz schist and quartzite (Cardiff conglomerate); these rocks are present for about

13 kilometers (8 miles) on either side of the Susquehanna, the southwest end of the belt reaching into Maryland. The basal conglomeratic unit rests on the quartzose schist unit (Peters Creek quartzite) mentioned in the last paragraph; detailed descriptions (Knopf and Jonas, 1929, p. 39; Agron, 1950, p. 1268) speak of the contact as conformable, but several writers have postulated an unconformity to explain regional relations. Freedman, Wise, and Bentley (1964, p. 628) consider that this syncline belongs to the period of the isoclinal recumbent folds farther north but that here the isoclinal folds are nearly vertical, perhaps tilted and accentuated by later folding. On the other hand, if the postulated unconformity exists, the syncline should logically belong to a later period of folding (perhaps the one that produced the domes around Baltimore). The syncline can be followed northeastward into the area north of the Doe Run-Avondale domes. Southwestward it has been mapped as following a continuous outcrop belt of the quartzose schist unit (Peters Creek quartzite) mentioned above, which swings around the northwest side of the Baltimore gneiss domes, but Fisher and Hopson have shown that that belt is not synclinal; perhaps instead the syncline traces between the northeastern domes of the Baltimore group.

The rocks of the Baltimore zone are variably metamorphosed. Biotite and garnet are generally present, and staurolite and kyanite (more rarely andalusite and sillimanite) occur along the Potomac, immediately around the Baltimore gneiss domes, and near Philadelphia, although in places they are retrograded. Near the Susquehanna River, however, in the depression between the groups of domes, chlorite is abundant, and in places even biotite is scarce and retrograded. Here, close to the Coastal Plain, a belt of intermediate volcanic rocks at least 40 kilometers (25 miles) long and a few wide is now mostly greenstone and actinolite schist (Marshall, 1937; James Run gneiss of Southwick and Fisher, 1967, p. 4–5). Traced northeastward into northern Delaware, what may be the same rocks become amphibolite and then banded pyroxene-bearing gneiss (Ward, 1959), one of the few areas of granulite-facies rocks in the whole Appalachian chain; traced southwestward toward Baltimore, they may become the gabbro sheet and associated felsic gneisses there, always regarded as intrusive until the work of Crowley (1969, and ms.).

The gneiss domes around Baltimore were recognized by Eskola (1949, p. 470) as classic examples of the type. On the other hand, Bailey and Mackin (1937) showed that the gneiss in the Doe Run-Avondale area forms the cores of nappe-like recumbent folds that have in turn been folded into domes (see also later discussions by Mackin, 1950, p. 69–71; McKinstry, 1961; Mackin, 1962), and the map pattern and associated lineation pattern in the northernmost and westernmost of the domes around Baltimore almost demand a similar interpretation. Presumably the recumbent folding corresponds to the isoclinal folding in the zones farther north, the doming to the later, more upright folds there or to a still later folding that appears only in this zone (F35 of Freedman, Wise, and Bentley, 1964, p. 631). The dominant lineation around the Baltimore domes is generally radial to them and probably belongs to the later period of deformation.

The gneiss cores of the domes have been regarded as Precambrian basement by all observers, and the Precambrian age of their original metamorphism, roughly coeval with that of the basement in the Blue Ridge, Highlands, and Green Mountains anticlinoria, has been proved by radiometric dates (Hopson, 1964, p. 193–207, and references there cited). The metasedimentary mantle (Glenarm group), on the other hand, was metamorphosed in Paleozoic, probably Cambrian or Ordovician time (Wetherill and others, 1966), and as its upper part is continuous with the schist next south of the Martic line, its age has been a part of the controversy that raged over the line. Thus the resemblance of the stratigraphic sequence next above the gneiss cores to the Paleozoic sequence over the basement in the Mine Ridge anticline north of the line has frequently been cited as evidence for hypothesis 2 above. Adherents of hypothesis 1, however, have either denied the implied correlation or suggested that the Martic overthrust reappears around the domes, separating the main body of schist from the quartzitic and carbonate units next to the gneiss, which would thus appear in windows up to 50 kilometers (30 miles) southeast of the Martic line. According to the work of Cloos, Fisher, and Hopson (Hopson, 1964, p. 72ff.), graded bedding shows that in Maryland at least the schist forms a continuous stratigraphic sequence, tops to the west or northwest, from the Martic line on the northwest side of the Westminster zone to the vicinity of the domes; Hopson therefore supports hypothesis 3 and considers that the carbonate and quartzitic units lie at the base of this (basal Paleozoic and uppermost Precambrian) sequence and have no equivalents north of the Martic line. Radiometry has also been used to support a latest Precambrian age for the sequence, on the grounds that felsic intrusive rocks cutting its upper part are themselves dated as Early Cambrian, but the exact correspondence of the numbers from those rocks with numbers from the definitely meta-volcanic rocks nearby (James Run gneiss; Tilton, Doe, and Hopson, 1970, p. 431–432), which lie along strike from some of the supposed intrusives, suggests that the latter may be simply more highly metamorphosed volcanic rocks and thus that the upper part of the sequence around Baltimore includes strata as young as Early Cambrian.

Northeast along the strike, the Baltimore zone disappears where the Coastal Plain sediments lap over the Triassic rocks in New Jersey, but, as noted at the beginning of this section, only 55 kilometers (35 miles) farther northeast is the southwest tip of the New England province. The geology in this corner of the New England province, in New York City and Westchester County, New York (Chapter 5, p. 94), is remarkably like that in the Baltimore zone; the stratigraphy is grossly similar (although the quartzitic unit is thinner in New York), and the structure consists of large isoclinal folds that have been refolded, partly into domical structures. The carbonate unit around New York City can now be correlated with assurance with the (autochthonous) Cambro-Ordovician carbonate sequence of the Taconic region (Chapter 5, p. 94), and one must therefore consider the possibility that the carbonate rocks in the Baltimore zone are also Cambro-Ordovician, whatever the age of the overlying schist. Around Baltimore, the carbonate unit exhibits two facies (Choquette, 1960, p. 1031), a northern facies of do-lostone and limestone and a southern facies of calcareous shale and shaly limestone. One might compare these two facies with the two Cambro-Ordovician carbonate facies on either side of the Welsh Mountain-Chickies anticline, the northern with the normal carbonate sequence in the Lititz zone and the Great Valley (or in New York City), the southern with the shaly limestone in the Lancaster synclinorium (Conestoga limestone), speculating that that anticline was displaced northward 40 to 50 kilometers (25 to 30 miles) from the vicinity of Baltimore, before any of the metamorphism. The rear margin of such a displaced mass might be at the top of the carbonate unit in the domes or, more likely, just above the zone of submarine slide breccias and chaotic structure west and northwest of the domes which, if the underlying rocks around the domes are indeed Cambro-Ordovician, might record the regional emplacement of the displaced mass. A formal analogy between this rather far-fetched speculation and the gravity-slide hypothesis for the Taconic slate mass is evident; indeed a relation between the Martic and Taconic problems was first suggested by Kay (1941), although he did not involve the Baltimore gneiss domes. The distance from the

Taconic-type clastic rocks in the Great Valley near Harrisburg to the southernmost carbonate rocks north of the Martic line (in Chester Valley) is about 70 kilometers (45 miles), to the south-easternmost carbonate rocks around Baltimore over 100 (over 60); if one assumes that the various facies of the Cambro-Ordovician—platform carbonates (Kittatinny group), basin carbonates (Conestoga limestone), basin clastics of Taconic type—originally succeeded each other oceanward in simple parallel belts, then these distances would be minimum measures of the total displacement of Taconic-type rocks in this region (minimum because of the later shortening in the region recorded by the ubiquitous isoclinal recumbent folds).

To return from this speculative flight, this part of the Piedmont displays two lines of basement highs, one in the Baltimore zone and one in the Honeybrook-Hanover zone, in addition to the line marked out by the Highlands and South Mountain-Blue Ridge anticlinoria. All three lines show a depression centered at or just east of the Susquehanna River and culminations on either side. To judge by the geology of southwestern New England and adjacent New York, these lines must converge northeastward, squeezing out any synclinoria between them, but the critical area is hidden under Triassic strata. Strikes in this part of the Piedmont outline the Central Appalachian salient, swinging from N75°E in eastern Pennsylvania (even east-west in the Lititz zone) to N20°E in southern Maryland, but the curvature is less pronounced in the Baltimore zone.

An additional complication is the slate (with its basal conglomeratic unit) in the Peach Bottom syncline. Its age is unknown, but similar slate is known in similar synclines to the southwest almost on strike, notably the Quantico syncline at the Coastal Plain border 30 to 70 kilometers (18 to 42 miles) southwest of Washington and the Arvonia syncline (or synclinorium) on the James River, some 120 kilometers (75 miles) farther on; in the slate in both those synclines, Upper Ordovician fossils have been found. (The strike line of the Quantico syncline would project southeast of the westernmost of the Baltimore domes, just as that of the Peach Bottom syncline could be interpreted as passing southeast of the northernmost.) As noted above detailed descriptions speak of conformity at the base of the slate in the Peach Bottom syncline, but Stose and Jonas (1939, p. 106), Hopson (1964, Fig. 19), and Southwick and Fisher (1967, p. 6–8) all conclude that an unconformity is required; the relations at the base of the slate in the other synclines are also disputed, but I believe that an unconformity can be demonstrated in the Arvonia syncline. If the unconformities are real, and if the correlation of the slate in the three synclines is warranted, then the first major deformation (recumbent folding) and the main progressive metamorphism (also the displacement of the carbonate facies boundary, if it is real) probably occurred before the Late Ordovician, whereas the later periods of deformation and the associated retrogressive metamorphism (also the metamorphism of the slate in the synclines) would be later, perhaps late Paleozoic.

Main Body of the Piedmont Province, Virginia to Alabama

The southern end of the largest Triassic basin follows the east flank of the Blue Ridge anticlinorium for some 125 kilometers (80 miles) into northern Virginia; indeed its western border fault encroaches southwestward onto that flank and its south tip lies within the volcanic rocks (Catoctin group). On the southeast side of this tip and on to the southwest, the volcanic rocks are succeeded southeastward by quartz-bearing phyllite (Candler phyllite; see above, p. 166–167), which probably represents the postvolcanic clastic sequence (Chilhowee group). Southeast of the phyllite is a narrow band of limestone (Everona limestone; Mack, 1965, but Mack includes in his discussion a belt of mainly dolomitic marble at or near the base of the Catoctin group on the east flank of the Blue Ridge *west* of the main Triassic basin, which has nothing to do with the Everona limestone), more metamorphosed than the limestone around Frederick, Maryland, but probably correlative, to judge by a poor fossil or two that have been found in it. Not quite 40 kilometers (25 miles) south-southwest of the tip of the main basin and placed slightly en echelon is a small Triassic basin, 25 kilometers (15 miles) long, which covers the outcrop belt of the limestone again.

Beyond the small Triassic basin, limestone, or rather marble of more than one kind, reappears as part of a group of rocks (Evington group) also including quartzite, greenstone, and several varieties of phyllite or schist; these rocks can be followed along strike for at least 80 kilometers (50 miles), always just southeast of the main belt of quartz-bearing phyllite (Candler phyllite) on the southeast flank of the Blue Ridge anticlinorium. A stratigraphic sequence has been worked out here, but no fossils are known and opinions are divided on which end of the sequence is up (cf. Furcron, 1935, and Redden, 1963, with Brown, 1953, p. 91–94; 1958; 1970, Table 1 and p. 345; and

Espenshade, 1954, p. 22–23) and hence on whether it outlines a synclinorium or not. If it does (as I tend to believe), the rocks are probably Lower Paleozoic, beginning with the Lower Cambrian clastics (like the sequence in the Murphy synclinorium, which it somewhat resembles; Chapter 8, p. 179), although the sequence is not particularly similar to that on the northwest flank of the Blue Ridge anticlinorium in the Valley and Ridge province; if it does not, their relation to the rocks in the Blue Ridge anticlinorium is not clear. Redden's map suggests the possibility that recumbent folds have been folded and domed, scrambling the sequence. As the James River is deflected northeastward along the northeast half of the outcrop belt of these rocks, the belt is called the James River marble belt or the James River synclinorium; it is nowhere more than 8 kilometers (5 miles) wide. If it is a synclinorium, it can be regarded as the continuation of the Frederick limestone area, itself a continuation of the York syncline in the Honeybrook-Hanover belt of Pennsylvania.

The rocks of the James River belt show relatively low-grade metamorphism—at most chloritoid and biotite in the phyllite or schist and albite and actinolite in the volcanics—except in the southern part of the belt, where garnet and staurolite and even sillimanite appear, mainly on the southeast side; even here, however, the belt, or its central part, appears to be lower in grade than the rocks on either side. Here also several domes of mica gneiss appear to have risen through the other rocks, bringing up the older part of the clastic sequence (but probably not basement).

On the southeast side, the James River belt is bordered by wide areas of mica schist with bands of hornblende schist and bands or domes of mica gneiss. These rocks are not unlike the postbasement rocks on the east flank of the Blue Ridge anticlinorium at this latitude (Lynchburg gneiss and Candler phyllite, perhaps with a thinned representative of the Catoctin group), and if the James River belt is a synclinorium, they are probably correlative and anticlinorial (Brown, 1958, p. 53; 1969, p. 38–39; 1970, p. 345). Farther northeast, however, north of the James River and east and southeast of the small Triassic basin, the same rocks have been interpreted (Smith, Milici, and Greenberg, 1964) as a mixed clastic and volcanic sequence becoming generally younger southeastward from the narrow band of probably Paleozoic limestone (Everona limestone) exposed between the Triassic basins to the certainly Upper Ordovician slate in the Arvonia syncline (mentioned above, p. 191). The rocks here are mostly low-grade, biotite appearing only well east of the limestone band and garnet only on the east side of the Arvonia syncline. This interpretation seems questionable as it does not jibe with the interpretation of the James River belt as a synclinorium nor for that matter with Hopson's evidence that the schist along the Potomac (West minster zone of Maryland) becomes generally younger northwestward, but large unmapped areas remain between the areas that have been studied in detail, and they may contain unforeseen complications.

The Arvonia syncline is the southwesternmost of several en echelon synclines of dark, locally graphitic slate, the northernmost of which is the Quantico syncline, not far southwest of Washington, D. C., which, as mentioned above, has also yielded Upper Ordovician fossils. In the Arvonia syncline, the fossiliferous slate occurs in the lower part of a sequence (Arvonia formation) about 1000 meters (about 3500 feet) thick, the upper part of which includes quartzite and conglomerate, although minor volcanic rocks are also present. Quartzite and conglomerate also occur locally at the base and lie unconformably on granodioritic rock, which may be intrusive into the surrounding rocks or may only be metavolcanic material within them. To be sure, some recent workers (Brown and Sunderman, 1954; Smith, Milici, and Greenberg, 1964 p. 14, but see Fig. 3) have denied the unconformity on the grounds that tourmaline and andalusite in the overlying slate were produced by contact metamorphism around the intrusive, but they agree that the intrusion would have been earlier than the regional metamorphism, which could have produced the minerals observed. Field observation convinces me that the unconformity is real, and Brown (1969, p. 31–32; 1970, p. 345) now agrees. Gold has been mined in many places along the synclinal belt, both above and below the presumed unconformity, and there are some base metal deposits; moreover, Ordovician slate has been quarried commercially in the Arvonia syncline, and indeed the fossils were discovered during the quarrying.

How far southwest the James River belt extends is not certain; its characteristic rocks are still present at the Roanoke River where available detailed maps end (Redden, 1963). As mentioned in Chapter 8 (p. 167), the quartz-bearing phyllite on the northwest side of the belt can be followed topographically for some 100 kilometers (60 miles) southwest of the James, and it may then double back, as though around a syncline or synclinorium. Espenshade reports (Reed, Bryant, and Myers, 1970, p. 263) tracing some of the James River rocks even farther to the west-southwest, into a belt of similar rocks at the southeast foot of the Blue Ridge that crosses the North Carolina line northeast of Mount Airy, North Carolina. We have, however, no detailed maps of these areas.

The James River belt and the limestone band (Everona limestone) that points from it toward the Paleozoic limestone around Frederick strike regularly N40°–45°E, roughly parallel to the trends in the Valley and Ridge province on the other side of the Blue Ridge anticlinorium, on the straight southwestern wing of the Central Appalachian arc. The synclinal belts to the east are more irregular, however, and their trend is more nearly N30°E. The known south end of the James River belt is about opposite the angular recess in the Valley and Ridge province at Roanoke, at the junction of the Central and Southern Appalachian arcs, and the topographic trend of the quartz-bearing phyllite appears to show an angle here, bending around to about N60°E. Along this trend, the James River belt would project southwestward just northwest of the main strand of the Brevard zone, intersecting it at a low angle in northernmost North Carolina, near Mount Airy, but many tens of kilometers (tens of miles) of unmapped country still intervene. One might nevertheless suggest a relationship between the James River synclinorium (if it is a synclinorium) and the original downfold (if any) along the Brevard zone; thus the Brevard zone, southwest of the point where its strands coalesce in northern North Carolina, could well include a continuation of the James River synclinorium as well as being the root zone of the entire Blue Ridge anticlinorium, or the zone of *Verschluckung* where the roots have disappeared (Burchfiel and Livingston, 1967).

From North Carolina to the Coastal Plain the Brevard zone is bounded on the southeast by a broad belt of monotonous-appearing gneiss and schist, interspersed with large masses of granitoid rock and containing a few scattered bodies of mafic and ultramafic rock, including serpentine. The metamorphic grade here is persistently high, sillimanite being present over a larger area probably than in any other part of the Piedmont. Van Hise in 1896, seeing these rocks in Alabama, pronounced them "the original Jacob," the true Archean (Adams, 1926, p. 29); actually of course virtually nothing is known of their age. This belt, called the Dadeville belt in Alabama and Georgia and the Inner Piedmont in the Carolinas, is 80 to 90 kilometers (50 to 60 miles) wide from southern North Carolina to western Georgia but tapers at both ends. To the southwest it is only about 40 kilometers (25 miles) wide where it passes beneath the Coastal Plain; to the northeast it may end where the southern strand of the Brevard zone (Stony Ridge fault) bevels across its N50°E trend or, if it does continue across, it would trace into the southeast side of the James River belt. Its southeastern margin is well marked only in certain areas, notably in western Georgia and easternmost Alabama where the northwest-dipping Towaliga fault separates it from the Pine Mountain belt, and athwart the boundary between the Carolinas where it adjoins less dramatically the Kings Mountain belt—the boundary there, though perhaps locally faulted, is principally a drop in metamorphic grade (Overstreet and Bell, 1965, p. 54) but might nevertheless be interpreted as a southeast-facing structural front. The Pine Mountain and Kings Mountain belts are distinguished from the Dadeville or Inner Piedmont belt by the presence of well differentiated metasediments—especially quartzite and marble—and in general by lower metamorphism. Elsewhere the southeastern boundary is much vaguer; to the northeast and especially to the southwest along the strike of the Kings Mountain belt there are isolated strips or patches of lower grade metasedimentary rocks, but otherwise the Dadeville or Inner Piedmont belt simply merges southeastward into a similar or even more plutonic zone.

Remarkably little is known of this belt. In North Carolina, Griffitts and Overstreet (1952; Overstreet and Griffitts, 1955; Overstreet, Yates, and Griffitts, 1963) have painstakingly outlined the distribution of metamorphic minerals and worked out a sequence of intrusions. In Georgia, a few intrusive bodies have been studied with care and a few isolated areas have been mapped. Seams of schist (locally with marble) like that along the Brevard zone are reported a few kilometers (miles) in from the northwestern margin in Georgia and South Carolina, with trends slightly oblique to that zone. One characteristic of the belt as a whole seems to be a generally low and irregular dip of foliation, which in several places outlines fairly broad folds more or less transverse to the trend; such structure is quite unexpected in what appears to be, at least from central North Carolina south, the central, highest-grade core of the whole chain. Dips are steeper near the margins where they are mostly inward; in places indeed the belt has the appearance of a broad and rather simple foliation syncline, but this apparent simplicity almost certainly masks unknown complexities. Thus Griffin (1967, 1969a) has shown that in northwestern South Carolina earlier recumbent folds have later been refolded or even torn apart, and he has mapped two large northwest-facing recumbent nappes underlain by sole faults (Walhalla and Six Mile nappes). The age of the rocks is uncertain; from scattered radiometric ages, Overstreet and Bell (1965, p. 114) assign the major metamorphism and some of the granitic intrusions in the belt to the

Ordovician, but admit the possibility of older metasedimentary and metavolcanic rocks—back to the late Precambrian—and of younger intrusions—up to the Carboniferous.

Concerning the Pine Mountain and Kings Mountain belts we know a little more; they are roughly on strike with each other but nearly 300 kilometers (200 miles) apart, although patches of rock somewhat like those in the Kings Mountain belt can be followed across South Carolina. Furthermore, although they share some rock types, the apparent stratigraphic sequences in the belts show no obvious similarities.

The Pine Mountain belt is perhaps the better known, thanks to two quadrangle reports in Georgia (Hewett and Crickmay, 1937, and Clarke, 1952; the rocks in the Alabama portion are described by Adams, 1930, p. 273–275, and the associated faults by Bentley, 1969). Gneiss, exposed in an elongate anticlinorium and a dome or two, is overlain, possibly unconformably, by quartzite and muscovite schist containing kyanite (also lenses of dolomite marble in Alabama), thrown into moderately open folds, remarkably simple for rocks in the kyanite grade. The quartzite upholds ridgelike mountains such as Pine Mountain in Georgia (not to be confused with Pine Mountain on the Appalachian Plateau in Kentucky and adjacent Tennessee and Virginia at the northwest margin of the Pine Mountain thrust sheet); these mountains resemble the mountains in the Valley and Ridge province more than any in the intervening Piedmont (except Talladega Mountain in Alabama; Chapter 8, p. 181). The two margins of the belt, which is 15 to 25 kilometers (10 to 15 miles) wide, are thrust faults marked by intensely mylonitized zones up to several hundreds of meters (thousands of feet) thick. The Towaliga fault on the north dips moderately steeply to the north-northwest and the Goat Rock fault on the south somewhat less steeply to the south-southeast; thus the belt is downthrown relative to the belts on either side (unless, as Clarke, 1952, p. 78–80, suggests, the bounding faults are the same, anticlinally folded, and the belt between is an enormous window—the Dadeville belt to the north being the complementary syncline). The characteristic rocks of the belt lie mainly along the north side of the belt; southward and eastward toward the Goat Rock fault the schists at the top of the sequence fade into a terrain of granitic gneiss and charnockitic rocks. East-northeastward, the characteristic schist and quartzite disappear about 100 kilometers (60 miles) from the Georgia-Alabama line or 140 kilometers (90 miles) from the Coastal Plain. The Towaliga fault can be followed some kilometers (miles) farther east, but beyond that no continuation of the belt is known.

The Kings Mountain belt has been studied because deposits of kyanite, barite, beryl, spodumene, tin, manganese, and gold are associated with it (Keith and Sterrett, 1931; Kesler, 1955; Espenshade and Potter, 1960, p. 64—94; Overstreet and Bell, 1965, p. 43—54). Minor but conspicuous beds of quartzite (including kyanite quartzite), conglomerate, and marble (chiefly dolomitic) are interbedded in the upper part of a considerable thickness of phyllite and schist, mostly but not entirely of low grade. Especially prevalent are sericite or muscovite schist, some of it strongly manganiferous, and actinolite or hornblende schist, parts of each being clearly metavolcanic. Such rocks can be followed readily for some 60 kilometers (nearly 40 miles) along strike in the two Carolinas; they are intruded by at least two generations of granitic rocks (perhaps Ordovician and Carboniferous), and ultramafic bodies are more common here than in the belts on either side. The margins of the belt are mainly gradational, being determined rather by grade of metamorphism than by structural features, although faulting has been reported along the northwest side (such faulting could be Triassic, a southwestward continuation of the border fault of the Dan River basin). The ends are even less precise. Northeastward, the typical rocks of the belt occur discontinuously for 25 kilometers (15 miles) farther along strike, disappearing amid masses of mica and hornblende gneiss. Southwestward, marble can be found here and there two-thirds of the way across South Carolina, associated with higher grade but still partly metavolcanic schists; the latter, once again at low grade and including the typical manganiferous schist, continue thence to the Georgia line and 60 kilometers (40 miles) beyond, finally disappearing amid plutonic rocks, still more than 100 kilometers (65 miles) from the northeasternmost schist of the Pine Mountain belt, which in any case they do not greatly resemble.

The stratigraphy of these rocks is not clearly established; for example, whether the quartzite occurs as one, three, or many layers or sets of lenses, and whether the hornblende schist occurs mainly low in the sequence or is in good part the higher grade metamorphic equivalent of the calcareous upper part. A significant unconformity has been postulated in the lower part of the sequence between two units of mica schist (roughly between the Bessemer and Battleground schists), but the similarity of these schists is admitted by all the later workers; the unconformity seems dubious to me. Ideas on the overall structure

have also been varied. Keith and Sterrett (1931) mapped two synclinoria in the belt at the state line, whereas Kesler (1955, p. 381—382) recognized only an anticlinorium in the eastern part of the belt. Espenshade and Potter (1960, p. 82) cite evidence of compound deformation, and their map pattern (cf. their Pl. 7 and Fig. 42) almost demonstrates the refolding of recumbent folds into a synclinorium in the eastern part of the main Kings Mountain belt and an anticline just to the east. Thus the structure is probably far from simple.

The north half of the main Kings Mountain belt (in North Carolina) trends N25°E, the south half (mainly in South Carolina) N60°E, the bend taking place within a few kilometers (miles) close to Kings Mountain, North Carolina, just north of the state line. Across the rest of South Carolina and in Georgia the trend, though irregular and somewhat imprecise, averages about N45°E. The trend of the Pine Mountain belt lies within 5 degrees of N65°E throughout.

The age and significance of these isolated belts ("dejective zones"; see King, 1955, p. 350—351) of lower grade metasedimentary rocks is not clear. Age guesses have ranged from Precambrian (Hewett and Crickmay, 1937, p. 26, for the sediments of the Pine Mountain belt) to Mississippian (Overstreet and Bell, 1965, p. 108—109, for the marble near the top of the sequence in the Kings Mountain belt). A possible correlation with the Carolina slate belt is discussed below; it suggests a lower Paleozoic age for the Kings Mountain belt. Projected northeastward along strike, the Kings Mountain belt seems to point toward the Sauratown Mountains area of quartzite (Chapter 8, p. 183), but that area lies north of the southern strand of the Brevard zone, the Stony Ridge fault. One might better project the trend more easterly, avoiding the Stony Ridge fault and following a line of marble occurrences not far southeast of it; one then comes (on the southeast side of the Dan River Triassic basin) to several small districts in Virginia in which kyanite quartzite reappears (Espenshade and Potter, 1960, p. 34—35), intricately interfolded with schist and gneiss that could be middle-grade equivalents of the muscovite and hornblende schists of the Kings Mountain district. The northern of these districts lies just east of the southern end of the Arvonia syncline and its rocks seem to be considerably higher grade than those of the syncline, hinting once again at an unconformity between; moreover, kyanite is reported locally in subcommercial quantities still farther northeast on the eastern side of the syncline and its en echelon continuations to the point where their trend is overlapped once more by the Coastal Plain, not far southwest of the Potomac River. If (as I believe) the unconformity beneath the rocks in the Arvonia syncline is real, their Upper Ordovician age demands an age no younger than Middle Ordovician for the rocks with kyanite quartzite and hence, if the correlation is correct, for the Kings Mountain rocks. (That unconformity could not be equivalent to the one postulated in the Kings Mountain belt, which would lie below the kyanite quartzite there.) The flimsiness of this chain of inferences is evident, but unfortunately it is typical of Piedmont correlations today.

The rest of the Piedmont in the Carolinas and Georgia (and a very small corner of Alabama) appears to consist of irregular stripes or belts formed either of relatively high-grade rocks dominantly of plutonic aspect or of low-grade rocks in good part volcanic; considerable bodies of metasedimentary rocks are present with both, however, at the appropriate metamorphic grade. The western stripe is dominantly plutonic and is called the Charlotte belt in the Carolinas, the Uchee belt in Georgia and Alabama; it is continuous except in northern South Carolina, where relatively low-grade metavolcanic rocks like those in the Kings Mountain belt can apparently be followed southeastward across it into the main stripe of low-grade rocks, the Carolina slate belt.

The rocks of the Charlotte belt have been most intensively studied near Charlotte in southern North Carolina (Bell and Overstreet, 1959; W. C. Overstreet, personal communication), where a complicated sequence of intrusions appears to be present; similar rock types, probably forming a similar sequence, characterize the belt through South Carolina as well (Overstreet and Bell, 1965, p. 32—43). The "matrix" for the intrusions consists of granodioritic or granitic gneiss, in places containing great swarms of angular to rounded inclusions of other, mainly plutonic, rocks; strong compositional layering is common, however, and streaks of obviously metasedimentary rocks occur locally. This gneiss has generally been considered an intrusive rock; one is reminded, however, of the Sykesville "granite" in Maryland (see above, p. 189), which Cloos and Hopson have shown is a metamorphosed sedimentary breccia, probably a great gravity slide. Other parts of the gneiss may be metavolcanic, perhaps equivalent to some of the volcanic rocks in the Kings Mountain belt to the west and especially in the Carolina slate belt to the east; on the other hand, some true plutonic rocks may be present. Overstreet and Bell indeed attempt to distinguish an older metaplutonic and a younger metavolcanic unit in the Charlotte belt in South Carolina, but they admit the two are

lithologically similar (1965, p. 35).

These "matrix" rocks are cut: first by swarms of mafic dikes, now metamorphosed to amphibolite, second by granite, some gneissic and concordant but much of it forming large elliptical plutons, up to 15 kilometers (10 miles) across, and third by smaller cross-cutting bodies of gabbro, norite, and pyroxenite, with which are associated lesser masses of augite syenite; the most conspicuous mass of syenite forms a ring dike around a gabbro-pyroxenite core in Cabarrus County, North Carolina, about 20 kilometers (15 miles) northeast of Charlotte. The older rocks in the belt are mainly in the lower amphibolite grade but drop off into the greenschist facies locally; sillimanite occurs only near the later plutons.

Similar higher grade rocks (up to the kyanite and staurolite zones) appear again beyond the Carolina slate belt, half hidden under the Coastal Plain sediments in Georgia and South Carolina but forming a fairly distinct belt in North Carolina, which may be called the Raleigh belt (Parker, 1968). This belt includes a large anticlinorium (Wake-Warren anticlinorium), which plunges steeply southward at the south end of the belt; a granite pluton some 80 kilometers (50 miles) long lies in its core east of Raleigh, and other large and small bodies are present as far north as Richmond, Virginia (e.g., the Petersburg granite). Several dunite bodies occur on the west side of the belt north of Raleigh, thoroughly isolated from the principal zones of ultramafic bodies in the southern Appalachians, which are found mainly in the Blue Ridge and in the James River synclinorium and secondarily in and near the Kings Mountain belt (Larrabee, 1966).

The main low-grade dominantly volcanic stripe, the Carolina slate belt, can be followed continuously from about 50 kilometers (35 miles) north of the Virginia-North Carolina border across both Carolinas (except where cut out by a late granitic pluton in South Carolina) and over 100 kilometers (60 miles) into Georgia, a total distance of 600 kilometers (350 miles). Once again the best information comes from North Carolina, where the rocks have been described in reports on copper, copper-gold, and pyrophyllite mining districts (see especially Laney, 1917) and more recently in several areal reports and articles (Conley, 1962a, 1962b; Conley and Bain, 1965; Stromquist and Sundelius, 1969; see summary by Sundelius, 1970). The dominant rock types are volcanic tuff, breccia, and flows, both mafic and felsic, and sedimentary mudstone, argillite, and graywacke, though these too may contain much volcanic material. The rocks are poorly sorted, and their bedding ranges from fine lamination to thick graded beds; slaty cleavage is present in all the fine-grained rocks. Quartzite, some of it kyanitic (metamorphosed chert?), conglomerate, and carbonate rock are very minor constituents. A fairly detailed stratigraphic succession has been deduced from the studies mentioned, dominantly but not exclusively metasedimentary above, metavolcanic below (mainly felsic in southern North Carolina). (Conley, 1962a, p. 14—15, reported a strong angular unconformity beneath an uppermost unit of volcanics, but it has not been confirmed by later work [Stromquist and Sundelius, 1969, p. B20] and seems dubious to me, judging by the pattern on published maps and by some reconnaissance observations.) The succession is not less than 3000 meters (10,000 feet) thick, perhaps much more. The rocks are remarkably little metamorphosed in some parts of the belt; in southern North Carolina the units outline large fairly broad anticlines and synclines up to 20 kilometers (13 miles) apart, plunging southwest. Elsewhere the grade is somewhat higher, and the folds are tighter and less easily deciphered, but the belt appears generally synclinorial. Axial-plane cleavage in these rocks is mainly steep; in general it dips northwest except along the northwest side of the belt in northern North Carolina and adjacent Virginia. In southern North Carolina, along or near the northwest margin of the belt is a steep northwest-dipping fault (Gold Hill fault), probably a thrust fault (Laney, 1910, p. 68—71). Other parallel shear zones are reported in the vicinity, especially to the west in the eastern part of the Charlotte belt, and faulting may also occur at other contacts of the slate belt with higher grade rocks.

Quite recently (St. Jean, 1965), fossils have finally been found in these rocks in southern North Carolina—two headless trilobites, probably Middle Cambrian, on a loose piece of partly volcanic argillite, probably from fairly high in the stratigraphic sequence, though outside the area recently mapped in detail. Thus the main part of the volcanic slate succession is lower Paleozoic (if the lower unit does not extend into the latest Precambrian), as had been many times suggested but never before proved.

The same rocks continue into northern South Carolina where, as noted above, they can apparently be followed northwestward into the Kings Mountain belt, suggesting a similar age for at least the larger part of the schists in that belt. A tentative stratigraphy has been postulated to cover both belts here (Overstreet and Bell, 1965, p. 19, 44, Table 4; see also Secor and Wagener, 1968), but its relation to that in North Carolina is not yet clear. Mafic as well as felsic volcanics are recognized in the lower part, whereas the upper part includes a mixture of volcanic and sedimentary rocks; the

unconformity postulated in the Kings Mountain belt (see above) lies in this upper part, but beneath the characteristic kyanite quartzite and manganiferous schist of that belt.

Similar rocks appear also in eastern Georgia, not only on strike with the Kings Mountain belt but also with the main Carolina slate belt, where the kyanite quartzite is found again (Hurst, 1959). Finally, to return to North Carolina, low-grade volcanic rocks reappear around the south end of the Raleigh higher grade belt and continue northeastward into an eastern volcanic stripe at the Coastal Plain border (Parker, 1968); if it is connected with the main slate belt, however, the connection is hidden under the Cretaceous rocks of the Coastal Plain or broken by the Deep River Triassic basin. This eastern belt is virtually unknown; it does appear to extend northward a short distance into Virginia.

Despite the low grade of the Carolina slate belt and its appendages, it contains a number of igneous intrusions, which are in general the same as those in the Charlotte belt: mafic dike swarms (at least in the rocks below the reported unconformity), granitic plutons, perhaps of two generations, and a few late gabbro bodies that cut the edge of the belt in South Carolina. In the slate belt, in contrast to the Charlotte belt, the late granite plutons have distinct metamorphic aureoles.

In the present state of knowledge, it is not certain whether the lower grade rocks of the slate belt rest unconformably upon the higher grade rocks of the Charlotte and Raleigh belts, simply grade into them with increasing metamorphism, or both. No unequivocal evidence of unconformity between has been found, but the mafic dike swarms cutting the granitoid gneiss of the Charlotte belt might be the feeders for some of the volcanic rocks, implying that the gneiss is older. Overstreet and Bell (1965, p. 97, Table 2) accept an unconformity above at least part of the gneisses of the Charlotte belt and, on the basis of radiometric determinations, date the latter as late Precambrian (?) and Cambrian. The volcanic sequence above they tentatively consider to range from the Ordovician to the Mississippian, but the units below the unconformity that they recognize within that sequence they regard as most probably Ordovician. The fossils found in the upper part of the volcanic sequence in North Carolina (below the postulated unconformity) date those rocks, however, as probably Cambrian, thus favoring the interpretation that the gneisses of the Charlotte belt are in large part simply more metamorphosed equivalents of the felsic volcanics of the slate belt. In any case, the early granitic bodies here as elsewhere are probably Ordovician, and the late granite plutons may be Carboniferous. The gabbro-syenite masses are presumably younger still, though probably no younger than Triassic.

The northern continuation of these stripes through Virginia is quite unclear. The Charlotte belt loses its distinctness in northern North Carolina, where the Kings Mountain belt fades out and the Inner Piedmont belt is cut across by the Stony Ridge fault; moreover, the proportion of rocks of plutonic aspect may decrease here also. The Carolina slate belt is not recognized much more than 50 kilometers (35 miles) north of the North Carolina line, but its disappearance may perhaps be the result of rising metamorphic grade, the volcanic belt masquerading as a belt of granodioritic and hornblendic gneiss that extends northward east of the kyanite quartzite districts mentioned above (p. 195) as possible continuations of the Kings Mountain belt. If so, however, we cannot yet distinguish it from the adjoining belts. Several observers have suggested that it may reappear as the slate in the Arvonia syncline, which contains some volcanic materials. The Arvonia belt is considerably off strike, however, and the difference in age (Cambrian for an upper part of the Carolina volcanic sequence, Upper Ordovician for the Arvonia slate) is unfavorable to the correlation. Moreover, metavolcanic materials are also present in the older rocks on either side (Brown, 1969). Not enough is known of the wedge of the Virginia Piedmont lying between the Arvonia line of synclines and the Coastal Plain to make any intelligent guesses about other connections through that region.

Strikes in these belts are rather irregular, but a general trend can be made out. They average N20°E in southern Virginia and northern North Carolina, but in crossing North Carolina they bend rather abruptly to N50° or 60°E, then more gradually back to N30° or 35°E. The abrupt bend reflects the Roanoke recess of the Valley and Ridge province and occurs about on a line trending S30°E from Roanoke and passing close to the area where the strands of the Brevard zone may die out. Moreover, it seems to be reflected still farther southeastward by the Cape Fear arch, the most prominent structural feature in the entire Atlantic Coastal Plain. In north-central South Carolina the strikes shift again, this time as far as N75°E in the Carolina slate belt, then back to N50°–55°E in western South Carolina and eastern Georgia; this bend reflects the bend in the Kings Mountain belt but nothing farther northwest. In western Georgia the Uchee (Charlotte) belt is bevelled by the Coastal Plain border, but its trend changes to the N65°E trend of the adjacent Pine Mountain belt; this change might be said to reflect the Rome

recess. As noted above, the dip of foliation is generally steeply northwest, except in part of northern North Carolina and southern Virginia; before Triassic tilting, however, it may have been steeply southeast through much of the belt.

Extension of Piedmont Rocks beneath the Coastal Plain

The Piedmont province is overlapped on its seaward side, from northeast of Trenton, New Jersey, to southwest of Columbiana, Alabama, by the Cretaceous and later sediments of the Atlantic Coastal Plain. Drill holes have penetrated these sediments, however, in many places from New Jersey to Alabama to reveal the kinds of rock that form the subsurface extension of the Piedmont as far as the coast (see Richards, 1945; Spangler, 1950; Applin, 1951; Bonini and Woollard, 1960; King, 1961b; Milton and Hurst, 1965), and seismic soundings have determined the general shape of the upper surface of these rocks even beyond the present shore line (see summary in Murray, 1961, p. 21–47; also Drake, Ewing, and Sutton, 1959, Fig. 29; Emery and others, 1970, Figs. 38 and 40).

Except in southernmost Georgia and adjacent Florida and Alabama, the rocks beneath the Coastal Plain sediments appear to be the same as those of the nearby Piedmont—"granite," gneiss, schist, and metavolcanic slate, also dolerite and red sandstone that are presumably Triassic. Even in the 3000-meter (10,000-foot) well at Cape Hatteras, North Carolina, some 200 kilometers (125 miles) from the nearest outcrop of Piedmont rocks, the pre-Cretaceous basement consists of granitoid rock (though badly weathered; Spangler, 1950, p. 122–123). Thus here the Piedmont geologic province seems to have a total width of not less than 400 kilometers (250 miles), half of it hidden beneath the later sediments. Belts of low-grade metavolcanic rock can apparently be followed in the shallower subsurface of Georgia and the Carolinas, and Triassic basins can be outlined under several parts of the Coastal Plain.

In southernmost Georgia and northern Florida, on the other hand, wells penetrating the Coastal Plain sediments have encountered unmetamorphosed, unfolded Paleozoic sedimentary rocks, containing fossils ranging in age from Early Ordovician to probably Middle Devonian (Applin, 1951, p. 13–15, 22–25; Bridge and Berdan, 1952; Puri and Vernon, 1964, Pl. 1 and p. 16–23). With one exception which may be cross-bedding, these rocks show no dips greater than 10 degrees. They are known in a triangular area whose base extends east-west from near the Georgia-Florida boundary at the Atlantic to the southeasternmost part of Alabama and whose apex lies on the west coast of the Florida Peninsula about 280 kilometers (180 miles) farther south (Fig. 8A). The southwest side of the triangle is bounded by ignorance, for the Gulf of Mexico encroaches here and the thickness of the Coastal Plain sediments either is unknown or is known to increase very rapidly southwestward— in either case the older rocks are lost to view. Furthermore, in the western part of the triangle the Paleozoic rocks underlie presumably Triassic redbeds. The southeast side of the triangle, on the other hand, is fairly precisely located; in one well indeed the base of the Paleozoic sediments (probably Lower Ordovician but not fossiliferous in this well) was reached, resting on rhyolitic agglomerate and tuff. Similar volcanic rocks have been found farther east and south under the central part of the Florida Peninsula, and several wells encountered coarse-grained plutonic rocks (granite and diorite); radiometry suggests a late Precambrian or earliest Paleozoic age, at least for the plutonic rocks (Bass, 1969, p. 307). The northern boundary of the triangle, between the unfolded Paleozoic rocks on the south and typical Piedmont rocks on the north, is somewhat less precisely located, and the nearest wells north of it, in southeastern Georgia, again encountered volcanic or low-grade metavolcanic rocks, whereas farther west the boundary is hidden by Triassic (?) redbeds.

The Paleozoic rocks here are all clastic—sandstone (or quartzite) in the lower part of the Ordovician and the probable Middle Devonian, black shale between; they cannot be less than 1000 meters (3000 feet) thick, and twice that is more probable. The fossils are distinctly European in aspect.

The unexpected presence of these virtually undeformed Paleozoic rocks must indicate the far side of the Appalachian orogenic belt, and the granitic rocks still farther southeast under central Florida may represent a fragment of the Precambrian or at least pre-Ordovician floor onto which the Paleozoic rocks (and perhaps the underlying volcanic rocks) overlap. The east-west boundary between the Paleozoic rocks and the Piedmont may mark the original limit of the Appalachian deformed and metamorphosed belt, or it may follow a later fault, Triassic or other.

To what can one compare these enigmatic rocks? They do not recall any other sequence known in eastern North America, not even in Nova Scotia or southeastern Newfoundland, the southeasternmost belts in the widest visible part of the Appalachians. If however one looks across the Atlantic Ocean (Fig. 8B), to the high Fouta-Djallon Plateau of Guinea in western Africa

(Arnould, Aymé, and Guillaume, 1959, and references there given), one finds a comparable if somewhat thinner sequence, a sandwich of dark shale between sandstone units (the lowest fossils here are Silurian graptolites in the shale), lying nearly horizontal and resting unconformably on a north- or north-northwest-trending orogenic belt of latest Precambrian or earliest Paleozoic age (Rokelides of Sierra Leone; see Allen, 1968). North of the Plateau along the Guinea-Senegal border (Bassot, 1966), however, the lowest beds above the unconformity are also folded with generally northeast strikes (probably east-west or even northwest farther west in Portuguese Guinea), and the zone of younger deformation swings in a broad arc northward across southeastern Senegal and western Mauritania, merging with or overlapping the older orogenic belt to form the Mauritanide folded belt (Sougy, 1962, 1969). East of this belt, the older Precambrian basement of the Sahara platform is overlain by a typical gently warped platform cover ranging in age from latest Precambrian to Carboniferous; the Ordovician to Devonian portion is like that in Guinea but thins rapidly eastward. The Mauritanide belt itself includes a narrow eastern zone of folding, involving rocks as high as Upper Devonian, and a broader western zone of low-grade metamorphic rocks, probably also largely but not entirely Paleozoic, which in places at least are thrust out over the folded rocks or even the Precambrian basement. The western side of the belt and its northern continuation are concealed by a coastal plain of Mesozoic and Cenozoic sediments (the oldest beds recorded are Upper Jurassic); probably, however, the belt is continued northward by the well-known Paleozoic folded belt of the Anti-Atlas in southern Morocco and perhaps also by the low-grade metamorphic terrain of the central Moroccan Meseta, and it may ultimately connect with the Hercynian orogenic belts of Spain and western France. Are we looking here at the southeastern margin of the Appalachians?

Comparison of the Piedmont with New England

New England and the Appalachian Piedmont have very similar positions in the Appalachian chain, and one might expect them to show common features. At the western edge of each, in the Green Mountains and the Blue Ridge, is a major anticlinorium exposing Precambrian basement, and the most persistent string of ultramafic bodies in the Appalachians passes not far to the east of both (Hess, 1939, Fig. 13). The northeastern extre-

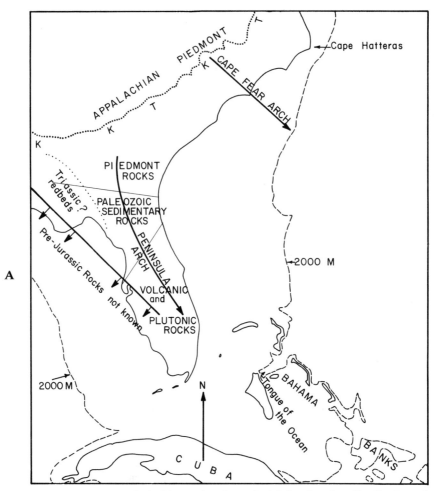

FIGURE 8. **(A) Map of Florida Peninsula and vicinity showing distribution of pre-Jurassic rocks beneath the Coastal Plain cover in relation to the continental margin (depth of 2000 meters). (B) Map of West Africa showing distribution of latest Precambrian or early Paleozoic (Rokelide) and late Paleozoic (Mauritanide) orogenic belts in relation to the coastal plain and the continental margin (depth of 2000 meters). Dotted lines are unconformities; letter symbols as on Plate 1.**

mity of the Piedmont at Trenton, New Jersey, is only 55 kilometers (35 miles) from the southwest end of the New England metamorphic province on Staten Island, ans as noted above (p. 191) there are strong similarities in both stratigraphy and structure between the rocks that lie on strike from these two extremities—in the Baltimore zone in the northeast appendix of the Piedmont on the one hand and in Westchester County, New York, in the southwest prong of the New England province on the other. Remarkably few other belt-for-belt parallels are possible, however. The zones between the Baltimore zone and the Blue Ridge have no counterpart in Westchester County, and neither the Baltimore zone nor the Westchester County structure seems to persist far along strike into the main areas of the Piedmont or New England.

Forty years ago, indeed, the two provinces seemed more similar than they do today; each

appeared to consist of vast areas of indecipherable schist, gneiss, and "granite," mostly called Precambrian because they are so much more altered than the folded but unmetamorphosed Paleozoic strata of the Valley and Ridge province to the west and because undoubted Precambrian metamorphic rocks occur in the anticlinoria between. Here and there a few more obviously metasedimentary bands and a few fossil localities were known, but they provided remarkably little information about the age of the major metamorphic terrains. Yet in those forty years, the geology of New England has been transformed, largely as the result of the work of Marland P. Billings, his students, and others using and extending his combination of the methods of stratigraphy, structural geology, and metamorphic petrology; we know now that New England records a complex Paleozoic geosyncline containing a succession of major anticlinoria and

B

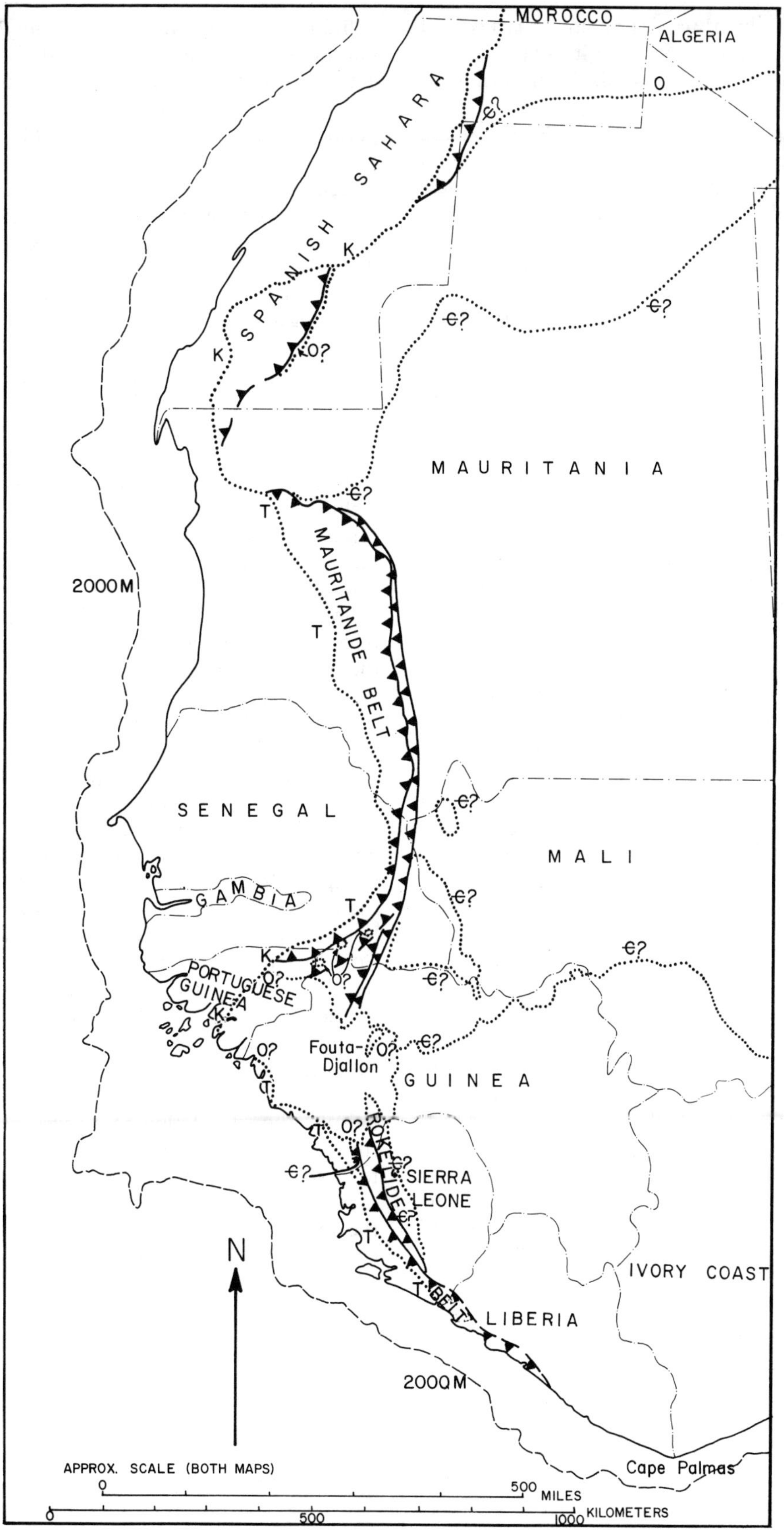

MOROCCO
ALGERIA
O
SPANISH SAHARA
€?
K
O?
€?
MAURITANIA
T
MAURITANIDE BELT
2000M
SENEGAL
MALI
GAMBIA
PORTUGUESE GUINEA
Fouta-Djallon
GUINEA
ROKELIDE
SIERRA LEONE
BELT
LIBERIA
IVORY COAST
N
2000M
Cape Palmas
APPROX. SCALE (BOTH MAPS)
0
500 MILES
0
500
1000 KILOMETERS

synclinoria, which were probably marked out early and which have each their own particular character and history. A similar transformation is now beginning in Piedmont geology; as it proceeds, analogy with the structure of New England should therefore suggest working hypotheses to apply to the probably equally complex but less well exposed and more extensive Piedmont Province.

Thus we may anticipate that the Piedmont also will contain major anticlinoria and synclinoria alternating with one another across strike but arranged en echelon along it and composed rather of Paleozoic or latest Precambrian metasediments and metavolcanics than of Precambrian basement rocks. In the anticlinoria we may expect more volcanics, more conglomerates, and more unconformities; in the synclinoria, more complete and more monotonous sections of pelites or calcareous pelites, thrown into great recumbent folds or nappes, rooting perhaps on the anticlinoria and folded again across elongate gneiss domes or pinched between them. The example of New England further suggests that alternating belts of high-grade and low-grade metamorphic rocks are relatively independent of the anticlinoria and synclinoria and may indeed be related to upthrown and downthrown blocks along (Triassic?) normal faults. Some plutonic rocks will turn out to be simply metamorphosed piles of volcanics; others should be groupable into distinct igneous series, like Billings' "magma series" in New Hampshire and vicinity, each containing many members from mafic to salic but distinguished from the others by chemical trends and structural position and in part related to different orogenic events or interorogenic periods. Furthermore, we should be prepared to find complex deformation—folding of older folds, remetamorphism, retrograde metamorphism—not the exception but the rule, whether within a single orogenic period or as a result of several superposed events.

How may such events there may have been we still do not know. The overwhelming importance of the late Paleozoic Alleghany orogeny in the Valley and Ridge province has led to the standard interpretation that whatever Piedmont deformation, metamorphism, and igneous intrusion is not definitely Precambrian must be late Paleozoic—Carboniferous or Permian. On the other hand, detailed study of the Blue Ridge has increasingly emphasized the importance of an early Paleozoic period of deformation there, probably Ordovician and hence roughly (but it may be very roughly) correlative with the Taconic movements of New England. Much of the recent work in the Piedmont also hints at the importance of such a period of deformation, but the indications are still mostly indirect or uncertain; perhaps the most significant is the unconformity beneath the fossiliferous Upper Ordovician Arvonia slate, yet even that unconformity is denied by some. I am strongly inclined to believe indeed that Taconic movements will ultimately prove to have been the most important of all in the Piedmont, as the Acadian movements were in New England and the Canadian Appalachians, but the evidence is still far from compelling; certainly in the virtual absence of dated Lower Paleozoic deposits we are hardly in a position to reconstruct the Cambrian and Ordovician history. What other periods of movement will be recognized is even less certain; evidence of Acadian movements seems to be absent, for middle and late Paleozoic rocks other than intrusives are as yet unknown. On the other hand, latest Precambrian (Avalonian?) movements may have been important in supplying the vast quatities of presumed latest Precambrian sediments in the Ocoee group of the Great Smoky Mountains, the Lynchburg gneiss of the Virginia Blue Ridge, the Glenarm group of Maryland and Pennsylvania, and the many undated terrains in the Piedmont that may be correlative with these. Finally as in New England, the importance or indeed the very existence of pre-Appalachian Precambrian basement in the Piedmont east of the Blue Ridge remains uncertain, except for its obvious presence in the Baltimore gneiss domes (and perhaps in the Pine Mountain belt of Georgia); the evidence still permits the speculation that the central belts of the Appalachian geosyncline from Newfoundland to Alabama never had a Precambrian sialic basement but were originally floored by simatic crust, the present sial having evolved there during the course of the Appalachian orogenies.

CHAPTER **10**

The Triassic Basins and Related Rocks

Aligned along the crystalline core of the Appalachian Mountains from Nova Scotia to the Carolinas, mostly within the Piedmont province and its Northern Appalachian equivalent, are a series of faulted basins or half-grabens containing Triassic sedimentary rocks, dominantly redbeds, little deformed and resting with profound unconformity on the rocks affected by the Appalachian orogenies (Fig. 9). These rocks locally contain remains of dinosaurs and other reptiles and especially their tracks, and also amphibians, fresh-water fish, estherian crustaceans, fresh-water molluscs, and plants; these exclusively nonmarine fossils indicate a Late Triassic—Keuper—age (Colbert and Gregory, *in* Reeside and others, 1957, p. 1459–1461). Commonly associated with the sedimentary rocks are igneous rocks of basaltic composition, in the form of lava flows, sills, and stocks within the basins and of persistent dikes both within and without—similar dikes crop out in the Piedmont as far as Alabama. Furthermore, entirely similar rocks, both sedimentary and igneous, have been found by the drill beneath the Cretaceous and Cenozoic cover of the Coastal Plain from Long Island to Alabama and Florida, and there is little reason to doubt that these too represent faulted basins within the buried extension of the Piedmont province.

Triassic Sedimentary Rocks

The largest of the Triassic sedimentary basins, the New York-Virginia or Newark basin, begins on the west bank of the Hudson River opposite New York City, where a dolerite sill within the sediments forms the great cliff of the Palisades, and extends nearly to Charlottesville, Virginia, 500 kilometers (over 300 miles) away to the southwest. The outcrop belt is broadly curved, following fairly closely the curving strike of the underlying Paleozoic and older rocks as they swing out of the New York recess and around the Pennsylvania salient; it reaches a maximum width of 45 kilometers (30 miles) in western New Jersey and eastern Pennsylvania, but it is actually interrupted for less than 2 kilometers (1 mile) near Frederick, Maryland—this interruption and a constriction east of the Susquehanna River in Pennsylvania divide the basin into three subbasins, each 150 to 200 kilometers (100 to 140 miles) long (Newark-Delaware, Gettysburg, and Culpeper subbasins). With only local exceptions, the Triassic strata dip northwest or north away from the southeastern margin of the basin, where the basal beds rest unconformably on rocks ranging from Precambrian gneiss to Ordovician carbonate and slate. The dips, though variable, average about 20 degrees, and in the

203

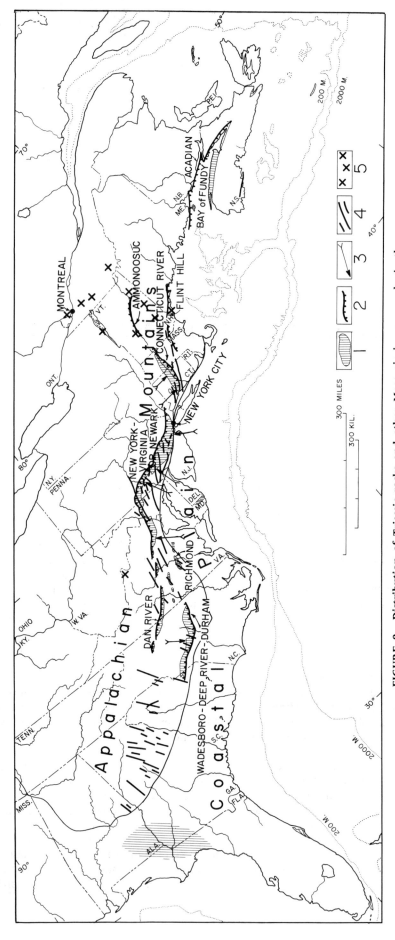

FIGURE 9. Distribution of Triassic rocks and other Mesozoic igneous rocks in the Appalachians. (1) Basin of Triassic rocks. Those reported beneath the Coastal Plain are indicated without borders or by question marks. (2) Basin-border fault active during Triassic deposition (also Ammonoosuc and Flint Hill faults). (3) Probable center of intrusion of sills (center is generally close to border fault). (4) General trend of dolerite dikes. (5) Center of later (mainly alkalic) Mesozoic igneous activity (much generalized).

wider parts of each of the three subbasins, the total thickness of beds is estimated to be at least 5 kilometers (3 miles) and may be considerably more. These rocks have been studied for a century and a half and are reasonably well known; among the most detailed recent studies are those by the late Dean B. McLaughlin in New Jersey and Pennsylvania, though his results are scattered through a number of small papers (for short summaries, see McLaughlin *in* Reeside and others, 1957, p. 1491–1498, and *in* Johnson and McLaughlin, 1957, p. 31–36), and that by Glaeser (1966) of the northern two subbasins.

Roughly the lower third of the Triassic section where it is thickest consists of pinkish and reddish arkose, associated with pale feldspathic conglomerate and red siltstone and silty shale (named Stockton, New Oxford, and Manassas in the three subbasins); the source of the highly feldspathic debris appears to have been in the Piedmont province to the southeast. The bulk of the upper part of the section (Brunswick, Gettysburg, and Bull Run formations) is bright red silty shale, siltstone, and micaceous quartz sandstone (arkose is rare), probably also derived from the southeast, but coarse fanglomerate beds (with fragments up to 0.3 meter—1 foot—but rarely larger) occur throughout the section close to the northwest margin of the basin, interfingering southeastward into the finer grained sediments, and obviously derived from the northwest. All these deposits are clearly fluviatile; the coarser parts are probably piedmont fan deposits, and the finer are flood-plain deposits of short streams. In the northeastern (Newark-Delaware) subbasin, however, a great lens of fine-grained lacustrine sediments (Lockatong formation) up to 1 kilometer (3800 feet) thick is intercalated between the arkosic beds below and the dominantly shaly beds above; it consists of dark gray and dull red argillite and shale and includes a few beds of clayey limestone. Three separate mappable units of lava occur high in the section in this subbasin, a remnant or two of lava is preserved at the top in the central (Gettysburg) subbasin, and lava and pyroclastics have been found in the western part of the Culpeper subbasin (Toewe, 1966, p. 8–13).

The fanglomerate along the northwest side of the basin contains pebbles and cobbles of the Precambrian and lower Paleozoic rocks immediately adjacent on the northwest, and also pebbles of Paleozoic sedimentary rocks as young as Devonian derived from the Valley and Ridge province farther northwest. (In Virginia, fanglomerate consisting of lower Paleozoic carbonate pebbles in a red matrix has been widely quarried as "Potomac marble.") As beds in all parts of the section turn into such fanglomerate wherever they approach the northwest border of the basin, that border must have been a steep mountain front almost throughout Triassic deposition, like mountain fronts in the Great Basin today, though probably not as high. The border itself is formed in large part by en echelon normal faults, and probably these faults were active during deposition, like the faults that now follow the mountain fronts in the Great Basin. In places along this border, however, fanglomerate high in the section rests directly and unconformably on pre-Triassic rocks; presumably these are places where the top of the sediments accumulating along the mountain foot lapped up onto less subsided blocks between the en enchelon normal faults or across the main border fault onto the mountain front beyond. Faults also occur far out in the basin, cutting the Triassic rocks or even bringing up the pre-Triassic floor, but there is no evidence that any of these faults were active during deposition.

The predominance of redbeds led some earlier observers to suppose that these are desert deposits. The presence of nonred lacustrine deposits (and of coal in other basins) suggests, however, a warm climate with seasonal rainfall, like that of present-day savannas, perhaps drier and warmer in the valleys where deposition was going on than in the surrounding mountains.

The Triassic basin in the Connecticut Valley in Connecticut and Massachusetts is very similar in dimensions and structure to the subbasins of the New York-Virginia basin, but the structural elements are reversed; the beds dip eastward toward a major eastern border fault that was active during deposition, as shown by fanglomerate throughout the section (here also the deposits lapped over the main fault in a few places onto fault blocks or the mountain front). In this basin, however, virtually all the sediments are arkosic and came from the east; on the west there is local material only at the very base (Krynine, 1950). The section is not less than 5 kilometers (about 3 miles) thick (Sanders, 1963, suggests 9 kilometers—30,000 feet), but here three units of lava appear about at the middle; lacustrine sediments, including thin beds of limestone, are intercalated between them, as though the lava flows had disrupted the drainage. Numerous faults cut the rocks in the basin, but again there is no evidence that they moved during deposition. Where Triassic faults cut pre-Triassic rocks, those rocks are commonly silicified for several meters (several yards) from the fault. A couple of small fault basins to the west of the main basin are probably erosional remnants of that basin, for the sediments in them have the same eastern source, and the larger one (Pomperaug basin) contains the same three lava units. If the Ammonoosuc fault of western New Hampshire is in fact a Triassic normal fault (Chapter 5, p. 99), then another subbasin may once have existed along the Connecticut River north of the present basin.

The Connecticut Valley basin illustrates another structural peculiarity of several of these basins. The dip is not uniformly eastward near the border fault; rather it outlines a series of gentle anticlines and synclines more or less perpendicular to the border fault and the trend of the basin. Wheeler (1939) has pointed out that the anticlines generally lie opposite salients of the border fault that project into the basin, synclines opposite recesses, and he suggested that subsidence was partly impeded by friction along the projections of the fault. In other places, the dips increase abruptly close to the eastern border fault, to as much as 60 degrees, instead of decreasing as one would expect along a normal fault; such dips can perhaps be explained by lack of support below blocks close to the fault, either because of the outpouring of lava from beneath or by the play of antithetic faults near the main fault.

South of the New York-Virginia basin, Triassic rocks form a number of basins in Virginia and North Carolina. The long, narrow Dan River basin, crossing the state line, and two smaller ones, one in each direction, are aligned (slightly offset en echelon) along the trend of the New York-Virginia basin so as to extend it southwestward an additional 300 kilometers (200 miles); the beds in these basins dip northwest toward a border fault next which they grade into fanglomerate, just as in the New York-Virginia basin with which they may once have been continuous. East of this line in Virginia, several small basins form two additional lines, the dips still mainly to the west; these basins may be simply erosional remnants of the main western basin, although in at least one of them, fanglomerate is reported next the western border fault (Brown, 1969, p. 35, 42). In the Richmond basin, west of Richmond, Virginia, in the eastern line, some of the rocks are dark gray and are probably lake and swamp deposits; coal has been mined there from near the base of the sequence off and on since the eighteenth century. In the largest of all the southern basins, however, the Wadesboro-Deep River-Durham basin in North and South Carolina (overlapping Cretaceous sediments divide the outcrop belt into two parts), the arrangement is like that in the Connecticut Valley basin, with the border fault, fanglomerates, and principal source area on the east (Reinemund, 1955). This basin extends for nearly 250 kilometers (150 miles) along the strike of the older rocks and contains up to 3 kilometers (2 miles) of

strata. Here a middle dark, fine-grained lacustrine unit (Cumnock formation) separates two coarser moderately feldspathic units (Pekin and Sanford formations) and contains mineable coal. A similar median dark coal-bearing unit is known also in the Dan River basin and one of the smaller basins in Virginia, but the coal is not mineable.

The Dan River and Deep River basins form a pair facing each other as across a plane of symmetry; the opposed dips indicate an arch, but it is clearly postdepositional, for the beds must have originally lain flat or even sloped gently toward the plane of symmetry from the source-area mountain fronts beyond the active border faults on either side (these lie 100 kilometers or more—60 to 80 miles—apart). If either the north end of the New York-Virginia basin or the south end of the Connecticut Valley basin were extended a few tens of kilometers (tens of miles), those basins too would face each other across an arch. The rather similar stratigraphy in the Dan River and Deep River basins, the presence of three units of lava in both the New York-Virginia and Connecticut Valley basins, and the presence of intermediate basins in both Connecticut and Virginia (the Pomperaug basin in western Connecticut even contains the three lava units) suggest that Triassic deposits were once continuous across the whole area from eastern to western border faults, forming the filling of a great graben or rift-valley, averaging perhaps 100 kilometers (60 miles) in width and extending 1000 kilometers (700 miles) along the metamorphic core of the Appalachian chain from southern New England to the Carolinas.

It must be mentioned that the border faults and some of the faults within the basins have also been interpreted as pre-Triassic thrust faults (Bain, 1932, p. 71–72) and as wrench faults (Bain, 1941; 1957, p. 497; Sanders, 1963, pp. 512–514). Exposures of the fault surfaces are rare, but those that have been uncovered tend to support the normal-fault hypothesis for the border faults; that some of the faults within the basins are wrench or oblique-slip faults remains possible.

Still another major Triassic basin with an entirely comparable pattern is known under and around the Bay of Fundy. Dips are mainly northwest; the unconformable southeastern contact can be followed for nearly 250 kilometers (150 miles) in western Nova Scotia, and fragments of the northern border, with local fanglomerate, are exposed on the north shore of the bay in Nova Scotia and New Brunswick. There are even outliers in eastern Nova Scotia, 130 kilometers (80 miles) east of the main basin. A thick lava unit crowns the exposed section, which is nearly a kilometer (half a mile) thick and consists mainly of red sandstone and shale (Klein, 1962); lacustrine deposits occur but coal is absent. Klein (1963) has shown that in this basin, as in the New York-Virginia basin, the sediments were derived from both sides. Triassic rocks not only underlie most of the Bay of Fundy but have been followed about 120 kilometers (75 miles) southwest into the northern part of the Gulf of Maine (Uchupi, 1966); no outcrops are known along the eastern Maine coast, but a submarine declivity off that coast may represent the northwestern fault scarp. As noted in Chapter 5 (p. 107), the Flint Hill zone in southeastern New Hampshire and its extensions into southwestern Maine and eastern Massachusetts may represent a Triassic normal fault en echelon to the border fault of the Fundy basin; like that fault it would be downthrown on the southeast (redbed material has actually been found in the glacial drift in one area in eastern Massachusetts— Oldale, 1962). Neither of these faults could be the continuation of either of the border faults of the graben or rift-valley postulated in the preceding paragraphs, but they might represent one side of another comparable graben.

Drill holes in several parts of the Atlantic Coastal Plain have discovered red sandstone, with or without doleritic intrusions, beneath the Cretaceous sediments at a level where Piedmont crystalline rocks would normally be expected. Where such sandstone is found near the inner edge of the Coastal Plain in western Long Island and in Virginia, it could easily represent outliers of the Connecticut Valley or Richmond basins, but sandstone in three wells in far southeastern Maryland lies much too far to the east and must indicate an eastern basin, perhaps in line with the Fundy basin, as may a smaller basin or basins reported in South Carolina, somewhat southeast of the trend of the Deep River basin. Finally, a large area underlain by such sandstone in southwestern Georgia, southeastern Alabama, and northwestern Florida, mainly north and west of but in part overlapping the unmetamorphosed Paleozoic sediments there, must represent a very large basin, larger perhaps than any of the exposed ones and hundreds of kilometers (hundreds of miles) southwest of them. A similar but smaller red sandstone basin in southern Arkansas (Eagle Mills formation) has been known for years, but it has been variously classed as Permian, Triassic, and Jurassic. If all these areas of red sandstone are part of the Triassic graben or rift-valley system, then it rivalled the present East African system in extent.

Whether or not the Triassic sedimentary basins add up to such a grandiose rift-valley system, the dominant normal faulting associated with them, with displacements measured in kilometers

(miles), suggests an active extension perpendicular to the trend of the faults and basins. This trend was strongly influenced by the preexisting structure of the older rocks (as shown first by Davis, 1888, p. 486–488, for the Connecticut Valley basin), for it lies parallel to that structure or cuts it at low angles and faithfully follows the major salients and recesses of the Appalachian chain. Furthermore, the basins are aligned more or less along the central axis of the chain, within its metamorphic core, and a linear positive gravity anomaly that follows the Appalachian trend from Georgia to Vermont, east of the gradient whose steepest part coincides with the basement anticlinoria and the Brevard zone, is neatly bracketed by the opposed border faults of the main line of paired basins. It does not take much imagination, therefore, to envisage the Triassic fault troughs as subsided keystone blocks along the crest of a broad early Mesozoic uplift collinear with the Appalachian orogenic belt, the uplift representing the first and perhaps the largest isostatic rebound of the thickened crust within that belt, finally released from whatever orogenic forces had produced and deformed it. Similarly, Hans Cloos (1939) regarded the Rhine and Red Sea grabens as keystone blocks on broad uplifts. The later arching of the sediments, expressed in the present opposed dips of paired basins, might be a further continuation of the same process.

Triassic and Other Post-Paleozoic Igneous Rocks

Although the basaltic or doleritic igneous rocks associated with the Triassic sedimentary rocks take varied forms—lava flows (with rare tuffs), sills, stocks, dikes—their chemistry is remarkably uniform and banal and their mineralogy hardly less so. Indeed both are entirely comparable to those of postorogenic dolerites all over the world and of many ages—for example, the nearly contemporaneous Karroo dolerites of South Africa and those in the Permian of Tasmania, the Devonian Old Red Sandstone, the Keweenawan of Lake Superior, and the Athabaska group of western Canada, all associated with redbeds. The mineralogy and texture (the latter ranges from fine-grained basalt to moderately coarse gabbro) depends chiefly on the size of the body and the rate of cooling; if cooling was very slow, differentiation into granophyre and picritic basalt was possible, as in the Palisades sill opposite New York City and in other large Triassic sills. Sanders (1963, p. 514) points out that the dikes in Connecticut, although similar in chemistry to the flows and sills, differ in being markedly porphyritic.

As noted above, lava flows are known in the Triassic sediments from Nova Scotia to northern Virginia; in Connecticut and New Jersey, three separate units of lava flows have been mapped, and their correlation is suggested by such peculiarities as the near-restriction of pillow lava to the lowest unit in each region. Large sills are present in the Connecticut Valley, New York-Virginia, and Deep River basins, being especially widespread in the New York-Virginia basin. They show a strong tendency to assume bowl or saucer forms (Hotz, 1952), rising gradually across the strata from some central point; the few well authenticated stocks seem to occur at such central points (indicated by arrows on Fig. 9). Carey (1958b) has provided a satisfying explanation of these relations, which are observed in many other dolerite areas; a basaltic magma, rising through vertical fractures or necks in a thoroughly solidified substratum and entering an overlying poorly consolidated and presumably lighter sedimentary sequence (the poor consolidation of the Triassic sediments is proved by dikes of clastic material found cutting both sills and lava flows; see, for example, Walton and O'Sullivan, 1950), would tend to spread out laterally along the bedding and lift the overlying sediments instead of cutting vertically through them in the form of dikes or vents. The sill-like extensions would nevertheless rise across the strata away from the original point of entry, either gradually or in steps across better consolidated layers, producing cone-sheets. (According to Carey, the Tasmanian cone-sheets flare upward like the mouth of a trumpet, in contrast to the bowl or saucer shapes of the North American ones.)

In contrast to the other forms, dikes extend far outside the limits of the known sedimentary basins beyond the major border faults on both sides; in places they desert the crystalline zones of the chain and extend into the Valley and Ridge province. Their total distribution is still incompetely known; they are present at least from southern Nova Scotia to Alabama, but they seem to be commoner southwest than northeast of New Jersey. They are generally practically vertical, and in any one area the majority tend to lie roughly parallel, so that taken as a whole they form a grandiose dike swarm (Fig. 9; also King, 1961a) whose known extent is at least 2200 kilometers (1400 miles). At the southwest end of the Appalachians, individual dikes trend northwest, almost perpendicular to the general strike, but northeastward their trend swings through north (in Virginia) to northeast (in eastern Pennsylvania and New England); in southern Nova Scotia the trend is east-northeast,

parallel to the coast. Moreover, whereas the trend of the sedimentary basins follows the strike of the pre-Triassic rocks through salients and recesses, the trend of the dikes does not; for example, it continues evenly across the New York recess as if the recess were not there. (In detail, to be sure, the course of individual dikes may be influenced by the surrounding rocks; thus in steeply dipping schists the dikes tend to consist of alternate concordant and sharply cross-cutting segments, the total trend of which adds up to the local trend of the swarm.)

That the trend of the dike swarm is independent of the older strike and of the trend of the Triassic basins and normal faults poses a problem in mechanics. As mentioned above, the normal faulting indicates extension across the Appalachian chain and hence suggests that at the time of Triassic deposition the axis of least compressive stress was oriented perpendicular to the chain (and presumably nearly horizontal), compatible with the broad arching of the crust postulated in the preceding section. But the dikes indicate a quite different pattern of stress; the axis of least compression should lie perpendicular to the dikes; that is, roughly across the chain at the north but along it at the south, ignoring bends in the chain. At present, explanations for the discrepancy can only be speculative. Perhaps the stress system governing the distribution of the dikes lay deeper than that governing the faulting and basin formation, in the upper mantle instead of the crust. Perhaps the dikes are entirely younger than the Triassic deposition and associated igneous activity; Sanders (1963, p. 514) considers them later than the other Triassic events because they seem to follow already formed, postdepositional faults, and according to de Boer (1967) paleomagnetic data suggest that they are Jurassic. Although similar dolerite is known beneath the Coastal Plain as far as southern Alabama and northern Florida, nonetheless the dikes seem generally limited to the Appalachian edifice and therefore should have shared its post-Triassic history, which appears to have been one of continued, though lesser, broad arching; it is not clear how the stress distribution indicated by the dikes can be reconciled with this history, unless it be subcrustal. Perhaps the two explanations must be combined.

There appears to have been other Mesozoic igneous activity in the Appalachian region, however. As noted in Chapter 5 (p. 111), the alkalic rocks of the White Mountain magma series of New Hampshire were long considered early Carboniferous, postorogenic with respect to the Acadian orogeny, by correlation with the alkalic Quincy igneous series in eastern Massachusetts and Rhode

Island, known to be pre-Pennsylvanian, but radio-metric determinations now strongly suggest a Jurassic age (curiously enough, some of the asso-ciated basic dikes are difficult to distinguish from the "Triassic" ones); likewise the Ascutney stock in Vermont and the Megantic stock in southeast-ern Quebec, plus lamprophyre and mica peridotite dikes in the Champlain Valley, give early Cre-taceous dates, and the Monteregian intrusives around Montreal are the same age or younger.

Another small group of mafic alkalic intrusions has been known for a long time in the Valley and Ridge province of central Virginia and adjacent West Virginia. These are also postorogenic (pre-sumably post-Permian), and radiometric data sug-gest that their age is early Cretaceous (Zartman and others, 1967, p. 861) or even early Cenozoic (Fullagar and Bottino, 1969). They may indeed be related to mica-periodite dikes that are wide-spread though insignificant in volume in the Appalachian Plateau of Pennsylvania and New York. Similar dikes also occur across much of the southern part of the central platform of the United States (Brock and Heyl, 1961, Fig. 1), but there they seem to be of different ages—Permian in Kentucky and vicinity, late Cretaceous farther west.

Postscript: Post-Triassic history of the Appalachians

In thorough contrast to the Triassic rocks, which, though postorogenic, nevertheless seem an integral part of the Appalachian orogenic edifice, are the Coastal Plain sediments, marine and non-marine, Cretaceous and younger, that lap up upon that edifice, burying its southeastern margin and its southwestern end and extending far to the west beyond its limits, indeed all round the Gulf of Mexico (Murray, 1961). In the subsurface, more-over, Jurassic rocks are found at the base of the overlapping sequence, at least from Alabama westward and perhaps as far north as North Caro-lina, and also under the Grand Banks of New-foundland (Bartlett, 1969, p. 7). The clastic material in this sequence east of the Mississippi River, and as far west as Texas at certain times (e.g., Lower and Middle Eocene; Todd and Folk, 1957), was derived mainly from erosion of the Appalachian Mountains; hence it constitutes a record of their later Mesozoic and Cenozoic history, but attempts to study the deposits in that light are still relatively few (Gilluly, 1964; Owens, 1970). In principle, that history should also be recorded in the land forms of the mountains themselves, and for a cen-tury physiographers and geomorphologists have

been attempting to read it there, but the different readings are so various, not to say contradictory, that this record must be accounted inadequately deciphered. Probably only when the land surfaces in the mountains have been traced into and cor-related with dated surfaces, erosional and depos-itional, within the Coastal Plain sequence, and when the deposits upon the surfaces in the moun-tains have been adequately studied (a start in this direction has been made; see King, 1949; Hack, 1965; Pierce, 1966, p. 60 ff.), can we hope for a satisfactory interpretation of the postorogenic history of the mountain chain.

In this book, therefore, no attempt is made to discuss the post-Triassic history of the Appalach-ians in any detail, even though it would certainly be an important chapter of the tectonic history if we understood it; broad and vague generalizations must suffice. Judging by the present gentle dip of the Coastal Plain sediments away from the moun-tains, which is notably quaquaversal around their southern end and which everywhere increases downward and seaward, but even so hardly ex-ceeds a degree or two, the mountains have been uplifted as a very broad low arch, roughly collinear with the orogenic belt; the attitude of erosion surfaces within the mountains, and indeed the continued presence of the mountains themselves despite a couple of hundred million years of eros-ion, enforces the same conclusion. It is harder to answer the questions whether that uplift was at a nearly constant rate or decreased through time, and whether it was continuous or interrupted; the sediments of the Coastal Plain suggest the second alternative to each of these questions. To the first question, Cretaceous *clastic* sediments appear to be two or three times as voluminous as Cenozoic under Georgia (cf. Applin, 1952, p. 1163, and Toulmin, 1952, p. 1168) and North Carolina (estimated from sections in Spangler, 1950); if the sediments under the continental rise were included, however, these imbalances might be lessened (see Emery and others, 1970, Figs. 38, 42, and 43). To the second, there appear to have been bursts of clastic sediments at certain times, such as the Early and early Late Cretaceous, the Eocene, and the Miocene, separated by times of lessened clastic sedimentation, if not regression and erosion, as in the middle Late Cretaceous, the Paleocene, and the Oligocene. The Paleocene still-stand seems to have been a period of bauxite formation over much of the eastern Gulf Coastal Plain (Overstreet and others, 1964–1967), and there may have been an approximately contem-poraneous period of especially intense chemical weathering in the mountains, recorded by deposits of iron, manganese, and silicon oxides in residual clay (e.g., Rodgers, 1948, esp. p. 15–17, 40) and by sink-hole fillings in the Valley and Ridge province that contain bauxite, kaolinite, and lignite deposits, of either late Cretaceous or early Cenozoic (Paleocene) age (Bridge, 1950, p. 193–195; Tschudy, 1965; Pierce, 1965). These sink-hole fillings lie well below the ridge crests of the Valley and Ridge province, and their presence thus implies that much of the present relief of that province already existed in the early Cenozoic or earlier. Those very ridge crests, held up by resistant sandstone or quartzite, have often been considered erosional remnants of a major peneplain, variously dated from Cretaceous to mid-Tertiary, but Cooper (1944, p. 213–214), by quantitative measurement of the sandstone debris still present on the lower slopes of one of the ridges, has shown that the ridge crests have been lowered tens of meters (probably more than 100 feet) since the present topographic relief was established, let alone since erosion first reached the rocks that form the crest of the mountains. It is possible to argue, therefore, that the mountains have never ceased to be mountains since the Triassic or indeed the Paleozoic.

The last chapter in the geologic history of the Appalachians was that of the Pleistocene glaciations, which covered the entire northern half of the chain but encroached only slightly on the southern half, although periglacial phenomena are known as far south as the Great Smoky Mountains of Tennessee and North Carolina (King, 1964, p. 134 ff.). The tectonic consequences of the glaciation were simply down-bowing of the northern segment (presumably several times) in company with a much vaster area of the Canadian shield to the northwest, followed by rebound when the ice sheets melted; the mild earthquakes that still occur in the northeastern United States and eastern Canada, especially in the Saint Lawrence Valley, are traditionally attributed to this rebound. A geologically more important consequence, perhaps, was the virtually complete replacement in the northern Appalachians of the preexisting mantle of soil and residual weathered material by a new mantle of glacial drift; this glacial mantle has been studied assiduously for a century and has revealed a fascinating chapter of the geologic (if not tectonic) history, whereas study of the nonglacial mantle of the southern Appalachians, which should record an equally fascinating history, has barely begun.

CHAPTER 11

Summary of the Geologic History of the Appalachians*

Appalachian history proper, during which the Appalachian region was distinct from other parts of North America, was preceded by a sort of pre-history, represented by the Precambrian basement that underlies the western provinces of the chain. This basement consists, at least as far southwest as Tennessee, of high-grade metamorphic and plutonic rocks that clearly belong to the Grenville province of the Canadian shield, especially to its southeastern part as exposed in the Adirondacks and the Frontenac axis; characteristic, though not necessarily abundant, are coarse graphitic marble and associated metasediments, charnockitic rocks, and anorthosite. Not only lithology but radiometry attests to the correlation. Basement is found as far east in the Appalachians as the line of great anticlinoria forming the Blue Ridge province and its northern Appalachian equivalents, and locally a little farther east still, in the folded gneiss domes near Baltimore, Philadelphia, and New York and perhaps also in southeastern Vermont. In these areas, the basement rocks have been remetamorphosed; in the anticlinoria they are retrogressed to the greenschist facies but are still recognizable, whereas in the gneiss domes they

have been completely reconstituted in the amphibolite facies. Where wells have reached the basement beneath the Appalachian Plateau, on the other hand, they have found it quite unaltered and undisturbed. Whether the basement is equally undisturbed under the Valley and Ridge province is, as discussed in Chapter 3, controversial; to date no wells have penetrated to it, and the few that were drilled to reach it showed only that it lies far deeper than had been suspected. In any case, what later became the western Appalachian region was then simply part of a broader orogenic belt, the Grenville belt, extending along the east or southeast side of the North American continent from Labrador at least to Tennesse; this belt went through a long and probably very complicated orogenic history (de Waard and Walton, 1967; Wynne-Edwards and others, 1966; Wynne-Edwards, 1967, Fig. 1), ending 850 million years ago or a little less, and then was subjected to a period of subaerial erosion that stripped away all superficial structures and exposed the metamorphic core of the orogenic belt, over much of it down to the granulite facies (rocks of the granulite facies are exposed over a larger

*In the hope of presenting in this summary chapter a clear and concise outline of the geologic history of the Appalachians, I have quite deliberately oversimplified the data and suppressed the qualifications and doubts that attach to many of the principal conclusions, trusting that the preceding chapters contain enough data, enough qualifications, and enough references to enable a serious reader to determine for himself what is well established and what is only personal belief.

area in the Grenville belt than in any other orogenic belt in North America). There is no evidence that the Appalachian part of this belt was marked off in any way at that time.

Late Precambrian history

Evidence that the Appalachian region was beginning to differ systematically from the rest of North America is found first in rocks of apparently very late Precambrian age. On the west side of the chain, these appear as great clastic wedges, resting unconformably on the basement and lapping upon it so that the thinner the wedge the younger the beds at its base. These wedges are distributed irregularly along the line of basement anticlinoria already mentioned; they probably extend some distance northwestward under the Valley and Ridge province or its equivalents, although their rocks are nowhere brought to the surface there, and they may also extend far into the Piedmont and perhaps into the interior zones of parts of the northern Appalachians (e.g., west-central Newfoundland). Almost everywhere Lower Cambrian fossils occur in the highest beds of these clastic wedges (probably nowhere more than 300 meters—1000 feet—from the top), but as these fossils do not appear to represent the lowest Lower Cambrian faunal zones, an indefinite thickness of strata below them may also correlate with Lower Cambrian rocks elsewhere. (All these rocks, Lower Cambrian and older, are referred to throughout this book as the basal clastic sequence.) The thickest such clastic sequence known is in the Great Smoky Mountains of Tennessee and North Carolina, near or just beyond the southwestern end of basement exposure in the Blue Ridge anticlinorium. Here clastic rocks apparently totalling more than 8 kilometers (5 miles) in thickness have been divided into four groups (the first three constitute the Ocoee "series" or supergroup, the last is the Chilhowee group), dominated respectively by arkose, graywacke, siltstone and silty argillite, and arkosic quartzite and quartzite. Great thicknesses of such strata also appear to be present to the southwest in Georgia and Alabama. To the northeast, the thickness decreases into Virginia, more rapidly along the northwest than along the southeast flank of the Blue Ridge anticlinorium; only the highest of the four groups, about 1 kilometer (about 3000 feet) thick, persists along the northwest flank, but two large piles of volcanics appear below it, one in southwestern Virginia (Mt. Rogers volcanic group) and one in northern Virginia, Maryland, and southern Pennsylvania

(Catoctin greenstone). Farther northeast in Pennsylvania, the thickness decreases further, and in New Jersey and adjacent Pennsylvania and New York, in the New York recess, the basal clastic sequence is reduced to 100 meters or so (300 to 400 feet) of clean Lower Cambrian quartzite.

In western New England, the reverse transition takes place, the basal clastic sequence thickening northward, especially on the east side of the Green Mountains anticlinorium and over its crest in northern Vermont and adjacent Quebec, although the total thickness seems to be only about 1-kilometer (3000 feet). Greenstone (Tibbitt Hill volcanics) appears at the visible base of the section athwart the international border. Farther northeast, the anticlinorium does not rise high enough to expose these rocks. In northwestern Newfoundland, they appear again (Labrador group), again associated with basaltic volcanics, but the thickness seems to be only about $\frac{1}{2}$ kilometer (1500 feet), except perhaps to the southeast where they are metamorphosed.

The source areas of these vast accumulations of sediments are not known. In the vicinity of the Great Smoky Mountains, they seem to have been derived successively from the southeast, the northeast, and the northwest (Hadley and Goldsmith, 1963, p. B47, B68; King, 1964, p. 62–70; Whisonant, 1968); the great thicknesses and evidence of rapid deposition and poor sorting of some strata show that nearby areas were strongly uplifted while the basins where we now find the deposits were sinking. It seems unlikely that these source areas could have been the remnants of mountains originally raised during orogeny of the Grenville belt, for nothing comparable is known in the broad areas of that belt outside the Appalachian region. More probably, this first distinctively Appalachian sedimentation was accompanied if not caused by sharp local uplifts and downwarps, although their nature—whether broad arches and basins, narrow anticlines and synclines, or fault blocks—remains obscure.

A similar and perhaps clearer picture, though on a smaller scale, emerges from the late Precambrian history of the Avalon Peninsula in southeastern Newfoundland, on the other side of the Appalachians from the rocks just discussed. In some belts there, a continuous sequence of late Precambrian clastic sediments as much as 6 kilometers (20,000 feet) thick, beginning with graywacke and continuing up through arkose into quartzite, is capped by rocks with the first Lower Cambrian fossils; volcanics are locally present in the sequence. But on the Holyrood horst between two such belts, the Cambrian rests unconformably on the graywacke and both of them in turn in different places on a still older group of rocks including volcanics (Harbour Main group) intruded by granodiorite (Holyrood granodiorite), still very late Precambrian if radiometric ages (580 million years) are to be trusted. Here we have evidence not only of probably blocklike uplifts and downwarps, the former presumably supplying sediment to the latter, but also of intrusion of granitoid rocks and at least some metamorphism. The same period of metamorphism may be recorded in Cape Breton Island (George River group) and in southern New Brunswick (Green Head formation), and the same period of granitoid intrusion in New Brunswick and in southeastern Massachusetts (Dedham granodiorite).

This period of late Precambrian orogenic events has recently been christened the Avalonian orogeny (Lilly, 1966, p. 572); the thick sediments suggest that it produced a chain of islands along the east side of the present northern Appalachians. Similarly, the sediments along the line of basement anticlinoria may record an Avalonian event along the west side of the chain, or perhaps a similar event of slightly different age. In any case, all these facts confirm Hess' theoretical insight (1939, p. 282; 1940—he expressed it in other words) that sedimentation and tectonic activity are not successive phases in the history of a geosyncline but accompany one another from the beginning.

In the area intervening between the two zones where such late Precambrian sedimentation and Avalonian tectonism are known, evidence of Precambrian events is obscure or absent, perhaps in part because later orogeny has wiped it out, but probably in large part because no continental Precambrian rocks ever existed there. Yet around Baltimore, according to Hopson (1964), we have an immense thickness of clastic sediments (Wissahickon schist), nearly as thick as those in the Great Smoky Mountains and probably correlative, including gravity slide breccias that testify to high relief and hence suggest accompanying orogeny entirely subsequent to the Grenville-belt orogeny recorded in the basement gneiss of the same region. Here we are perhaps looking at a part of the western belt of Avalonian movements, which may have affected other parts of the Piedmont as well.

Early Paleozoic History

Very shortly after the appearance of the first Early Cambrian life in the western Appalachian region, the seas there cleared, and for a long period, lasting into the Middle Ordovician, clastic sedi-

mentation was almost wholly replaced by carbonate deposition, at least as far east as the present line of basement anticlinoria. As the Cambrian wore on, basal sands followed by carbonate deposits encroached farther and farther west onto the central platform of the continent, until an immense shallow-water carbonate bank, comparable to the modern Bahama, Florida, and Yucatán Banks around the Gulf of Mexico or the Sahul Shelf off northwestern Australia, reached from the Appalachian region to Minnesota and Texas and probably connected with similar bank areas in and near the present eastern Cordillera and Arctic Islands. The Appalachian margin of this bank differed from its central portions (but not from its Cordilleran and Arctic margins) in having been established earlier (Early Cambrian instead of Late Cambrian) and in being constantly downwarped, so that far greater thicknesses of carbonate rock, all deposited in shallow water, accumulated there than in the interior of the continent (miogeosyncline versus craton). What clastic material reached the Appalachian part of the bank during this period, for example during a pronounced regressive phase at the end of the Early Cambrian, came from the interior of the continent and *not* from farther east in the Appalachian region.

Probably, again as in modern carbonate banks, the bank edge in the Appalachian region was generally a very abrupt declivity into deep water to the east (Rodgers, 1968; Bailey, 1929, p. 69–70, made a somewhat similar proposal, starting from a suggestion by Logan, 1862); it can perhaps still be seen in a couple of areas: northwestern Vermont and south-central Pennsylvania (see Chapter 4, p. 73, and Chapter 9, p. 187). Its position was fairly stable through the time concerned, although perhaps in places it migrated to and fro when downwarping temporarily became too fast for shallow-water sedimentation to keep pace. It was also the boundary between major faunal provinces (so-called Pacific or American and Atlantic or European faunas; see Wilson, 1957). As the eastern margin of the carbonates follows or rather lies a little east of the present line of basement anticlinoria, extending out to include the gneiss dome region from Baltimore to New York, it may record the eastern margin of continental crust at that time.

East of that margin, Cambrian and Early Ordovician history was quite different, but it appears to reflect already a pattern of strike belts—of anticlinoria and synclinoria—that is thoroughly Appalachian. At present our evidence for this part of the history comes almost exclusively from the Northern Appalachians. Near the carbonate bank, sedimentation was slow and fine grained, except that lime-conglomerate and lime-breccia, locally with blocks the size of boxcars, accumulated along the foot of the bank; chert is found farther out. Farther east, the sediments coarsen and thicken markedly—estimates of thickness range up to 15 kilometers (10 miles)—and largely mafic volcanic rocks appear in abundance. Here also ultramafic masses appear, whether associated with the mafic volcanics or intruded later in the Ordovician. Volcanic activity, including acid as well as mafic lava and tuff, seems to have reached a maximum, especially in the Early or early Middle Ordovician, along and east of the line of the present-day Bronson Hill anticlinorium, which perhaps at that time resembled a volcanic island arc. Yet quartzitic sediments of uncertain age (Late Cambrian?) underlie the volcanics in a few areas along the anticlinorium. Near the former Avalonian islands farther east, the sediments are shale, siltstone, and fine-grained, thin-bedded quartzite, but here also there are bodies of volcanic rock, notably in the Middle Cambrian; the thickness is relatively small in the Avalonian belt proper, but immense on both sides (Charlotte group of southwestern New Brunswick and adjacent Maine, Meguma group of southern Nova Scotia). In any case, there is no evidence whatever in the Northern Appalachians for the existence at this time of the subcontinental land mass that was long postulated under the name of Appalachia.

Whether the picture in the eastern part of the Central and Southern Appalachians was similar we do not know. Fairly thick carbonate strata, probably of bank types, are known in Alabama, Georgia, and North Carolina (Sylacauga, Tate, and Murphy marble belts) in the westernmost Piedmont or within the Blue Ridge province, and perhaps the bank extended as far east as the Brevard zone. Beyond that our only bits of firm evidence are the Cambrian (Middle Cambrian?) fossils found in the upper part of the sequence in the main volcanic slate belt of North Carolina; how old the base of that sequence is we can only guess. In the subsurface of northern Florida, however, Lower Ordovician quartzite, still virtually undeformed, appears to overlap on an older "basement" to the south (about 530 million years old, i.e., roughly Avalonian), entirely beyond the Appalachian region.

New deformation had already begun before the Middle Ordovician in the central part of the Northern Appalachians; Middle Ordovician rocks rest unconformably on older undated but probably Paleozoic rocks in northern Maine (Penobscot orogeny), southern Quebec, and southern Gaspé,

and perhaps also in north-central Newfoundland, and graywacke began to appear in abundance in more western belts in the Early Ordovician in Newfoundland, in the early Middle Ordovician on the mainland. The Middle Ordovician was a time of great paleogeographic variety and great changes. In the western belts, where carbonate deposition had been nearly continuous since the Early or Middle Cambrian, black mud and then graywacke spread westward, the mud ultimately reaching beyond the present Mississippi River, and the great Taconic slide masses followed, slipping off new uplifts in the western part of the former deep-water basin onto the by now rapidly subsiding eastern margin of the former shallow-water bank. Black organic mud, chert and graywacke (these two mutually exclusive), and basaltic volcanics were dominant from there to well east of the Bronson Hill anticlinorium (or an equivalent zone farther northeast). The anticlinorium itself was probably being converted from a volcanic island arc into a large linear tectonic highland made of continental crust, as granodiorite was intruded into it; the same thing was happening in west-central Newfoundland and probably in central New Brunswick. The Avalonian island belt, already partly continental perhaps, may also have coalesced at this time into a single land mass, for no Ordovician rocks younger than Early Ordovician (Arenig) are known in that region. Yet in between these growing lands lay a vast area of tranquil sea far from any source of sediment, where only very fine clay was rhythmically mixed with lime-mud to produce the "ribboned" clayey limestone (Carys Mills formation and other units) of northeastern Maine and northern New Brunswick, rendzina soils on which support the major potato culture of those areas where otherwise spruce forest would reign supreme. The belt of limy rocks can be traced northeastward to eastern Gaspé and perhaps central Newfoundland and southwestward, though interruptedly and mostly as metamorphosed equivalents such as diopside schist, as far as eastern Connecticut (Hebron formation).

The uplifts mentioned above were almost certainly simply the surface effects of orogenic deformation at depth, accompanied by (mainly low-grade) metamorphism and granodiorite intrusion (true pre-Devonian granite is rare in the Appalachians); this period of deformation is called the Taconic orogeny, and radiometric data suggest that it took place between 500 and 450 million years ago, very probably spread over much of that time. In the western part of the Northern Appalachians, uplift went on into the Upper

Ordovician—also deformation, at least in out-lying regions such as the Saint Lawrence Valley and eastern Pennsylvania—and floods of coarse sediment poured westward to form the Queenston delta in New York and adjacent states and far down the western side of the Appalachians to Tennessee and Alabama. As always through the Paleozoic, deposits were far thicker within these western Appalachian provinces than to the west on the central platform of the continent; indeed it was precisely the relations in this part of the Appalachians that first led James Hall to the idea of a trough of excess sedimentation that James D. Dana later christened the geosynclinal. Curiously enough, Anticosti Island, now far closer to the uplifted zone than, say, central Pen-nsylvania, received only black mud, and that only during a short period at the end of the Middle Ordovician. On the other hand, the open sea to the east in the present "potato belt" was entirely undisturbed, and shaly limestone con-tinued to be deposited there uninterruptedly into the Silurian.

The corresponding history in the eastern part of the Central and Southern Appalachians is still obscure. We do know that a flood of sediments, entirely comparable to that in the Queenston delta, though less voluminous, spread into Tennessee and Virginia from the southeast in the middle Middle Ordovician (Blount group and Bays formation), reaching its maximum there indeed before mud had even got to central New York State. Furthermore, rather coarse polymictic conglomerate is known at several places in the easternmost belts of these Middle Ordovician sediments preserved in the Valley and Ridge province, from near Roanoke, Virginia, to north-ernmost Georgia (Kellberg and Grant, 1956); the conglomerate contains pebbles of rock from the base of the Middle Ordovician down to the basal Cambrian clastic sequence (Chilhowee group), which must all have been exposed to erosion not far to the southeast at that time. We also know that this burst of sediment was accompanied by the first of a series of cataclysmic volcanic eruptions, the ash from which is now found as beds in Middle Ordovician strata over the whole eastern United States and into Ontario. In the Virginia Piedmont, moreover, slate with lower Upper Ordovician fossils (Arvonia slate) rests with a basal sandstone on already weathered granodiorite. All these facts suggest that the climax of Taconic orogeny was earlier here than in the northern Appalachians. Radiometry of the Piedmont rocks further suggests the import-ance of Ordovician, Taconic, orogeny in the southern Appalachians, but we are still unable to assess its full significance. We do not know of any younger Paleozoic sedimentary deposits in the entire Blue Ridge-Piedmont region, except at the extreme west edge in Alabama (in the Talla-dega group), and perhaps the whole region be-came at this time continental crust and dry land, as the northern Appalachians did in the Devonian. South of the Piedmont in northern Florida, on the other hand, the period from Early Ordovician to Early Devonian is re-presented by undeformed black shale with a remarkably European or African marine fauna.

Middle Paleozoic History

Berry and Boucot (1970) have given us a clear picture of Silurian paleogeography in the Northern Appalachians. At the beginning of the period, the seas were restricted to the belt of shaly limestone and a few other spots (notably Anticosti), but through the period they encroached steadily on the new tectonic highlands. Basal quartz-pebble conglomerate and quartzite are known in many areas, obviously not always of the same age, and in places carbonate rocks are intimately inter-bedded with clastics in the overlying deposits, especially in the Connecticut Valley-Gaspé syncli-norium and north of it in Gaspé. A bank edge can apparently be recognized along the northern margin of this synclinorium in and near the Gaspé Peninsula. Volcanic rocks are common along the Bronson Hill and also on the other anticlinoria (except the basement anticlinoria to the west), particularly on the northwest flank of the old Avalonian belt in southern New Brunswick and down strike into southeastern Maine and eastern Massachusetts.

In the western part of the Central and Southern Appalachians, the Silurian began with the deposi-tion of a great sheet of clean quartz sand, beach and shallow marine, and above it the seas en-croached more and more as the quantity of sedi-ment coming in from the east became less and less. Farther west on the platform, carbonate deposition had continued, interrupted only briefly during the Late Ordovician (not at all in central Tennessee and farther south), and it now encroached again into the Appalachian region. There was a temporary check in the Late Silurian, when a mild disturbance (Salinic disturbance) produced slight angular unconformities in places in eastern Quebec, and a flood of partly red clastics invaded New York (Salina group) and Pennsyl-vania (reaching momentarily as far as northern Vir-ginia), but by the end of the period, limestone had encroached again well into the Valley and

TABLE 2   Orogenic Movements in the Appalachian Region

Orogenic episode and approximate date	Known area of influence	Maximum manifestation
Appalachian movements **Palisades** Late Triassic (Carnian-Norian) 190–200 m.y.	Belt along central axis of already completed mountain chain	Fault troughs, broad warping, basaltic lava, dike swarm
Alleghany Pennsylvanian and/or Permian (Westphalian and later) 230–260 m.y.	West side of central and southern Appalachians, southeast side of northern Appalachians, perhaps also in Carolina Piedmont	Strong folding, also middle-grade metamorphism and granite intrusion at least in southern New England
Early Ouachita Mid-Mississippian through early Pennsylvanian (Viséan to early Westphalian)	Only in southernmost Appalachians in central Alabama	Clastic wedge, also possibly broad east-west structures that influenced later deformation
Acadian Devonian, mainly Middle but episodic into Mississippian (Emsian-Eifelian) 360–400 m.y.	Whole of northern Appalachians, except along northwest edge; as far southwest as Pennsylvania	Medium- to high-grade metamorphism, granite intrusion
Salinic Late Silurian (Ludlow)	Local on northwest side of northern Appalachians	Mild angular unconformity, minor clastic wedge
Taconic Middle (and Late) Ordovician (Caradoc, locally probably older) 450–500 m.y.	General on northwest side of northern Appalachians, local elsewhere; an early phase in Carolinas and Virginia, perhaps general in Piedmont province	Strong angular unconformity, gravity slides (?), at least low-grade metamorphism, granodioritic and ultramafic intrusion
Penobscot Early Ordovician or older (Arenig or older)	Local on northwest side of northern Appalachians	Strong angular unconformity, slaty cleavage, possibly some intrusion
Avalonian Latest Precambrian	Southeastern Newfoundland, Cape Breton Island, southern New Brunswick; probably also central and southern Appalachians (Florida?)	Probably some deformation, uplift of sources of coarse arkosic debris, gravity slides(?)
Late Precambrian about 580 m.y.	Southeastern Newfoundland, Cape Breton Island, southern New Brunswick; perhaps eastern Massachusetts	Mostly low-grade metamorphism, granitic intrusion

Orogenic episode and approximate date	Known area of influence	Maximum manifestation
Grenville (pre-Appalachian) movements Late Precambrian 800–1100 m.y.	Eastern North America including western part of Appalachian region	High-grade metamorphism, granitic and other intrusion

Ridge province. Along the east side of the province from Tennessee southwest, however, deposition had ceased in the Middle Ordovician, to resume only in the Devonian or even the Carboniferous; perhaps we see here the edge of a major Piedmont land mass produced in the Ordovician, but the stratigraphy farther west does not suggest any important source of sediment here after the Middle Ordovician.

Carbonate rocks seem to have reached a maximum in the earliest part of the Early Devonian, but then clastics started to advance again. In the interior belts of the Northern Appalachians, vast thicknesses of quartz sandstone and graywacke, generally rhythmically interbedded with siltstone and shale, were rapidly deposited in the major synclinoria (Littleton and Seboomook formations, etc.); volcanics still appeared in force along the anticlinorial trends. But by the Middle Devonian, deposition had ceased throughout the region, and in most of it the rocks then suffered their most severe period of deformation, metamorphism, and granite intrusion, the Acadian orogeny. Radiometry dates this period as 400 to 360 million years ago and strongly suggests at least two pulses of granitic plutonism (Faul and others, 1963). It may be suggested that at this time virtually the whole of the Northern Appalachians became continental crust and thus an integral part of the continent. Only the northern part of Gaspé and perhaps some other areas in eastern Quebec, western Vermont, the Hudson Valley, and western Newfoundland, all of which had been severely deformed in the Ordovician, escaped with only mild folding. Clastics appeared in the western belts already in the Early Devonian in Gaspé, western Newfoundland, and southeastern New York State; in the Middle and Late Devonian, vast floods of clastic sediments again invaded New York, Pennsylvania, and adjacent states to form the Catskill delta, and in the earliest Carboniferous mud again reached as far as the present Mississippi River. By that time, intramontane basins containing red continental deposits had formed in many places in the interior of the chain, especially in the Maritime Provinces, the first already in the Middle Devonian, more in the late Devonian, and the vast ramified basin

around the present Gulf of Saint Lawrence by the early Carboniferous. Volcanics appeared locally among these deposits, and angular unconformities testify that orogenic movement continued.

The Southern Appalachians appear to have escaped this storm, except that the clastics crept down the west side, mud extending the full length, coarser clastics advancing in a series of bursts and reaching Tennessee in the Late Devonian and again in the Early Carboniferous. Carbonate deposition reasserted itself however, first on the platform in the Mississippi Valley, then advancing east and northeast into the Virginias and western Pennsylvania. It reached its maximum in Sainte Genevieve or early Chester (mid-Viséan) time; at almost exactly the same time the sea broke into the Gulf of Saint Lawrence basin and deposited several layers of marine limestone and also bodies of evaporite (Windsor formation).

Late Paleozoic History

Even before this, however, a new wave of clastics had appeared at the south end of the Appalachians in Alabama, this time coming from the south. Because the stratigraphy of these strata is like that of beds of the same age in the Ouachita Mountains of Arkansas and Oklahoma, they probably reflect the beginning of the uplift and orogenic movement that swept from south to north in those mountains during the Carboniferous (Ham and Wilson, 1967, p. 383–388). In the visible portion of the Appalachians, Ouachita deformation seems to have been minor, but perhaps it is responsible for the remarkable east-west trends that cut across the typical northeast-striking Appalachian structures of Alabama.

In any case, the Early Carboniferous respite was short. The sea was quickly driven out of the basins in the Maritime Provinces and Newfoundland, and continental clastics were again deposited there, coarse fanglomerates around the margins, lake and then fluvial and swamp (coal-bearing) strata in the centers. Deformation continued, including considerable strike-slip faulting, but it was more and more confined to the southern and eastern sides of the Gulf of Saint Lawrence basin and to smaller basins in Nova Scotia and Newfoundland, where deformation was especially intense. A basin or two also developed in Rhode Island and eastern Massachusetts in the Late Carboniferous, and the deposits were then very badly deformed and in part metamorphosed and intruded by granite. Final movements in all these areas were apparently Late Carboniferous or Permian (possibly even Early Triassic); radiometry suggests an age between 260 and 230 million years.

In the late Early Carboniferous, clastics from the southeast also replaced limestone again throughout the Valley and Ridge province and into the Appalachian Plateau, and in the Late Carboniferous they spread westward across the continent as far as Kansas above a widespread surface of erosion, the whole area becoming a vast plain where coal swamps and river flood plains alternated rhythmically with shallow seas. For the first time carbonate deposition ceased to be dominant on the platform east of Texas; for the first time also sediment thicknesses in the western Appalachians were not significantly greater than on the platform. All the sediments in the Valley and Ridge province and the eastern half of the Plateau, including beds as young as Early Permian, were then folded and faulted, apparently together. Since this deformation was the first to be understood (by the Rogers brothers and their assistants in the 1830's), it has always been considered the chief Appalachian orogeny or revolution and was long considered to mark the end of the Paleozoic era. But as the above account should make clear, it was only one of a whole series of orogenic events spread over the entire Paleozoic, and probably not even the most significant of them, especially if, as seems probable, its role in the southern Appalachian Piedmont is less than used to be thought. Moreover, its age is perhaps the least well established of all; it must have ended after the Early Permian and probably long before the Late Triassic, but the sedimentary evidence rather suggests it began before the end of the Early Carboniferous, and it may have reached its climax slightly earlier in the Southern than in the Central Appalachians. By accepting for it Woodward's name Alleghany orogeny, for the Allegheny Mountains (see fn. p. 30) in the Central Appalachians, we can range it properly as one of the numerous Appalachian orogenies, of which the current roster, probably not yet complete, is given in Table 2 (from Rodgers, 1967, p. 421).

Post-Paleozoic History

Our next glimpse of the Appalachians is in the Late Triassic; they were now a chain of mountains, though not necessarily lofty ones, and the core areas were already deeply eroded. Along the crest of the chain for almost its full length was a great rift-valley graben system, which rivers were filling with debris from the mountains on either side; temporary lakes were present in some parts of the rift valley, coal swamps in others, and thrice volcanoes or fissure eruptions poured out basaltic lava. A little later alkalic magma broke through to the surface in New Hampshire and vicinity, accompanied by the formation of several great calderas. Only in the Cretaceous or the Late Jurassic did the sea once more enter the region, and then only to wash the southeastern and southern margins of the Appalachian chain, which repeated archlike uplifts kept high and subject to erosion, the debris accumulating as a great clastic wedge under the Coastal Plain and continental shelf from the Grand Banks off Newfoundland as far as Louisiana and at times Texas. During this period the mountains approached the forms we see today.

Finally the Pleistocene ice sheets covered the north half of the chain, modifying the topography and especially creating great numbers of lakes; perhaps at the same time the sea encroached more widely than before into the Northern Appalachians, reaching entirely across it in the Gulf and Estuary of Saint Lawrence and separating Newfoundland from the rest of the chain. Following the most recent disappearance of ice from the Appalachian region, man invaded the area, and geologic history merges into human history, first of the red race and then of the white.

CHAPTER **12**

Generalities and Speculations

Limits and Possible Continuations of the Appalachian Orogenic Belt

The Appalachian orogenic belt is that part of eastern North America where Paleozoic deformation was strong. The northwestern boundary of this belt is fairly obvious and generally fairly sharp, especially in the Northern Appalachians; even where the Appalachian Plateau forms a sort of transition zone between strongly folded and unfolded strata, the transition is not evenly gradational but steplike. The decollement hypothesis for the structure of the Plateau and the Valley and Ridge province explains these steps as the surface expression of differing thicknesses of affected strata above different parts of a stepped decollement surface, so that the deeper one looks in the pile of sediments the farther southeast would lie the northwestern limit of deformation. At the level of the basement indeed, it would lie at the southeast margin of the Valley and Ridge province along or under the overturned west flank of the series of basement anticlinoria— Blue Ridge, Highlands, Green Mountains, Long Range. In any case, the contrast is strong between the deformed Appalachian belt and the vast central platform of the continent where the sialic continental crust has remained stable for a thousand million years or more and overlying sediments have been affected mostly or only by vertical movements such as differential warping.

To the southeast, on the other hand, rock show-ing Appalachian deformation and, generally, metamorphism continues as far as evidence is available beneath the Atlantic Coastal Plain and continental shelf sediments, and it appears to be directly contiguous on that side with typical ocean crust, the age of which is unknown but may actually be post-Paleozoic if one accepts current ideas on the production of oceanic crust by spreading from the mid-ocean ridges and current estimates of the rate of spreading. Only in the extreme south, under the Coastal Plain of southernmost Georgia and northern Florida, do we find on the continent rock unaffected by Paleozoic orogeny. As discussed in Chapter 9, typical Piedmont rocks reach only to an east-west line in southern Georgia; beyond they are succeeded by virtually undeformed Paleozoic strata, which farther southeast in central Florida are adjacent to and seem to rest upon pre-Ordovician rocks including granite and diorite. Apparently we are looking here at a fragment of older sialic crust, on the other side of the Appalachian orogenic belt from the central North American platform (another possibility would be that this block was originally a "median massif" within the orogenic belt). The extent of the Florida fragment is not clear; presumably it reaches from the oceanic crust beneath the Gulf of Mexico to that beneath the Atlantic Ocean (east of the Blake Plateau) and extends southeastward an unknown distance under the thick Mesozoic and Cenozoic carbonate strata of southern Florida and perhaps the Bahamas.

To the southwest, it has long been evident that the Appalachian orogenic belt is related in some way to the Ouachita Mountains of Arkansas and Oklahoma, but the nature of the connection has not been clear; subsurface information has gradually provided some light on the question (see summary by King, 1961b). The Ouachitas are one of several areas in the south-central United States where strongly deformed Paleozoic rocks are known, either in outcrop or in the subsurface; such areas fall into two main groups. In the first group, the Paleozoic strata are relatively competent, largely carbonate, and of platform type, although in some areas—the Arbuckles, for example—they are far thicker than the equivalent strata on the platform on either side. These Paleozoic rocks were deformed on the margins of large blocks of Precambrian basement uplifted in the late Paleozoic, and the group forms a complex double or triple belt of such uplifts, including the Arbuckle and Wichita Mountains of Oklahoma and extending west-northwestward across the southwestern part of the North American platform from under the edge of the Coastal Plain in southeastern Oklahoma and adjacent Texas into southeastern Colorado and indeed beyond, into the Eastern Rocky Mountains where very similar uplifts of Laramide age have further complicated the picture. In the second group, which includes the Ouachitas, a less competent, much more shaly, and in its upper part geosynclinal sequence was deformed by parallel folds and thrust faults not involving the basement so far as known. This group forms a single but highly sinuous belt traceable along the southern margin of the platform from the Ouachita Mountains under the Coastal Plain cover to the Marathon region of West Texas, and beyond into Mexico; mild metamorphism is present along the side of the belt away from the platform. In both groups deformation was largely Carboniferous (locally Early Permian) and took place in a series of episodes (Ham and Wilson, 1967, p. 387–392). In the first or Arbuckle-Wichita group, the stratigraphy has considerable similarity to that in the western Appalachians, especially in the lower part of the section where carbonate rocks dominate in both, but the structure is quite unlike anything in the Appalachians; in the second or Ouachita group the structure is more like that of the Valley and Ridge province, but the stratigraphy is rather different, except that some strata in central Alabama show certain Ouachita-like features, especially in the upper part of the section.

The easternmost exposures in the Ouachitas are nearly 500 kilometers (300 miles) west-northwest of the southwesternmost exposures of folded rocks

in the Appalachians, but in the subsurface the two deformed belts come much closer. Carbonate rocks of Valley and Ridge type have been followed beneath the Coastal Plain of western Alabama for 100 kilometers (60 miles) southwest along their strike, but there they encounter a major flexure where the Coastal Plain sediments thicken enormously, so that the older rocks drop down beyond the reach of the drill. From the other side, the shaly rocks of the Ouachitas can apparently be followed 300 kilometers (200 miles) south-southeast and southeast along their strike into eastern Mississippi, where they are bevelled by the same flexure. Just to the southeast of the last of these rocks, carbonate rocks of Valley and Ridge type appear on strike with them but well to the northwest of the projected strike of the Valley and Ridge itself, suggesting that the Valley and Ridge province may turn a sharp corner in the vicinity of the flexure.

The flexure mentioned extends east-southeastward roughly parallel with the Ouachita trend from northeasternmost Texas to eastern Mississippi but then cuts almost perpendicularly across all the Appalachian trends and continues southeastward into western Florida and roughly along the Gulf Coast of peninsular Florida; here it forms the southwest side of the triangle of undeformed Paleozoic rocks in northern Florida (p. 198–199, Fig. 9A) and perhaps the western side of the Florida fragment of sialic crust mentioned above. Indeed all along its course it may lie along or near the southern limit of pre-Mesozoic sialic crust, whether that was an original continental margin or was produced by tearing apart a larger continental block.

Even though the flexure makes it impossible to be sure, probably the Ouachita rocks in eastern Mississippi originally extended "behind," i.e., south of the Valley and Ridge rocks there and in Alabama, and possibly they connected with the shaly rocks of the Talladega belt at the west edge of the Piedmont in Alabama. If so, the relations in Mississippi are like those in southernmost Quebec, where a more external zone with a dominantly carbonate section (that of the Champlain Valley) disappears northward along strike, apparently beneath a more internal zone with a dominantly shaly section (the "Taconic" belt along the southeast side of the Saint Lawrence; see p. 117–119). Beyond the Northern Appalachians, the carbonate zone reappears in western Newfoundland in its normal position at the edge of the orogenic belt; west of the Ouachitas, on the other hand, it reappears in the Arbuckle Mountains and farther northwest in an entirely different position, as a belt with a greatly thickened stratigraphic section entirely inside the platform.

At their northeastern end, the Appalachians clearly strike out into the open Atlantic at the south end of the Labrador Channel between Labrador and Greenland, and no trace of Appalachian structure is known on the floor of the deep ocean; on the contrary all known trends there strike north-south or northwest-southeast, at high angles to the Appalachian trends but roughly parallel to the continental margins on either side of the channel (e.g., Godby, Baker, Bower, and Hood, 1966; Mayhew, Drake, and Nafe, 1968). According to the theory of continental drift, the continuation of the Appalachians should be sought in the western part of the British Isles, where two Paleozoic orogenic belts converge— the Caledonian belt striking southwest from Scotland and northwestern England across Wales and northern and central Ireland, the Hercynian belt striking west from southern England and Wales across southern Ireland; Bailey (1929, p. 74–76), following out an idea of Bertrand (1887, p. 443, Fig. 5), suggested that the convergence is completed in North America and explicitly invoked continental drift as an explanation. The timing of orogenies on the two sides of the Atlantic has generally been considered to contradict this idea, however, as shown in the following table, based on the conventional assignments of orogenies to the ends of periods:

North America		Europe	
"Appalachian"	Permian		
		Hercynian	Carboniferous
Acadian	Devonian		
		Caledonian*	Silurian
Taconic	Ordovician		

But more thorough analyses of orogenic timing in the two areas have largely dispelled this contradiction. In the Appalachians, as indicated in preceding chapters, the Alleghany orogeny was probably going on through much of the Carboniferous period, especially in the Maritime Provinces and Newfoundland, ending in the Permian perhaps but not necessarily at the end of the period; it is thus strictly coeval with the main Hercynian orogenic episodes of Europe. Likewise, as McKerrow (1962) has shown and as indeed Bailey (1929, p. 60–62) had seen, the Caledonian orogeny of Great Britain was not simply a single or double pulse at the end of the Silurian period but a long complex process, lasting at least from the Early Ordovician if not the Late Cambrian to the Middle Devonian and including phases roughly contemporaneous with the Taconic and Acadian orogenies of the Northern Appalachians (themselves not single pulses); even the late Silurian or earliest Devonian phase, dominant only in the eastern part of the British Caledonian belt, may have its Appalachian representative in the Salinic disturbance, though that was quantitatively insignificant beside its British counterpart and perhaps a bit earlier. Finally, the Avalonian orogeny of the northern Appalachians seems to have its counterpart in the Cadomian orogeny of Brittany and the British Isles.

When one compares the northern Appalachians and the British Isles geologic belt by geologic belt, one can find a large number of more or less exact parallels, some involving only rough likenesses, other astonishingly close similarities down to stratigraphic details. Some of these parallels are listed in Table 3.

Table 3 emphasizes the parallels, of course, and the data were selected for this purpose (see also Dewey and Kay, 1968); doubtless data could have been selected to emphasize the differences instead. But on any reasonable reconstruction the present continental shelves off northeastern Newfoundland and western Ireland, each on the order of 300 kilometers (200 miles) wide, would have intervened between the now visible portions of the Appalachians and their supposed British continuation; one should not expect therefore any closer resemblance between them than across the Gulf of Saint Lawrence or between the Maritime Provinces and central New England across Maine and the Gulf of Maine. In both the latter cases there are many differences as well as similarities in stratigraphy and structure, but no one doubts the original continuity.

If one accepts the hypothesis of continental drift and recognizes the British Caledonides and Hercynides as the northeastern continuation of the Appalachians, one is then forced to examine the whole eastern coast of the North Atlantic south of Britain and ask if it also was once contiguous with the Appalachian belt. Tight and loose reconstructions become possible here, depending on whether one fits the continental margins together as Bullard and others (1965) have done or assumes that an older but narrower ocean intervened (Nafe and Drake, 1969, p. 83). The Hercynides of Brittany and the Vendée strike westward out to sea south of the British Hercynides and are likewise cut off at the continental margin, on the north side of the deep part of the Bay of Biscay. The Hercynides of the Iberian Peninsula, the Iberian Meseta, on the

---

*Reports of strictly Caledonian (i.e., post-Silurian, pre-Devonian) orogeny in Newfoundland have not been confirmed.

TABLE 3

Northern Appalachians	British Isles, etc.
Cambrian and Lower Ordovician carbonate section—western Newfoundland, the Champlain Valley, and farther southwest	Durness limestone—northwest Scotland, long known to have a fauna more like the American fauna than like that of the Baltic province; likewise the physical stratigraphy shows some remarkable parallels, e.g., black asphaltic dolostone in the Upper Cambrian
Zone of Taconic, and locally older, deformation, metamorphism, and granitoid intrusion—west-central Newfoundland, northern Maine, and western New England	Zone of Dalradian (and Moine) schists, metamorphosed in Late Cambrian or Early Ordovician—northwest Ireland and Highlands of Scotland
Zone of dominantly Acadian metamorphism and granitic intrusion—central Newfoundland, central New Brunswick, and central New England	Zone with late Precambrian (Cadomian) deformation granite)—central Ireland and Midlands of Scotland and vicinity
Post-Acadian basins, mainly continental Carboniferous and Upper Devonian—Maritime Provinces and southwest Newfoundland	Old Red Sandstone and Lower Carboniferous basins—central Ireland, Midlands of Scotland, etc.
Zone with late Precambrian (Avalonian) deformation followed by latest Precambrian volcanics and sediments, then by Cambrian and Lower Ordovician shale section with European or Baltic fauna—southeastern Newfoundland, Cape Breton Island, southern New Brunswick, and eastern Massachusetts	Zone with late Precambrian (Cadomian) deformation followed by latest Precambrian volcanics, then by Cambro-Ordovician shale section, again with striking stratigraphic similarities—southeast Ireland, southwest Wales, Anglesey, Welsh Border, and western Midlands (also Ordovician iron ore in Brittany is remarkably similar in petrology and stratigraphy to Wabana iron ore of southeastern Newfoundland)
Triassic basins—Nova Scotia, etc.	New Red Sandstone basins—Midlands of England
Alleghany folded zones—southwestern Newfoundland, Nova Scotia, southern New Brunswick, and southeastern New England	Hercynian folded belt—southern Ireland, southern Wales, southwestern England, and Brittany

other hand, trend at a quite different angle; the strike is northwest across much of the Meseta, but at the northwestern corner of the peninsula it swings through north to northeast, into the Bay of Biscay, and many have considered the metamorphic core of the Meseta to be the continuation of Brittany, especially those who accept the 45 degree rotation of Iberia in the Cenozoic proposed by Carey (1958a, p. 257—261) to open up the deep part of the Bay of Biscay and force up the Pyrenees. (Mattauer, 1968, on the other hand, explains the same discrepancy neatly by 500 kilometers—300 miles—of very late Paleozoic dextral strike slip on the North Pyreneean "fundamental fault.") South of the younger Alpine belt of southern Spain and northern Morocco, Hercynian deformed and metamorphic rocks appear again in central Morocco (the Moroccan Meseta) and beneath the High Atlas; here the strike is northeast, roughly parallel to the Atlantic Coast. One is tempted therefore to postulate a further rotation of the Iberian block in the late Paleozoic, to permit its

restoration to a proper position and trend between Brittany and Morocco. The true southeast margin of the Hercynian (and Appalachian?) belt would then be represented by the folded sedimentary terrains of the Montagne Noire in southern France (and Sardinia?), the Cantabrian Mountains in north-central Spain, and the Anti-Atlas in southern Morocco.

A further southwestward continuation of the European Hercynides has recently been recognized in the Mauritanide fold belt of West Africa (Sougy, 1962, 1969; see Chapter 9, 199, and Fig. 8B), which can be interpreted as a Hercynian metamorphic core thrust eastward over a Paleozoic folded belt at the margin of the Sahara platform. In southeastern Senegal, this belt appears to branch, the Hercynian trend curving westward to disappear under the coastal plain of southern Senegal and northern Portuguese Guinea, whereas an older, probably late Precambrian (Avalonian?) trend continues south and then south-southeast, diving under the flat-lying middle Paleozoic strata of the Fouta-Djallon Plateau in Guinea but reappearing beyond as the Rokelide belt, which can apparently be followed all along the coast of Sierra Leone (east of a narrow coastal plain) and at least half the length of Liberia.

A tight reconstruction of the Atlantic would readily permit one to connect the southeastern front of the Hercynian branch with the southern front of the Appalachians under the Coastal Plain of southern Georgia, but only if the reconstruction of Bullard and others (1965) is modified by shifting North America about 250 kilometers (150 miles) southward relative to Africa. Such a modification has the added advantage that the sharp angle in the present North American continental margin opposite the Tongue of the Ocean in the Bahama Bank would not lie on the African continent in Portuguese Guinea, as in the Bullard reconstruction, but would fit the similar angle in the African continental margin southwest of the Guineas; furthermore, the Bahama Banks would not overlap the Sahara platform but would fit rather neatly into the acute angle left in the Bullard reconstruction where the African and South American continental margins diverge west of Cape Palmas (in easternmost Liberia) and the Amazon Delta. On the other hand, North America can hardly be shifted this much relative to Europe, and hence Africa and Europe must be brought 250 kilometers (150 miles) closer together, perhaps by eliminating the entire width of the geosynclinal Alpine zone in southern Spain (Betic Cordillera) and northern Morocco (Rif and pre-Rif). Thus the Mauritanide belt would be the missing eastern side of the central and southern Appalachians, and the Florida fragment and its possible southeastern continuation under the Bahamas would be a piece of the Sahara platform or a sliver from an original Sahara-Guiana shield.

Once one has gone this far, the Guiana platform of northern South America must be brought into the reconstruction. That the Caribbean Sea is a late development seems evident, and it and the Bartlett Deep can simply be closed up in the reconstruction with few if any qualms. The Gulf of Mexico is a different matter, yet it too has an oceanic crust and there is no evidence of its existence before the Jurassic. If a tight reconstruction of the North Atlantic be permitted, then northwestern South America (*without* the Mesozoic and Cenozoic additions to the Andes) might be replaced nearly against the pre-Mesozoic continental margin on the northeast and northwest sides of the Gulf, Paleozoic portions of the Greater Antilles (if any) being slivers from the fracture zone. If so, the interior belts of the Ouachita chain and the southwestward continu-

ation of the Appalachian Piedmont should be sought along the northwest margin of the Guiana platform, in the Paleozoic (at least partly Taconic) fold belt since reworked into the eastern part of the northern Andes (Bürgl, 1967, p. 431 ff.). On the other hand, the east-west Paleozoic fold belt of northern Honduras, southern Guatemala, and southeastern and southern Mexico (south of the transverse volcanic range from Orizaba to Colima) does not fit into this reconstruction any better than into Bullard's, whether because it originally lay farther west but remained attached to North rather than South America or because, as is perhaps more probable, the whole reconstruction is faulty. (In Carey's reconstruction, 1958a, Fig. 24, the eastern half of this belt is separated from the western half and rotated back into the western Gulf of Mexico, but there are no obvious parallels with the Ouachitas and it does not seem reasonable to separate the two halves of the belt.)

The timing of all this rifting and drifting is by no means clear. In Chapter 7, it was pointed out that if Newfoundland has rotated and is separated from the Maritime Provinces by a right-handed strike-slip movement of a couple of hundred kilometers (over 100 miles), the movement must have taken place before the full development of the Carboniferous basin under and around the Gulf of Saint Lawrence, for that basin has not been torn apart. The known strike-slip faulting in the same area also suggests that fragmentation at the north end of the Appalachians began in the Carboniferous, and perhaps the cessation of compression in the Caledonian belt in northwestern Europe and its transference to the Hercynian belt is another expression of the beginning of rifting in or at least of strike-slip movement along the future northern North Atlantic (Harland, 1965). Farther south, there is no reason to assume any rifting until the Triassic, yet by the Jurassic the Gulf of Mexico and the central North Atlantic were present or had at least begun to form. Perhaps one could interpret the curious orientation of the "Triassic" (perhaps Jurassic) dike swarm in the Appalachians as a record of tension related not to isostatic adjustment in the Appalachians but to the incipient separation of North America from South America and Africa.

To sum up this drifting speculation, the Appalachians might be considered one large segment of a global Paleozoic orogenic belt, other fragments of which are now found in northwestern South America, the Ouachita system of the south-central United States and eastern Mexico, the Mauritanide belt of West Africa, the Moroccan and Iberian Mesetas, and Brittany and the western British Isles, beyond which two branches lead off, the older one into Scandinavia, East Greenland, and

Svalbard (Spitsbergen), the younger one across central Europe to the Scythian "platform" along the north shore of the Black Sea.

Mechanism of Orogeny

All that has gone before should make it clear that, although in many ways the Appalachians can claim to be a "type" mountain range—here indeed a major folded belt was first clearly worked out and here the geosyncline was first recognized and named—their history is far more complex than implied by the simple scheme of successive geosyncline, orogeny, and uplift found in textbooks; all three of these accompanied one another almost from beginning to end, even if perhaps they predominated in the given order. In each orogenic "episode" (except perhaps the last), maximum orogeny took place in a linear core belt, where metamorphism and plutonism acted upon a thick shale and graywacke section, generally stuffed with volcanics or even dominantly volcanic. These rocks, and any floor on which they may have rested, were as if gripped and squeezed between the jaws of a giant vise, and at the same time heated up enough to become quite plastic and to stew in their own juice, in the fluids released as they transformed into mineral assemblages stable at these higher pressures and temperatures or as they reached the partial melting point. Away from the belt of maximum orogeny, the stratigraphic section, itself different—containing few or no volcanics but generally far more carbonate rock—was deformed at low pressure and temperature partly or wholly independent of its here thick, rigid sialic floor, as though it had escaped from and spilled out over the jaws of the vise (to be sure, only the western marginal belt is visible in the Appalachians, except perhaps in Newfoundland). Near the transition from core to western marginal belt, part of the sialic floor, perhaps its eastern margin, was semiplastically forced upward to form the great basement anticlinoria, as if the inner surface of the vise itself became more plastic and was forced upward and outward under the pressure it was exerting, while material originally deposited upon it slid by gravity outward into the adjacent part of the marginal belt.

From episode to episode, not only the intensity of compression within the core belt but also its position varied, although it was always linear and aligned generally northeast-southwest. The basic

difference between the northern and southern segments of the Appalachians, as Shatsky saw years ago (1945), is that in the northern segment the core belt migrated generally southeastward away from the North American continent, in the southern segment northwestward toward the continent* (curiously, the Avalonian movements seem to disobey this rule in both segments, although they may appear to do so simply because we can observe them only where later deformation has not overprinted them). A graph of intensity versus time, especially if integrated over the whole chain, would not, I believe, be either a series of sharp isolated peaks or a smooth sine curve but would resemble the stock market, with some major highs and lows, most of them compound, but (despite the word "episode" I have used above) with no sharp separation into orogenic and non-orogenic periods or phases and no true periodicity.

Furthermore, for me the vise is not a metaphor but a fairly exact model. Thus the evidence of intense shortening perpendicular to the length of the chain, not only in the folded marginal belts but also in the central core belt, is too clear for me to doubt that there was not only confining but directed pressure, the greatest compressive stress being consistently directed roughly horizontally across the orogenic belt. The western jaw of the vise was I believe the Precambrian sialic crust forming the platform of the North American continent, as it then existed; the eastern jaw may have been the Sahara platform; in between lay the main Appalachian "geosyncline," which at the beginning probably had an oceanic floor but which gradually became clogged with sialic debris produced from the sediments and volcanics between the jaws of the vise during the various metamorphic and plutonic episodes, until the whole was welded together into new, thick crust. Compression then relaxed, and the thickened crust rose isostatically to form mountains and has continued to do so ever since. Tension then threatened to tear the mountains apart along the Triassic keystone graben system, and eventually did along a different line of fracture that became the North Atlantic Ocean. The cause of such compression and tension I do not look for in the crust but deeper in the body of the Earth, in the form of slow but irresistible movements driven by heat energy, above which the shallow crust has floated passively to and fro, now smashed together, now rifted apart, like a half-plastic, half-brittle scum on a convecting liquid.

*Shatsky further pointed out that the Appalachian Plateau, a typical "foredeep," occurs only in front of the segment in which migration was toward the continent; he believed this to illustrate a general rule.

APPENDIX

Small-Scale Geologic Maps of the Appalachians

North America

Geologic map of North America (2 sheets), 1965, 1/5,000,000
 U.S. Geological Survey, Washington, D.C.
Tectonic map of North America (2 sheets), 1969, 1/5,000,000
 U.S. Geological Survey, Washington, D.C.
 See also The Tectonics of North America—a discussion to accompany the
 Tectonic map of North America (P. B. King), 1969, U.S. Geological Survey
 Professional Paper 628.

Canada

Geological map of Canada, 1969, 1/5,000,000
 Geological Survey of Canada (Map 1250A), Ottawa, Ont.
Tectonic map of Canada, 1969, 1/5,000,000
 Geological Survey of Canada (Map 1251A), Ottawa, Ont.

United States of America

Geologic map of the United States (4 sheets), 1932, 1/2,500,000
 U.S. Geological Survey, Washington, D.C.
National Atlas of the United States, Geology, 1967, 1/7,500,000
 U.S. Geological Survey (Atlas sheet 75), Washington, D.C.
Tectonic map of the United States (2 sheets), 1944 (1st ed.), 1961 (2nd ed.),
 1/2,500,000
 U.S. Geological Survey, Washington, D.C.; American Association of Petroleum
 Geologists, Tulsa, Okla.
National Atlas of the United States, Tectonic features, 1967, 1/7,500,000
 U.S. Geological Survey (Atlas sheet 70), Washington, D.C.

226

Newfoundland

Geology—Island of Newfoundland, 1967, 1/1,000,000
  Geological Survey of Canada (Map 1231A), Ottawa, Ont.
Geological map of Newfoundland, 1954, 1/760,320
  Newfoundland, Mines Branch, Geological Survey, St. John's, Newf.

Nova Scotia, Prince Edward Island, and New Brunswick

Geological map of the Maritime Provinces, 1949, 1/760,320
  Geological Survey of Canada (Map 910A), Ottawa, Ont.

Nova Scotia

Geological map of the province of Nova Scotia, 1965, 1/506,880 Nova Scotia,
  Department of Mines, Halifax, N. S.

New Brunswick

Geological map—New Brunswick, 1968, 1/500,000
  New Brunswick, Department of Natural Resources (Map N.R.-1), Fredericton,
  N.B.

Quebec

(Geological map) Southern Quebec (3 sheets), 1943, 1/760,320
  Geological Survey of Canada (Maps 703A, 704A, 705A), Ottawa, Ont.
Carte géologique—Péninsule de Gaspé, 1953 (1st ed.), 1967 (2nd ed.), 1/253,440
  Québec, Ministère des Richesses naturelles (Cartes 1000, 1642), Québec, P.Q.
Carte géologique des basses terres du St-Laurent, 1961, 1/253,440
  Québec, Ministère des Richesses naturelles (Carte 1407), Québec, P.Q.

Maine

Preliminary geologic map of Maine, 1967, 1/500,000
  Maine Geological Survey, Augusta, Me.

New Hampshire

Geologic map of New Hampshire, 1955, 1/250,000
  U.S. Geological Survey, Washington, D.C.; New Hampshire State Planning and
  Development Commisson, Concord, N.H.
    See also The geology of New Hampshire, Part II—Bedrock geology (M. P.
    Billings), 1956, New Hampshire State Planning and Development Com-
    mission

Vermont

Centennial geologic map of Vermont, 1961, 1/250,000
  Vermont Geological Survey, Montpelier, Vt.

Massachusetts and Rhode Island

Geologic map of Massachusetts and Rhode Island, 1916, 1/250,000
U.S. Geological Survey *in* Geology of Massachusetts and Rhode Island (B. K. Emerson), 1917, U.S. Geological Survey Bulletin 597.

Connecticut

Preliminary geological map of Connecticut, 1956, 1/253,440
Connecticut Geological and Natural History Survey, Middletown, Conn.
See also Explanatory text for preliminary geological map of Connecticut, 1956 (John Rodgers, R. M. Gates, and John L. Rosenfeld), 1959, Connecticut Geological and Natural History Survey Bulletin 84.

New York

Geologic map of New York (5 sheets), 1961, 1/250,000
New York State Museum, Geological Survey (Map and Chart Series 5), Albany, N.Y.

New Jersey

Geologic map of New Jersey, 1910–1912, 1/250,000
New Jersey Bureau of Geology and Topography (Sheet 40), Trenton, N.J.

Pennsylvania

Geologic map of Pennsylvania (2 sheets), 1960, 1/250,000
Pennsylvania Topographic and Geologic Survey, Harrisburg, Pa.

Ohio

Geologic map of Ohio, 1920 (rev. ed. 1947), 1/500,000
Ohio Division of Geological Survey, Columbus, Ohio

Delaware

Generalized geologic map of Delaware, 1966, appr. 1/300,000
Delaware Geological Survey, Newark, Del.

Maryland

Geologic map of Maryland, 1968, 1/250,000
Maryland Geological Survey, Baltimore, Md.

Virginia

Geologic map of Virginia, 1963, 1/500,000
Virginia Division of Mineral Resources, Charlottesville, Va.

West Virginia

Geologic map of West Virginia (2 sheets), 1968, 1/250,000
  West Virginia Geological and Economic Survey, Morgantown, W.Va.

Kentucky

Geologic map of Kentucky, 1929, 1/500,000
  Kentucky Geological Survey, Series 6, Lexington, Ky.

Tennessee

Geologic map of Tennessee (4 sheets), 1966, 1/250,000
  Tennessee Division of Geology, Nashville, Tenn.

North Carolina

Geologic map of North Carolina, 1958, 1/500,000
  North Carolina Division of Mineral Resources, Raleigh, N.C.
  See also Explanatory text for geologic map of North Carolina (J. L. Stuckey
  and S. G. Conrad), 1958, North Carolina Division of Mineral Resources
  Bulletin 71.

South Carolina

Geologic map of the crystalline rocks of South Carolina, 1965, 1/250,000
  U.S. Geological Survey (Map I–413), Washington D.C.
  See also The crystalline rocks of South Carolina (W. C. Overstreet and Henry
  Bell, III), 1965, U.S. Geological Survey Bulletin 1183.

Georgia

Geologic map of Georgia, 1939, 1/500,000
  Georgia Geological Survey, Atlanta, Ga.

Alabama

Geological map of Alabama, 1926, 1/500,000
  Geological Survey of Alabama, University, Ala.
  See also Geology of Alabama (G. I. Adams, Charles Butts, L. W. Stephenson, and
  C. W. Cooke), 1926, Geological Survey of Alabama Special Report 14.

Bibliography and author index

Adams, G. I., 1926, The crystalline rocks [of Alabama]: Alabama Geol. Survey Spec. Rept. 14, p. 25–40. **193, 229***

——1930, The significance of the quartzites of Pine Mountain in the crystallines of west central Georgia: Jour. Geology, v. 38, p. 271–279. **194**

Agar, W. M., 1927, The geology of the Shepaug Aqueduct Tunnel, Litchfield County, Connecticut: Connecticut Geol. Nat. History Survey Bull. 40, 38 p. **94**

——1932, The petrology and structure of the Salisbury–Canaan district of Connecticut: Am. Jour. Sci., 5th ser., v. 23, p. 31–48. **88**

Agron, S. L., 1950, Structure and petrology of the Peach Bottom slate, Pennsylvania and Maryland, and its environment: Geol. Soc. America Bull., v. 61, p. 1265–1306. **189, 190**

Albee, A. L., 1961, Boundary Mountain anticlinorium, west-central Maine and northern New Hampshire: U.S. Geol. Survey Prof. Paper 424-C, p. C51–C54. **123**

——1968, Metamorphic zones in northern Vermont: in Zen, E-an, White, W. S., Hadley, J. B., and Thompson, J. B., Jr., eds., Studies of Appalachian geology: northern and maritime (Billings vol.), p. 329–341 **75, 96**

Albee, A. L. See also Cady, Albee, and Chidester, 1963.

Alcock, F. J., 1935, Geology of Chaleur Bay region: Geol. Survey Canada Mem. 183, 146 p. **133**

——1938, Geology of Saint John region, New Brunswick: Geol. Survey Canada Mem. 216, 65 p. **136**

Allen, P. M., 1968, The stratigraphy of a geosynclinal succession in western Sierra Leone, West Africa: Geol. Mag., v. 105, p. 62–73. **199**

Alterman, I. B., 1969, An Ordovician boulder conglomerate at the base of the Hamburg Klippe, east-central Pennsylvania (abs.): Geol. Soc. America Abstracts with Programs for 1969, pt. 1 [v. 1, no. 1], p. 1–2. **89**

Alvord, D. C. See Drake, Davis, and Alvord, 1960.

Amos, D. H., 1963, Petrology and age of plutonic rocks, extreme southeastern Maine: Geol. Soc. America Bull., v. 74, p. 169–193. **137**

Anderson, F. D., 1965, Geology, Belleoram, Newfoundland: Geol. Survey Canada, Prelim Ser., Map 8-1965. **159**

——1967, Structural studies in the Baie d'Espoir Group, Newfoundland: Geol. Assoc. Canada Spec. Paper 4 (Lilly vol.), p. 193–200. **157, 157fn**

Anderson, F. D., and Poole, W. H., 1959, Geology, Woodstock-Fredericton, York, Carleton, Sunbury and Northumberland Counties, New Brunswick: Geol. Survey Canada, Prelim Ser., Map 37-1959. **134**

Applin, P. L., 1951, Preliminary report on buried pre-Mesozoic rocks in Florida and adjacent states: U.S. Geol. Survey Circ. 91, 28 p. **198**

——1952, Sedimentary volumes in Gulf Coastal Plain of the United States and Mexico. Part 1: Volume of Mesozoic sediments in Florida and Georgia: Geol. Soc. America Bull., v. 63, p. 1159–1163. **209**

Armstrong, R. L. See Pierce and Armstrong, 1966.

Arndt, H. H. See Trexler, Wood, and Arndt, 1961.

Arnould, Michel, Aymé, J.-M., and Guillaume, Raymond, 1959 [1960], Nouvelle stratigraphie des séries primaires du nord du Fouta-Djallon, (Guinée, Sénégal): Soc. géol. France Bull., sér. 7, v. 1, p. 631–634. **199**

Ashley, G. H., 1908, Studies in mechanics of Allegheny structure (abs.) Science, new ser., v. 27, p. 924–925. **19**

Aubert de la Rüe, Edgar, 1951, Recherches géologiques et minières aux Îles Saint-Pierre et Miquelon: Office de la Recherche scientifique Outre-Mer [Paris, France], 75 p. **160**

Aymé, J.-M. See Arnould, Aymé, and Guillaume, 1959.

Ayrton, W. G., 1967, Chandler–Port-Daniel area, Bonaventure and Gaspé-South Counties: Quebec Dept. Nat. Resources Geol. Rept. 120, 91 p. **132**

Bachinski, D. J. See Davies, Tupper, Bachinski, Boyle, and Martin, 1969.

Badgley, P. C., 1956, New Carlisle map-area, electoral district of Bonaventure: Quebec Dept. Mines, Geol. Surveys Branch, Geol. Rept. 70, 36 p. **132**

* Boldface numerals at the right of an entry refer to pages in this book on which the reference is cited.

Bailey, E. B., 1929, The Palæozoic mountain systems of Europe and America: British Assoc. Adv. Sci. Rept., 96th Ann. Mtg., Glasgow, 1928, p. 57–76; extended abs. *in:* Nature, v. 122, p. 811–814, 1928.   **213, 221**

Bailey, E. B., Collet, L. W., and Field, R. M., 1928, Paleozoic submarine landslips near Quebec City: Jour. Geology, v. 36, p. 577–614.   **117, 118**

Bailey, E. B., and Mackin, J. H., 1937, Recumbent folding in the Pennsylvania Piedmont—preliminary statement: Am. Jour. Sci., 5th ser., v. 33, p. 187–190.   **190**

Bain, G. L. See Conley and Bain, 1965.

Bain, G. W., 1932, The northern area of Connecticut Valley Triassic: Am. Jour. Sci., 5th ser., v. 23, p. 57–77.   **206**

———1941, The Holyoke Range and Connecticut Valley structure: Am. Jour. Sci., v. 239, p. 261–275.   **206**

———1957, Triassic age rift structure in eastern North America: New York Acad. Sci. Trans., ser. 2, v. 19, p. 489–502.   **206**

Baird, D. M., 1966, Carboniferous rocks of the Conche-Groais Island area, Newfoundland: Canadian Jour. Earth Sci., v. 3, p. 247–257.   **153**

Baird, D. M. See also Clifford and Baird, 1962; Tuke and Baird, 1967.

Baker, R. C. See Godby, Baker, Bower, and Hood, 1966.

Balk, Robert, 1927, Die primäre Struktur des Noritmassivs von Peekskill am Hudson, nördlich New York (auch bekannt als "Cortlandt Norit"): Neues Jahrb., Beilage-Bd. 57, Abt. B, p. 249–303.   **94**

———1936, Structural and petrologic studies in Dutchess County, New York, Part I. Geologic structure of sedimentary rocks: Geol. Soc. America Bull., v. 47, p. 685–774.   **80, 88, 93**

———1946, Gneiss dome at Shelburne Falls, Massachusetts: Geol. Soc. America Bull., v. 57, p. 125–159.   **100**

———1953, Structure of graywacke areas and Taconic Range, east of Troy, New York: Geol. Soc. America Bull., v. 64, p. 811–864.   **85**

Barghoorn, E. S. See Grew, Mamay, and Barghoorn, 1970.

Barss, M. S., and Hacquebard, P. A., 1967, Age and the stratigraphy of the Pictou Group in the Maritime Provinces as revealed by fossil spores: Geol. Assoc. Canada Spec. Paper 4 (Lilly vol.), p. 267–282.   **138**

Barth, T. F. W., 1936, Structural and petrologic studies in Dutchess County, New York, Part II. Petrology and metamorphism of the Paleozoic rocks: Geol. Soc. America Bull., v. 47, p. 775–850. (Note discussion, p. 2000–2008.)   **88, 93**

Bartlett, G. A., 1969, Cretaceous biostratigraphy of the Grand Banks of Newfoundland: Maritime Sediments (Halifax, N.S.), v. 5, p. 4–14.   **209**

Bass, M. N., 1969, Petrography and ages of crystalline basement rocks of Florida—some extrapolations: Am. Assoc. Petroleum Geologists Mem. 11, p. 283–310. **199**

Bassot, J. P., 1966, Étude géologique du Sénégal oriental et de ses confins guinéo-maliens: Bur. Recherches géol. min. Mém. 40, 322 p.   **199**

Bastin, E. S., and Williams, H. S., 1914, Description of the Eastport quadrangle [Maine]: U.S. Geol. Survey Geol. Atlas, Folio 192, 15 p.   **137**

Bates, R. L., 1936, The Big A Mountain area, Virginia: Virginia Geol. Survey Bull. 46-M, p. 167–204.   **28, 43**

Bayles, R. E., Henry, W. H., Fettke, C. R., Harris, L. D., Flowers, R. R., and Haught, O. L., 1956, Wood County deep well: West Virginia Geol. Econ. Survey Rept. Invs. 14, 62 p.   **19**

Bean, R. J., 1953, Relation of gravity anomalies to the geology of central Vermont and New Hampshire: Geol. Soc. America Bull., v. 64, p. 509–537.   **98**

Béland, Jacques, 1957, St. Magloire and Rosaire–St. Pamphile areas, southern Quebec: Quebec Dept. Mines, Geol. Surveys Branch, Geol. Rept. 76, 49 p.   **117**

———1967, Contributions from systematic studies of minor structures in the southern Québec Appalachians: Royal Soc. Canada Spec. Pub. 10, p. 48–56.   **119**

———1969, The geology of Gaspé: Canadian Min. Met. Bull., v. 62, p. 811–818; Canadian Inst. Min. Metallurgy, Trans., v. 72, p. 213–220.   **120, 121**

Béland, Jacques. See also Lajoie, Lespérance, and Béland, 1968.

Bell, Henry, III, and Overstreet, W. C., 1959, Relations among some dikes in Cabarrus County, North Carolina: South Carolina Div. Geology Geol. Notes, v. 3, no. 2, 5 p.   **196**

Bell, Henry, III. See also Overstreet and Bell, 1965.

Bell, K. G., 1968, Faults in eastern Massachusetts (abs.): Geol. Soc. America Spec. Paper 115, p. 250.   **113**

Belt, E. S., 1965, Stratigraphy and paleogeography of Mabou Group and related middle Carboniferous facies, Nova Scotia, Canada: Geol. Soc. America Bull., v. 76, p. 777–801.   **142**

———1968a, Carboniferous continental sedimentation, Atlantic Provinces, Canada: Geol. Soc. America Spec. Paper 106, p. 127–176.   **142**

———1968b, Post Acadian rifts and related facies, eastern Canada: in Zen, E-an, White, W. S., Hadley, J. B., and Thompson, J. B., Jr., eds., Studies of Appalachian geology: northern and maritime (Billings vol.), p. 95–113.   **138, 144, 145, 153**

———1969, Newfoundland Carboniferous stratigraphy and its relation to the Maritimes and Ireland: Am. Assoc. Petroleum Geologists Mem. 12, p. 734–753. **154**

Bentley, R. D., 1969, Strike slip faults in Lee County, Alabama (abs.): Geol. Soc. America Abstracts with Programs for 1969, pt. 4 [v. 1, no. 4], p. 5.   **194**

Bentley, R. D., and Neathery, T. L., 1970, Brevard fault zone of Alabama (abs.): Geol. Soc. America Abstracts with Programs, v. 2, p. 194–195.   **183**

Bentley, R. D. See also Freedman, Wise, and Bentley, 1964; Neathery and Bentley, 1970.

Berdan, J. M. See Bridge and Berdan, 1952.

Bergin, M. J. See Wood and Bergin, 1970.

Bernold, Stanley, ms. 1962, The bedrock geology of the Guilford 7½-minute quadrangle, Connecticut: Ph.D. dissertation, Yale University.   **105, 109**

Berry, W. B. N., 1960, Graptolite faunas of the Marathon region, west Texas: Texas Univ. Bur. Econ. Geology Pub. 6005, 179 p.   **78**

———1961, Graptolite fauna of the Poultney slate: Am. Jour. Sci., v. 259, p. 223–228.   **79**

———1962a, On the Magog, Quebec, graptolites: Am. Jour. Sci., v. 260, p. 142–148.   **97, 119**

————1962b, Stratigraphy, zonation, and age of Schaghticoke, Deepkill, and Normanskill shales, eastern New York: Geol. Soc. America Bull., v. 73, p. 695–718.   **79, 85**

————1963a, On the "Snake Hill Shale": Am. Jour. Sci., v. 261, p. 731–737.   **85**

————1963b, Ordovician correlations in the Taconic and adjacent regions: in Bird, J. M., ed., Stratigraphy, structure, sedimentation and paleontology of the southern Taconic region, eastern New York (Geol. Soc. America 76th Ann. Mtg., New York 1963, Gdbk. Trip 3), Albany, N.Y., p. 21–31.   **79**

————1968, Ordovician paleogeography of New England and adjacent areas based on graptolites: in Zen, E-an, White, W. S., Hadley, J. B., and Thompson, J. B., Jr., eds., Studies of Appalachian geology: northern and maritime (Billings vol.), p. 23–34.   **79**

Berry, W. B. N., and Boucot, A. J., 1970, Correlation of the Silurian rocks of North America: Geol. Soc. America Spec. Paper 102.   **215**

Berry, W. B. N. See also Bird, Zen, Berry, and Potter, 1963; Harwood and Berry, 1967.

Bertrand, Marcel, 1887, La chaîne des Alpes, et la formation du continent européen: Soc. géol. France Bull., sér. 3, v. 15, p. 423–447.   **221**

Betz, Frederick, Jr., 1943, Late Paleozoic faulting in western Newfoundland: Geol. Soc. America Bull., v. 54, p. 687–706.   **154**

Bick, K. F., 1960, Geology of the Lexington quadrangle, Virginia: Virginia Div. Min. Resources Rept. Invs. 1, 40 p.   **38**

Billings, M. P., 1929, Structural geology of the eastern part of the Boston basin: Am. Jour. Sci., 5th ser., v. 18, p. 97–137.   **112**

————1937, Regional metamorphism of the Littleton–Moosilauke area, New Hampshire: Geol. Soc. America Bull., v. 48, p. 463–565.   **102**

————1945, Mechanics of igneous intrusion in New Hampshire: Am. Jour. Sci., v. 243-A (Daly vol.), p. 40–68.   **100**

————1950, Stratigraphy and the study of metamorphic rocks: Geol. Soc. America Bull., v. 61, p. 435–447. **10**

————1956, The geology of New Hampshire, Part II. Bedrock geology: New Hampshire Planning and Development Comm., 200 p.   **102, 105, 227**

Billings, M. P., Rodgers, John, and Thompson, J. B., Jr., 1952, Geology of the Appalachian highlands of east-central New York, southern Vermont, and southern New Hampshire: Geol. Soc. America 65th Ann. Meeting, Boston 1952, Gdbk. (Guidebook for field trips in New England), p. 1–71.   **81, 86, 91, 93, 96, 97**

Billings, M. P. See also Doll, Cady, Thompson, and Billings, 1961 and 1963.

Bird, J. M., 1963, Sedimentary structures in the Taconic sequence rocks of the southern Taconic region: in Bird, J. M., ed., Stratigraphy, structure, sedimentation and paleontology of the southern Taconic region, eastern New York (Geol. Soc. America, 76th Ann. Mtg., New York 1963, Gdbk. Trip 3), Albany, N.Y., p. 5–20.   **84**

————1969, Middle Ordovician gravity sliding—Taconic region: Am. Assoc. Petroleum Geologists Mem. 12, p. 670–686.   **77fn., 84**

Bird, J. M., and Rasetti, Franco, 1968, Lower, Middle, and Upper Cambrian faunas in the Taconic sequence of eastern New York: Stratigraphic and biostratigraphic significance: Geol. Soc. America Spec. Paper 113, 66 p.   **79**

Bird, J. M., Zen, E-an, Berry, W. B. N., and Potter, D. B., 1963, Stratigraphy, structure, sedimentation and paleontology of the southern Taconic region, eastern New York: Albany, N.Y. (Geol. Soc. America, 76th Ann. Mtg., New York 1963, Gdbk. Trip 3), 67 p.   **87**

Bloomer, R. O., and Werner, H. J., 1955, Geology of the Blue Ridge region in central Virginia: Geol. Soc. America Bull., v. 66, p. 579–606.   **165, 166, 167**

Bodine, M. W., Jr., 1965, Stratigraphy and metamorphism in southwestern Casco Bay: New England Intercoll. Geol. Conf., 57th Ann. Mtg., Brunswick, Me., 1965, Gdbk., p. 57–72.   **128**

Boer, Jelle de, 1967, Paleomagnetic-tectonic study of Mesozoic dike swarms in the Appalachians: Jour. Geophys. Res., v. 72, p. 2237–2250.   **208**

Bonini, W. E., and Woollard, G. P., 1960, Subsurface geology of North Carolina–South Carolina Coastal Plain from seismic data: Am. Assoc. Petroleum Geologists Bull., v. 44, p. 298–315.   **198**

Booth, V. H., 1950, Stratigraphy and structure of the Oak Hill succession in Vermont: Geol. Soc. America Bull., v. 61, p. 1131–1168.   **74**

Born, K. E., and Wilson, C. W., Jr., 1939, The Howell structure, Lincoln County, Tennessee: Jour. Geology, v. 47, p. 371–388.   **15**

Bottino, M. L. See Fairbairn, Bottino, Pinson, and Hurley, 1966; Fullagar and Bottino, 1969.

Boucot, A. J., 1954, Age of the Katahdin granite: Am. Jour. Sci., v. 252, p. 144–148.   **124, 125**

————1961, Stratigraphy of the Moose River synclinorium, Maine: U.S. Geol. Survey Bull. 1111-E, p. 153–188.   **124**

————1962, Appalachian Siluro-Devonian: in Some aspects of the Variscan fold belt, p. 155–163, Manchester (Manchester University Press).   **121**

————1968, Silurian and Devonian of the northern Appalachians: in Zen, E-an, White, W. S., Hadley, J. B., and Thompson, J. B., Jr., eds., Studies of Appalachian geology: northern and maritime (Billings vol.), p. 83–94.   **122**

————1969, Geology of the Moose River and Roach River synclinoria, northwestern Maine: Maine Geol. Survey Bull. 21, 117 p.   **124**

Boucot, A. J., Cumming, L. M., and Jaeger, H., 1967, Contributions to the age of the Gaspé Sandstone and Gaspé Limestone: Geol. Survey Canada Paper 67-25, 27 p.   **121**

Boucot, A. J., and Drapeau, Georges, 1968 [1969], Siluro-Devonian rocks of Lake Memphremagog and their correlatives in the Eastern Townships: Quebec Dept. Nat. Res., Mines Branch, Spec. Paper 1, 44 p.   **122**

Boucot, A. J., Field, M. T., Fletcher, Raymond, Forbes, W. H., Naylor, R. S., and Pavlides, Louis, 1964, Reconnaissance bedrock geology of the Presque Isle quadrangle, Maine: Maine Geol. Survey Quad. Mapping Ser. 2, 123 p.   **129, 135**

Boucot, A. J.   See also Berry and Boucot, 1970; Pavlides, Mencher, Naylor, and Boucot, 1964.

Boudette, E. L.   See Espenshade and Boudette, 1967.

Bower, M. E.   See Godby, Baker, Bower, and Hood, 1966.

Bowin, C. O.   See Emery, Uchupi, Phillips, Bowin, Bunce, and Knott, 1970.

Boyle, R. W.   See Davies, Tupper, Bachinski, Boyle, and Martin, 1969.

Brace, W. F., 1953, The geology of the Rutland area, Vermont: Vermont Geol. Survey Bull. 6, 124 p.   **77, 91**

———1955, Quartzite pebble deformation in central Vermont: Am. Jour. Sci., v. 253, p. 129–145.   **96**

Bradley, D. A., 1962, Gisborne Lake and Terrenceville map-areas, Newfoundland: Geol. Survey Canada Mem. 321, 56 p.   **160**

Brent, W. B., 1960, Geology and mineral resources of Rockingham County: Virginia Div. Min. Resources Bull. 76, 174 p.   **37**

Bridge, Josiah, 1950, Bauxite deposits of the Southeastern United States: in Snyder, F. G., ed., Symposium on mineral resources of the Southeastern United States, 1949 Proc.: Knoxville, Tenn., Univ. Tennessee Press, p. 170–201.   **210**

———1955, Disconformity between Lower and Middle Ordovician series at Douglas Lake, Tennessee: Geol. Soc. America Bull., v. 66, p. 725–730.   **47**

———1956, Stratigraphy of the Mascot-Jefferson City zinc district, Tennessee: U.S. Geol. Survey Prof. Paper 277, 76 p.   **49**

Bridge, Josiah, and Berdan, J. M., 1952, Preliminary correlation of the Paleozoic rocks from test wells in Florida and adjacent parts of Georgia and Alabama: Assoc. Am. State Geologists, 44th Ann. Mtg., Tallahassee 1952, Gdbk., p. 29–38 (Florida Geol. Survey, 1952); U.S. Geol. Survey Press Release (1951, 8 p.).   **198**

Brobst, D. A., 1962, Geology of the Spruce Pine district, Avery, Mitchell, and Yancey Counties, North Carolina: U.S. Geol. Survey Bull. 1122-A, 26 p.   **171**

Brock, M. R., and Heyl, A. V., Jr., 1961, Post-Cambrian igneous rocks of the central craton, western Appalachian Mountains and Gulf Coastal Plain of the United States: U.S. Geol. Survey Prof. Paper 424, p. D33–D35.   **209**

Brock, M. R.   See also Zartman, Brock, Heyl, and Thomas, 1967.

Broedel, C. H., 1937, The structure of the gneiss domes near Baltimore, Maryland: Maryland Geol. Survey, v. 13, p. 149–187.   **189**

Brokaw, A. L., 1950, Geology and mineralogy of the East Tennessee zinc district: Internat. Geol. Congress, 18th, London 1948, Rept., pt. 7, p. 70–76.   **49**

Brokaw, A. L., and Jones, C. L., 1946, Structural control of ore bodies in the Jefferson City area, Tennessee: Econ. Geology, v. 41, p. 160–165.   **49**

Bromery, R. W.   See Griscom and Bromery, 1968.

Brosgé, W. P.   See Miller and Brosgé, 1954.

Brown, W. R., 1953, Structural framework and mineral resources of the Virginia Piedmont: Kentucky Geol. Survey, Ser. 9, Special Pub. 1, p. 88–111.   **192**

———1958, Geology and mineral resources of the Lynch-burg quadrangle, Virginia: Virginia Div. Min. Resources Bull. 74, 99 p.   **167, 192**

———1969, Geology of the Dillwyn quadrangle, Virginia: Virginia Div. Min. Resources Rept. Invs. 10, 77 p.   **192, 193, 198, 206**

———1970, Investigations of the sedimentary record in the Piedmont and Blue Ridge of Virginia: in Fisher, G. W., Pettijohn, F. J., Reed, J. C., Jr., and Weaver, K. N., eds., Studies of Appalachian geology: central and southern (Cloos vol.), p. 335–349.   **166, 192, 193**

Brown, W. R., and Sunderman, H. C., 1954, Geologic relations in and between the Esmont and Arvonia slate districts, Virginia (abs.) Geol. Soc. America Bull., v. 65, p. 1356.   **193**

Brückner, W. D., 1966, Stratigraphy and structure of west-central Newfoundland: Geol. Assoc. Canada and Mineralog. Assoc. Canada, 19th Ann. Mtg., Halifax 1966, Gdbk. (Geology of parts of Atlantic Provinces), p. 137–151.   **151, 152**

———1969, Geology of eastern part of Avalon Peninsula, Newfoundland—a summary: Am. Assoc. Petroleum Geologists Mem. 12, p. 130–138.   **158**

Bryant, Bruce, 1962, Geology of the Linville quadrangle, North Carolina–Tennessee—a preliminary report: U.S. Geol. Survey Bull. 1121-D, 30 p.   **171**

Bryant, Bruce, and Reed, J. C., Jr., 1961, The Stokes and Surry Counties quartzite area, North Carolina—a window?: U.S. Geol. Survey Prof. Paper 424, p. D61–D63.   **183**

———1962, Structural and metamorphic history of the Grandfather Mountain area, North Carolina: a preliminary report: Am. Jour. Sci., v. 260, p. 161–180.   **171**

———1970, Structural and metamorphic history of the southern Blue Ridge; in Fisher, G. W., Pettijohn, F. J., Reed, J. C., Jr., and Weaver, K. N., eds., Studies of Appalachian geology: central and southern (Cloos vol.), p. 213–225.   **171, 172**

Bryant, Bruce.   See also Reed and Bryant, 1964; Reed, Bryant, and Myers, 1970.

Bucher, W. H., 1936, Cryptovolcanic structures in the United States: Internat. Geol. Congress, 16th, Washington 1933, Rept., v. 2, p. 1055–1083.   **15**

———1956, Role of gravity in orogenesis: Geol. Soc. America Bull., v. 67, p. 1295–1318.   **62**

———1957, Taconic klippe: a stratigraphic-structural problem: Geol. Soc. America Bull., v. 68, p. 657–673.   **80, 88**

Buckman, R. C.   See Zartman, Snyder, Stern, Marvin, and Buckman, 1965.

Buckwalter, T. V.   See Geyer, Buckwalter, McLaughlin, and Gray, 1963.

Bullard, Edward, Everett, J. E., and Smith, A. G., 1965, The fit of the continents around the Atlantic: Royal Soc. London Philos. Trans., ser. A, v. 258, p. 41–51.   **221, 223**

Bumgarner, J. G., Houston, P. K., Ricketts, J. E., and Wedow, Helmuth, Jr., 1964, Habit of the Rocky Valley thrust fault in the West New Market area, Mascot-Jefferson City zinc district, Tennessee: U.S. Geol. Survey Prof. Paper 501, p. B112–B115.   **49**

Bunce, E. T.   See Emery, Uchupi, Phillips, Bowin, Bunce, and Knott, 1970.

Burchfiel, B. C., and Livingston, J. L., 1967, Brevard Zone compared to Alpine root zones: Am. Jour. Sci., v. 265, p. 241–256.   **184, 193**

Bürgl, Hans, 1967, The orogenesis in the Andean system of Colombia: Tectonophysics, v. 4, p. 429–443.   **223**

Butler, J. R., and Dunn, D. E., 1968, Geology of the Sauratown Mountains anticlinorium and vicinity, North Carolina: Southeastern Geology Spec. Pub. 1 (Geol. Soc. America, Southeastern Sect., 17th Ann. Mtg., Durham 1968, Gdbk.), p. 19–47.   **183**

Butler, J. R.   See also Dunn, Butler, and Centini, 1966.

Butts, Charles, 1926, The Paleozoic rocks [of Alabama]: Alabama Geol. Survey Spec. Rept. 14, p. 41–230.
            60, 181, 229

———1927, Fensters in the Cumberland overthrust block in southwestern Virginia: Virginia Geol. Survey Bull 28, 12 p.   **22**

———1933, Geologic map of the Appalachian Valley of Virginia with explanatory text: Virginia Geol. Survey Bull. 42, 56 p.   **167**

———1939, Tyrone quadrangle, Geology and mineral resources: Pennsylvania Geol. Survey, 4th Ser., Atlas [A]96, 118 p.   **34**

———1940, Description of the Montevallo and Columbiana quadrangles [Alabama]: U.S. Geol. Survey Geol. Atlas, Folio 226, 20 p.   **60, 181**

Butts, Charles, and Edmundson, R. S., 1939, Geology of Little North Mountain in northern Virginia: Virginia Geol. Survey Bull. 51-H, p. 161–179.   **37**

———1943, Geology of the southwestern end of Walker Mountain, Virginia: Geol. Soc. America Bull., v. 54, p. 1669–1691.   **45**

———1966, Geology and mineral resources of Frederick County: Virginia Div. Min. Resources Bull. 80, 142 p.   **37**

Cady, W. M., 1945, Stratigraphy and structure of west central Vermont: Geol. Soc. America Bull., v. 56, p. 515–587.   **73, 74, 81, 84, 119**

———1960, Stratigraphic and geotectonic relationships in northern Vermont and southern Quebec: Geol. Soc. America Bull., v. 71, p. 531–576.   **92, 97, 119, 123**

———1968, Tectonic setting and mechanism of the Taconic slide: Am. Jour. Sci., v. 266, p. 563–578.   **81**

Cady, W. M., Albee, A. L., and Chidester, A. H., 1963, Bedrock geology and asbestos deposits of the upper Missisquoi Valley and vicinity, Vermont: U.S. Geol. Survey Bull. 1122-B, 78 p.   **97**

Cady, W. M.   See also Doll, Cady, Thompson, and Billings, 1961 and 1963.

Callaghan, Eugene, 1931, A contribution to the structural geology of central Massachusetts: New York Acad. Sci. Annals, v. 33, p. 27–75.   **109**

Cameron, E. N., 1951, Preliminary report on the geology of the Mt. Prospect complex: Connecticut Geol. Nat. History Survey Bull. 76, 44 p.   **94**

Carey, S. W., 1958a, The tectonic approach to continental drift: Continental Drift—a symposium (Univ. Tasmania Geology Dept., Symposium 2), p. 177–355, Hobart, Tasmania.   **222, 223**

———1958b, The isostrat, a new technique for the analysis of the structure of the Tasmanian dolerite:

Dolerite—a symposium (Univ. Tasmania Geology Dept., Symposium 4), p. 130–164, Hobart, Tasmania.
            208

Carroll, G. V., ms. 1952, Geology of the Dover Plains quadrangle of New York and Connecticut: Ph.D. dissertation, Yale University.   **87, 88**

Carswell, L. D., Hollowell, J. R., and Platt, L. B., 1968, Geology and hydrology of the Martinsburg Formation in Dauphin County, Pennsylvania: Pennsylvania Geol. Survey, 4th Ser., Bull. (Ground Water Rept.) W24, 54 p.   **89**

Cashion, W. W.   See Cooper and Cashion, 1970.

Cate, A. S., 1962, Subsurface structure of the Plateau region of north-central and western Pennsylvania on top of the Oriskany formation: Penna. Geol. Survey, 4th Ser. [Map 9].   **13, 16**

Causey, L. V.   See Warman and Causey, 1962.

Centini, B. A.   See Dunn, Butler, and Centini, 1966.

Chadwick, G. H., 1944, Geology of the Catskill and Kaaterskill quadrangles. Part II: Silurian and Devonian geology, with a chapter on glacial geology: New York State Mus. Bull. 336, 251 p.   **68**

Chapman, C. A., 1962, Bays-of-Maine igneous complex: Geol. Soc. America Bull., v. 73, p. 883–887.   **137**

———1968, Intersecting belts of post-tectonic "alkaline" intrusions in New England: Illinois State Acad. Sci. Trans., v. 61, p. 46–52.   **111**

Chidester, A. H., 1968, Evolution of the ultramafic complexes of northwestern New England: in Zen, E-an, White, W. S., Hadley, J. B., and Thompson, J. B., Jr., eds., Studies of Appalachian geology: northern and maritime (Billings vol.), p. 343–354.   **99**

Chidester, A. H.   See also Cady, Albee, and Chidester, 1963.

Choquette, P. W., 1960, Petrology and structure of the Cockeysville formation (pre-Silurian) near Baltimore, Maryland: Geol. Soc. America Bull., v. 71, p. 1027–1052.   **191**

Christensen, M. N., 1963, Structural analysis of Hoosac nappe in northwestern Massachusetts: Am. Jour. Sci., v. 261, p. 97–107.   **92**

Church, W. R., 1969, Metamorphic rocks of Burlington Peninsula and adjoining areas of Newfoundland, and their bearing on continental drift in North Atlantic: Am. Assoc. Petroleum Geologists Mem. 12, p. 212–233.
            155

Clark, G. S., and Kulp, J. L., 1968, Isotopic age study of metamorphism and intrusion in western Connecticut and southeastern New York: Am. Jour. Sci., v. 266, p. 865–894.   **102**

Clark, S. K., 1932, The mechanics of the Plains–type folds of the Mid–Continent area: Jour. Geology, v. 40, p. 46–61.   **15**

Clark, S. K., and Royds, J. S., 1948, Structural trends and fault systems in Eastern Interior Basin: Am. Assoc. Petroleum Geologists Bull., v. 32, p. 1728–1749.   **15**

Clark, T. H., ed., 1967, Appalachian tectonics: Royal Soc. Canada Spec. Pub. 10, 99 p.   **10**

Clark, T. H.   See also Houde and Clark, 1962.

Clarke, J. W., 1952, Geology and mineral resources of the Thomaston quadrangle, Georgia: Georgia Geol. Survey Bull. 59, 103 p.   **194**

————1958, The bedrock geology of the Danbury quadrangle: Connecticut Geol. Nat. History Survey Quad. Rept. 7, 47 p.   **94**

Cleaves, A. B. See Willard and Cleaves, 1939.

Clifford, P. M., and Baird, D. M., 1962, Great Northern Peninsula of Newfoundland—Grenville inlier: Canadian Min. Met. Bull., v. 55, p. 150–157, 276–277; Canadian Inst. Min. Metallurgy Trans., v. 65, p. 95–103.   **149**

Clifford, T. N. See Thompson, Robinson, Clifford, and Trask, 1968.

Cloos, Ernst, 1947, Oölite deformation in the South Mountain fold, Maryland: Geol. Soc. America Bull., v. 58, p. 843–917.   **33, 39, 166**

————1950, The geology of the South Mountain anticlinorium, Maryland: Johns Hopkins Univ. Studies in Geology, no. 16, pt. 1, 28 p. (Geol. Soc. America, 63rd Ann. Mtg., Washington 1950, Gdbk. 1).   **166**

————1951, Structural geology of Washington County: Maryland Dept. Geology, Mines and Water Resources, The physical features of Washington County, p. 124–163.   **37, 166**

————1953, Appalachenprofil in Maryland: Geol. Rundschau, v. 41, p. 145–160.   **189**

————1957, Blue Ridge tectonics between Harrisburg, Pennsylvania, and Asheville, North Carolina: Natl. Acad. Sci. Proc., v. 43, p. 834–839.   **173**

————1964a, Wedging, bedding plane slips, and gravity tectonics in the Appalachians: in Lowry, W. D., ed., Tectonics of the Southern Appalachians: Virginia Polytech. Inst. Dept. Geol. Sci. Mem. 1, p. 63–70.   **37**

————1964b [1965], Appalachenprofil 1964: Geol. Rundschau, v. 54, 812–834.   **167, 184**

Cloos, Ernst, and Hietanen, Anna, 1941, Geology of the "Martic overthrust" and the Glenarm series in Pennsylvania and Maryland: Geol. Soc. America Spec. Paper 35, 207 p.   **188, 188fn.**

Cloos, Hans, 1939, Hebung—Spaltung—Vulkanismus: Geol. Rundschau, v. 30, p. 401–527.   **207**

Cloud, P. E., Jr., 1967, Geology and bauxite deposits of the Rock Run and Goshen Valley areas, northeast Alabama: U.S. Geol. Survey Bull. 1199-N, 74 p.   **60**

Cohen, C. J., 1937, Structure of the metamorphosed gabbro complex at Baltimore, Maryland: Maryland Geol. Survey, v. 13, p. 215–236.   **189**

Collet, L. W. See Bailey, Collet, and Field, 1928.

Colton, G. W., 1970, The Appalachian basin—its depositional sequences and their geologic relationships: in Fisher, G. W., Pettijohn, F. J., Read, J. C., Jr., and Weaver, K. N., eds., Studies of Appalachian geology: central and southern (Cloos vol.), p. 5–47.   **12, 32**

Conley, J. F., 1962a, Geology of the Albemarle quadrangle, North Carolina: North Carolina Div. Min. Resources Bull. 75, 26 p.   **196, 197**

————1962b, Geology and mineral resources of Moore County, North Carolina: North Carolina Div. Min. Resources Bull. 76, 40 p.   **196**

Conley, J. F., and Bain, G. L., 1965, Geology of the Carolina slate belt west of the Deep River–Wadesboro Triassic basin, North Carolina: Southeastern Geology, v. 6, p. 117–138.   **196**

Cooper, B. N., 1936, Stratigraphy and structure of the Marion area, Virginia: Virginia Geol. Survey Bull.

46-L, p. 125–166.   **45**

————1939, Geology of the Draper Mountain area, Virginia: Virginia Geol. Survey Bull. 55, 98 p.   **45**

————1944, Geology and mineral resources of the Burkes Garden quadrangle, Virginia: Virginia Geol. Survey Bull. 60, 299 p.   **44, 210**

————1946, Metamorphism along the "Pulaski" fault in the Appalachian Valley of Virginia: Am. Jour. Sci., v. 244, p. 95–104.   **45**

————1948, Status of Mississippian stratigraphy in the central and northern Appalachian region: Jour. Geology, v. 56, p. 255–263.   **44**

————1961, Grand Appalachian field excursion: Virginia Polytech. Inst. Eng. Ext. Ser., Geol. Gdbk. 1 (Geol. Soc. America, 74th Ann. Mtg., Cincinnati 1961, Gdbk. Trip 1), 187 p.   **41, 44, 45, 47, 62, 64**

————1964, Relation of stratigraphy to structure in the Southern Appalachians: in Lowry, W. D., ed., Tectonics of the Southern Appalachians: Virginia Polytech. Inst. Dept. Geol. Sci. Mem. 1, p. 81–114.
                                       41, 44, 47, 62, 64

————1968, Profile of the folded Appalachians of western Virginia: U M R (University of Missouri at Rolla) Journal, no. 1, p. 27–64.   **45, 62, 64**

————1970, The Max Meadows breccias: a reply: in Fisher, G. W., Pettijohn, F. J., Reed, J. C., Jr., and Weaver, K. N., eds., Studies of Appalachian geology (Cloos vol.), p. 179–191.   **47**

Cooper, B. N., and Cashion, W. W., 1970, Relation of the Pulaski and Seven Springs faults in southwestern Virginia: Am. Jour. Sci., v. 268, p. 385–396.   **41, 45**

Cooper, B. N., and Haff, J. C., 1940, Max Meadows fault breccia: Jour. Geology, v. 48, p. 945–974.   **45**

Cooper, G. A., 1956, Chazyan and related brachiopods: Smithsonian Misc. Coll., v. 127, 1245 p.   **78**

Cooper, J. R., 1954, La Poile-Cinq Cerf map-area, Newfoundland: Geol. Survey Canada Mem. 276, 62 p.
                                                      156

Craddock, J. C., 1957, Stratigraphy and structure of the Kinderhook quadrangle, New York, and the "Taconic klippe": Geol. Soc. America Bull., v. 68, p. 675–723.
                                                   80, 87

Craig, L. C. See King, Ferguson, Craig, and Rodgers, 1944.

Cressler, C. W., 1964, Geology and ground-water resources of Walker County, Georgia: Georgia Geol. Survey Inf. Circ. 29, 15 p.   **53**

Crickmay, G. W., 1936, Status of the Talladega series in southern Appalachian stratigraphy: Geol. Soc. America Bull., v. 47, p. 1371–1392.   **181**

————1952, Geology of the crystalline rocks of Georgia: Georgia Geol. Survey Bull. 58, 56 p.   **180**

Crickmay, G. W. See also Hewett and Crickmay, 1937.

Crowley, W. P., 1968, The bedrock geology of the Long Hill and Bridgeport quadrangles, Connecticut: Connecticut Geol. Nat. History Survey Quad. Rept. 24, 81 p.   **101**

————1969, Stratigraphic evidence for a volcanic origin of part of the Bel Air belt of Baltimore gabbro complex in Baltimore County, Maryland (abs.): Geol. Soc. America Abstracts with Programs for 1969, pt. 1 [v. 1, no. 1], p. 10.   **190**

Cumming, L. M., 1967, Geology of the Passamaquoddy Bay region, Charlotte County, New Brunswick: Geol. Survey Canada Paper 65–29, 36 p.   **137**

——1968, St. George-Table Head disconformity and zinc mineralization, western Newfoundland: Canadian Min. Met. Bull., v. 61, p. 721–725; Canadian Inst. Min. Met. Trans., v. 121, p. 144–148.   **150**

Cumming, L. M. See also Boucot, Cummings, and Jaeger, 1967.

Currier, L. W., 1935, Zinc and lead region of southwestern Virginia: Virginia Geol. Survey Bull. 43, 122 p.   **46, 167**

Currier, L. W., and Jahns, R. H., 1952, Geology of the "Chelmsford granite" area: Geol. Soc. America, 65th Ann. Mtg., Boston 1952, Gdbk. (Guidebook for field trips in New England), p. 103–117.   **108, 113**

Cushing, H. P., and Ruedemann, Rudolf, 1914, Geology of Saratoga Springs and vicinity: New York State Mus. Bull. 169, 177 p.   **80, 86**

Dale, T. N., 1893, The Rensselaer grit plateau in New York: U.S. Geol. Survey 13th Ann. Rept., pt. 2, p. 291–340.   **85**

——1899, The slate belt of eastern New York and western Vermont: U.S. Geol. Survey 19th Ann. Rept., pt. 3, p. 153–300.   **80, 84**

——1904, The geology of the north end of the Taconic Range: Am. Jour. Sci., 4th ser., v. 17, p. 185–190.   **76**

Dale, T. N. See also Pumpelly, Wolff, and Dale, 1894.

Daly, R. A., 1903, The geology of Ascutney Mountain, Vermont: U.S. Geol. Survey Bull. 209, 122 p.   **100**

Dana, J. D., 1873, On some results of the earth's contraction from cooling, including a discussion of the origin of mountains, and the nature of the earth's interior: Am. Jour. Sci., 3rd ser., v. 5, p. 423–443, 474–475; v. 6, p. 6–14, 104–115, 161–172, 304, 381–382.   **9**

——1888, A brief history of Taconic ideas: Am. Jour. Sci., 3rd ser., v. 36, p. 410–427.   **76**

Darton, N. H., 1940, Some structural features of the Northern Anthracite coal basin, Pennsylvania: U.S. Geol. Survey Prof. Paper 193-D, p. 69–81.   **66, 67**

Dasch, E. J. See Hills and Dasch, 1969.

Davies, J. L., Tupper, W. M., Bachinski, D. J., Boyle, R. W., and Martin, R. F., 1969, Geology and mineral deposits of the Nigadoo River–Millstream River area, Gloucester County, New Brunswick: Geol. Survey Canada Paper 67–49, 70 p.   **134**

Davis, G. L. See Wetherill, Tilton, Davis, Hart, and Hopson, 1966.

Davis, R. E. See Drake, Davis, and Alvord, 1960.

Davis, W. M., 1888, The structure of the Triassic formation of the Connecticut Valley: U.S. Geol. Survey 7th Ann. Rept., p. 455–490.   **207**

Dennis, J. G., 1956, The geology of the Lyndonville area, Vermont: Vermont Geol. Survey Bull. 8, 98 p.   **100**

——1960 [1961], Zum Gebirgsbau der nördlichen Appalachen: Geol. Rundschau, v. 50, p. 554–577.   **120**

Dennis, J. G. See also Eric and Dennis, 1958.

Dewey, John, and Kay, Marshall, 1968, Appalachian and Caledonian evidence for drift in the North Atlantic: in

Phinney, R. A., ed., The history of the earth's crust: Princeton, N.J., Princeton University Press, p. 161–167.   **221**

Dieterich, J. H., 1968, Multiple folding in western Connecticut: a reinterpretation of structure in the New Haven–Naugatuck–Westport area: Connecticut Geol. Nat. History Survey Gdbk. 2, Trip D-2, 13 p.   **101**

Dieterich, J. H., ms. 1968, Sequence and mechanics of folding in the area of New Haven, Naugatuck and Westport, Connecticut: Ph.D. dissertation, Yale University, 153 p.   **101**

Dietrich, R. V., 1954, Geology of the Pilot Mountain area, Virginia: Virginia Polytech. Inst. Bull., v. 47, no. 4 (Eng. Expt. Sta. Ser. 91), 32 p.   **167**

——1959, Geology and mineral resources of Floyd County of the Blue Ridge Upland, southwestern Virginia: Virginia Polytech. Inst. Bull., v. 52, no. 12, (Eng. Expt. Sta. Ser. 134), 160 p.   **167**

Diment, W. H., 1968, Gravity anomalies in northwestern New England: in Zen, E-an, White, W. S., Hadley, J. B., and Thompson, J. B., Jr., eds., Studies of Appalachian geology: northern and maritime (Billings vol.), p. 399–413.   **95**

Dineley, D. L., and Williams, B. P. J., 1968a, Sedimentation and paleoecology of the Devonian Escuminac Formation and related strata, Escuminac Bay, Quebec: Geol. Soc. America Spec. Paper 106, p. 241–264.   **133**

——1968b, The Devonian continental rocks of the lower Restigouche River, Quebec: Canadian Jour. Earth Sci., v. 5, p. 945–953.   **133**

Dixon, H. R., and Lundgren, Lawrence, Jr., 1968, Structure of eastern Connecticut: in Zen, E-an, White, W. S., Hadley, J. B., and Thompson, J. B., Jr., eds., Studies of Appalachian geology: northern and maritime (Billings vol.), p. 219–229.   **108, 109, 110**

Dixon, H. R., Lundgren, Lawrence, Jr., Snyder, G. L., and Eaton, G. P., 1963, Colchester nappe of eastern Connecticut (abs.): Geol. Soc. America Spec. Paper 73, p. 139.   **109**

Dixon, H. R. See also Goldsmith and Dixon, 1968.

Doe, B. R. See Tilton, Doe, and Hopson, 1970.

Doll, C. G., Cady, W. M., Thompson, J. B., Jr., and Billings, M. P., 1961, Centennial geologic map of Vermont: Vermont Geol. Survey.   **96, 97, 104, 227**

——1963, Reply to Zen's discussion of the Centennial Geologic Map of Vermont: Am. Jour. Sci., v. 261, p. 94–96.   **83**

Dott, R. H., Jr., 1961, Squantum "tillite," Massachusetts—evidence of glaciation or subaqueous mass movements?: Geol. Soc. America Bull., v. 72, p. 1289–1305.   **112**

Dowse, A. M., 1950, New evidence on the Cambrian contact at Hoppin Hill, North Attleboro, Massachusetts: Am. Jour. Sci., v. 248, p. 95–99.   **113**

Drake, A. A., Jr., 1970, Structural geology of the Reading Prong: in Fisher, G. W., Pettijohn, F. J., Reed, J. C., Jr., and Weaver, K. N., eds., Studies of Appalachian geology: central and southern (Cloos vol.), p. 271–291.   **70**

Drake, A. A., Jr., Davis, R. E., and Alvord, D. C., 1960, Taconic and post-Taconic folds in eastern Pennsylvania and western New Jersey: U.S. Geol. Survey Prof. Paper 400, p. B180–B181.   **70**

Drake, A. A., Jr., and Epstein, J. B., 1967, The Martins-burg Formation (Middle and Upper Ordovician) in the Delaware Valley, Pennsylvania–New Jersey: U.S. Geol. Survey Bull. 1244-H, 16 p.   **69**

Drake, A. A., Jr. See also Ryan, Drake, Sherwood, and others, 1961.

Drake, C. L., Ewing, Maurice, and Sutton, G. H., 1959, Continental margins and geosynclines: the east coast of North America north of Cape Hatteras: Physics and Chemistry of the Earth, v. 3, p. 110–198.   **198**

Drake, C. L. See also Mayhew, Drake, and Nafe, 1968; Nafe and Drake, 1969.

Drapeau, Georges. See Boucot and Drapeau, 1968.

Dunbar, C. O. See Schuchert and Dunbar, 1934.

Dunlop, G. M. See Phillips, Kennedy, and Dunlop, 1969.

Dunn, D. E., Butler, J. R., and Centini, B. A., 1966, Brevard fault zone, North Carolina: new interpretation (abs.): Geol. Soc. America Spec. Paper 87, p. 247.   **183**

Dunn, D. E. See also Butler and Dunn, 1968.

Eaton, G. P., and Rosenfeld, J. L., 1960, Gravimetric and structural investigations in central Connecticut: Internat. Geol. Cong., 21st, Copenhagen 1960, Rept., pt. 2, p. 168–178.   **105**

Eaton, G. P. See also Dixon, Lundgren, Snyder, and Eaton, 1963; Rosenfeld and Eaton, 1956.

Edmundson, R. S. See Butts and Edmundson, 1939, 1943, and 1966.

Eisbacher, G. H., 1969, Displacement and stress field along part of the Cobequid Fault, Nova Scotia: Canadian Jour. Earth Sci., v. 6, p. 1095–1104.   **143**

Eldredge, Niles. See Kay and Eldredge, 1968.

Elmore, P. L. D. See Faul, Stern, Thomas, and Elmore, 1963.

Emerson, B. K., 1898, Geology of old Hampshire County, Massachusetts: U.S. Geol. Survey Mon. 29, 790 p.   **91, 100**

———1917, Geology of Massachusetts and Rhode Island: U.S. Geol. Survey Bull. 597, 289 p.   **91, 100, 228**

Emery, K. O., Uchupi, Elazar, Phillips, J. D., Bowin, C. O., Bunce, T. E., and Knott, S. T., 1970, Continental rise off eastern North America: Am. Assoc. Petroleum Geologists Bull., v. 54, p. 44–108.   **198, 209**

Emmons, Ebenezer, 1842, Natural History of New York, Div. 4, Geology of New-York. Part II: comprising the survey of the second geological district: Albany, N.Y., 437 p.   **75**

———1844, The Taconic system: Albany, N.Y., 65 p.; Natural History of New York, Div. 5, Agriculture of New York, v. 1, Soils of the state, p. 45–112, 1846.   **75, 86**

Englund, K. J., 1968, Geology and coal resources of the Elk Valley area, Tennessee and Kentucky: U.S. Geol. Survey Prof. Paper 572, 59 p.   **22**

Englund, K. J., and Roen, J. B., 1963, Origin of the Middlesboro Basin, Kentucky: U.S. Geol. Survey Prof. Paper 450, p. E20–E22.   **22**

Enos, Paul, 1969, Cloridorme Formation, Middle Ordovician flysch, northern Gaspé Peninsula, Quebec: Geol. Soc. America Spec. Paper 117, 66 p.   **120**

Epstein, A. G. See Epstein and Epstein, 1969.

Epstein, J. B., and Epstein, A. G., 1969, Geology of the Valley and Ridge province between Delaware Water Gap and Lehigh Gap, Pennsylvania: Geol. Soc. America 82nd Ann. Mtg., Atlantic City 1969, Gdbk. (Geology of selected areas in New Jersey and eastern Pennsylvania and guidebook of excursions: Rutgers Univ. Press), p. 132–205.   **70**

Epstein, J. B. See also Drake and Epstein, 1967.

Eric, J. H., and Dennis, J. G., 1958, Geology of the Concord-Waterford area, Vermont: Vermont Geol. Survey Bull. 11, 66 p.   **98fn.**

Ern, E. H., Jr., 1963, Bedrock geology of the Randolph quadrangle, Vermont: Vermont Geol. Survey Bull. 21, 96 p.   **98**

———1964, Major recumbent structure in the Vermont Piedmont? (abs.): Geol. Soc. America Spec. Paper 76, p. 243.   **98**

Eskola, P. E., 1949, The problem of mantled gneiss domes: Geol. Soc. London Quart. Jour., v. 104, p. 461–476.   **105, 190**

Espenshade, G. H., 1954, Geology and mineral deposits of the James River–Roanoke River manganese district, Virginia: U.S. Geol. Survey Bull. 1008, 155 p.   **192**

———1970, Geology of the northern part of the Blue Ridge anticlinorium: in Fisher, G. W., Pettijohn, F. J., Reed, J. C., Jr., and Weaver, K. N., eds., Studies of Appalachian geology: central and southern (Cloos vol.), p. 199–211.   **165**

Espenshade, G. H., and Boudette, E. L., 1967, Geology and petrology of the Greenville quadrangle, Piscataquis and Somerset Counties, Maine: U.S. Geol. Survey Bull. 1241-F, 60 p.   **128**

Espenshade, G. H., and Potter, D. B., 1960, Kyanite, sillimanite, and andalusite deposits of the Southeastern States: U.S. Geol. Survey Prof. Paper 336, 121 p.   **195**

Espenshade, G. H., and Rankin, D. H., 1970, Probable Precambrian crystalline rocks in the Sauratown Mountains anticlinorium, a major structural feature in the Piedmont of North Carolina (abs.): Geol. Soc. America Abstracts with Programs, v. 2, p. 207.   **183**

Everett, J. E. See Bullard, Everett, and Smith, 1965.

Ewing, Maurice. See Drake, Ewing, and Sutton, 1959; Heezen, Tharp, and Ewing, 1959.

Fairbairn, H. W., Bottino, M. L., Pinson, W. H., Jr., and Hurley, P. M., 1966, Whole-rock age and initial $^{87}Sr/^{86}Sr$ of volcanics underlying fossiliferous Lower Cambrian in the Atlantic provinces of Canada: Canadian Jour. Earth Sci., v. 3, p. 509–521.   **140, 162**

Fairbairn, H. W., Moorbath, Stephen, Ramo, A. O., Pinson, W. H., Jr., and Hurley, P. M., 1967, Rb-Sr age of granitic rocks of southeastern Massachusetts and the age of the Lower Cambrian at Hoppin Hill: Earth Planetary Science Letters, v. 2, p. 321–328.   **113**

Fairley, W. M., 1965, The Murphy Syncline in the Tate quadrangle: Georgia Geol. Survey Bull. 75, 71 p.   **179, 180**

Faul, Henry, Stern, T. W., Thomas, H. H., and Elmore, P. L. D., 1963, Ages of intrusion and metamorphism in the northern Appalachians: Am. Jour. Sci., v. 261, p. 1–19.   **92, 125, 146, 217**

Faul, Henry. See also Lyons and Faul, 1968.

Feininger, Tomas, 1968, The updip termination of a large dike of Westerly Granite and the regional distribution of the Westerly and Narragansett Pier Granites in Rhode Island and Connecticut: U.S. Geol. Survey Prof. Paper 600, p. D181–185.   **109**

Fellows, R. E., 1943, Recrystallization and flowage in Appalachian quartzite: Geol. Soc. America Bull., v. 54, p. 1399–1431.   **33**

Ferguson, H. W., and Jewell, W. B., 1951, Geology and barite deposits of the Del Rio district, Cocke County, Tennessee: Tennessee Div. Geology Bull. 57, 235 p.   **173**

Ferguson, H. W. See also King, Ferguson, Craig, and Rodgers, 1944; King and Ferguson, 1960.

Fettke, C. R., 1950, Henderson dome, a unique structure in northwestern Pennsylvania (abs.): Geol. Soc. America Bull., v. 61, p. 1458.   **13, 15**
———1954, Structure-contour maps of the Plateau region of north-central and western Pennsylvania: Pennsylvania Geol. Survey, 4th Ser., Bull. G 27, 50 p.   **13, 14, 16**

Fettke, C. R. See also Bayles, Henry, Fettke, Harris, Flowers, and Haught, 1956.

Field, M. T. See Boucot, Field, Fletcher, Forbes, Naylor, and Pavlides, 1964.

Field, R. M. See Bailey, Collet, and Field, 1928.

Finks, R. M., 1968, Taconian islands and the shores of Appalachia: New York State Geol. Assoc., 40th Ann. Mtg., Flushing, Queens, N.Y., 1968, Gdbk., p. 117–153 and addendum.   **71**

Fisher, D. W., 1961, Stratigraphy and structure in the southern Taconics (Rensselaer and Columbia Counties, New York): New York State Geol. Assoc., 33rd Ann. Mtg., Troy, N.Y., 1961, Gdbk., p. D1–D22.   **79, 87**
———1962, Correlation of the Ordovician rocks in New York State: New York State Mus. Map and Chart Ser. 3.   **78**

Fisher, G. W., 1970, The metamorphosed sedimentary rocks along the Potomac River near Washington, D.C.: in Fisher, G. W., Pettijohn, F. J., Reed, J. C., Jr., and Weaver, K. N., eds., Studies of Appalachian geology: central and southern (Cloos vol.), p. 299–315.   **188**

Fisher, G. W., Pettijohn, F. J., Reed, J. C., Jr., and Weaver, K. N., eds., 1970, Studies of Appalachian geology: central and southern (Cloos vol.): New York, Wiley-Interscience, 460 p.   **10, 186**

Fisher, G. W. See also Southwick and Fisher, 1967.

Fletcher, Raymond. See Boucot, Field, Fletcher, Forbes, Naylor, and Pavlides, 1964.

Flowers, R. R. See Bayles, Henry, Fettke, Harris, Flowers, and Haught, 1956.

Fluhr, T. W., 1950, The Delaware aqueduct: some geological data: New York Acad. Sci. Trans., ser. 2, v. 12, p. 182–186.   **94**

Foland, K. A., Quinn, A. W., and Giletti, B. J., 1970, Jurassic and Cretaceous isotopic ages of the White Mountain magma series (abs.): Geol. Soc. America Abstracts with Programs, v. 2, no. 1, p. 19–20.   **111**

Folk, R. L. See Todd and Folk, 1957.

Forbes, W. H. See Boucot, Field, Fletcher, Forbes, Naylor, and Pavlides, 1964.

Forrest, J. T., 1969, Stratigraphy and structure of the Murphy belt in the Murphy, North Carolina 7½ quadrangle (abs.): Geol. Soc. America Abstracts with Programs for 1969, pt. 4 [v. 1, no. 4], p. 23–24.   **179**

Fox, H. D., 1950, Structure and origin of two windows exposed on the Nittany arch at Birmingham, Pennsylvania: Am. Jour. Sci., v. 248, p. 153–170, 368.   **34, 35**

Frankel, Larry, 1966, Geology of southeastern Prince Edward Island: Geol. Survey Canada Bull. 145, 70 p.   **138**

Freedman, Jacob, 1950, Stratigraphy and structure of the Mt. Pawtuckaway quadrangle, southeastern New Hampshire: Geol. Soc. America Bull., v. 61, p. 449–491.   **107**

Freedman, Jacob, Wise, D. U., and Bentley, R. D., 1964, Pattern of folded folds in the Appalachian Piedmont along Susquehanna River: Geol. Soc. America Bull., v. 75, p. 621–638.   **187, 190**

Fritts, C. E., 1962, Age and sequence of metasedimentary and metavolcanic formations northwest of New Haven, Connecticut: U.S. Geol. Survey Prof. Paper 450-D, p. D32–D36.   **100**

Fullagar, P. D., and Bottino, M. L., 1969, Tertiary felsite intrusions in the Valley and Ridge province, Virginia: Geol. Soc. America Bull., v. 80, p. 1853–1857.   **209**

Fuller, J. O. See Miller and Fuller, 1954.

Furcron, A. S., 1935, James River iron and marble belt, Virginia: Virginia Geol. Survey Bull. 39, 124 p.   **192**
———1953, Comments on the geology of the Ellijay quadrangle, Georgia–North Carolina–Tennessee: Georgia Geol. Survey Bull. 60, p. 32–40.   **180**

Furcron, A. S., and Teague, K. H., 1945, Sillimanite and massive kyanite in Georgia (a preliminary report): Georgia Geol. Survey Bull. 51, 76 p.   **180**

Gair, J. E., 1950, Some effects of deformation in the central Appalachians: Geol. Soc. America Bull., v. 61, p. 857–876.   **37**

Gates, R. M., 1952, The geology of the New Preston quadrangle, Connecticut. Part 1. The bedrock geology: Connecticut Geol. Nat. History Survey Misc. Ser. 5 [Quad. Rept. 2], p. 5–34.   **94**
———1959, Bedrock geology of the Roxbury quadrangle, Connecticut: U.S. Geol. Survey Geol. Quad. Map GQ–121.   **101**

Gates, R. M., and Martin, C. W., 1967, The bedrock geology of the Waterbury quadrangle: Connecticut Geol. Nat. History Survey Quad. Rept. 22, 36 p.   **101**

Gates, R. M. See also Rodgers, Gates, and Rosenfeld, 1959.

Geddes, Wilburt. See Zietz, King, Geddes, and Lidiak, 1966.

Geyer, A.. R, Buckwalter, T. V., McLaughlin, D. B., and Gray, Carlyle, 1963, Geology and mineral resources of the Womelsdorf quadrangle: Pennsylvania Geol. Survey, 4th Ser., Atlas A177c, 96 p.   **70**

Geyer, A. R., Gray, Carlyle, McLaughlin, D. B., and Moseley, J. R., 1958, Geology of the Lebanon [7½′] quadrangle: Pennsylvania Geol. Survey, 4th Ser., Atlas A167C.   **69**

Geyer, A. R. See also Gray, Geyer, and McLaughlin, 1958.

Giles, A. W., 1927, The geology of Little North Mountain in northern Virginia and West Virginia: Jour. Geology, v. 35, p. 32–57.   **37**

Giletti, B. J. See Foland, Quinn, and Giletti, 1970.

Gilluly, James, 1960, A folded thrust in Nevada—inferences as to time relations between folding and faulting: Am. Jour. Sci., v. 258-A (Bradley vol.), p. 68–79.   **170**

———1964, Atlantic sediments, erosion rates, and the evolution of the Continental Shelf: Geol. Soc. America Bull., v. 75, p. 483–492.   **209**

Giovanella, C. A. See Wynne-Edwards, Gregory, Hay, Giovanella and Reinhardt, 1966.

Glaeser, J. D., 1966, Provenance, dispersal, and depositional environments of Triassic sediments in Newark-Gettysburg basin: Pennsylvania Geol. Survey, 4th Ser., Gen. Geology Rept. G43, 168 p.   **205**

Godby, E. A., Baker, R. C., Bower, M. E., and Hood, P. J., 1966, Aeromagnetic reconnaissance of the Labrador Sea: Jour. Geophys. Research, v. 71, p. 511–517.   **163, 221**

Goldring, Winifred, 1943, Geology of the Coxsackie quadrangle, New York: New York State Mus. Bull. 332, 374 p.   **68, 87**

Goldsmith, Richard, 1961, Axial-plane folding in southeastern Connecticut: U.S. Geol. Survey Prof. Paper 424, p. C54–C57.   **109**

Goldsmith, Richard, and Dixon, H. R., 1968, Bedrock geology of eastern Connecticut: Connecticut Geol. Nat. History Survey Gdbk. 2, Sect. F-O, 9 p.   **109**

Goldsmith, Richard. See also Hadley and Goldsmith, 1963; Lundgren, Goldsmith, and Snyder, 1958.

Gooch, E. O., 1958, Infolded metasedimentary rocks near the axial zone of the Catoctin Mountain–Blue Ridge anticlinorium in Virginia: Geol. Soc. America Bull., v. 69, p. 569–574.   **166**

Goodwin, B. K., 1962 [1963], An alternate interpretation for the structure of east-central and northeastern Vermont: Pennsylvania Acad. Sci. Proc., v. 36, p. 200–207.   **98**

———1963, Geology of the Island Pond area, Vermont: Vermont Geol. Survey Bull. 20, 111 p.   **98, 100**

Grant, L. F. See Kellberg and Grant, 1956.

Gray, Carlyle, Geyer, A. R., and McLaughlin, D. B., 1958, Geology of the Richland [7½′] quadrangle: Pennsylvania Geol. Survey, 4th Ser., Atlas A167D.   **69**

Gray, Carlyle. See also Geyer, Buckwalter, McLaughlin, and Corey, 1963; Geyer, Gray, McLaughlin, and Moseley, 1958.

Green, J. C., 1968, Geology of the Connecticut Lakes–Parmachenee area, New Hampshire and Maine: Geol. Soc. America Bull., v. 79, p. 1601–1638.   **123**

Green, J. C., and Guidotti, C. V., 1968, The Boundary Mountains anticlinorium in northern New Hampshire and northwestern Maine: in Zen, E-an, White, W. S., Hadley, J. B., and Thompson, J. B., Jr., eds., Studies of Appalachian geology: northern and maritime (Billings vol.), p. 255–266.   **104, 123**

Greenberg, S. S. See Smith, Milici, and Greenberg, 1964.

Gregory, A. F. See Wynne-Edwards, Gregory, Hay, Giovanella, and Reinhardt, 1966.

Greiner, H. R. See Lespérance and Greiner, 1969.

Grew, E. S., 1970, Stratigraphy of the Worcester area, central Massachusetts (abs.): Geol. Soc. America Abstracts with Programs, v. 2, no. 1, p. 21–22.   **108**

Grew, E. S., Mamay, S. H., and Barghoorn, E. S., 1970, Age of plant fossils from the Worcester coal mine, Worcester, Massachusetts: Am. Jour. Sci., v. 268, p. 113–126.   **108**

Griffin, R. H., 1951, Structure and petrography of the Hillabee sill and associated metamorphics of Alabama: Alabama Geol. Survey Bull. 63, 74 p.   **182**

Griffin, V. S., Jr., 1967, Folding styles and migmatization within the Inner Piedmont belt in portions of Anderson, Oconee, and Pickens Counties, South Carolina: South Carolina Div. Geology, Geol. Notes, v. 11, p. 37–53.   **194**

———1969a, Migmatitic Inner Piedmont belt of northwestern South Carolina: South Carolina Div. Geology, Geol. Notes, v. 13, p. 87–104, 146–147.   **194**

———1969b, Inner Piedmont tectonics in the vicinity of Walhalla, South Carolina: South Carolina Div. Geology, Geol. Notes, v. 14, p. 15–28.   **183**

Griffitts, W. R., and Overstreet, W. C., 1952, Granitic rocks of the western Carolina Piedmont: Am. Jour. Sci., v. 250, p. 777–789.   **194**

Griffitts, W. R. See also Overstreet and Griffitts, 1955; Overstreet, Yates, and Griffitts, 1963.

Griscom, Andrew, and Bromery, R. W., 1968, Geologic interpretation of aeromagnetic data for New England: in Zen, E-an, White, W. S., Hadley, J. B., and Thompson, J. B., Jr., eds., Studies of Appalachian geology: northern and maritime (Billings vol.), p. 425–436.   **95**

Guidotti, C. V. See Green and Guidotti, 1968.

Guillaume, Raymond. See Arnould, Aymé, and Guillaume, 1959.

Gwinn, V. E., 1964, Thin-skinned tectonics in the Plateau and northwestern Valley and Ridge provinces of the Central Appalachians: Geol. Soc. America Bull., v. 75, p. 863–899.   **16, 20, 20, 28, 35, 62, 64**

———1970, Kinematic patterns and estimates of lateral shortening, Valley and Ridge and Great Valley Provinces, Central Appalachians, south-central Pennsylvania: in Fisher, G. W., Pettijohn, F. J., Reed, J. C., Jr., and Weaver, K. N., eds., Studies of Appalachian geology: central and southern (Cloos vol.), p. 127–146.   **33, 35, 36, 64, 166**

Hack, J. T., 1965, Geomorphology of the Shenandoah Valley, Virginia and West Virginia, and origin of the residual ore deposits: U.S. Geol. Survey Prof. Paper 484, 84 p.   **209**

Hacquebard, P. A. See Barss and Hacquebard, 1967.

Hadley, J. B., 1964, Correlation of isotopic ages, crustal heating and sedimentation in the Appalachian region: in Lowry, W. D., ed., Tectonics of the Southern Appalachians: Virginia Polytech. Inst. Dept. Geol. Sci. Mem. 1, p. 33–44.   **185**

———1970, The Ocoee Series and its possible correlatives: in Fisher, G. W., Pettijohn, F. J., Reed, J. C., Jr., and Weaver, K. N., eds., Studies of Appalachian geology: central and southern (Cloos vol.), p. 247–259.   **174, 180**

Hadley, J. B., and Goldsmith, Richard, 1963, Geology of the eastern Great Smoky Mountains, North Carolina and Tennessee: U.S. Geol. Survey Prof. Paper 349-B, 118 p.   **174, 177, 212**

Hadley, J. B. See also King, Hadley, Neuman, and Hamilton, 1958; Zen, White, Hadley, and Thompson, 1968.

Haff, J. C. See Cooper and Haff, 1940.

Hall, B. A., ms. 1964, Stratigraphy and structure of the Spider Lake quadrangle, Maine: Ph.D. dissertation, Yale University, 153 p.   **125**

Hall, B. A., 1969, Pre–Middle Ordovician unconformity in northern New England and Quebec: Am. Assoc. Petroleum Geologists Mem. 12, p. 467–476.   **125, 126**

Hall, James, 1883, Contributions to the geological history of the North American continent: Am. Assoc. Adv. Sci. Proc., 31st Ann. Mtg., Montreal, 1882, p. 31–69; abs. *in* Canadian Naturalist and Geologist, v. 2, p. 284–286, 1857; see also Natural History of New York, Div. 6, Paleontology, v. 3, p. 1–96, 1859.   **9**

Hall, L. M., 1959, The geology of the St. Johnsbury quadrangle, Vermont and New Hampshire: Vermont Geol. Survey Bull. 13, 105 p.   **100**

———1968a, Bedrock geology in the vicinity of White Plains, New York: New York State Geol. Assoc., 40th Ann. Mtg., Flushing, Queens, N.Y., 1968, Gdbk., p. 7–31.   **94**

———1968b, Times of origin and deformation of bedrock in the Manhattan Prong: *in* Zen, E-an, White, W. S., Hadley, J. B., and Thompson, J. B., Jr., eds., Studies of Appalachian geology: northern and maritime (Billings vol.), p. 117–127.   **94**

Ham, W. E., and Wilson, J. L., 1967, Paleozoic epeirogeny and orogeny in the central United States: Am. Jour. Sci., v. 265, p. 332–407.   **217, 220**

Hamilton, J. B., 1965, Limestone in New Brunswick: New Brunswick Mines Br. Geol. Div. Min. Resources Rept. 2, 147 p.   **136**

Hamilton, Warren, 1961, Geology of the Richardson Cove and Jones Cove quadrangles, Tennessee: U.S. Geol. Survey Prof. Paper 349-A, 55 p.   **174**

Hamilton, Warren. See also King, Hadley, Neuman, and Hamilton, 1958.

Hansen, W. R., 1956, Geology and mineral resources of the Hudson and Maynard quadrangles, Massachusetts: U.S. Geol. Survey Bull. 1038, 104 p.   **108**

Harland, W. B., 1965, Tectonic evolution of the Arctic–North Atlantic region: Royal Soc. London Philos. Trans., Ser. A., v. 258, p. 59–75.   **223**

———1969, Fleur de Lys "tilloid": Am. Assoc. Petroleum Geologists Mem. 12, p. 234–235.   **155**

Harper, C. T., 1968, Isotopic ages from the Appalachians and their tectonic significance: Canadian Jour. Earth Sci., v. 5, p. 49–59.   **68**

Harris, L. D., 1967, Geology of the L. S. Bales well, Lee County, Virginia—a Cambrian and Ordovician test: Kentucky Geol. Survey, Ser. 10, Spec. Pub. 14, p. 50–55.   **23**

———1970, Details of thin-skinned tectonics in parts of Valley and Ridge and Cumberland Plateau provinces of the southern Appalachians: *in* Fisher, G. W., Pettijohn, F. J., Reed, J. C., Jr., and Weaver, K. N., eds., Studies of Appalachian geology: central and southern (Cloos vol.), p. 161–173.   **23, 24–25**

Harris, L. D., and Miller, R. L., 1958, Geology of the

Duffield quadrangle, Virginia: U.S. Geol. Survey Geol. Quad. Map GQ-111.   **48**

Harris, L. D. See also Bayles, Henry, Fettke, Harris, Flowers, and Haught, 1956.

Hart, S. R. See Wetherill, Tilton, Davis, Hart, and Hopson, 1966.

Hartshorn, J. H. See Zen and Hartshorn, 1966.

Harwood, D. S., and Berry, W. B. N., 1967, Fossiliferous lower Paleozoic rocks in the Cupsuptic quadrangle, west central Maine: U.S. Geol. Survey Prof. Paper 575, p. D16–D23.   **123**

Hatch, N. L., Jr., Schnabel, R. W., and Norton, S. A., 1968, Stratigraphy and correlation of the rocks on the east limb of the Berkshire anticlinorium in western Massachusetts and north-central Connecticut: *in* Zen, E-an, White, W. S., Hadley, J. B., and Thompson, J. B., Jr., eds., Studies of Appalachian geology: northern and maritime (Billings vol.), p. 177–184.   **99**

Hatch, N. L., Jr., and Stanley, R. S., 1970, Stratigraphic continuity and facies changes in formations of early Paleozoic age in western Massachusetts and tentative correlations with Connecticut (abs.): Geol. Soc. America Abstracts with Programs, v. 2, no. 1, p. 23–24.   **101**

Hatcher, R. D., Jr., 1969, Stratigraphy, petrology, and structure of the low rank belt and part of the Blue Ridge of northwesternmost South Carolina: South Carolina Div. Geology, Geol. Notes, v. 13, p. 105–141, 143–145.   **183**

———1970a, Stratigraphy of the Brevard zone and Poor Mountain area, northwestern South Carolina: Geol. Soc. America Bull., v. 81, p. 933–939.   **183**

———1970b, Stratigraphic controls and thrusting along the Brevard Zone (abs.): Geol. Soc. America Abstracts with Programs, v. 2, p. 214–215.   **183**

Haught, O. L., 1968, Structural contour map; datum: Greenbrier Limestone: West Virginia Geol. Econ. Survey.   **16**

Haught, O. L. See also Bayles, Henry, Fettke, Harris, Flowers, and Haught, 1956.

Hawkes, H. E., Jr., 1941, Roots of the Taconic fault in west-central Vermont: Geol. Soc. America Bull., v. 52, p. 649–666.   **81**

Hawley, David, 1957, Ordovician shales and submarine slide breccias of northern Champlain Valley in Vermont: Geol. Soc. America Bull., v. 68, p. 55–94.   **72, 84, 117**

Hay, P. W. See Wynne-Edwards, Gregory, Hay, Giovanella, and Reinhardt, 1966.

Hayes, A. O., and Howell, B. F., 1937, Geology of Saint John, New Brunswick: Geol. Soc. America Spec. Paper 5, 146 p.   **136**

Hayes, C. W., 1891, The overthrust faults of the southern Appalachians: Geol. Soc. America Bull., v. 2, p. 141–154.   **57**

Heezen, B. C., Tharp, Marie, and Ewing, Maurice, 1959, The floors of the oceans, 1. The North Atlantic: Geol. Soc. America Spec. Paper 65, 122 p.   **163**

Helwig, James, and Sarpi, Ernesto, 1969, Plutonic-pebble conglomerates, New World Island, Newfoundland, and history of eugeosynclines: Am. Assoc. Petroleum Geologists Mem. 12, p. 443–466.   **157, 163**

Helwig, James. See also Horne and Helwig, 1969.

Henderson, W. R. S., 1958, "Blountian" allochthone in Appalachians of Quebec: Alberta Soc. Petroleum Geologists Jour., v. 6, p. 120–128.   **82, 118**

Henningsmoen, Gunnar, 1969, Short account of Cambrian and Tremadocian of Acado-Baltic province: Am. Assoc. Petroleum Geologists Mem. 12, p. 110–114.   **162**

Henry, W. H. See Bayles, Henry, Fettke, Harris, Flowers, and Haught, 1956.

Herz, Norman, 1961, Bedrock geology of the North Adams quadrangle, Massachusetts–Vermont: U.S. Geol. Survey Quad. Map GQ–139.   **86, 92, 93**

Hess, H. H., 1939, Island arcs, gravity anomalies and serpentinite intrusions. A contribution to the ophiolite problem: Internat. Geol. Congress, 17th, Moscow 1937, Rept., v. 2, p. 263–283. (Edition in Russian, p. 279–300.)   **199, 213**

———1940, Appalachian peridotite belt: its significance in sequence of events in mountain building (abs.): Geol. Soc. America Bull., v. 51, p. 1996.   **213**

Hewett, D. F., and Crickmay, G. W., 1937, The Warm Springs of Georgia, their geologic relations and origin—a summary report: U.S. Geol. Survey Water-Supply Paper 819, 40 p.   **194, 195**

Hewett, D. F. See also Stose, Miser, Katz, and Hewett, 1919.

Hewitt, P. C., 1961, The geology of the Equinox quadrangle and vicinity, Vermont: Vermont Geol. Survey Bull. 18, 83 p.   **80**

Heyl, A. V. See Brock and Heyl, 1961; Zartman, Brock, Heyl, and Thomas, 1967.

Hietanen, Anna. See Cloos and Hietanen, 1941.

Higgins, M. W., 1968, Geologic map of the Brevard fault zone near Atlanta, Georgia: U.S. Geol. Survey Misc. Geol. Invs. Map I-511.   **182**

Hills, F. A., and Dasch, E. J., 1969, Rb-Sr evidence for metamorphic remobilization of the Stony Creek Granite, southeastern Connecticut (abs.): Geol. Soc. America Spec. Paper 121, p. 136–137.   **105**

Hollowell, J. R. See Carswell, Hollowell, and Platt, 1968.

Hood, P. J. See Godby, Baker, Bower, and Hood, 1966.

Hopson, C. A., 1964, The crystalline rocks of Howard and Montgomery Counties: Maryland Geol. Survey, The geology of Howard and Montgomery Counties, p. 27–215.   **188, 189, 190, 191, 213**

Hopson, C. A. See also Tilton, Doe, and Hopson, 1970; Wetherill, Tilton, Davis, Hart, and Hopson, 1966.

Horne, G. S., ms. 1968, Stratigraphy and structural geology of southwestern New World Island area: Ph.D. dissertation, Columbia Univ., 280 p.   **156**

Horne, G. S., 1969, Early Ordovician chaotic deposits in the central volcanic belt of northeastern Newfoundland: Geol. Soc. America Bull., v. 60, p. 2451–2464.   **157**

Horne, G. S., and Helwig, James, 1969, Ordovician stratigraphy of Notre Dame Bay, Newfoundland: Am. Assoc. Petroleum Geologists Mem. 12, p. 388–407.   **156**

Hoskins, D. M., 1970, Alternative interpretation of the Catskill–Pocono contact in the anthracite area of Pennsylvania (abs.): Geol. Soc. America Abstracts with Programs, v. 2, no. 1, p. 25.   **67**

Hotz, P. E., 1952, Form of diabase sheets in southeastern Pennsylvania: Am. Jour. Sci., v. 250, p. 375–388.   **208**

Houde, M., and Clark, T. H., 1962, Geological map of St. Lawrence Lowlands: Quebec Dept. Nat. Resources, Map. No. 1407.   **116, 117, 227**

Houston, P. K. See Bumgarner, Houston, Ricketts, and Wedow, 1964.

Howell, B. F. See Hayes and Howell, 1937.

Hoy, R. B. See Moebs and Hoy, 1959.

Hubbert, M. K., and Rubey, W. W., 1959, Role of fluid pressure in mechanics of overthrust faulting: Geol. Soc. America Bull., v. 70, p. 115–205.   **64, 81**

Hubert, Claude, 1967, Tectonics of part of the Sillery Formation in the Chaudière-Matapédia segment of the Québec Appalachians: Royal Soc. Canada Spec. Pub. 10, p. 33–40.   **118**

Hurley, P. M. See Fairbairn, Bottino, Pinson, and Hurley, 1966; Fairbairn, Moorbath, Ramo, Pinson, and Hurley, 1967.

Hurst, V. J., 1955, Stratigraphy, structure, and mineral resources of the Mineral Bluff quadrangle, Georgia: Georgia Geol. Survey Bull. 63, 137 p.   **179**

———1956, Geologic map of the Kennesaw Mtn.–Sweat Mtn. area, Cobb County, Georgia: [Georgia Dept. Mines, Mining, and Geology].   **182**

———1959, The geology and mineralogy of Graves Mountain, Georgia: Georgia Geol. Survey Bull. 68, 33 p.   **197**

———1970, The Piedmont in Georgia: in Fisher, G. W., Pettijohn, F. J., Reed, J. C., Jr., and Weaver, K. N., eds., Studies of Appalachian geology: central and southern (Cloos vol.), p. 383–396.   **180, 182**

Hurst, V. J., and Schlee, J. S., 1962, Field excursion—Ocoee rocks in north central Georgia and southeast Tennessee: Georgia Geol. Survey Gdbk. 3, 28 p.   **178, 179**

Hurst, V. J. See also Milton and Hurst, 1965.

Hussey, A. M., II, 1968, Stratigraphy and structure of southwestern Maine: in Zen, E-an, White, W. S., Hadley, J. B., and Thompson, J. B., Jr., eds., Studies of Appalachian geology: northern and maritime (Billings vol.), p. 291–301.   **127, 128**

Hutchinson, R. D., 1952, The stratigraphy and trilobite faunas of the Cambrian sedimentary rocks of Cape Breton Island, Nova Scotia: Geol. Survey Canada Mem. 263, 124 p.   **140**

———1956, Cambrian stratigraphy, correlation, and paleogeography of eastern Canada: Internat. Geol. Congress, 20th, México 1956, El sistema Cambrico, su paleogeografía y el problema de su base-Symposium, v. 2, p. 289–314.   **120**

———1962, Cambrian stratigraphy and trilobite faunas of southeastern Newfoundland: Geol. Survey Canada Bull. 88, 156 p.   **160, 161**

Isachsen, Y. W., 1964, Extent and configuration of the Precambrian in northeastern United States: New York Acad. Sci. Trans., ser. 2, v. 26, p. 812–829.   **70**

Jaeger, H. See Boucot, Cumming, and Jaeger, 1967.

Jahns, R. H., 1941, Stratigraphy of the Lowell-Fitchburg area, Massachusetts (abs.): Geol. Soc. America Bull., v. 52, p. 1910–1911.   **108**

Jahns, R. H. See also Currier and Jahns, 1952; White and Jahns, 1950.

Jenness, S. E., 1963, Terra Nova and Bonavista map-areas, Newfoundland: Geol. Survey Canada Mem. 327, 184 p.   **159**

———1966, The anorthosite of northern Cape Breton Island, Nova Scotia, a petrological enigma: Geol. Survey Canada Paper 66–21, 25 p.   **141**

Jewell, W. B. See Ferguson and Jewell, 1951.

Joesting, H. R., Keller, Fred, Jr., and King, E. R., 1949, Geologic implications of aeromagnetic survey of Clearfield–Philipsburg area, Pennsylvania: Am. Assoc. Petroleum Geologists Bull., v. 33, p. 1747–1766.   **64**

Joesting, H. R. See also Woollard, Chairman, Joesting, and others, 1964.

Johnson, M. E., and McLaughlin, D. B., 1957, Triassic formations in the Delaware Valley: Geol. Soc. America, 70th Ann. Mtg., Atlantic City, N.J., Gdbk., p. 29–68.   **205**

Jonas, A. I. (Stose, A. J.). See Knopf and Jonas, 1929. Stose and Jonas, 1935 and 1939.

Jones, C. L. See Brokaw and Jones, 1946.

Katz, F. J. See Stose, Miser, Katz, and Hewett, 1919.

Kay, Marshall, 1937, Stratigraphy of the Trenton group: Geol. Soc. America Bull., v. 48, p. 233–302.   **78, 118**

———1941, Taconic allochthone and the Martic thrust: Science, new ser., v. 94, p. 73.   **89, 191**

———1942, Development of the northern Allegheny synclinorium and adjoining regions: Geol. Soc. America Bull., v. 53, p. 1601–1657.   **12, 42**

———1945, Paleogeographic and palinspastic maps: Am. Assoc. Petroleum Geologists Bull., v. 29, p. 426–450.   **152**

———1958, Ordovician Highgate Springs sequence of Vermont and Quebec and Ordovician classification: Am. Jour. Sci., v. 256, p. 65–96.   **73**

———1959, Excursions at north end of the Taconic Range near Sudbury: New England Intercoll. Geol. Conf., 51st Ann. Mtg., Rutland, Vt., 1959, Gdbk., p. 17–18.   **84**

———1967, Stratigraphy and structure of northeastern Newfoundland bearing on drift in North Atlantic: Am. Assoc. Petroleum Geologists Bull., v. 51, p. 579 600.   **156**

———1969, Silurian of northeast Newfoundland coast: Am. Assoc. Petroleum Geologists Mem. 12, p. 414–424.   **156**

Kay, Marshall, ed., 1969, North Atlantic—geology and continental drift: Am. Assoc. Petroleum Geologists Mem. 12, 1082 p.   **10**

Kay, Marshall, and Eldredge, Niles, 1968, Cambrian trilobites in central Newfoundland volcanic belt; Geol. Mag., v. 105, p. 372–377.   **157**

Kay, Marshall, and Williams, Harold, 1963, Ordovician–Silurian relations on New World Island, Notre Dame Bay, northeast Newfoundland (abs.): Geol. Soc. America Bull., v. 74, p. 807.   **156**

Kay, Marshall. See also Dewey and Kay, 1968.

Kehn, T. M. See Wood and Kehn, 1961; Wood, Trexler, and Kehn, 1969.

Keith, Arthur, 1912, New evidence on the Taconic question (abs.): Geol. Soc. America Bull., v. 23, p. 720–721.   **76**

———1913, Further discoveries in the Taconic Mountains (abs.): Geol. Soc. America Bull., v. 24, p. 680.   **76, 81**

———1932, Stratigraphy and structure of northwestern Vermont: Washington [D.C.] Acad. Sci. Jour., v. 22, p. 357–379, 393–406.   **77, 81**

Keith, Arthur, and Sterrett, D. B., 1931, Description of the Gaffney and Kings Mountain quadrangles [South Carolina–North Carolina]: U.S. Geol. Survey Geol. Atlas, Folio 222, 13 p.   **195, 195**

Kellberg, J. M., and Grant, L. F., 1956, Coarse conglomerates of the Middle Ordovician in the southern Appalachian Valley: Geol. Soc. America Bull., v. 67, p. 697–716.   **215**

Keller, Fred, Jr. See Joesting, Keller, and King, 1949.

Kelley, D. G., and Mackasey, W. O., 1965, Basal Mississippian volcanic rocks in Cape Breton Island: Geol. Survey Canada Paper 64–34, 10 p.   **141**

Kelley, D. G. See also Poole, Kelley, and Neale, 1964.

Kennedy, M. J. See Neale and Kennedy, 1967; Phillips, Kennedy and Dunlop, 1969.

Kesler, T. L., 1950, Geology and mineral deposits of the Cartersville district, Georgia: U.S. Geol. Survey Prof. Paper 224, 97 p.   **58, 180**

———1955, The Kings Mountain area: Geol. Soc. America, 68th Ann. Mtg., New Orleans 1955, Gdbk. (Guides to Southeastern geology), p. 374–387.   **195**

Kindle, C. H., 1942, A Lower (?) Cambrian fauna from eastern Gaspé, Quebec: Am. Jour. Sci., v. 240, p. 633–641.   **130**

———1948, Crepicephalid trilobites from Murphy Creek, Quebec, and Cow Head, Newfoundland: Am. Jour. Sci., v. 246, p. 441–451.   **130**

Kindle, C. H., and Whittington, H. B., 1958, Stratigraphy of the Cow Head region, western Newfoundland: Geol. Soc. America Bull., v. 69, p. 315–342.   **151**

———1959, Some stratigraphic problems of the Cow Head area in western Newfoundland: New York Acad. Sci. Trans., ser. 2, v. 22, p. 7–18.   **151**

Kindle, C. H. See also Whittington and Kindle, 1969.

King, E. R. See Joesting, Keller, and King, 1949; Zeitz, King, Geddes, and Lidiak, 1966.

King, P. B., 1949, The floor of the Shenandoah Valley: Am. Jour. Sci., v. 247, p. 73–93.   **209**

———1950, Geology of the Elkton area, Virginia: U.S. Geol. Survey Prof. Paper 230, 82 p.   **165, 166**

———1955, A geologic section across the southern Appalachians: an outline of the geology in the segment in Tennessee, North Carolina, and South Carolina: Geol. Soc. America, 68th Ann. Mtg., New Orleans 1955, Gdbk. (Guides to Southeastern geology), p. 332–373.   **195**

———1961a, Systematic pattern of Triassic dikes in the Appalachian region: U.S. Geol. Survey Prof. Paper 424, p. B93–B95.   **208**

———1961b [1962], The subsurface Ouachita structural belt east of the Ouachita Mountains: Univ. Texas, Bur. Econ. Geology, Pub. 6120, p. 83–98, 347–361.   **198, 220**

——1964, Geology of the central Great Smoky Mountains, Tennessee: U.S. Geol. Survey Prof. Paper 349-C, 148 p.   **174, 176, 178, 210, 212**

——1969, The tectonics of North America—a discussion to accompany the tectonic map of North America: U.S. Geol. Survey Prof. Paper 628, 95 p. **226**

King, P. B., and Ferguson, H. W., 1960, Geology of northeasternmost Tennessee: U.S. Geol. Survey Prof. Paper 311, 136 p.   **168, 170**

King, P. B., Ferguson, H. W., Craig, L. C., and Rodgers, John, 1944, Geology and manganese deposits of northeastern Tennessee: Tennessee Div. Geology Bull. 52, 283 p.   **168**

King, P. B., Hadley, J. B., Neuman, R. B., and Hamilton, Warren, 1958, Stratigraphy of Ocoee series, Great Smoky Mountains, Tennessee and North Carolina: Geol. Soc. American Bull., v. 69, p. 947–966.   **174**

Klein, G. D., 1962, Triassic sedimentation, Maritime Provinces, Canada: Geol. Soc. America Bull., v. 73, p. 1127–1145.   **207**

——1963, Regional implications of Triassic paleocurrents, Maritime Provinces, Canada: Jour. Geology, v. 71, p. 801–808.   **207**

Knopf, E. B., 1927, Some results of recent work in the southern Taconic area: Am. Jour. Sci., 5th ser., v. 14, p. 429–458.   **77, 88**

——1946, Stratigraphy of the lower Paleozoic rocks surrounding Stissing Mountain, Dutchess County, New York (abs.): Geol. Soc. America Bull., v. 57, p. 1211–1212.   **77**

——1956, Stratigraphy and structure of the Stissing area, Dutchess County, New York (abs.): Geol. Soc. America Bull., v. 67, p. 1817–1818.   **77**

——1962, Stratigraphy and structure of the Stissing Mountain area, Dutchess County, New York: Stanford Univ. Pub. Geol. Sciences, v. 7, no. 1, 55 p.   **77, 87**

Knopf, E. B., and Jonas, A. I., 1929, Geology of the McCalls Ferry–Quarryville district, Pennsylvania: U.S. Geol. Survey Bull. 799, 156 p.   **188, 188fn., 190**

Knopf, E. B. See also Prindle and Knopf, 1932.

Knott, S. T. See Emery, Uchupi, Phillips, Bowin, Bunce, and Knott, 1970.

Knowles, R. R. See Ratcliffe and Knowles, 1969.

Knox, A. S., 1944, A Carboniferous flora from the Wamsutta formation of southeastern Massachusetts: Am. Jour. Sci., v. 242, p. 130–138.   **111**

Krynine, P. D., 1950, Petrology, stratigraphy, and origin of the Triassic sedimentary rocks of Connecticut: Connecticut Geol. Nat. History Survey Bull. 73, 239 p.   **205**

Kulp, J. L., and Poldervaart, Arie, 1956, The metamorphic history of the Spruce Pine District: Am. Jour. Sci., v. 254, p. 393–403.   **171**

Kulp, J. L. See also Clark and Kulp, 1968; Long and Kulp, 1962.

LaForge, Laurence, 1932, Geology of the Boston area, Massachusetts: U.S. Geol. Survey Bull. 839, 105 p.   **113**

Lajoie, Jean, Lespérance, P. J., and Béland, Jacques, 1968, Silurian stratigraphy and paleogeography of Matapédia-Témiscouata region, Québec: Am. Assoc.

Petroleum Geologists Bull., v. 52, p. 615–640.   **121**

Lane, M. A. See Potter and Lane, 1969.

Laney, F. B., 1910, The Gold Hill mining district: North Carolina Geol. Econ. Survey Bull. 21, 137 p.   **197**

——1917, The geology and ore deposits of the Virgilina district, Virginia and North Carolina: Virginia Geol. Survey Bull. 14, 176 p.; North Carolina Geol. Econ. Survey Bull. 26, 176 p.   **196**

Larrabee, D. M., 1966, Map showing distribution of ultramafic and intrusive mafic rocks from northern New Jersey to eastern Alabama: U.S. Geol. Survey Misc. Geol. Invs. Map I–476.   **196**

Larrabee, D. M., Spencer, C. W., and Swift, D. J. P., 1965, Bedrock geology of the Grand Lake area, Aroostook, Hancock, Penobscot, and Washington Counties, Maine: U.S. Geol. Survey Bull. 1201-E, 38 p.   **135, 137**

Laurence, R. A., 1960, Geologic problems in the Sweetwater barite district, Tennessee: Am. Jour. Sci., v. 258-A (Bradley vol.), p. 170–179.   **47**

Lespérance, P. J., and Greiner, H. R., 1969, Squatec-Cabano area, Rimouski, Rivière-du-Loup and Témiscouata Counties: Quebec Dept. Nat. Resources, Mines Branch, Geol. Rept. 128, 111 p.   **122**

Lespérance, P. J. See also Lajoie, Lespérance, and Béland, 1968.

Lesure, F. G., 1957, Geology of the Clifton Forge iron district, Virginia: Virginia Polytech. Inst. Bull., v. 50, no. 7 (Eng. Expt. Sta. Ser. no. 118), 130 p.   **40**

Lidiak, E. G. See Zeitz, King, Geddes, Wilburt, and Lidiak, 1966.

Lilly, H. D., 1963, Geology of Hughes Brooks–Goose Arm area, West Newfoundland: Memorial Univ. Newfoundland Geol. Rept. 2, 123 p.   **151**

——1966, Late Precambrian and Appalachian tectonics in the light of submarine exploration of the Great Bank of Newfoundland and in the Gulf of St. Lawrence. Preliminary views: Am. Jour. Sci., v. 264, p. 569–574.   **152, 159, 161, 213**

——1967, Some notes on stratigraphy and structural style in central west Newfoundland: Geol. Assoc. Canada Spec. Paper 4 (Lilly vol.), p. 201–211.   **151**

Livingston, J. L. See Burchfiel and Livingston, 1967.

Lochman, Christina, 1956, Stratigraphy, paleontology, and paleogeography of the *Elliptocephala asaphoides* strata in Cambridge and Hoosick quadrangles, New York: Geol. Soc. America Bull., v. 67, p. 1331–1396.   **79, 80**

Lock, B. E., 1969, Silurian rocks of west White Bay area, Newfoundland: Am. Assoc. Petroleum Geologists Mem. 12, p. 433–442.   **153**

Logan, W. E., 1861, Remarks on the fauna of the Quebec group of rocks and the primordial zone of Canada: Am. Jour. Sci., 2nd ser., v. 31, p. 216–220; Canadian Naturalist, v. 5, p. 472–477 [1860].   **10, 117**

——1862, Considerations relative to the Quebec group, and the upper copper-bearing rocks at Lake Superior: Am. Jour. Sci., 2nd ser., v. 33, p. 320–327.   **213**

Long, L. E., 1962, Isotopic age study, Dutchess County, New York: Geol. Soc. America Bull., v. 73, p. 997–1006.   **90**

Long, L. E., and Kulp, J. L., 1962, Isotopic age study of the metamorphic history of the Manhattan and

Reading Prongs: Geol. Soc. America Bull., v. 73, p. 969–995.   **96**

Loring, R. B.   See Platt, Loring, and Stephens, 1969.

Loveridge, W. D.   See McCartney, Poole, Wanless, Williams, and Loveridge, 1966.

Lowman, S. W., 1961, Some aspects of turbidite sedimentation in the vicinity of Troy, New York: New York State Geol. Assoc., 33rd Ann. Mtg., Troy, N.Y., 1961, Gdbk., Trip B, 15 p.   **79**

Lowry, W. D., 1957, Implications of gentle Ordovician folding in western Virginia: Am. Assoc. Petroleum Geologists Bull., v. 41, p. 643–655.   **47, 62**

————1960, Relationship between tectonism and sedimentation in Early Silurian time in Virginia: Virginia Polytech. Inst. Min. Industries Jour., v. 7, no. 3, p. 1–7.   **41, 47**

Lowry, W. D., ed., 1964, Tectonics of the southern Appalachians: Virginia Polytech. Inst. Dept. Geol. Sci. Mem. 1, 114 p.   **10**

Ludlum, J. C., 1958, Relation of surface and subsurface structure in West Virginia to future drilling for natural gas: West Virginia Engineer, v. 20, no. 7.   **20**

Lundgren, Lawrence, Jr., 1962, Deep River area, Connecticut: stratigraphy and structure: Am. Jour. Sci., v. 260, p. 1–23.   **108**

————1966, Muscovite reactions and partial melting in southeastern Connecticut: Jour. Petrology, v. 7, p. 421–453.   **110**

————1968, Late Paleozoic metamorphism in southeastern Connecticut (abs.): Geol. Soc. America Spec. Paper 101, p. 266–267.   **110**

————1969, Cataclastic deformation of the Hebron Formation, southeastern Connecticut (abs.): Geol. Soc. America Abstracts with Programs for 1969, pt. 1 [v. 1, no. 1], p. 38.   **109**

Lundgren, Lawrence, Jr., Goldsmith, Richard, and Snyder, G. L., 1958, Major thrust fault in southeastern Connecticut (abs.): Geol. Soc. America Bull., v. 69, p. 1606.   **109**

Lundgren, Lawrence, Jr.   See also Dixon and Lundgren, 1968; Dixon, Lundgren, Snyder, and Eaton, 1963.

Lyons, J. B., and Faul, Henry, 1968, Isotope geochronology of the northern Appalachians: in Zen, E-an, White, W. S., Hadley, J. B., and Thompson, J. B., Jr., eds.: Studies in Appalachian geology: northern and maritime (Billings vol.), p. 305–318.   **113**

McCartney, W. D., 1967, Whitbourne map–area, Newfoundland: Geol. Survey Canada Mem. 341, 135 p.   **158, 159**

————1969, Geology of Avalon Peninsula, southeast Newfoundland: Am. Assoc. Petroleum Geologists Mem. 12, p. 115–129.   **158**

McCartney, W. D., Poole, W. H., Wanless, R. K., Williams, Harold, and Loveridge, W. D., 1966, Rb-Sr age and geological setting of the Holyrood granite, southeast Newfoundland: Canadian Jour. Earth Sci., v. 3, p. 947–957.   **159**

McCord, W. R., 1960, Map of West Virginia showing structural contours on top of Onandaga Limestone–Huntersville chert with deep well locations: West Virginia Geol. Econ. Survey (see also ibid., Rept. Invs.

20, p. 15–25).   **16**

McCoy, A. W., 1934, An interpretation of local structural development in Mid-Continent areas associated with deposits of petroleum: Problems of Petroleum geology (Sidney Powers memorial volume), p. 581–627: Tulsa, Am. Assoc. Petroleum Geologists.   **15**

MacFadyen, J. A., Jr., 1956, The geology of the Bennington area, Vermont: Vermont Geol. Survey Bull. 7, 72 p.   **77, 80**

McGerrigle, H. W., 1950, The geology of eastern Gaspé: Quebec Dept. Mines, Geol. Surveys Branch, Geol. Rept. 35, 168 p.   **121**

————1953, Geological map, Gaspé Peninsula: Quebec Dept. Mines, Geol. Surveys Branch, Map No. 1000.   **120, 227**

McGerrigle, H. W., and Skidmore, W. B., 1967, Geological map, Gaspé Peninsula: Quebec Dept. Nat. Resources, Geol. Explor. Service, Map No. 1642.   **120, 227**

McGregor, D. C., and Owens, B., 1966, Illustrations of Canadian fossils: Devonian spores of eastern and northern Canada: Geol. Survey Canada Paper 66–30, 66 p.   **121**

Mack, Tinsley, 1965, Characteristics of the Everona Formation in Virginia: Virginia Div. Min. Resources Inf. Circ. 10, 16 p.   **192**

Mackasey, W. O.   See Kelley and Mackasey, 1965.

McKerrow, W. S., 1962, The chronology of Caledonian folding in the British Isles: Natl. Acad. Sci. Proc., v. 48, p. 1905–1913.   **221**

Mackin, J. H., 1950, The down-structure method of viewing geologic maps: Jour. Geology, v. 58, p. 55–72.   **70, 114, 190**

————1962, Structure of the Glenarm Series in Chester County, Pennsylvania: Geol. Soc. America Bull., v. 73, p. 403–409.   **190**

Mackin, J. H.   See also Bailey and Mackin, 1937.

McKinstry, Hugh, 1961, Structure of the Glenarm series in Chester County, Pennsylvania: Geol. Soc. America Bull., v. 72, p. 557–577.   **190**

McLaughlin, D. B.   See Geyer, Buckwalter, McLaughlin, and Gray, 1963; Geyer, Gray, McLaughlin, and Moseley, 1958; Gray, Geyer, and McLaughlin, 1958; Johnson and McLaughlin, 1957.

Maclure, William, 1809, Observations on the geology of the United States, explanatory of a geological map: Am. Philos. Soc. Trans., v. 6, p. 411–428, Jour. physique, chimie, hist. nat., t. 69, p. 201–213; t. 72, p. 137–165, 1811. 2nd ed., privately published, Philadelphia, 1817; also Am. Philos. Soc. Trans., new ser., v. 1, p. 1–91, 1818.   **8**

Mamay, S. H.   See Grew, Mamay, and Barghoorn, 1970.

Marleau, R.-A., 1968, Woburn-East Megantic-Armstrong area, Frontenac and Beauce Counties: Quebec Dept. Nat. Resources, Mines Branch, Geol. Rept. 131, 55 p.   **122**

Marshall, John, 1937, The structures and age of the volcanic complex of Cecil County, Maryland: Maryland Geol. Survey, v. 13, p. 189–213.   **190**

Martin, C. W., ms. 1962, Petrology, metamorphism, and structure of the Hartland Formation in the central Western Connecticut Highlands: Ph.D. dissertation, Univ. Wisconsin, 99 p. (not seen).   **101**

Martin, C. W.   See also Gates and Martin, 1967.

Martin, R. F. See Davies, Tupper, Bachinski, Boyle, and Martin, 1969.

Marvin, R. F. See Zartman, Snyder, Stern, Marvin, and Buckman, 1965.

Mather, W. W., 1843, Natural History of New York, Div. 4, Geology of New York. Part I, comprising the geology of the first geological district: Albany, N.Y., 653 p.   **94**

Mattauer, Maurice, 1968, Les traits structuraux essentials de la chaîne pyrénéenne: Rev. géographie phys. géologie dynamique, sér. 2, v. 10, p. 3–11.   **222**

Mattinson, C. R., 1964, Mont Logan area, Matane and Gaspé–North Counties: Quebec Dept. Nat. Resources Geol. Rept. 118, 97 p.   **120**

Maxwell, J. C., 1962, Origin of slaty and fracture cleavage in the Delaware Water Gap area, New Jersey and Pennsylvania: *in* Petrologic Studies—a volume in honor of A.F. Buddington: Geol. Soc. America, p. 281–311.   **70**

Mayhew, M. A., Drake, C. L., and Nafe, J. E., 1968, Marine geophysical evidence for sea-floor spreading in the Labrador Sea (abs.): Am. Geophys. Union Trans. v. 49, p. 202.   **163, 221**

Mencher, Ely. See Pavlides, Mencher, Naylor, and Boucot, 1964.

Milici, R. C., 1962, The structural geology of the Harriman Corner, Roane County, Tennessee: Am. Jour. Sci., v. 260, p. 787–793.   **52**

————1963, Low-angle overthrust faulting, as illustrated by the Cumberland Plateau–Sequatchie Valley fault system: Am. Jour. Sci., v. 261, p. 815–825.   **23, 26**

Milici, R. C. See also Smith, Milici, and Greenberg, 1964.

Miller, B. L., 1935, Age of the schists of the South Valley Hills, Pennsylvania: Geol. Soc. America Bull., v. 46, p. 715–756.   **188**

————1944, Specific data on the so-called "Reading overthrust": Geol. Soc. America Bull., v. 55, p. 211–254.   **70**

Miller, R. L., 1944, Geology and manganese deposits of the Glade Mountain district, Virginia: Virginia Geol. Survey Bull. 61, 150 p.   **46**

————1962, The Pine Mountain overthrust at the northeast end of the Powell Valley anticline, Virginia: U.S. Geol. Survey Prof. Paper 450, p. D69–D72.   **23**

Miller, R. L., and Brosgé, W. P., 1954, Geology and oil resources of the Jonesville district, Lee County, Virginia: U.S. Geol. Survey Bull. 990, 240 p.   **23**

Miller, R. L., and Fuller, J. O., 1954, Geology and oil resources of the Rose Hill district—the fenster area of the Cumberland overthrust block—Lee County, Virginia: Virginia Geol. Survey Bull. 71, 383 p.   **23**

Miller, R. L. See also Harris and Miller, 1958.

Milton, Charles, and Hurst, V. J., 1965, Subsurface "basement" rocks of Georgia: Georgia Geol. Survey Bull. 76, 56 p.   **198**

Milton, D. J., 1960, Geology of the Old Speck Mountain quadrangle: New England Intercoll. Geol. Conf., 52nd Ann. Mtg., Rumford, Me., 1960, Gdbk., p. 25–32.   **123**

Miser, H. D. See Stone, Miser, Katz, and Hewett, 1919.

Moebs, N. N., and Hoy, R. B., 1959, Thrust faulting in Sinking Valley, Blair and Huntingdon Counties,

Pennsylvania: Geol. Soc. America Bull., v. 70, p. 1079–1088.   **34, 35**

Moench, R. H. See Osberg, Moench, and Warner, 1968.

Moorbath, Stephen. See Fairbairn, Moorbath, Ramo, Pinson, and Hurley, 1967.

Moore, G. E., Jr. See Quinn and Moore, 1968.

Moseley, J. R. See Geyer, Gray, McLaughlin, and Moseley, 1958.

Munyan, A. C., 1951, Geology and mineral resources of the Dalton quadrangle, Georgia-Tennessee: Georgia Geol. Survey Bull. 57, 128 p.   **54, 58**

Murray, G. E., 1961, Geology of the Atlantic and Gulf coastal province of North America: New York, Harper and Brothers, 692 p.   **198, 209**

Murthy, V. R., 1957, Bed rock geology of the East Barre Area, Vermont: Vermont Geol. Survey Bull. 10, 121 p.   **98**

————1958, A revision of the Lower Paleozoic stratigraphy in eastern Vermont: Jour. Geology, v. 66, p. 276–287 (see also discussions and replies: ibid., v. 67, p. 577–584, 1959).   **98**

Mutch, T. A., 1968, Pennsylvanian nonmarine sediments of the Narragansett Basin, Massachusetts–Rhode Island: Geol. Soc. America Spec. Paper 106, p. 177–209.   **111**

Myers, W. B. See Reed, Bryant, and Myers, 1970.

Nafe, J. E., and Drake, C. L., 1969, Floor of the North Atlantic—summary of geophysical data: Am. Assoc. Petroleum Geologists Mem. 12, p. 59–87.   **221**

Nafe, J. E. See also Mayhew, Drake, and Nafe, 1968.

Nash, W. A. See Neale and Nash, 1963.

Naylor, R. S., 1968, Origin and regional relationships of the core-rocks of the Oliverian domes: *in* Zen, E-an, White, W. S., Hadley, J. B., and Thompson, J. B., Jr., eds., Studies of Appalachian geology: northern and maritime (Billings vol.), p. 231–240.   **105**

————1969, Age and origin of the Oliverian Domes, central-western New Hampshire: Geol. Soc. America Bull., v. 80, p. 405–427.   **105**

Naylor, R. S. See also Boucot, Field, Fletcher, Forbes, Naylor, and Pavlides, 1964; Pavlides, Mencher, Naylor, and Boucot, 1964.

Neale, E. R. W., and Kennedy, M. J., 1967, Relationship of the Fleur de Lys Group to younger groups of the Burlington Peninsula, Newfoundland: Geol. Assoc. Canada Spec. Paper 4 (Lilly vol.), p. 139–169.   **155**

Neale, E. R. W., and Nash, W. A., 1963, Sandy Lake (east half), Newfoundland: Geol. Survey Canada Paper 62-28, 40 p.

Neale, E. R. W., and Williams, Harold, eds., 1967, Collected papers on geology of the Atlantic region (Lilly vol.): Geol. Assoc. Canada Spec. Paper 4, 292 p.   **10**

Neale, E. R. W. See also Poole, Kelley, and Neale, 1964; Rodgers and Neale, 1963.

Neathery, T. L., and Bentley, R. D., 1970, Southern terminus of the Brevard fault zone (abs.): Geol. Soc. America Abstracts with Programs, v. 2, p. 233.   **183**

Neathery, T. L. See also Bentley and Neathery, 1970.

Nelson, W. H. See Neuman and Nelson, 1965.

Neuman, R. B., 1967, Bedrock geology of the Shin Pond and Stacyville quadrangles, Penobscot County, Maine: U.S. Geol. Survey Prof. Paper 524-I, 37 p. **125**

——1968, Paleogeographic implications of Ordovician shelly fossils in the Magog belt of the northern Appalachian region: in Zen, E-an, White, W. S., Hadley, J. B., and Thompson, J. B., Jr., eds., Studies of Appalachian geology: northern and maritime (Billings vol.), p. 35–48. **126, 134**

Neuman, R. B., and Nelson, W. H., 1965, Geology of the western Great Smoky Mountains, Tennessee: U.S. Geol. Survey Prof. Paper 349-D, 81 p. **174, 176**

Neuman, R. B., and Rankin, D. W., 1966, Bedrock geology of the Shin Pond region: New England Intercoll. Geol. Conf., 58th Ann. Mtg., Katahdin, Me., 1966, Gdbk., p. 8–17. **125**

Neuman, R. B. See also King, Hadley, Neuman, and Hamilton, 1958.

Newell, M. F. See Rankin, Stern, Reed, and Newell, 1969.

Nichols, D. R., 1956, Bedrock geology of the Narragansett Pier quadrangle, Rhode Island: U.S. Geol. Survey Geol. Quad. Map, GQ–91. **111**

Nickelsen, R. P., 1956, Geology of the Blue Ridge near Harpers Ferry, West Virginia: Geol. Soc. America Bull., v. 67, p. 239–269. **166**

——1963, Fold patterns and continuous deformation mechanisms of the central Pennsylvania folded Appalachians: in Tectonics and Cambro-Ordovician stratigraphy in the central Appalachians of Pennsylvania, Pittsburgh and Appalachian Geol. Socs. Field Conf. 1963, Gdbk., p. 13–29. **32, 33**

Norton, S. A., 1969, Unconformities at the northern end of the Berkshire Highlands: New England Intercoll. Geol. Conf., 61st Ann. Mtg., Albany, N.Y., 1969, Gdbk., Trip 21, 20 p. **92**

Norton, S. A. See also Hatch, Schnabel, and Norton, 1968; Thompson and Norton, 1968.

Novotny, R. F., 1961, A regional fault in east-central Massachusetts and southern New Hampshire: U.S. Geol. Survey Prof. Paper 424, p. D48–D49. **107**

Oder, C. R. L., and Ricketts, J. E., 1961, Geology of the Mascot–Jefferson City zinc district, Tennessee: Tennessee Div. Geology Rept. Invs. 12, 29 p. **47, 49**

Offield, T. W., 1967, Bedrock geology of the Goshen-Greenwood Lake area, N. Y.: New York State Mus. Sci. Service Map and Chart Ser. 9, 77 p. **70, 78**

Oldale, R, N., 1962, Sedimentary rocks of Triassic age in northeastern Massachusetts: U.S. Geol. Survey Prof. Paper 450, p. C31–C32. **207**

Oliver, W. A., Jr. See Quinn and Oliver, 1962.

Ollerenshaw, N. C., 1967, Cuoq-Langis area, Matane and Matapédia Counties: Quebec Dept. Nat. Resources Geol. Rept. 121, 192 p. **120**

Ordway, R. J., 1959, Geology of the Buffalo Mountain-Cherokee Mountain area, northeastern Tennessee: Geol. Soc. America Bull., v. 70, p. 619–635. **170**

Oriel, S. S., 1950, Geology and mineral resources of the Hot Springs window, Madison County, North Carolina: North Carolina Div. Min. Resources Bull. 60, 70 p. **173**

Osberg, P. H., 1952, The Green Mountain anticlinorium in the vicinity of Rochester and East Middlebury, Vt.: Vermont Geol. Survey Bull. 5, 127 p. **96**

——1956, Stratigraphy of the Sutton Mountains, Quebec; key to stratigraphic correlation in Vermont (abs.): Geol. Soc. America Bull., v. 67, p. 1820. **97**

——1965, Structural geology of the Knowlton-Richmond area, Quebec: Geol. Soc. America Bull., v. 76, p. 223–250 **119**

——1968, Stratigraphy, structural geology, and metamorphism of the Waterville-Vassalboro area, Maine: Maine Geol. Survey Bull. 20, 64 p. **128**

——1969, Lower Paleozoic stratigraphy and structural geology, Green Mountain–Sutton Mountain anticlinorium, Vermont and southern Quebec: Am. Assoc. Petroleum Geologists Mem. 12, p. 687–700. **97, 118, 120**

Osberg, P. H., Moench, R. H., and Warner, Jeffrey, 1968, Stratigraphy of the Merrimack synclinorium in west-central Maine: in Zen, E-an, White, W. S., Hadley, J. B., and Thompson, J. B., Jr., eds., Studies of Appalachian geology: northern and maritime (Billings vol.), p. 241–253. **127**

Osborne, F. F., 1956, Geology near Quebec City: Naturaliste Canadien, v. 83, p. 157–223. **117, 118**

O'Sullivan, R. B. See Walton and O'Sullivan, 1950.

Overstreet, E. F., and others, 1964–1967, Bauxite deposits of the Southeastern United States: U.S. Geol. Survey Bull. 1199, 16 chapters, 518 p. **209**

Overstreet, W. C., and Bell, Henry, III, 1965, The crystalline rocks of South Carolina: U.S. Geol. Survey Bull. 1183, 126 p. (see also ibid., Misc. Geol. Invs. Map I–413). **194, 195, 196, 197, 229**

Overstreet, W. C., and Griffitts, W. R., 1955, Inner Piedmont belt: Geol. Soc. America, 68th Ann. Mtg., New Orleans 1955, Gdbk. (Guides to Southeastern geology), p. 549–577. **194**

Overstreet, W. C., Yates, R. G., and Griffitts, W. R., 1963, Geology of the Shelby quadrangle, North Carolina: U.S. Survey Misc. Geol. Invs. Map I–384. **194**

Overstreet, W. C. See also Bell and Overstreet, 1959; Griffitts and Overstreet, 1952.

Owens, B. See McGregor and Owens, 1966.

Owens, J. P., 1970, Post-Triassic tectonic movements in the central and southern Appalachians as reported by sediments of the Atlantic Coastal Plain: in Fisher, G. W., Pettijohn, F. J., Reed, J. C., Jr., and Weaver, K. N., eds., Studies of Appalachian geology: central and southern (Cloos vol.), p. 417–427. **209**

Oxley, Philip, 1953, Stratigraphy and structure of the Western Brook, St. Paul's, and Parsons Pond areas, St. Barbe district, western Newfoundland: Newfoundland Geol. Survey Rept. 5, 53 p. **151**

Parker, J. M., 3rd, 1968, Structure of easternmost North Carolina Piedmont: Southeastern Geology, v. 9, p. 117–131. **196, 197**

Pavlides, Louis, 1968, Stratigraphic and facies relationships of the Carys Mills Formation of Ordovician and Silurian age, northeast Maine: U.S. Geol. Survey Bull. 1264, 44 p. **129**

Pavlides, Louis, Mencher, Ely, Naylor, R. S., and Boucot, A. J., 1964, Outline of the stratigraphic and tectonic features of northeastern Maine: U.S. Geol. Survey Prof. Paper 501, p. C28–C38.   **126, 129**

Pavlides, Louis. See also Boucot, Field, Fletcher, Forbes, Naylor, and Pavlides, 1964.

Perry, W. J., Jr., 1964, Geology of Ray Sponaugle well, Pendleton County, West Virginia: Am. Assoc. Petroleum Geologists Bull., v. 48, p. 659–669.   **39**

Pettijohn, F. J. See Fisher, Pettijohn, Reed, and Weaver, 1970.

Phillips, J. D. See Emery, Uchupi, Phillips, Bowin, Bunce, and Knott, 1970.

Phillips, W. E. A., Kennedy, M. J., and Dunlop, G. M., 1969, Geologic comparison of western Ireland and northeastern Newfoundland: Am. Assoc. Petroleum Geologists Mem. 12, p. 194–211.   **155**

Pierce, K. L., 1965, Geomorphic significance of a Cretaceous deposit in the Great Valley of southern Pennsylvania: U.S. Geol. Survey Prof. Paper 525, p. C152–C156.   **210**

———1966, Bedrock and surficial geology of the McConnellsburg quadrangle, Pennsylvania: Pennsylvania Geol. Survey, 4th Ser., Atlas A109a, 111 p.   **209**

Pierce, K. L., and Armstrong, R. L., 1966, Tuscarora fault, an Acadian (?) bedding-plane fault in central Appalachian Valley and Ridge province: Am. Assoc. Petroleum Geologists Bull., v. 50, p. 385–390.   **32, 67**

Pinson, W. H., Jr. See Fairbairn, Bottino, Pinson, and Hurley, 1966; Fairbairn, Moorbath, Ramo, Pinson, and Hurley, 1967.

Platt, L. B., 1969, Some aspects of conglomerates in the Taconics, Cossayuna area, New York: New England Intercoll. Geol. Conf., 61st Ann. Mtg., Albany, N.Y., 1969, Gdbk., Trip 18, 11 p.   **80**

Platt, L. B., Loring, R. B., and Stephens, G. C., 1969, Taconic events in the Hamburg 15′ quadrangle, Pennsylvania (abs.): Geol. Soc. America Abstracts with Programs for 1969, pt. 1 [v. 1, no. 1], p. 48–49.   **69**

Platt, L. B., See also Carswell, Hollowell, and Platt, 1968; Sanders, Platt, and Powers, 1961.

Poldervaart, Arie. See Kulp and Poldervaart, 1956; Wilcox and Poldervaart, 1958.

Poll, H. W. van de, 1967 [1968], Carboniferous volcanic and sedimentary rocks of the Mount Pleasant area, New Brunswick: New Brunswick Min. Resources Branch Rept. Invs. 3, 52 p.   **139**

Pollard, Melvin, 1965, Age, origin, and structure of the post-Cambrian Boston strata, Massachusetts: Geol. Soc. America Bull., v. 76, p. 1065–1068.   **112**

Poole, W. H., 1963, Geology, Hayesville, New Brunswick: Geol. Survey Canada, Prelim. Ser., Map 6–1963.   **134**

———1967, Tectonic evolution of Appalachian region of Canada: Geol. Assoc. Canada Spec. Paper 4 (Lilly vol.), p. 9–51.   **134, 139, 143, 144, 147, 154, 161**

Poole, W. H., Kelley, D. G., and Neale, E. R. W., 1964, Age and correlation problems in the Appalachian region of Canada: Royal Soc. Canada Spec. Pub. 8, p. 61–84.   **119, 120, 134, 137, 140, 146**

Poole, W. H. See also Anderson and Poole, 1959; McCartney, Poole, Wanless, Williams, and Loveridge, 1966.

Potter, D. B., 1963, Stratigraphy and structure of the Hoosick Falls area: in Bird, J. M., ed., Stratigraphy, structure, sedimentation and paleontology of the southern Taconic region, eastern New York (Geol. Soc. America, 76th Ann. Mtg., New York 1963, Gdbk. Trip 3), Albany, N. Y., p. 58–67, also p. 43–48.   **84, 85**

Potter, D. B., and Lane, M. A., 1969, Some major structural features of the Taconic allochthon in the Hoosick Falls area, New York–Vermont: New England Intercoll. Geol. Conf., 61st Ann. Mtg., Albany, N.Y., 1969, Gdbk., Trip 12, 23 p.   **84**

Potter, D. B. See also Bird, Zen, Berry, and Potter, 1963; Espenshade and Potter, 1960.

Powers, R. W. See Sanders, Platt, and Powers, 1961.

Powers, Sidney, 1931, Structural geology of northeastern Oklahoma: Jour. Geology, v. 39, p. 117–132.   **15**

Price, P. H., 1931, The Appalachian structural front: Jour. Geology, v. 39, p. 24–44.   **19, 26**

Price, P. H. See also Reeves and Price, 1950.

Prindle, L. M., and Knopf, E. B., 1932, Geology of the Taconic quadrangle: Am. Jour. Sci., 5th ser., v. 24, p. 257–302.   **77, 93**

Prouty, W. F. 1923, Geology and mineral resources of Clay County: Alabama Geol. Survey County Rept. 1, 190 p. (map separately published in 1922).   **181**

Prucha, J. J., 1956, Stratigraphic relationships of the metamorphic rocks in southeastern New York: Am. Jour. Sci., v. 254, p. 672–684.   **94**

———1968, Salt deformation and decollement in the Firtree Point anticline of central New York: Tectonophysics, v. 6, p. 273–299.   **20, 28**

Prucha, J. J., Scotford, D. M., and Sneider, R. M., 1968, Bedrock geology of parts of Putnam and Westchester Counties, New York, and Fairfield County, Connecticut: New York State Mus. Map and Chart Ser. 11, 26 p.   **94**

Pumpelly, Raphael, Wolff, J. E., and Dale, T. N., 1894, Geology of the Green Mountains in Massachusetts: U.S. Geol. Survey Mon. 23, 206 p.   **92**

Puri, H. S., and Vernon, R. O., 1964, Summary of the geology of Florida and a guidebook to the classic exposures: Florida Geol. Survey Spec. Pub. 5 (revised), 312 p.   **198**

Quinn, A. W., and Moore, G. E., Jr., 1968, Sedimentation, tectonism, and plutonism of the Narragansett Bay region: in Zen, E-an, White, W. S., Hadley, J. B., and Thompson, J. B., Jr., eds., Studies of Appalachian geology: northern and maritime (Billings vol.), p. 269–279.   **111, 113**

Quinn, A. W., and Oliver, W. A., Jr., 1962, Pennsylvanian rocks of New England: Pennsylvanian system in the United States, p. 60–73, Am. Assoc. Petroleum Geologists.   **111**

Quinn, A. W., Ray, R. G., and Seymour, W. L., 1949, Bedrock geology of the Pawtucket quadrangle, Rhode Island–Massachusetts: U. S. Geol. Survey Geol. Quad. Map [1].   **113**

Quinn, A. W. See also Foland, Quinn, and Giletti, 1970.

Ramo, A. O., See Fairbairn, Moorbath, Ramo, Pinson, and Hurley, 1967.

Rankin, D. W., 1967, Guide to the geology of the Mt. Rogers area, Virginia, North Carolina and Tennessee: Carolina Geol. Soc. Ann. Mtg. 1967, Gdbk., 48 p.
167, 171, 172

———1968, Volcanism related to tectonism in the Piscataquis volcanic belt, an island arc of Early Devonian age in north-central Maine: *in* Zen, E-an, White, W. S., Hadley, J. B., and Thompson, J. B., Jr., eds., Studies of Appalachian geology: northern and maritime (Billings vol.), p. 355–369.   **124, 126**

———1969, The Fries thrust: a major thrust in the Blue Ridge province of southwestern Virginia (abs.): Geol. Soc. America Abstracts with Programs for 1969, pt. 4 [v. 1, no. 4], p. 66–67.   **170**

———1970, Stratigraphy and structure of Precambrian rocks in northwestern North Carolina: *in* Fisher, G. W., Pettijohn, F. J., Reed, J. C., Jr., and Weaver, K. N., eds., Studies of Appalachian geology: central and southern (Cloos vol.), p. 227–245.   **167, 171, 172**

Rankin, D. W., Stern, T. W., Reed, J. C. Jr., and Newell, M. F., 1969, Zircon ages of felsic volcanic rocks in the upper Precambrian of the Blue Ridge, Appalachian Mountains: Science, v. 166, p. 741–744.   **165, 168**

Rankin, D. W.   See also Espenshade and Rankin, 1970; Neuman and Rankin, 1966.

Rasetti, Franco.   See Bird and Rasetti, 1968.

Ratcliffe, N. M., ms. 1965, Bedrock geology of the Great Barrington area, Massachusetts: Ph. D. dissertation, Penna. State Univ., 213 p. (not seen).   **77, 92**

———1968a, Stratigraphic and structural relations along the western border of the Cortlandt intrusives: New York State Geol. Assoc., 40th Ann. Mtg., Flushing, Queens, N. Y., 1968, Gdbk., p. 197–220.   **94**

———1968b, Contact relations of the Cortlandt complex at Stony Point, New York, and their regional implications: Geol. Soc. America Bull., v. 79, p. 777–786.
96

———1969a, Structural and stratigraphic relations along the Precambrian front in southwestern Massachusetts: New England Intercoll. Geol. Conf., 61st Ann. Mtg., Albany, N. Y., 1969, Gdbk. Trip 1, 21 p.   **92**

———1969b, Stratigraphy and deformational history of rocks of the Taconic Range near Great Barrington, Massachusetts: New England Intercoll. Geol. Conf., 61st Ann. Mtg., Albany, N. Y., 1969, Gdbk. Trip 2, 23 p.; abs. in Geol. Soc. America Spec. Paper 101, p. 274, 1968.   **77**

Ratcliffe, N. M., and Knowles, R. R., 1969 [1970], Stratigraphic relations along the western edge of the Cortlandt intrusives and their bearing on the Inwood-Manhattan problem: City Univ. New York, Queens Coll. Dept. Geology, Geol. Bull. 3, p. 49–64 (abs. in Geol. Soc. America Spec. Paper 121, p. 368).   **94**

Ratcliffe, N. M.   See also Zen and Ratcliffe, 1966.

Ray, R. G.   See Quinn, Ray, and Seymour, 1949.

Raymond, P. E., 1913, Quebec and vicinity: Internat. Geol. Congress, 12th, Toronto 1913, Gdbk. 1, p. 25–48.
117, 118

Redden, J. A., 1963, Stratigraphy and metamorphism of the Altavista area: Virginia Polytech. Inst. Eng. Ext. Ser., Geol. Gdbk. 2, p. 77–99; see also abs. in Geol. Soc. America Spec. Paper 76, p. 255, 1964.   **192, 193**

Reed, J. C., Jr., 1955, Catoctin formation near Luray, Virginia: Geol. Soc. America Bull., v. 66, p. 871–896.
165

Reed, J. C., Jr., and Bryant, Bruce, 1964, Evidence for strike–slip faulting along the Brevard zone in North Carolina: Geol. Soc. America Bull., v. 75, p. 1177–1195.   **182, 183**

Reed, J. C., Jr., Bryant, Bruce, and Myers, W. B., 1970, The Brevard zone: a reinterpretation: *in* Fisher, G. W., Pettijohn, F. J., Reed, J. C., Jr., and Weaver, K. N., eds., Studies of Appalachian geology: central and southern (Cloos vol.), p. 261–269   **183, 184, 193**

Reed, J. C., Jr.   See also Bryant and Reed, 1961, 1962, and 1970; Fisher, Pettijohn, Reed, and Weaver, 1970; Rankin, Stern, Reed, and Newell, 1969.

Reeside, J. B., Jr., Chairman, and Triassic subcommittee, 1957, Correlation of the Triassic formations of North America exclusive of Canada: Geol. Soc. America Bull., v. 68, p. 1451–1513, 2 charts,   **203, 205**

Reeves, Frank, and Price, P. H., 1950, Early Devonian gas in northern West Virginia and pre-Devonian oil prospects: Am. Assoc. Petroleum Geologists Bull., v. 34. 2095–2132.   **17, 20**

Reinemund, J. A., 1955, Geology of the Deep River coal field, North Carolina: U.S. Geol. Survey Prof. Paper 246, 159 p.   **206**

Reinhardt, E. W.   See Wynne-Edwards, Gregory, Hay, Giovanella, and Reinhardt, 1966.

Rich, J. L., 1934, Mechanics of low–angle overthrust faulting as illustrated by Cumberland thrust block, Virginia, Kentucky, and Tennessee: Am. Assoc. Petroleum Geologists Bull., v. 18, p. 1584–1596.
23, 26, 49

Richards, H. G., 1945, Subsurface stratigraphy of Atlantic Coastal Plain between New Jersey and Georgia: Am. Assoc. Petroleum Geol. Bull., v. 29, p. 885–955.   **198**

Rickard, L. V., 1962, Late Cayugan (Upper Silurian) and Helderbergian (Lower Devonian) stratigraphy in New York: New York State Mus. Bull. 386, 157 p.   **68**

———1969, Stratigraphy of the Upper Silurian Salina Group—New York, Pennsylvania, Ohio, Ontario: N.Y. State Mus. Map and Chart Ser. 12, 57 p.   **20**

Rickard, M. J. 1965, Taconic orogeny in the western Appalachians: experimental application of micro-textural studies to isotopic dating: Geol. Soc. America Bull., v. 76, p. 523–535.   **120**

Ricketts, J. E.   See Bumgarner, Houston, Ricketts, and Wedow, 1964; Oder and Ricketts, 1961.

Riva, John, 1968, Graptolite faunas from the Middle Ordovician of the Gaspé north shore: Naturaliste canadien, v. 95, p. 1379–1400.   **118**

———1969, Middle and Upper Ordovician graptolite faunas of St. Lawrence Lowlands of Quebec, and of Anticosti Island: Am. Assoc. Petroleum Geologists Mem. 12, p. 513–556.   **117**

Robertson, P. B., 1968, La Malbaie structure, Quebec—a Paleozoic meteorite impact site: Meteoritics, v. 4, p. 89–112.   **117**

Robinson, Peter.   See Thompson, Robinson, Clifford, and Trask, 1968.

Rodgers, John, 1948, Geology and mineral deposits of Bumpass Cove, Unicoi and Washington Counties,

Tennessee: Tennessee Div. Geology Bull. 54, 82 p. **170, 210**

———1949, Evolution of thought on structure of middle and southern Appalachians: Am. Assoc. Petroleum Geologists Bull., v. 33, p. 1643–1654. **9**

———1950, Mechanics of Appalachian folding as illustrated by Sequatchie anticline, Tennessee and Alabama: Am. Assoc. Petroleum Geologists, v. 34, p. 672–681. **26, 29, 52**

———1953a, Geologic map of East Tennessee with explanatory text: Tennessee Div. Geology Bull. 58, Pt. II, 168 p. **78fn., 170, 174, 176**

———1953b, The folds and faults of the Appalachian Valley and Ridge province: Kentucky Geol. Survey, Ser. 9, Spec. Pub. 1, p. 150–166. **61, 62, 64**

———1963, Mechanics of Appalachian foreland folding in Pennsylvania and West Virginia: Am. Assoc. Petroleum Geologists Bull., v. 47, p. 1527–1536. **20, 21, 30**

———1964, Basement and no-basement hypotheses in the Jura and the Appalachian Valley and Ridge: in Lowry, W. D., ed., Tectonics of the Southern Appalachians: Virginia Polytech. Inst. Dept. Geol. Sci. Mem. 1, p. 71–80. **36**

———1965, Long Point and Clam Bank Formations, western Newfoundland: Geol. Assoc. Canada Proc., v. 16, p. 83–94. **152**

———1967, Chronology of tectonic movements in the Appalachian region of eastern North America: Am. Jour. Sci., v. 265, p. 408–427. **218**

———1968, The eastern edge of the North American continent during the Cambrian and Early Ordovician: in Zen, E-an, White, W. S., Hadley, J. B., and Thompson, J. B., Jr., eds., Studies of Appalachian geology: northern and maritime (Billings vol.), p. 141–149. **73, 78, 114, 152, 187, 213**

———1970, The Pulaski fault, and the extent of Cambrian evaporites in the central and southern Appalachians: in Fisher, G. W., Pettijohn, F. J., Reed, J. C., Jr., and Weaver, K. N., eds., Studies of Appalachian geology: central and southern (Cloos vol.), p. 175–178. **47**

Rodgers, John, Gates, R. M., and Rosenfeld, J. L., 1959, Explanatory text for preliminary geological map of Connecticut, 1956: Connecticut Geol. Nat. History Bull. 84, 64 p. **100, 228**

Rodgers, John, and Neale, E. R. W., 1963, Possible "Taconic" klippen in western Newfoundland: Am. Jour. Sci., v. 261, p. 713–730. **81, 152**

Rodgers, John, and Shaw, C. E., Jr., 1963, Age of the Talladega Slate of Alabama (abs.): Geol. Soc. America Spec. Paper 73, p. 226–227. **181**

Rodgers, John. See also Billings, Rodgers, and Thompson, 1952; King, Ferguson, Craig, and Rodgers, 1944; Shaw and Rodgers, 1963.

Roen, J. B. See Englund and Roen, 1963.

Rogers, H. D. See Rogers and Rogers, 1843.

Rogers, W. B., and Rogers, H. D., 1843, On the physical structure of the Appalachian chain, as exemplifying the laws which have regulated the elevation of great mountain chains, generally: Assoc. Am. Geologists and Naturalists Repts., p. 474–531. **9**

Roliff, W. A., 1968, Oil and gas exploration—Anticosti Island, Quebec: Geol. Assoc. Canada Proc., v. 19, p. 31–36. **117**

Rondot, Jehan, 1968, Nouvel impact météorique fossile? La structure semi-circulaire de Charlevoix: Canadian Jour. Earth Sci., v. 5, p. 1305–1317. **117**

Root, S. I., 1970, Structure of the northern terminus of the Blue Ridge in Pennsylvania: Geol. Soc. America Bull., v. 81, p. 815–830. **165**

Rose, E. R., 1952, Torbay map area, Newfoundland: Geol. Survey Canada Mem. 265, 64 p. **158**

Rosenfeld, J. L., 1968, Garnet rotations due to the major Paleozoic deformations in southeast Vermont: in Zen, E-an, White, W. S., Hadley, J. B., and Thompson, J. B., Jr., eds., Studies of Appalachian geology: northern and maritime (Billings vol.), p. 185–202. **96, 97, 98**

Rosenfeld, J. L., and Eaton, G. P., 1956, Metamorphic geology of the Middle Haddam area, Connecticut: a progress report (abs.): Geol. Soc. America Bull., v. 67, p. 1823. **105**

Rosenfeld, J. L. See also Eaton and Rosenfeld, 1960; Rodgers, Gates, and Rosenfeld, 1959; Thompson and Rosenfeld, 1951.

Ross, M. H., 1949, Source and correlation of the Deepkill conglomerates (abs.): Geol. Soc. America Bull., v. 60, p. 1973. **79**

Royds, J. S. See Clark and Royds, 1948.

Rubey, W. W. See Hubbert and Rubey, 1959.

Ruedemann, Rudolf, 1901, Trenton conglomerate of Rysedorph hill Rensselaer Co. N.Y. and its fauna: New York State Mus. Bull. 49, p. 3–114. **79, 85**

———1909, Types of inliers observed in New York: New York State Mus. Bull. 133, p. 164–193. **76**

———1930, Geology of the capital district (Albany, Cohoes, Troy, and Schenectady quadrangles): New York State Mus. Bull. 285, 218 p. **80, 85**

———1942, Geology of the Catskill and Kaaterskill quadrangles. Part I: Cambrian and Ordovician geology of the Catskill quadrangle: New York State Mus. Bull. 331, 251 p. **87**

Ruedemann, Rudolf. See also Cushing and Ruedemann, 1914.

Ruffman, Alan, and Woodside, John, 1970, The Oddtwins magnetic anomaly and its possible relationship to the Humber Arm klippe of western Newfoundland, Canada: Canadian Jour. Earth Sci., v. 7, p. 326–337. **152**

Ruitenberg, A. A., 1968 [1969], Geology and mineral deposits, Passamaquoddy Bay area: New Brunswick Min. Resources Branch Rept. Invs. 7, 47 p. **137**

Ryan, J. D., Drake, A. A., Jr., Sherwood, W. C., and others, 1961, Structure and stratigraphy of the Reading Hills and Lehigh Valley in Northampton and Lehigh Counties, Pennsylvania: Pennsylvania Geologists Field Conf., 26th Ann. Mtg., Bethlehem 1961, Gdbk., 79 p. **70**

Safford, J. M., 1869, Geology of Tennessee: Nashville, Tenn., 550 p. **9, 22**

Salisbury, J. W., 1961, Geology and mineral resources of the northwest quarter of the Cohutta Mountain quadrangle: Georgia Geol. Survey Bull. 71, 61 p. **58, 178**

Sanders, J. E., ms. 1953, Geology of the Pressmen's Home area, Hawkins and Grainger Counties, Tennessee: Ph.D. dissertation, Yale University. See abs. in Geol. Soc. America Bull., v. 67, p. 1824, 1956. **49**

Sanders, J. E., 1963, Late Triassic tectonic history of northeastern United States: Am. Jour. Sci., v. 261, p. 501–524.   **205, 206, 207, 208**

Sanders, J. E., Platt, L. B., and Powers, R. W., 1961, Bald Mountain limestone, New York: new facts and interpretations relative to Taconic geology: Geol. Soc. America Bull., v. 72, p. 485–487.   **86**

Sanschagrin, Roland, 1964, Magdalen Islands: Quebec Dept. Nat. Resources Geol. Rept. 106, 58 p.   **138**

Sarpi, Ernesto. See Helwig and Sarpi, 1969.

Schiller, E. A. See Taylor and Schiller, 1966.

Schlee, J. S. See Hurst and Schlee, 1962.

Schnabel, R. W. See Hatch, Schnabel, and Norton, 1968.

Schopf, J. M., 1964, Middle Devonian plant fossils from northern Maine: U.S. Geol. Survey Prof. Paper 501, p. D43–D49.   **125, 129**

Schuchert, Charles, and Dunbar, C. O., 1934, Stratigraphy of western Newfoundland: Geol. Soc. America Mem. 1, 123 p.   **149**

Scotford, D. M., 1951, Structure of the Sugarloaf Mountain area, Maryland, as a key to Piedmont stratigraphy: Geol. Soc. America Bull., v. 62, p. 45–75.   **188**

———1956, Metamorphism and axial-plane folding in the Poundridge area, New York: Geol. Soc. America Bull., v. 67, p. 1155–1198.   **94**

Scotford, D. M. See also Prucha, Scotford, and Sneider, 1968.

Sears, C. E., 1964, Geophysics and Appalachian structure (abs.): Geol. Soc. America Spec. Paper 76, p. 257.   **64**

Secor, D. T., Jr., and Wagener, H. D., 1968, Stratigraphy, structure, and petrology of the Piedmont in central South Carolina: South Carolina Div. Geology, Geol. Notes, v. 12, p. 67–84.   **197**

Sever, C. W., 1964, Geology and ground-water resources of crystalline rocks, Dawson County, Georgia: Georgia Geol. Survey Inf. Circ. 30, 32 p.   **180**

Seymour, W. L. See Quinn, Ray, and Seymour, 1949.

Shaffner, M. N., 1958, Geology and mineral resources of the New Florence quadrangle, Pennsylvania: Pennsylvania Geol. Survey, 4th ser., Atlas A57, 165 p.   **20**

Shand, S. J., 1942, Phase petrology in the Cortlandt complex, New York: Geol. Soc. America Bull., v. 53, p. 409–428.   **94**

Shatsky, N. S., 1945, O sravnitel'noy tektonike Cevernoy Ameriki i Bostochnoy Evropy (A comparative study of tectonics of North America and the European platform): Akad. Nauk S.S.S.R. Izvestiya (Acad. Sci. U.S.S.R. Bull.), Ser. geol., 1945, no. 4, p. 10–26 (Russian with English summary).   **224**

Shaw, A. B., 1958, Stratigraphy and structure of the St. Albans area, northwestern Vermont: Geol. Soc. America Bull., v. 69, p. 519–567.   **73, 74**

Shaw, C. E., Jr., and Rodgers, John, 1963, Subdivisions of the Talladega Slate of Alabama (abs.): Geol. Soc. America Spec. Paper 73, p. 239–240.   **181**

Shaw, C. E., Jr. See also Rodgers and Shaw, 1963.

Sherrill, R. E., 1934, Symmetry of northern Appalachian foreland folds: Jour. Geology, v. 42, p. 225–247.   **19**

Sherwood, W. C., 1964, Structure of the Jacksonburg Formation in Northampton and Lehigh Counties, Pennsylvania: Pennsylvania Geol. Survey, 4th Ser., Gen. Geology Rept. G45, 64 p.   **70**

Sherwood, W. C. See also Ryan, Drake, Sherwood, and others, 1961.

Shumaker, R. C., 1967, Bedrock geology of the Pawlet quadrangle, Vermont. Part I: Central and western portions: Vermont Geol. Survey Bull. 30, p. 1–59.   **79**

Skehan, J. W., 1961, The Green Mountain anticlinorium in the vicinity of Wilmington and Woodford, Vermont: Vermont Geol. Survey Bull. 17, 159 p.   **86, 91, 93, 98**

———1968, Fracture tectonics of southeastern New England as illustrated by Wachusett–Marlborough tunnel, east-central Massachusetts: in Zen, E-an, White, W. S., Hadley, J. B., and Thompson, J. B., Jr., eds., Studies of Appalachian geology: northern and maritime (Billings vol.), p. 281–290.   **108, 113**

Skidmore, W. B., 1967, The Taconic unconformity in the Gaspé Peninsula and neighbouring regions: Royal Soc. Canada Spec. Pub. 10, p. 25–32.   **121, 130**

Skidmore, W. B. See also McGerrigle and Skidmore, 1967.

Smith, A. G. See Bullard, Everett, and Smith, 1965.

Smith, C. H., 1958, Bay of Islands igneous complex, western Newfoundland: Geol. Survey Canada Mem. 290, 132 p.   **150**

Smith, E. A., 1893, Underthrust folds and faults: Am, Jour. Sci., 3rd ser., v. 45, p. 305–306.   **9**

Smith, J. W., Milici, R. C., and Greenberg, S. S., 1964, Geology and mineral resources of Fluvanna County: Virginia Div. Min. Resources Bull. 79, 62 p.   **192, 193**

Smith, W. E. T., 1967, Some geological and tectonic considerations of eastern Canadian earthquakes: Royal Soc. Canada Spec. Pub. 10, p. 84–93.   **111**

Smith, W. H., 1948, Geology of Newport township, Washington County, Ohio: Ohio Jour. Sci., v. 48, p. 233–240 (Ohio Geol. Survey Rept. Invs. 5).   **18**

Sneider, R. M. See Prucha, Scotford, and Sneider, 1968.

Snyder, G. L. See Dixon, Lundgren, Snyder, and Eaton, 1963; Lundgren, Goldsmith, and Snyder, 1958; Zartman, Snyder, Stern, Marvin, and Buckman, 1965.

Sougy, Jean, 1962, West African fold belt: Geol. Soc. America Bull., v. 73, p. 871–876.   **199, 222**

———1969 [1970], Grandes lignes structurales de la chaîne des Mauritanides et de son avant-pays (socle précambrien et sa couverture infracambrienne et paléozoique), Afrique de l'Ouest: Soc. géol. France Bull., sér. 7, v. 11, p. 133–149.   **199, 222**

Southwick, D. L., and Fisher, G. W., 1967, Revision of stratigraphic nomenclature of the Glenarm Series in Maryland: Maryland Geol. Survey Rept. Invs. 6, 19 p.   **190, 191**

Spangler, W. B., 1950, Subsurface geology of Atlantic Coastal Plain of North Carolina: Am. Assoc. Petroleum Geologists Bull., v. 34, p. 100–132.   **198, 209**

Spencer, C. W. See Larrabee, Spencer, and Swift, 1965.

Spencer, E. W., 1968, Geology of the Natural Bridge, Sugarloaf Mountain, Buchanan, and Arnold Valley quadrangles, Virginia: Virginia Div. Min. Resources Rept. Invs. 13, 55 p.   **38, 40**

Stanley, R. S., 1964, The bedrock geology of the Collinsville quadrangle: Connecticut Geol. Nat. History Survey Quad. Rept. 16, 99 p.   **101**

———1969 [1970], Comments on the geology of western Connecticut: City Univ. New York, Queens Coll. Dept. Geology, Geol. Bull. 3, p. 11–15.   **101**

252 Bibliography and Author Index

Stanley, R. S. See also Hatch and Stanley, 1970.

Stead, F. W., and Stose, G. W., 1943, Manganese and quartzite deposits in the Lick Mountain district, Wythe County, Virginia: Virginia Geol. Survey Bull. 59, 16 p. **46**

Stearns, R. G., 1954, The Cumberland Plateau overthrust and geology of the Crab Orchard Mountains area, Tennessee: Tennessee Div. Geology Bull. 60, 47 p. **26**

———1955, Low-angle overthrusting in the central Cumberland Plateau, Tennessee: Geol. Soc. America Bull., v. 66, p. 615–628. **26**

Stearns, R. G. See also Wilson and Stearns, 1958.

Stephens, G. C. See Platt, Loring, and Stephens, 1969.

Stern, T. W. See Faul, Stern, Thomas, and Elmore, 1963; Rankin, Stern, Reed, and Newell, 1969; Zartman, Snyder, Stern, Marvin, and Buckman, 1965.

Sterrett, D. B. See Keith and Sterrett, 1931.

Stevens, R. K., ms. 1969, A note on the Quebec Group allochthon along the Gaspé North Shore. **118, 120**

Stevens, R. K. See also Williams and Stevens, 1969.

Stevenson, I. M., 1959, Shubenacadie and Kennetcook map-areas, Colchester, Hants and Halifax Counties, Nova Scotia: Geol. Survey Canada Mem. 302, 88 p. **143**

St. Jean, Joseph, Jr., 1965, New Cambrian trilobite from the Piedmont of North Carolina (abs.): Geol. Soc. America Spec. Paper 82, p. 307–308. **197**

St-Julien, Pierre, 1967, Tectonics of part of the Appalachian region of southeastern Québec (southwest of the Chaudière River): Royal Soc. Canada Spec. Pub. 10, p. 41–47. **119**

———1968, Les "argiles-à-blocs" du sud-ouest des Appalaches du Québec: Naturaliste canadien, v. 95, p. 1345–1356. **117, 118**

Stose, A. J., and Stose, G. W., 1946, Geology of Carroll and Frederick Counties: Maryland Dept. Geology, Mines and Water Resources, The physical features of Carroll and Frederick Counties, p. 11–131. **188**

———1957, Geology and mineral resources of the Gossan Lead district and adjacent area in Virginia: Virginia Div. Min. Resources Bull. 72, 291 p. **167**

Stose, A. J. (Jonas, A. I.) See also Knopf and Jonas, 1929; Stose and Jonas, 1935 and 1939.

Stose, G. W., 1930, Unconformity at the base of the Silurian in southeastern Pennsylvania: Geol. Soc. America Bull., v. 41, p. 629–657. **68, 89**

———1946, The Taconic sequence in Pennsylvania: Am. Jour. Sci., v. 244, p. 665–696. **89**

Stose, G. W., and Jonas, A. I., 1935, Highlands near Reading, Pennsylvania; an erosion remnant of a great overthrust sheet: Geol. Soc. America Bull., v. 46, p. 757–779. **70**

———1939, Geology and mineral resources of York County, Pennsylvania: Pennsylvania Geol. Survey, 4th Ser., Bull. C67, 199 p. **191**

Stose, G. W., Miser, H. D., Katz, F. J., and Hewett, D. F., 1919, Manganese deposits of the west foot of the Blue Ridge, Virginia: Virginia Geol. Survey Bull. 17, 166 p. **167**

Stose, G. W. See also Stead and Stose, 1943; Stose and Stose, 1946 and 1957.

Stromquist, A. A., and Sundelius, H. W., 1969, Stratigraphy of the Albemarle Group of the Carolina slate belt in central North Carolina: U.S. Geol. Survey Bull. 1274-B, 22 p. **196, 197**

Stuckey, J. L., and Conrad, S. G., 1958, Explanatory text for geologic map of North Carolina: North Carolina Div. Min. Resources Bull. 71, 51 p. **229**

Sundelius, H. W., 1970, The Carolina slate belt: in Fisher, G. W., Pettijohn, F. J., Reed, J. C., Jr., and Weaver, K. N., eds., Studies of Appalachian geology: central and southern (Cloos vol.), p. 357–367. **196**

Sundelius, H. W. See also Stromquist and Sundelius, 1969.

Sunderman, H. C. See Brown and Sunderman, 1954.

Sutton, G. H. See Drake, Ewing, and Sutton, 1959.

Swift, D. J. P. See Larrabee, Spencer, and Swift, 1965.

Swingle, G. D., 1961, Structural geology along the eastern Cumberland Escarpment, Tennessee: Tennessee Div. Geology Rept. Invs. 13, 46 p. **26, 52**

Taylor, F. C., 1965, Silurian stratigraphy and Ordovician–Silurian relationships in southwestern Nova Scotia: Geol. Survey Canada Paper 64-13, 24 p. **142**

Taylor, F. C., and Schiller, E. A., 1966, Metamorphism of the Meguma group of Nova Scotia: Canadian Jour. Earth Sciences, v. 3, p. 959–974. **141**

Teague, K. H. See Furcron and Teague, 1945.

Tharp, Marie. See Heezen, Tharp, and Ewing, 1959.

Theokritoff, George, 1968, Cambrian biogeography and biostratigraphy in New England: in Zen, E-an, White, W. S., Hadley, J. B., and Thompson, J. B., Jr., eds., Studies of Appalachian geology: northern and maritime (Billings vol.), p. 9–22. **79, 80**

Thomas, H. H. See Faul, Stern, Thomas, and Elmore, 1963; Zartman, Brock, Heyl, and Thomas, 1967.

Thompson, J. B., Jr., 1956, Skitchewaug nappe, a major recumbent fold in the area near Claremont, New Hampshire (abs.): Geol. Soc. America Bull., v. 67, p. 1826–1827. **103**

———1959, Stratigraphy and structure in the Vermont valley and the eastern Taconics between Clarendon and Dorset: New England Intercoll. Geol. Conf., 51st Ann. Mtg., Rutland, Vt., 1959, Gdbk., p. 71–87. **77**

———1967, Bedrock geology of the Pawlet quadrangle, Vermont. Part II: Eastern portion: Vermont Geol. Survey Bull. 30, p. 61–98. **77, 83, 84**

Thompson, J. B., Jr., and Norton, S. A., 1968, Paleozoic regional metamorphism in New England and adjacent areas: in Zen, E-an, White, W. S., Hadley, J. B., and Thompson, J. B., Jr., eds., Studies of Appalachian geology: northern and maritime (Billings vol.), p. 319–327. **101, 114**

Thompson, J. B., Jr., Robinson, Peter, Clifford, T. N., and Trask, N. J., Jr., 1968, Nappes and gneiss domes in west-central New England: in Zen, E-an, White, W. S., Hadley, J. B., and Thompson, J. B., Jr., eds., Studies of Appalachian geology: northern and maritime (Billings vol.), p. 203–218. **103, 104**

Thompson, J. B., Jr., and Rosenfeld, J. L., 1951, Tectonics of a mantled gneiss dome in southwestern Vermont (abs.): Geol. Soc. America Bull., v. 62, p. 1484–1485. **97**

Thompson, J. B., Jr. See also Billings, Rodgers, and Thompson, 1952; Doll, Cady, Thompson, and Billings, 1961 and 1963; Zen, White, Hadley, and Thompson, 1968.

Tiedemann, H. A., 1956, Geology of the Postoak window, Tennessee (abs.): Geol. Soc. America Bull., v. 67, p. 1760. **26, 52**

Tilton, G. R., Doe, B. R., and Hopson, C. A., 1970, Zircon age measurements in the Maryland Piedmont, with special reference to Baltimore Gneiss problems: in Fisher, G. W., Pettijohn, F. J., Reed, J. C., Jr., and Weaver, K. N., eds., Studies of Appalachian geology: central and southern (Cloos vol.), p. 429–434. **185, 189, 191**

Tilton, G. R. See also Wetherill, Tilton, Davis, Hart, and Hopson, 1966.

Todd, T. W., and Folk, R. L., 1957, Basal Claiborne of Texas, record of Appalachian tectonism during Eocene: Am. Assoc. Petroleum Geologists Bull., v. 41, p. 2545–2566. **209**

Toewe, E. C., 1966, Geology of the Leesburg quadrangle, Virginia: Virginia Div. Min. Resources Rept. Invs. 11, 52 p. **205**

Toulmin, L. D., 1952, Sedimentary volumes in Gulf Coastal Plain of United States and Mexico. Part II: Volume of Cenozoic sediments in Florida and Georgia: Geol. Soc. America Bull., v. 63, p. 1165–1175. **209**

Toulmin, Priestley, 3rd, 1961, Geological significance of lead-alpha and isotopic age determinations of "alkalic" rocks of New England: Geol. Soc. America Bull., v. 72, p. 775–779. **111**

Trask, N. J., Jr. See Thompson, Robinson, Clifford, and Trask, 1968.

Trexler, J. P., Wood, G. H., Jr., and Arndt, H. H., 1961, Angular unconformity separates Catskill and Pocono formations in western part of Anthracite region, Pennsylvania: U.S. Geol. Survey Prof. Paper 424, p. B84–B88. **66**

Trexler, J. P. See also Wood, Trexler, and Kehn, 1969.

Tschudy, R. H., 1965, An Upper Cretaceous deposit in the Appalachian Mountains: U.S. Geol. Survey Prof. Paper 525, p. B64–B68. **210**

Tuke, M. F., 1968, Autochthonous and allochthonous rocks in the Pistolet Bay area in northernmost Newfoundland: Canadian Jour. Earth Sci., v. 5, p. 501–513. **152**

Tuke, M. F., and Baird, D. M., 1967, Klippen in northern Newfoundland: Royal Soc. Canada Spec. Pub. 10, p. 3–9. **152**

Tupper, W. M. See Davies, Tupper, Bachinski, Boyle, and Martin, 1969.

Uchupi, Elazar, 1966, Structural framework of the Gulf of Maine: Jour. Geophys. Research, v. 71, p. 3013–3028. **143, 207**

Uchupi, Elazar. See also Emery, Uchupi, Phillips, Bowin, Bunce, and Knott, 1970.

Vernon, R. O. See Puri and Vernon, 1964.

Ver Wiebe, W. A., 1936, Geosynclinal boundary faults: Am. Assoc. Petroleum Geologists Bull., v. 20, p. 910–938. **26**

Waard, Dirk de, and Walton, M. S., Jr., 1967, Precambrian geology of the Adirondack highlands, a reinterpretation: Geol. Rundschau, v. 56, p. 596–629. **211**

Wagener, H. D. See Secor and Wagener, 1968.

Walcott, C. D., 1888, The Taconic System of Emmons, and the use of the name Taconic in geologic nomenclature: Am. Jour. Sci., 3rd ser., v. 35, p. 229–242, 307–327, 394–401. **76, 86**

Waldbaum, D. R., 1963, Stratigraphy and metamorphism of the carbonate rocks in Dutchess County, New York (abs.): Geol. Soc. America Spec. Paper 73, p. 257. **77**

Walthier, T. N., 1949, Geology and mineral deposits of the area between Corner Brook and Stephenville, western Newfoundland: Newfoundland Geol. Survey Bull. 35, p. 3–62. **151**

Walton, M. S., Jr., and O'Sullivan, R. B., 1950, The intrusive mechanics of a clastic dike: Am. Jour. Sci., v. 248, p. 1–21. **208**

Walton, M. S., Jr. See also Waard and Walton, 1967.

Wanless, R. K. See McCartney, Poole, Wanless, Williams, and Loveridge, 1966.

Ward, R. F., 1959, Petrology and metamorphism of the Wilmington complex, Delaware, Pennsylvania, and Maryland: Geol. Soc. America Bull., v. 70, p. 1425–1458. **190**

Warman, J. C., and Causey, L. V., 1962, Geology and ground-water resources of Calhoun County, Alabama: Alabama Geol. Survey County Rept. 7, 77 p. **60**

Warner, Jeffrey. See Osberg, Moench, and Warner, 1968.

Watkins, J. S., 1964, Regional geologic implications of the gravity and magnetic fields of a part of eastern Tennessee and southern Kentucky: U.S. Geol. Survey Prof. Paper 516-A, 17 p. **64**

Weaver, J. D., 1957, Stratigraphy and structure of the Copake quadrangle, New York: Geol. Soc. America Bull., v. 68, p. 725–761. **80, 87**

Weaver, K. N. See Fisher, Pettijohn, Reed, and Weaver, 1970.

Webb, G. W., 1963, Occurrence and exploration significance of strike-slip faults in southern New Brunswick, Canada: Am. Assoc. Petroleum Geologists Bull., v. 47, p. 1904–1927. **138, 139, 144**

———1969, Paleozoic wrench faults in Canadian Appalachians: Am. Assoc. Petroleum Geologists Mem. 12, p. 754–786. **136, 138, 139, 144, 145, 154**

Wedow, Helmuth, Jr. See Bumgarner, Houston, Ricketts, and Wedow, 1964.

Weeks, L. J., 1954, Southeast Cape Breton Island, Nova Scotia: Geol. Survey Canada Mem. 277, 112 p. **140, 143**

———1957, The Proterozoic of eastern Canadian Appalachia: Royal Soc. Canada Spec. Pub. 2, p. 141–149. **162**

Wentworth, C. K., 1921, Russell Fork fault of southwest Virginia: Jour. Geology, v. 29, p. 351–369; Virginia Geol. Survey Bull. 21, p. 53–66. **22**

Werner, H. J. See Bloomer and Werner, 1955.

Wetherill, G. W., Tilton, G. R., Davis, G. L., Hart, S. R., and Hopson, C. A., 1966, Age measurements in the Maryland Piedmont: Jour. Geophys. Research, v. 71, p. 2139–2155. **190**

Wheeler, Girard, 1939, Triassic fault-line deflections and associated warping: Jour. Geology, v. 47, p. 337–370. **206**

Whisonant, R. C., 1968, Stratigraphy and petrology of the basal Cambrian Chilhowee Group in central-eastern and southeastern Tennessee (abs.): Geol. Soc. America Special Paper 115, p. 236–237. **212**

Whitaker, J. C., 1955, Geology of Catoctin Mountain, Maryland and Virginia: Geol. Soc. America Bull., v. 66, p. 435–462. **165**

White, W. S., and Jahns, R. H., 1950, Structure of central and east-central Vermont: Jour. Geology, v. 58, p. 179–220. **96, 97**

White, W. S. See also Zen, White, Hadley, and Thompson, 1968.

Whittington, H. B., 1968, Zonation and correlation of Canadian and Early Mohawkian Series: in Zen, E-an, White, W. S., Hadley, J. B., and Thompson, J. B., Jr., eds., Studies of Appalachian geology: northern and maritime (Billings vol.), p. 49–60. **150**

Whittington, H. B., and Kindle, C. H., 1969, Cambrian and Ordovician stratigraphy of western Newfoundland: Am. Assoc. Petroleum Geologists Mem. 12, p. 655–664. **149**

Whittington, H. B. See also Kindle and Whittington, 1958 and 1959.

Wilcox, R. E., and Poldervaart, Arie, 1958, Metadolerite dike swarm in Bakersville–Roan Mountain area, North Carolina: Geol. Soc. America Bull., v. 69, p. 1323–1367. **172**

Willard, Bradford, 1943, Ordovician clastic sedimentary rocks in Pennsylvania: Geol. Soc. America Bull., v. 54, p. 1067–1121. **68**

Willard, Bradford, and Cleaves, A. B., 1939, Ordovician-Silurian relations in Pennsylvania: Geol. Soc. America Bull., v. 50, p. 1165–1198. **68, 69**

Williams, B. P. J. See Dineley and Williams, 1968a and 1968b.

Williams, Harold, 1963, Twillingate map-area, Newfoundland: Geol. Survey Canada Paper 63–36, 30 p. **156**
———1964, The Appalachians in northeastern Newfoundland—a two-sided symmetrical system: Am. Jour. Sci., v. 262, p. 1137–1158. **148, 156, 161**
———1967, Silurian rocks of Newfoundland: Geol. Assoc. Canada Spec. Paper 4 (Lilly vol.), p. 93–137. **155, 157**
———1969, Pre-Carboniferous development of Newfoundland Appalachians: Am. Assoc. Petroleum Geologists Mem. 12, p. 32–58. **148, 161**
———1970, Relationships between late Precambrian and Paleozoic rocks at Belle Bay, eastern Newfoundland (abs.): Geol. Soc. America Abstracts with Programs, v. 2, no. 1, p. 40–41. **160**

Williams, Harold, and Stevens, R. K., 1969, Geology of Belle Isle—northern extremity of the deformed Appalachian miogeosynclinal belt: Canadian Jour. Earth Sci., v. 6, p. 1145–1157. **149**

Williams, Harold. See also Kay and Williams, 1963; McCartney, Poole, Wanless, Williams, and Loveridge, 1966; Neale and Williams, 1967.

Williams, H. S. See Bastin and Williams, 1914.

Williams, M. Y., 1914, Arisaig-Antigonish district, Nova Scotia: Geol. Survey Canada Mem. 60, 173 p. **141**

Willis, Bailey, 1893, The mechanics of Appalachian structure: U.S. Geol. Survey 13th Ann. Rept., pt. 2, p. 211–281. **9, 42**

Wilson, C. W., Jr., and Stearns, R. G., 1958, Structure of the Cumberland Plateau, Tennessee: Geol. Soc. America Bull., v. 69, p. 1283–1296. **26, 27**

Wilson, C. W., Jr. See also Born and Wilson, 1939.

Wilson, J. L., 1952, Upper Cambrian stratigraphy in the central Appalachians: Geol. Soc. America Bull., v. 63, p. 275–322. **33**
———1957, Geography of olenid trilobite distribution and its influence on Cambro-Ordovician correlation: Am. Jour Sci., v. 255, p. 321–340. **213**

Wilson, J. L. See also Ham and Wilson, 1967.

Wilson, Tuzo, 1962, Cabot fault, an Appalachian equivalent of the San Andreas and Great Glen faults and some implications for continental displacement: Nature, v. 195, p. 135–138. **139, 144, 145, 154**

Wise, D. U., 1970, Multiple deformation, geosynclinal transitions and the Martic problem: in Fisher, G. W., Pettijohn, F. J., Reed, J. C., Jr., and Weaver, K. N., eds., Studies of Appalachian geology: central and southern (Cloos vol.), p. 317–333. **187, 188, 189**

Wise, D. U. See also Freedman, Wise, and Bentley, 1964.

Wolff, J. E. See Pumpelly, Wolff, and Dale, 1894.

Wood, G. H., Jr., and Bergin, M. J., 1970, Structural controls of the Anthracite region, Pennsylvania: in Fisher, G. W., Pettijohn, F. J., Reed, J. C., Jr., and Weaver, K. N., eds., Studies of Appalachian geology: central and southern (Cloos vol.), p. 147–160. **32, 66**

Wood, G. H., Jr., and Kehn, T. M., 1961, Sweet Arrow fault, east-central Pennsylvania: Am. Assoc. Petroleum Geologists Bull., v. 45, p. 256–263. **37**

Wood, G. H., Jr., Trexler, J. P., and Kehn, T. M., 1969, Geology of the west-central part of the southern Anthracite field and adjoining areas, Pennsylvania: U.S. Geol. Survey Prof. Paper 602, 150 p. **64, 66, 67**

Wood, G. H., Jr. See also Trexler, Wood, and Arndt, 1961.

Woodside, John. See Ruffman and Woodside, 1970.

Woodward, H. P., 1932, Geology and mineral resources of the Roanoke area, Virginia: Virginia Geol. Survey Bull. 34, 172 p. **39, 167**
———1957a, Structural elements of northeastern Appalachians: Am. Assoc. Petroleum Geologists Bull., v. 41, p. 1429–1440. **16, 30, 67, 68**
———1957b, Chronology of Appalachian folding: Am. Assoc. Petroleum Geologists Bull., v. 41, p. 2312–2327. **30, 64**
———1958, Alleghany orogeny: Am. Assoc. Petroleum Geologists Bull., v. 42, p. 193. **30fn.**
———1959, The Appalachian region: World Petroleum Cong., 5th, New York 1959, Proc. Sect. I, p. 1061–1079. **30fn.**
———1961, Preliminary subsurface study of southeastern Appalachian Interior Plateau: Am. Assoc. Petroleum Geologists Bull., v. 45, p. 1634–1655. **13**

Woodward, H. P., and others, 1959, A symposium on the Sandhill deep well, Wood County, West Virginia: West Virginia Geol. Econ. Survey Rept. Invs. 18, 182 p. **19**

Woollard, G. P., Chairman, Joesting, H. R., and others, 1964, Bouguer gravity anomaly map of the United States: U.S. Geol. Survey.   173

Woollard, G. P. See also Bonini and Woollard, 1960.

Wynne-Edwards, H. R., 1967, Senneterre-St. Jerome, a cross-section through the Grenville Province: Geol. Assoc. Canada–Mineralog. Assoc. Canada, 20th Ann. Mtg., Kingston, Ont., 1967, Gdbk., p. 99–107.   211

Wynne-Edwards, H. R., Gregory, A. F., Hay, P. W., Giovanella, C. A., and Reinhardt, E. W., 1966, Mont Laurier and Kempt Lake map-areas, Quebec (A preliminary report on the Grenville Project): Geol. Survey Canada Paper 66–32, 32 p.   211

Yates, R. G. See Overstreet, Yates, and Griffiths, 1963.

Young, D. M., 1957, Deep drilling through Cumberland overthrust block in southwestern Virginia: Am. Assoc. Petroleum Geologists Bull., v. 41, p. 2567–2573.   23

Zartman, R. E., 1969, Early Paleozoic plutonism near Boston, Massachusetts (abs.): Geol. Soc. America Abstracts with Programs for 1969, pt. 1 [v. 1, no. 1], p. 66.   113

Zartman, R. E., Brock, M. R., Heyl, A. V., and Thomas, H. H., 1967, K-Ar and Rb-Sr ages of some alkalic intrusive rocks from central and eastern United States: Am. Jour. Sci., v. 265, p. 848–870.   209

Zartman, R. E., Snyder, G. L., Stern, T. W., Marvin, R. F., and Buckman, R. C., 1965, Implications of new radiometric ages in eastern Connecticut and Massachusetts: U.S. Geol. Survey Prof. Paper 525, p. D1–D10.   108

Zen, E-an, 1961, Stratigraphy and structure at the north end of the Taconic Range in west-central Vermont: Geol. Soc. America Bull., v. 72, p. 293–338.   77fn., 79, 81, 82, 84

——1963, Age and classification of some Taconic stratigraphic units on the Centennial Geologic Map of Vermont: a discussion: Am. Jour. Sci., v. 261, p. 92–94.   83

——1964a, Stratigraphy and structure of a portion of the Castleton quadrangle, Vermont: Vermont Geol. Survey Bull. 25, 70 p.   79

——1964b, Taconic stratigraphic names: definitions and synonymies: U.S. Geol. Survey Bull. 1174, 95 p.   78

——1964c, Subdivision of the Stockbridge Limestone in southwestern Massachusetts and adjacent Connecticut (abs.): Geol. Soc. America Spec. Paper 76, p. 183–184.   77

——1967, Time and space relationships of the Taconic allochthon and autochthon: Geol. Soc. America Spec. Paper 97, 107 p.   75, 77fn., 78, 82, 83, 84, 86, 88, 93

——1968, Nature of Ordovician orogeny in the Taconic area: in Zen, E-an, White, W. S., Hadley, J. B., and Thompson, J. B., Jr., eds., Studies of Appalachian geology: northern and maritime (Billings vol.), p. 129–139.   78fn., 78, 81

——1969a, Stratigraphy, structure, and metamorphism of the Taconic allochthon and surrounding autochthon in Bashbish Falls and Egremont quadrangles and adjacent areas: New England Intercoll. Geol. Conf., 61st Ann. Mtg., Albany, N. Y., 1969, Gdbk., Trip 3, 41 p.   77

——1969b, Petrographic evidence for polymetamorphism in the western part of the northern Appalachians and a possible regional chronology: Geol. Soc. America Abstracts with Programs for 1969, pt. 7 [v. 1, no. 7], p. 297–299.   88

Zen, E-an, and Hartshorn, J. H., 1966, Geologic map of the Bashbish Falls quadrangle, Massachusetts, Connecticut, and New York: U.S. Geol. Survey Geol. Quad. Map GQ-507.   77

Zen, E-an, and Ratcliffe, N. M., 1966, A possible breccia in southwestern Massachusetts and adjoining areas, and its bearing on the existence of the Taconic allochthon: U.S. Geol. Survey Prof. Paper 550, p. D39–D46.   88

Zen, E-an, White, W. S., Hadley, J. B., and Thompson, J. B., Jr., eds., 1968, Studies of Appalachian geology: northern and maritime (Billings vol.): New York, Wiley–Interscience, 475 p.   10

Zen, E-an. See also Bird, Zen, Berry, and Potter, 1963.

Zietz, Isadore, King, E. R., Geddes, Wilburt, and Lidiak, E. G., 1966, Crustal study of a continental strip from the Atlantic Ocean to the Rocky Mountains: Geol. Soc. America Bull., v. 77, p. 1427–1447.   64

Subject index